asis

Volume

7

1972

Annual Review of Information Science and Technology

CARLOS A. CUADRA, Editor
ANN W. LUKE, Assistant Editor

Published by

AMERICAN SOCIETY FOR INFORMATION SCIENCE

Washington, D.C.

Major support for the preparation of Volume 7 of the *Annual Review of Information Science and Technology* was provided by the ERIC Clearinghouse on Library and Information Sciences operated for the U.S. Office of Education by the American Society for Information Science.

Library of Congress Catalog Card Number: 66-25096
International Standard Book Number: 0-87715-206-3
CODEN: ARISBC
Printed in the United States of America

List of Contributors

John L. Bennett
IBM Research Laboratory
San Jose, California

Alice Billingsley
U.S. Postal Service
Washington, D.C.

Alfred Blumstein
Carnegie-Mellon University
Pittsburgh, Pennsylvania

Wesley T. Brandhorst
ERIC Processing and Reference Facility
Bethesda, Maryland

Philip F. Eckert
NASA Scientific and Technical
Information Facility
College Park, Maryland

William D. Garvey
Johns Hopkins University
Baltimore, Maryland

Marvin C. Gechman
Information General, Inc.
Needham, Massachusetts

Heather Hudson
Stanford University
Stanford, California

Richard C. Kletter
Stanford University
Stanford, California

Ferdinand F. Leimkuhler
Purdue University
Lafayette, Indiana

Nan Lin
State University of New York
Albany, New York

Susan K. Martin
Harvard University Library
Cambridge, Massachusetts

Harold A. Olsen
University of Maryland
College Park, Maryland

Edwin E. Olson
University of Maryland
College Park, Maryland

Noah S. Prywes
University of Pennsylvania
Philadelphia, Pennsylvania

Joseph Raben
Queens College,
City University of New York
Flushing, New York

Phyllis A. Richmond
Case Western Reserve University
Cleveland, Ohio

Russell Shank
Smithsonian Institution
Washington, D.C.

Diane Pirog Smith
University of Pennsylvania
Philadelphia, Pennsylvania

R. L. Widmann
University of Pennsylvania
Philadelphia, Pennsylvania

John H. Wilson, Jr.
U.S. Atomic Energy Commission
Washington, D.C.

Chapter Reviewers

Henriette D. Avram
Phyllis Baxendale
Joseph Beard
Joseph Becker
Donald V. Black
Ralph C. Bledsoe
W. Douglas Climenson
Diana Crane
Maurice Geiger
Frederick G. Kilgour
Donald W. King
Joseph H. Kuney
Herbert B. Landau
Christine A. Montgomery
Richard H. Orr
William Paisley
Ruth Patrick
Alan M. Rees
Murray Rosenthal
M. E. Senko
Ralph Shoffner
Orrin Taulbee
Arthur Teplitz
Allen Veaner

Separate Cumulative Index to the *Annual Review*

Being published separately FOR THE FIRST TIME is the *Cumulative Index to the Annual Review of Information Science and Technology*. It covers Volumes 1 through 7 and is a significant revision of the "Combined Index" that appeared in previous volumes. Entries have been updated, expanded and systematized, producing a more informative and indispensable display of the wealth of topics presented in the seven *Annual Review* volumes.

The new *Cumulative Index* is the result of careful work by a team of experts including information specialists, lexicographers, librarians, and computer specialists. A merging process has significantly enhanced the precision of the index terms used. The various types of terms, e.g., acronyms, are entered in a standardized format throughout. An enumeration of the conventions adopted is provided. Finally, the total number of entries/access points is greater, reflecting an increase in cross references as well as more complete coverage of major terms.

Contents

Preface

In spite of concerns expressed in the literature about the health and vigor of the field of information science and of its service-oriented institutions—libraries and information centers—the progress reviews in this volume provide grounds for optimism. Some of the trends that were commented on in Volume 6 have proved to be solid and important. For example, the movement toward rapid interactive access to major public and commercial data bases is now very strong, and it will probably not be many years before satisfying experience with this new mode of information access will help it become not merely an experimental innovation but the standard means of searching and using centrally (or regionally) held data. Three chapters in this volume touch on related aspects of the movement: Bennett's review of the user interface in interactive systems, Gechman's report on machine-readable bibliographic data bases, and Brandhorst and Eckert's review of document retrieval and dissemination systems.

A second major trend—away from do-it-yourself library operations and toward cooperative system development and operations—is also confirmed this year in Martin's review of library automation and the review of library and information networks by Olson, Shank, and Olsen. Some of the economic pressures underlying this trend are discussed in Wilson's review on costs, budgeting and economics of library/information systems. This review marks the first inclusion in the *Annual Review* of a chapter specifically devoted to the economics of these systems; a similar chapter is also scheduled to appear in Volume 8, attesting to the growing importance of cost-effectiveness as a matter of major concern in library and information science.

This volume also introduces a new *Annual Review* topic of potentially great importance for future libraries: video cartridges and cassettes. It is widely accepted that libraries and information centers will, in the coming years, shift the balance of their holdings in the direction of some of the newer media, and the chapter by Kletter and Hudson helps to define the potential and problems of some of the promising new media. Other new areas of interest are information system applications in the criminal justice system and information system applications in the humanities.

In addition to these topics, this volume covers three of the core areas of information science, which we attempt to review on as close to an annual basis as possible: information needs and uses, document description and representation, and organization of information. This coverage is consistent with a newly developed *Annual Review* master plan for cyclic but flexible coverage of some 40 major areas of interest in library and information science.

In response to suggestions and criticisms about the orientation of the *Annual Review* toward United States publications, careful consideration was given toward having a chapter, or series of chapters, focussing on the information science activities of a number of countries in Western Europe. While these activities are important and should be described and appraised in the *Annual Review*, the consensus of opinion—including opinion from our friends abroad—was that these activities should be treated in the context of existing chapters, rather than as isolated activities. Accordingly, we have set aside plans to treat the non-U.S. literature separately and have, instead, given strong encouragement to all *Annual Review* authors to make their chapters as comprehensive as possible, from the standpoint of the world literature. Perhaps the forthcoming ASIS Annual Meeting in Washington, D.C., in October 1972, will provide added impetus to a much-needed concern for international exchange of information.

As in the past, the major personal contributions to the *Annual Review* series have come from our chapter authors, who commit themselves to the demanding task of sifting, analyzing, and critically appraising the extensive literature of the field, and who carry out their commitment in the face of very tight processing schedules. All of us who read and use the *Annual Review* are greatly in their debt.

Carlos A. Cuadra
Santa Monica, California

I

Planning Information Systems and Services

Planning information systems and services involves activities such as: identifying the information needs of the potential users of the systems, identifying or predicting the uses to which the information will be put, designing systems that can meet the requirements identified, and then evaluating and re-evaluating the resulting systems to close the gap between expectations and actual performances.

The two chapters in this section deal with two major aspects of information system planning: analysis of information needs and uses, and analysis of the economics of information processing. In the initial chapter, Lin and Garvey review recent activities in the study of information needs and uses of scientists, technologists, and laymen. They point out that the differing information needs of scientists and technologists are a function of many factors such as the kind of work in which an individual is engaged (basic or applied), the specific discipline within which he is working, and his knowledge of the availability of information. These needs often differ both in substance (nature of needed material) and in preferred and effective channels (sources of information). Recent studies dealing with types of information needs have concentrated on the needs for channels (e.g.,books, periodicals, films) rather than on the needs for substance (e.g., summaries, debates, application directions). More systematic studies are needed of the factors that determine different information needs.

Lin and Garvey examine the various patterns of informal information exchange among scientists and technologists and review progress made in understanding communication in organizations and professional meetings. They also discuss social networks (e.g., invisible colleges, communication stars), spatial arrangements, and other factors that affect the flow of information, and indicate why the layman's major sources of information—the mass media—are less effective than the scientist's communication channels.

Perhaps the most influential restrictions on information activities today are economic constraints. In the second chapter, Wilson examines the approaches, trends, and problems of responding to these forces in the area of costs, budgeting, and economics of information processing, especially as they relate to the planning of information systems. He reviews reported progress in cost analysis and reporting; cost-effectiveness analysis; programming, planning and budgeting systems; and, cost benefits and marketing.

In contrast with prior years, there now seems to be an abundance of literature reporting cost-related studies. Cost-reporting and accounting techniques are becoming more widely understood, and information on cost and systems analysis of libraries, particularly, is plentiful. It is still difficult to measure cost-effectiveness because clear statements of information system objectives—which are needed before the success of a system can be measured—are not always available.

The arguments about programming, planning and budgeting systems (PPBS) continue. Wilson urges the entire information community to adopt PPBS because it enhances the comparison of various methods of meeting objectives, and identifies future costs. If information services operations are to survive, vigorous marketing of the information services is essential. But can all the benefits received from information be measured in dollars? Economics techniques are being applied in assessing the value of information, and some criteria for measuring the benefits of information storage and retrieval systems are being usefully applied. This is, however, a very difficult area of inquiry and one that will require increasingly sharp attention in coming years.

1 Information Needs and Uses

NAN LIN
State University of New York at Albany
and
WILLIAM D. GARVEY
Johns Hopkins University

INTRODUCTION

The year 1971 saw a continued growth of literature reporting information needs and uses in science and technology. It also marked a period when a number of issues in information-needs-and-uses studies emerged above others as most significant by students in this field.

One most remarkable feature of this literature shows that systematic studies of information needs and uses have become truly international phenomena. Such studies continue to thrive in the United States, represented by activities of the American Psychological Association, of the Johns Hopkins University and of Stanford University. But the beginning of the 1970s also sees remarkable array of concerted efforts in other nations to study the information needs and uses of scientists and technologists, as exemplified in England, Canada, The Netherlands, Russia, and East Germany. Undoubtedly, there must be more studies outside the United States of which we are not aware at this time.

While investigations into the existing and potential needs and uses of information by scientists and technologists continue to grow, the decade of the 1970s probably will also see frequent debates on the basic structure of science and technology and its relation to the larger society. Such debates partially result from genuine concern for the health of science and technology and partially stem from the increasing reliance of science and technology upon resources and support from the society (Jencks & Riesman, 43; Lange, 52; Crawford & Biderman, 23; Greenberg, 33; Gouldner, 31; Archibald, 6; MacRae, 63; Crane, 22; Price, 83). There is more and more evidence that scientists and technologists are becoming more "applied" in their activities, and future scientists and technologists are turning to training programs and courses that promise to have practical applications. It remains to be determined whether such a trend is a genuine response to the society's needs or simply a temporary adjustment due to the limiting resources and the current restrictive job market. If any genuine change occurs for designers and policy-makers of information systems for scientists and technologists, its ramifications would be immense.

Also, there is a growing realization, among researchers of information needs and uses, of the lack of and need for a conceptual framework within which the enormous amount of data gathered and cumulated over the last decade can be meaningfully integrated (Skelton, 90). Such a framework could stem either from a summary of the global growth of literature on science and technology or from a summary of the information behavior patterns of individual scientists and technologists. Efforts in the former category have been attempted by Price (78, 80, 81, 82) and Griffith et al. (34) in the use of mathematical models of growth functions. Efforts in the latter category include Crane's use of a diffusion model to explain the growth of science (20) and Lin's discussion of a general communication model (54, 55).

International cooperation in science and technology also has drawn considerable discussion (Brittain, 12; Van Cott, 94; Crane, 22). Informal communication networks have existed among internationally prominent scientists in many fields; formal organizations, both intergovernmental and nongovernmental, serving science and technology in various ways are growing in number and variety. How should international organizations serve science and technology? Should they primarily provide forums for dialogues, or for collaborations in research, or should they eventually amass world banks of scientific and technological data? What should be the relation between these organizations and the national governments? How can possible conflicts between national interests and scientific advancement be best resolved? Furthermore, how are international cooperations to affect the brain-drain phenomenon—as observed by a group of British demographers (Bechhofer, 8; Kao, 50; Sabato, 85; and others)—in developing and less wealthy nations? Would such cooperations lessen or accelerate the flow?

While these issues will create further discussions among researchers and science policy-makers and have important ramifications for the design and studies of information systems, we shall in the rest of the chapter summarize studies of information needs and uses in science and technology that appeared or were completed in 1971.

For the purpose of this chapter, we shall draw a model, crudely parallel to the general model of human communication, specifying the phases of information needs, information seeking and exchange, information uses among scientists and technologists, and the organization of scientific and technological information (see Figure 1).

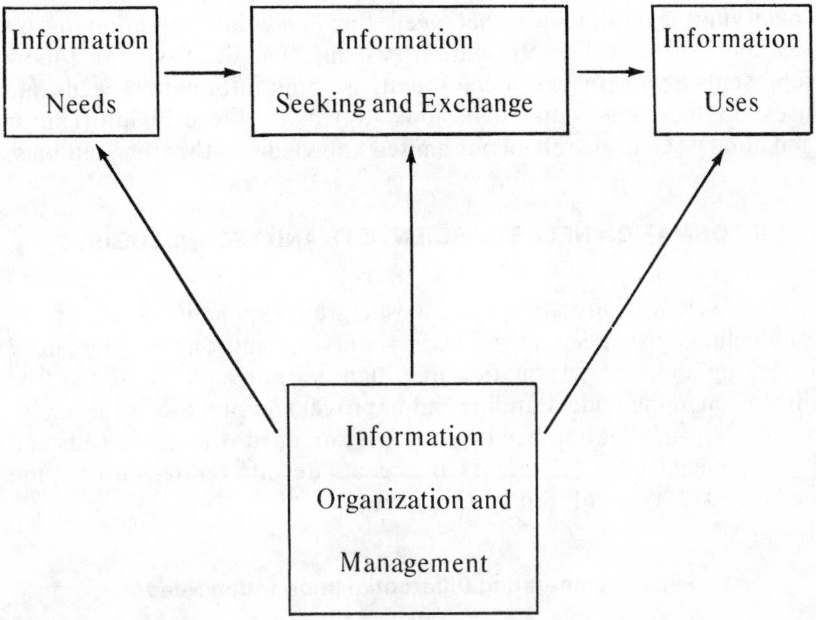

Figure 1. Phases in the Scientific Information System (SIS).

The approximation of the phases in the scientific information system (SIS) to those in the model of human communication is crude in the following senses. First, the SIS model focuses on information only, yet it must be assumed that the behavioral patterns of the scientist and technologists as well as the socioeconomic structure of science and technology are directly tied in with every phase. Second, each phase of the SIS model should be analyzed for both the system and the individual scientists and technologists. However, we shall only discuss (1) the attitudinal and behavioral patterns of information needs, exchange, and uses among scientists and technologists and (2) the organizational and institutional efforts to manage and improve the information system.

Third, the model introduces concepts that should be resolved and clarified. There have been discussions, for example, of the differentiation between information needs and demands (Brittain, 12). For our purpose, information needs and demands are considered synonymous.

After our summary of work up to and during 1971 regarding information needs, exchange, uses, and organization, we shall conclude by specifying several issues that need the immediate attention of researchers of scientific information systems. The discussion to follow represents a view of two social scientists about information needs and uses. In that sense, any omissions, especially those in information and library sciences, reflect our limited knowledge rather than our bias.

INFORMATION NEEDS OF SCIENTISTS AND TECHNOLOGISTS

While scientific literature continues to grow exponentially, scientists and technologists keep up their complaints that information they need is lacking and that information they find is irrelevant. Thus, the first dimension in the understanding and improvement of a SIS is the analysis of their information needs. A discussion of information needs can be sequenced into: (1) factors that generate differential information needs and (2) types of information needs.

Factors Generating Differential Information Needs

Probably the most important factor influencing the scientist's or technologist's needs is the type of work in which he is engaged. There is a distinction between a researcher and a teacher. While many are engaged in both research and teaching, priorities are usually assigned between the two. Since rewards differ for researchers and teachers, their information needs also differ. Merton & Lewis (68) point out that the intense competition to establish priority of scientific discovery has been in existence throughout the history of science. This competition for priority is a consequence of the fact that the primary reward for a scientist is to have his work recognized as significant by competent fellow scientists (Merton, 67). Priority is important, not only for significant discoveries, but for *any* new information. Thus, it should be expected that researchers, in general, should have greater need of information than nonresearchers. Furthermore, the researchers should rely less on documents, such as books that, by definition, contain older information. In a study of social scientists in England[1], it was found that library bookstocks tended to be more useful to teachers than to researchers (Line, 58). In interviews with education lecturers and schoolteachers, their need for information was far less urgent than that of other social scientists in the sample (Line et al., 60).

Similarly, specifications that identify whether work is relatively basic or applied also induces different information needs. In the English study (Line et al., 62), it was found that the need to use abstracts is substantially less for social scientists employed by the government (the applied group) than for those employed by educational institutions (the research group). We should also expect the basic researchers to use more up-to-date documents than practitioners. However, in a large-scale survey (of 34,000 specialties in different branches of science) in the Soviet Union (Goldberg, 30)[2], it was found that, in social sciences, practitioners usually need documents that have been published in the last ten years or less, whereas researchers need much older documents. Although the sample did not include a high proportion of historians, we suspect this surprising finding may be attributed to the Soviet social scientists' use of historical and census data in general. No empirical data were available to verify this suspicion.

---

[1]The Investigation into Information Requirements of the Social Sciences (INFROSS) project, sponsored by the Office of Scientific and Technological Information (OSTI), commenced in 1967 to study the information use of social scientists in Britain (Line, 58; Skelton, 90). It attempted to (1) identify information needs (and uses) of social scientists, (2) conduct an experimental information service in social sciences for information officials in university libraries, and (3) design information systems in the social scienes. At the time of our writing, reports regarding the first objective (to identify information needs and uses) have become available (Line, 58; Line et al., 59, 60, 61, 62; and Skelton, 90). The experimental Information Service has been completed, but reports are not yet available. The design of information systems will continue until the end of 1973. All INFROSS reports can be obtained from the National Lending Library for Science and Technology, Boston Spa, England.

[2]Goldberg reports a large-scale survey, carried out in the U.S.S.R. to ascertain and analyze the information needs in different branches of science. The survey enlisted the cooperation of many scientific institutions and over 200 libraries. Questionnaires, interviews, and open-ended questions (written suggestions) were the methods used for data collection. Furthermore, more than 470,000 readers' requests for publications and over 130,000 requests for bibliographical assistance and references were analyzed. Only a report on the data collected for social sciences (economics, sociology, law, psychology, philosophy and history) was available to these interviewers.

Another factor affecting different information needs of scientists and technologists is the discipline within which one is working. Goldberg (30) observes in the Russian study that social scientists in Russia tend to demand materials from libraries much more frequently than do scientists in other disciplines. Similar disciplinal differences in information needs had been observed in the United States (Garvey et al., 27).

Information needs can be stimulated simply by a knowledge of what facilities and/or materials are available. In a study, the Syracuse University Psychological Abstract Retrieval Service (SUPARS), conducted by researchers in the School of Library Science at Syracuse[3], it was found that many users tried the novel retrieval system simply because it became available. The study of social scientists in England also reveals that "availability of stock and services (in libraries) appears to have a considerable effect on demand and use" (Line, 58).

Information needs differ in substance as well as in source. In a study of a Single Article Service of the American Chemical Society, Paisley (70) analyzed the nature of articles being requested by each scientist. He found that co-occurrences of requested articles across specialties formed several distinctive clusters. Each cluster encompassed a number of conceptually related specialties within the discipline of chemistry.

More systematic efforts are needed, though, to isolate factors generating different information needs in terms of their substance and/or source. Research in human communication has provided us with some conceptual clues (Lin, 55). In general, the individual scientists and technologists are constrained by the spatial, social, and mass (communication) networks that they claim and of which they are considered members. Their needs frequently are generated by considerations of their relationships in the networks through which they eventually seek and receive rewards. The fragmentary data we have cited demonstrate that such networks also operate in the SIS. Future research may be fruitful in specifying the elements in the spatial, social, and mass networks surrounding scientists and technologists that may further explain the different information content and channelling the needs by scientists and technologists.

Types of Information Needs

Information needs can be categorized according to the substance-versus-channel dimension. Research into types of needs has been uneven, and while many studies have investigated the needs for channels

[3]All SUPARS reports are available from Dr. Pauline Atherton or Dr. Jeffrey Katzer, School of Library Science, Syracuse University.

(library facilities, audiovisual aids, training programs, etc.), few have focused on the needs for substance (the nature of the material).

For example, the American Psychological Association has conducted a number of studies on the pyschologists' needs for technological innovations. Prescott (76) reports a study of psychologists' interests and needs in audiotapes and other audiovisual media. Data from a random sample of members of the APA and Division 12 (Clinical Psychology) show that 75 percent of the respondents would use audiotapes if they were made available. In extrapolation, Prescott estimated that 10,000 psychologists would be interested in trying audiotapes, 5000 would consider subscribing to a service, and 4500 would contribute audiotapes to the service. The same study also showed that the preferences among various channels by the psychologists were: live (face-to-face audience), videotapes, films, audiotapes, books and manuals, and journals and abstracts—in that order.

In another APA study, Prescott (77) assessed the value of postdoctoral institutes for practitioners in psychology. Surveys of participants in the Postdoctoral Institutes (PDI), attended annually by approximately 100 psychological clinicians, show in general that clinicians gained knowledge from their participation in the PDI. However, they could not use or implement what they had learned because they lacked time or their institutions were perceived as not ready for such changes.

The INFROSS Project focused almost exclusively on the information needs and uses of references, indexes, abstracts, library catalogs and bibliographies, and on the use of books and libraries.

The data suggest the major deficiencies in the formal information system to be the lack of review articles, translation services, and services oriented to the practitioners (Line, 58). Formal bibliographical tools, including abstracting and indexing services, appeared to be underused, and the investigators report that there seems to be no great eagerness on the part of British social scientists to use them regularly. Where they did use them, it was for current awareness rather than for search of specific information (Line, 58, p. 431).

The Russian study (Goldberg, 30) also generated an enormous amount of data on scientists' needs for various formal channels such as books, periodicals, documents and libraries.

Crane (22) and Brittain (12) both point out the importance of international cooperation in meeting scientists' and technologists' demands for information. Brittain (12) reviews user studies conducted by international organizations in education. Crane (22) reviews international cooperative efforts in basic science. Again, the focus of discussions was on the improvement of international communication channels in meeting the needs of scientists and technologists.

With such large-scale studies conducted in England, Russia, and the United States (CRSC, 45, 46, 47, 48,), we have accumulated a large amount of data on the channel needs of scientists and technologists. However, how much do we know about their substance needs? In other words, do they need different types of materials? There have been some efforts made along this line, but they were smaller in scale and much less systematic, as compared with efforts to study channel needs.

Prescott (76), in her study of psychologists' interests in audiotapes, asked her respondents what they would like to have available on audiotapes. Fifty-six percent of the respondents suggested "how-to-do-it" instructions; 50 percent of them would like to have dialogues between prominent advocates with different points of view; 48 percent of them indicated "discussion of current hot issues"; and another 48 percent wanted "summaries of current research findings."

In another APA-sponsored study (49), data from a sample of graduate students in psychology showed the single most significant issue in psychology was "relevance" (mentioned by 34% of the respondents). They also considered that "relevance" (7%) and "writing" (9%) were major candidates for improvement in psychological journal articles.

One way of meeting the increasing information supply and demand made on the system by scientists and technologists is to support the primary journals in the system. The American Chemical Society, for example, attempted to solve the problem of the growing supply of materials to the primary journals by taking the following steps (Gushee, 35): (1) the creation of new journals; (2) imposition of page charges on the article authors, their institutions, or research sponsors; (3) solicitation of advertising and advertising revenues; and (4) subsidy of journals by nonmember subscribers and institutions.

Other efforts are directed toward developing innovations in the SIS to facilitate the linkage between information and scientists and technologists. This topic will be dealt with later.

PATTERNS OF INFORMATION EXCHANGE

We will restrict our attention here to the informal exchange among scientists and technologists. The informal communication patterns can be investigated on several levels, depending on the nature of the data.

On one level, data can be gathered from the general trend or structure of science and technology (such as number of scientists and volume of information) to induce some conceptualization of the informal communication structure. On a second level, data can be gathered from more or less permanent organizations and institutions (such as universities, industrial firms) to map the actual informal communication networks (based on indexes of advisorship, discussion partnership, or friendship). Such data then are used to construct the information exchange patterns.

On a third level, investigations can be conducted of scientists and technologists as they engage in exchanges in semipermanent organizational situations, such as national conventions, international meetings, and conferences. One important feature of this approach is that the structure provides an opportunity to trace a specific piece of information (for example, specific presentation material) as it is disseminated and assimilated among the participants.

Finally, information exchange data can be deduced from studies of the informal communication patterns and networks loosely defined over interest areas.

As we summarize studies of information exchanges at the several structural levels, we will also point out, where appropriate, the current conceptual confusion.

The Macroscopic Analysis of Information Exchange

Price (81) asserted that the number of elites in science is small relative to the total number of scientists ($\overline{N}$). Taking this clue, and further assuming that exchange among scientists in general is a rare event, Griffith et al. (34) suggest that informal contacts in a science might follow a Poisson distribution. Using data gathered by Crane (21), they attempted to find a single parameter for the Poisson distribution that would fit with empirical data. What they found was that the particular sets of data (from scientists in the areas of rural sociology and mathematically finite groups) suggested two groups: a majority having a low average rate of contact (thus fitting the distribution) and an elite whose frequencies of contacts deviated considerably from what the distribution would predict—being, in fact, about eight times higher than the majority. Thus, the study seemed to suggest that Price's elite concept must be valid, as far as the size of the elite group is concerned.

Crane (21, 20) has recently supplemented this concept of the "invisible colleges" by advancing a diffusion model for scientific growth. Using basically the interactive model of diffusion (Rogers, 84), Crane proposed that the growth of a scientific area is initially generated by a few innovators who are then joined by a large number of scientists. The interactions among these innovators and early adopters further attract other scientists and students. Such interactions account for the rapid increase in the number of participating scientists in the area. This model, while supporting the initial impetus provided by elites, attempts to explain the snowballing effect in science and the apparent communication between elites and nonelites.

A macroscopic model usually does not provide data on the specific patterns of exchange among scientists and technologists. It does provide, however, a conceptual framework within which hypotheses can be deduced about the exchange patterns.

The Analysis of Communication in Organizations

One distinctive feature of an organization is the fact that every member in the system is identifiable. This feature greatly aids studies of communication patterns, since it allows detailed sociometric mappings of the actual communication network of the members. The MIT group of researchers led by Allen has continued to advance our knowledge in this area. For example, they have found that, in a given working unit, there are identifiable communication "stars" (Allen, 1; Allen et al., 3). These persons, compared with their colleagues, tend to use external information sources much more frequently, to communicate more frequently with others in the same office or department (in terms of relative frequencies of communication-to-and communication-from), and to form a closer communication network among themselves. A conceptual deduction from such data is that these communication "stars" serve as the gatekeepers who facilitate the flow of information from outside and transmit the information to their colleagues. The implication of this deduction is that the transfer of technical information depends on the communication "stars."

The continuous changes of personnel in an industrial firm raises the problem of integration of the new hires into the existing communication networks. Gerstberger (29) compared the communication patterns between the newly hired engineers (with a firm two years or less) and other engineers in the firm. The 117 engineers (44 of them were the new hires) received weekly questionnaires for fourteen consecutive weeks. He found that the new hires, as expected, participated less in the interpersonal discussion networks than the veterans. However, communication among the new hires was just as frequent as was that among the veterans. The new hires also communicated with others outside their own sections as often as the veterans did.

The new hires differed from the veterans in the extent to which they communicated with others. Their communication was more intensive, and Gerstberger found two factors that contributed to this: (1) a larger number of colleagues with whom the new hire had interdependent working relations and (2) a larger number of contacts that his discussion partners (either new hires or veterans) maintained.

Communication within an organization is not only constrained by the social networks but is also affected by the spatial arrangements. The neighborhood effect and the territoriality concept have been observed in human communications (Hägerstrand, 36; Hall, 39; and Lin, 55). In general, communication is found to be more frequent and effective when the physical distance between the participants is small and when the participants consider a distance to be appropriate for the discussion of the specific topic. In a field experiment, Allen & Gerstberger (2) arranged a product engineering department office so that no physical barriers (no physical partitions) were present and no pieces of furniture were specifically assigned to any person. This "nonterritorial" office space arrangement lasted one year. The results showed a significant improvement in interpersonal communication, both in the average numbers of contacts made and the average frequencies of contacts within the office. However, the sample was too small (only 10 respondents participated in both the before-the-experiment and the after-the-experiment surveys). Furthermore, the participants' performance on the job, as rated by colleagues and officials outside the office, did not improve. More systematic research is needed before any conclusion can be drawn for the effect of spatial arrangements in organizations on the performance or productivity.

There is evidence, however, about the effect on performance of the relationship between the formally defined leaders and other members. Smith (91) did a partial correlational analysis (controlling on organizational factors such as proportion of Ph.D.'s and emphasis on coordination and research of 418 scientists and engineers engaged in petroleum engineering research in a large laboratory. He found that the more heterogeneous problem-solving approaches there were between leaders and members, the better the research team performed (in terms of papers published and patents obtained). This relation was found to be more significant for teams composed of younger members than for those of older members.

These studies of exchanges in organizations show that differential positions exist in the communication network and that information flow seems to be facilitated by the key communicators serving as the relayers. However, for communication to be effectively related to improvement of performance and productivity, other factors such as the quality of the staff, organizational emphasis on coordination and production, and leader-member relations must be taken into account (Hagstrom, 37).

The Analysis of Communication in Meetings

Exchange taking place in national and international meetings and its effect on the participants' work continues to draw research attention, following almost a decade's intensive and systematic examination of disciplines in the social, physical, and engineering sciences (CRSC, 48; Garvey et al., 28). Van Cott (94) recently summarized some factors that affect the quality of the International Congress of Psychology. Among these were (1) the program format, structure, and content; (2) the selection and scheduling of presentations; (3) the ability of the session chairmen and speakers; (4) the discussion and informal contacts; and (5) the efficiency of language translations. In their present form, international meetings need vast improvement before they can become effective media for international information exchanges. As more and more international cooperation in scientific and technological programs occur, the need for improvement of the quality of international meetings will become more urgent. In the opinion of these reviewers, more concerted research efforts are needed to help bring about such improvements.

For national meetings, research efforts are being continued in psychology (Sasmor, 86) and initiated for biomedical science at the Johns Hopkins Center for Research in Scientific Communication. A series of studies on conferences of the Council for Exceptional Children were conducted in 1970 (Paisley & Paisley, 73). The theme for the Conference on Instructional Technology held in San Antonio was instructional technology. Yet, the data showed the meeting attendants were "scarcely more 'attentive to' instructional technology than to the broad range of special education topics that the conference was not intended to emphasize." The data did not indicate if the attendants at the meeting were able to satisfy their information needs not covered formally by the presentations.

The Analysis of Informal Exchange Patterns

For the past seven or eight years, the most prevailing concept in the study of informal exchanges among scientists and technologists has been the "invisible college" concept (Price, 79). As more and more data have been gathered to test the existence of such groups or to use the "invisible colleges" as givens (Crawford, 25), it becomes clear that until the researchers agree on what they mean by the "invisible college" both *conceptually* and *operationally*, the concept will remain as provocative and confusing as it has been thus far.

Price's recent statement (81)[4] suggests that the definition of invisible colleges can be constructed in the following sequence:

1. The number of people in the invisible colleges of a given area of research front is empirically determined to be small, approximately the square root of the number of people in that area.
2. As their works are highly related and of high quality, the members are connected through cross-citations in their works and through interactions.

Price's own research effort demonstrates clearly that each of these propositions is empirically validated. However, as Price pointed out, it is easier to identify the characteristics of such groups when the groups have been historically identified than to find the groups by sorting the defined population in terms of the characteristics. The difficulty lies in the fact that the propositions did not eliminate the possibility of having others in the area of research front who do not belong to the invisible colleges and yet have contributed significantly to the area or are interconnected with the members in the invisible colleges. Thus, identifying such groups by the quality route or the communication network route becomes a matter of uncertainty. Several recent attempts in mapping communication networks among scientists and technologists demonstrate this problem.

Crawford (24) studied the communication network among scientists in sleep research. She found that 73 percent of the respondent-scientists (N=218) were directly or indirectly interconnected with one another in one large network. However, 37 scientists (15%) initiated or

---

[4]Price states, "These are not just groups of people working on a similar field of science and communicate amongst each other in some informal fashion behind the backs of the conventional journals. Invisible Colleges are not power groups in essence, nor must they be misunderstood as some upper one percent (or other fixed proportion) of the scientific population.

They are just the hierarchical elite resulting from an expectable inequality, and membering about the square root of the total population of people in that area of research front. They automatically reinforce their exclusiveness only by their excellence and by the overpowering effect of their contribution relative to that of the rest. They are highly connected with each other for within their small number they contain the greater part of the action. The only snag is that one can never know in advance that any particular people or papers or books or concepts will become part of the core or the elite. . . .The phenomenon is now becoming understood as a mechanism thrown up automatically by the scientific community."

received contacts from six or more scientists. This core group was also characterized by the greater number of papers they produced, the greater number of scientists who cited them, and the greater number of scientists who read their work. Information transmitted to these scientists could be transmitted through their informal contacts to 95 percent of the other scientists in the network, either directly or through an intermediary scientist.

In the study of the Irish Agriculture Institute, Allen et al. (3) found that the communication "stars" not only communicate among themselves, but also have substantial linkage with nonstars.

These studies started from a mapping of the communication networks and an attempt to differentiate the core group members ("stars") by the intensity of their communication contacts in the networks. There is some evidence that this method may reveal the ones who are also productive (Crawford, 24). However, other studies have shown that the overlapping between the centrality of communication and the productivity or quality is not a one-to-one relation (CRSC, 45, 46, 47). Among other kinds of relations, contacts are established between teachers-students, researchers-technicians, and so on.

Another research strategy is to identify the core group members based on some quality index. While there are many ways to measure quality, Cole & Cole (17) argue that, since straight citation counts are highly correlated with almost every refined index of quality, they may be used as an adequate, though not precise, measure of quality. Citation indices are readily available for most physical and life sciences and will become available in social sciences (Cole & Cole, 17). They should pave a potential route for investigations in the invisible colleges. Cole (16) showed that, in physics, the scientists who produced important discoveries depended almost wholly on the research produced by a relatively small number of scientists. It would be interesting to examine whether these other scientists—if they were the contemporaries of the discoverers—were also producers of quality work and reciprocated the citations.

The examination of the informal exchanges and the invisible colleges has reached a critical and uncertain point. A series of systematic investigations should be conducted to determine: (1) Which line of investigation to identify invisible colleges would be more effective: one that would use the quality measure first and the mapping of contacts second, or the mapping of contacts first and the indexing of quality second? (2) What is the extent to which quality of work and interconnectedness overlap in the constitution of the invisible colleges? (3) How we can determine the number of the invisible colleges in a given area?

and (4) How we can examine problems related to the boundary between members in the invisible colleges and nonmembers. Such examinations would not only clarify the problem of defining the invisible colleges empirically but also opens avenues for further investigations of the role played by the invisible colleges in the flow of scientific information.

INFORMATION USES OF SCIENTISTS, TECHNOLOGISTS, AND LAYMEN

Information use has remained the most popular topic in studies of the SIS. The past several years have seen growing interest outside the United States in surveys of library users or potential users. Reviews of most such studies before 1970 are available elsewhere (Hills, 41; Crane, 19; and Wood, 96). Our discussion here is restricted to research reports that become available in 1971 and those that appeared earlier but have not received adequate coverage. We shall report studies on information uses as they are related to (1) library materials and primary publications (journals and books), or interpersonal and informal communications; and (2) the use of scientific and technological information by laymen.

Uses of Primary Publications and Informal Channels

Several large-scale investigations of the uses of library materials and primary publications have been conducted outside the United States. Among them were (1) the Investigation into Information Requirements of the Social Sciences (INFROSS) project by the Bath University Library Group in England; (2) a large-scale survey of 34,000 specialties in different branches of science in the Soviet Union; and (3) a study of reading and researching habits of agricultural scientists and students in The Netherlands.

In the INFROSS project, the primary technique used in the investigations into information needs (and uses) was a questionnaire circulated to a national sample drawn from a population of all the identified social science researchers in England. The questionnaire went to 2602 individuals, approximately two-sevenths of the population. Only 1089 individuals returned the questionnaire—after two reminders. The low response rate was attributed to incorrect addresses, emigration, illness, death, and the length of the questionnaire (twenty pages). Two other methods, personal interviews and observations, were used on a small scale to supplement the data collected in the main study.

As expected, the data showed periodicals and books (monographs) as the formal channels most often used by the British social scientists in research (57% indicating frequent usage of each channel), followed by government documents (34%), proceedings (32%), research reports (28%), and computer printouts (21%). Colleagues in one's own institution and colleagues or experts elsewhere were the most frequently used informal channels (26% indicating frequent usage of each channel). Only 8 percent used conferences (an informal channel) often in their research.

The most used methods to locate references for their primary research interest at the time of response were bibliographies or references in books or journals (59%), consultants (34%), abstracts or indexes (32%), and colleagues in their own institute (27%).

One surprising finding was that in response to request to list library catalogues and published bibliographies they had used, 39 percent did not list any library catalogues at all. However, it was impossible to ascertain if no response indicated actual failures to use library catalogues for their current research or merely failure to answer the question.

Also, those who had the smallest collections of book volumes were those who least used formal methods of obtaining references, and those who owned most volumes were the heaviest users of libraries. The investigators suggested rather than a case of compensating for poor libraries by buying books or vice versa, people tend either to buy books *and* use libraries, or not to do either one. Surprisingly, 37 percent of the sampled British social scientists owned fewer than ten volumes and just over one-third owned over twenty-five.

On questions regarding use of libraries, the data showed the older and more experienced researchers tended to use fewer libraries than others. There was also a positive association between age of respondents and estimated library adequacy; the older respondents were more easily satisfied. Those wanting methodological and conceptual information were most easily satisfied, whereas those wanting historical and descriptive information were least likely to find the local bookstock adequate.

The most popular method of keeping up that was reported was the use of abstracting and indexing periodicals, mentioned by 40 percent of the respondents. Very little mention was made of review articles or of printed bibliographies.

The most common method of keeping track of currently published material and of research in progress was some form of personal or informal contact, mentioned by 37 percent of the respondents. Only 18 percent mentioned use of formal methods, such as research registers.

Asked about the extent to which they delegated searching, only 7 percent reported that they delegated extensively, and 72 percent did not delegate at all. The older, senior respondents were more likely to delegate (only 43% of professors did not delegate at all), and researchers in non-university environments delegated far more than those in universities. Some observations at the Bath University Library suggested that researchers were more willing to delegate retrospective searching than current searching. The delegation process certainly is a most important variable for SIS designers to remember in planning innovations such as the use of information officers in libraries.

Informal channels were found to be used often for locating relevant references, for keeping abreast of new publications, and for keeping up with current research. The investigators found meetings and conferences to be of marginal information-bearing value to their respondents. They did find that in meetings and conferences, formal papers and informal discussion were considered to be equally useful. This finding supports earlier evidence in the study of national meetings in the United States (CRSC, 48). However, no data were provided about whether information obtained through formal presentations was used differently from that obtained through informal discussions.

On the basis of their findings, the investigators suggest that the major deficiencies in the formal system at present appear to be a lack of review articles, poor translation services, lack of services oriented to the practitioners, and the underdeveloped state of information services (either person-to-person services such as those of an information officer, or impersonal such as the use of organized SDI).

Specific information needs and uses of social scientists in government departments, in colleges of education, in schools, and in social work are discussed by the investigations (Line et al., 59, 60, and 62). Skelton (90) provides a comparison of results of INFROSS with thirteen other science-user studies.

In the Russian study (30), some 1350 social scientists were questioned in person and 2670 were surveyed in libraries. Books and periodicals were the publications demanded most by the respondents from the libraries. In general, the social scientists in the U.S.S.R. were found to use libraries more frequently than did specialists in other sciences. Sixty-five percent of the social scientists indicated use of libraries at least once a week, compared to 59 percent in other specialties. Seventy-five percent of the respondents spent two to seven hours in the library on each visit. Unfortunately, other reports of the survey were only available in Russian and details cannot be reviewed here.

A similar survey of agricultural scientists was recently conducted in The Netherlands (Halászi, 38). A questionnaire was distributed to 66 libraries in Wageningen, The Netherlands, on three consecutive days. Additionally, 36 University staff members and 58 Institute staff members were interviewed. The University libraries returned 255 nonstudent responses and 192 student responses; the Institute libraries returned 204 nonstudent responses and 13 student responses. The data from these 664 questionnaires were analyzed to determine the frequency of library visits, the priorities the visitors gave to different types of literature, the purposes of library visits, the ages of the literature used, the means of tracing the literature, the help the visitors received, and the success of finding the literature. Other studies have dealt with the structure of formal channels and the interactions between formal and informal channels in the uses by scientists and technologists. Readers proficient in the Dutch language can examine the report (Halászi, 38) for descriptions of the data. However, it is impossible for us to evaluate the reliability and validity of the reported data critically because of the nonrandom sampling techniques used.

In a review of citation studies in social science, Broadus (13) found that citations of books or monographs were more frequent in humanities than in social sciences. Also, the citations in humanities tended to be older than those in social sciences.

Not only do scientists in different disciplines use information channels differently, but different groups within a discipline also use channels differently. In a recent study (SoGSIP, 49), questionnaires were sent to a sample of graduate students and faculty members (stratified by region and size of department) in psychology departments in the United States. With a response rate of between 40 and 50 percent, the data showed that the responses given by the graduate students and by the faculty differed on the sources of valuable information. Asked to indicate the sources from which they got the most valuable ideas relevant to their work and interests or the best single sources of ideas, an equal number of the graduate student respondents mentioned "professional journals (59%) and conversations with faculty members" (58%). These two sources were followed by "fellow graduate students" (43%), courses and seminars (35%), textbooks (30%), and other nonfiction books (21%). For the faculty, professional journals were the overwhelming choice (80%), followed by "conversations with faculty members" (50%), graduate students (37%), courses and seminars (28%), professional meetings (27%). The psychology faculty apparently finds the professional journals much more useful than do the graduate students while books were not as useful to the faculty as they were to the graduate students. The faculty found professional meetings much more useful than did the graduate students. In general, the faculty used journals and professional meetings as information sources more frequently than did the graduate students, who often had to rely on interpersonal channels and textbooks to get their information.

The selective use of journal information received substantial research attention. A series of studies was made of authors of articles and the people they named as principal workers in the subject-matter areas as reported in their articles in sociology and geography (CRSC, 46, 47). The principal workers who were named were asked how they first were exposed to the materials contained in the authors' articles and whether they found the articles useful. About 60 percent of these principal workers indicated that they had familiarized themselves with the content of the articles before the articles appeared in journals. Most of them became familiar with the information through direct contacts with the authors, or indirectly through contacts with their colleagues. Furthermore, there was an inverse relation between such prior acquaintance with the material and the perceived usefulness of the articles. Thus, it can be concluded that the usefulness of journal articles is restricted to those who do not have access to the interpersonal network of which the article authors are members.

Not only are journal uses found to be constrained by the involvement in the interpersonal network, but different uses are found to be made of journals. Research evidence shows that the prestige of journals varies and that journals from a stratified system (Lin & Garvey 56; Lin & Nelson, 57). In American sociology, for example, the status of major journals is positively related to the frequency with which each journal was cited, the prestige of the academic affiliation of the article authors, and the occurrence of self-reference in the articles. The journals of higher status also contain references that are more current. The scientists are very much aware of the status of the journals, as indicated by their journal preference for submitting manuscripts and the filtering down of manuscripts from top journals to less prestigious journals.

In general, knowledge about the relation between uses of information channels and the nature of information sought is limited. One outstanding exception was a study of a particular scientific specialty (polymer chemistry) recently summarized by Menzel and his associates (Menzel, 66). Questionnaires and personal interviews from a stratified sample of 161 polymer chemists in 36 institutions (including government, university, industrial, and independent research laboratories) showed that the scientists put emphasis on different channels in their deliberate searches, brushing-up, or accidental acquisition. For deliberate searches, scientists mentioned uses of articles and reprints (25%), books (18%), and other colleagues (15%), in that order, as the "main final channels" that provided the information being searched for. For brushing-up, the main final channels tended to be books (39%), articles and reprints (22%), and ex-colleagues (10%). Accidental acquisition of useful information mainly came from articles and reprints (45%); persons other than one's workmates, colleagues, ex-colleagues, or suppliers' representatives (17%), and books (12%). The effectiveness of articles and "other persons" in transmitting accidental acquisition has major implications for SIS designers and administrators. It demonstrates that peripheral literature and interpersonal channels supplement the more organized and salient publication and interpersonal networks in delivering useful information to scientists. Menzel warned us that a "perfect" and "closed" SIS may actually reduce the flow of scientific information.

In sum, the empirical evidence shows that to understand the differential use of information contained in various channels by scientists and technologists, it is important to understand the internal structure of and the interrelation of the various channels as they provide a network of information sources for scientists and technologists as individuals and groups.

Use of Scientific and Technological Information by the Layman

Most of the studies that we have reviewed pertain to the information-related behaviors of scientists and technologists. Few have discussed the use of scientific and technological information by laymen or practitioners.

In a comparison between the scientific communication model and the mass communication model, Lin (54) points out that scientific communication is much more effective than mass communication in information exchanges, owing to differences in the participants (participants in scientific communication are more like one another in their characteristics relevant to the information, and they are more flexible in the roles—either as a source or as a receiver); in the content (scientific communication is single-purpose); in the channels (scientific communication usually initiates in interpersonal channels, whereas mass communication usually initiates through mass media); and in the rewards (participants in scientific communication seek recognition more often than material gain). As scientific information is being transmitted to the public, the process fits into the mass communication model rather than into the scientific communication model. Lin proposes more research efforts and possible improvements in such a process.

Havelock (40) and his associates have examined rather extensively the process of the flow of scientific knowledge to the public and practitioners. However, from the scientific and technological point of view, our understanding of the process is lacking. For example, Tagliacozzo et al. (93) conducted interviews with 50 decision-makers in three types of organizations (assistant directors in hospitals, assistant superintendents in public school systems, and assistant administrators and department directors in city governments) to find out the information sources and content these organizations sought and used in their most recent typical decisions. Sources they most often used included internal documents, personal conversation, and telephone conversation; in terms of content, they sought costs, census data, and psychological data. For the kinds of information they needed, sources other than the internal documents and personal contact might have proved more useful.

Funkhouser & Maccoby (26) conducted a quasi-experiment testing the effects of textual variables in scientific writing, such as use of examples, readability, and use of activity words (words or phrases suggesting images of physical activity), on a group of lay subjects. They found that information gain was positively related to the use of examples, that the degree of reading enjoyment was positively related to readability and use of activity words used in the writing, and that a more favorable attitude toward scientific writing was also positively related to readability and use of activity words. Continued studies of this nature should be conducted to seek factors that affect communication effectiveness (especially information gain) of scientific information to the public.

INNOVATIONS IN SCIENTIFIC AND TECHNOLOGICAL INFORMATION SYSTEMS

How to best serve the information needs of scientists and technologists continues to be the question to which many societies and groups address their efforts. One answer seems to be the introduction of various innovations with the objective of improving the information delivery system or the use of the information. In this section, we will discuss several such attempts and evaluate the interplay between innovations and user studies.

Innovations attempting to restructure the delivery system can be exemplified by the recent efforts in the U.S.S.R. and the German Democratic Republic (G.D.R.) (East Germany).

Goldberg (30) reports innovative SISs in the U.S.S.R. and in the G.D.R. for social sciences. In the G.D.R., a separate system for information and documentation services was set up for each of the social science disciplines and was placed under each major research library that specialized in the particular field and acted as the support point for this center. In the U.S.S.R., a combined library-information center, the Institute of Scientific Information for the Social Sciences (INIBON), was established (1) to receive a deposit copy of "all Soviet publications and all foreign social-science literature of scientific interest," (2) to produce bibliographical bulletins and indexes, (3) to publish collections of abstracts, (4) to produce analytic surveys of literature, and (5) to give prompt replies to informational queries by individual institutions and specialists. Such monumental innovations (complete centralization of the SIS for a given science) certainly deserve assistance from systematic user evaluations to achieve the best results.

Innovations to modify or supplement the technical mechanisms in the delivery system continue to flourish around the world, most notably in the United States.

The American Institute of Physics is developing a National Information System for Physics and Astronomy (NISPA), to be implemented in the next six years (4, 5). The foremost function of NISPA is to "supply the presently unfilled needs of research and development scientists and engineers for current physics information" (AIP, 4). To achieve the current function, NISPA has developed a journal of preview abstracts entitled *Current Physics Advance Abstracts* (CPAA) to be published monthly. The CPAA contains abstracts and bibliographic data from referred and accepted manuscripts in the selected core journals of physics and astronomy some two months prior to journal publication. Certain selected information from each manuscript (source identification, title of article, author information, indexing and classification, article abstract, identification of references cited) will then be put on magnetic tape as unit records that form the *Searchable Physics Information Notices* (SPIN). The SPIN tapes issued monthly have been offered for lease or license since January 1971.

Eventually, the SPIN will be used not only to produce the traditional journals but also to establish a *Current Physics Microform* (CPM). The CPM will contain all of the articles from the core journals published by AIP. Finally, the SPIN tapes will be used to construct a printed journal, entitled *Current Physics Titles* (CPT), which will serve as a current-awareness journal and as an index to CPM. The CPAA, CPM, and CPT were all scheduled for sale starting in January 1972.

For an innovation of this scale, surprisingly few empirical studies have been undertaken to examine the need and potential use of the National Information System for Physics and Astronomy. One outstanding study was conducted for high energy physicists (Libby & Zaltman, 53); "distinguished physicists and astronomists" were consulted, and journal editors and review article authors were interviewed (AIP, 4). The preliminary effort by Libby & Zaltman has not been repeated for any other subgroups. In fact, that study was not even intended as feasibility research for the information system as now being implemented. A look over the planned activities related to the system shows that no future potential user study is being contemplated (AIP, 4). A proposal to study the specification achievement (whether the system is used as it was designed) was rejected by the funding agency.

Lack of a user study component in an innovation may cause serious problems. Take the example of the Educational Resources Information Centers (ERIC). The objectives of ERIC include: (1) collecting, abstracting, indexing, and making available the significant literature in the field of education; (2) preparing reviews and syntheses to place the literature in perspective; and (3) bringing the ERIC knowledge base to the attention of practitioners, so that educational practice might be benefited (Paisley, 71). After almost five full years of operation, the system is said to have accomplished the first two objectives in "fine order." However, as a former ERIC clearinghouse director points out (Paisley, 72), ". . .the third objective—bringing the ERIC knowledge base to the attention of practitioners—has eluded ERIC's outreach efforts thus far. Furthermore, knowledge of ERIC's existence is mostly in the possession of 'cosmopolite' researchers and professors rather than of 'localite' administrators and teachers."

It would be interesting to ask, in the historical perspective, why such an enormous investment was made without any empirical examinations of: (1) the definition and characteristics of potential users; (2) the communication behaviors and information needs of these potential users; (3) the information diffusion and dissemination strategies for the new system; and (4) strategies to facilitate user feedback and system modifications. Only now, for example, has the wisdom and efficiency of using microfilms as the means for retrieval in the system been questioned. Microfilm services are not widespread and the current facilities are poor for visually examining documents and receiving clear copies (Paisley, 72).

Schneider (87) stressed that examinations of the actual uses of the innovations should play a crucial role in the planning and implementation of an innovation. For example, the CAN/SDI project was developed by the Canadian National Science Library as a national service to alert scientists and technologists to current information in specific fields of research. It provided personalized bibliographies purchased from the Chemical Abstract Service, the Institute for Scientific Information, and the British Institute of Electrical Engineers. Wolters & Brown (95) conducted a survey of the users. Based on 406 returned questionnaires (a response rate of 67% from 604 questionnaires sent out), the study revealed that the major deficiencies of the system to the users were that the system did not provide possibilities for retrospective searching (mentioned by 43% of the respondents) and that hard copy documents were not available (22%). Most of the users became aware of the CAN/SDI through local libraries (40%). Only 17 percent of the respondents heard about the system from professional colleagues. Mauerhoff (65) points out that significantly more CAN/SDI users came from the government sector and few from industry and education. The adoption rate of the system was low; only 2400 of 28,000 potential users were actually using the SDI.

Such data support the need for and importance of integrating studies of users and potential users as a major component in any information system innovation.

One oustanding example of such a collaborative effort has been demonstrated in the Syracuse University Psychological Abstracts Retrieval Service (SUPARS), which attempted to test the viability of an on-line reference retrieval system using free-text indexing (Atherton, 7; Cook, 18; Katzer, 51; SUPARS, 92). Two years (1969-1970) of *Psychological Abstracts* on machine-readable tape were used to develop a data base of over 35,000 documents containing the original bibliographic citations and abstracts. After a pilot study, the fully operational system was made available to the students, staff, and faculty on campus for two and one-half months in the fall of 1970. Access to the system was via any one of 75 IBM 2741 telephone communication terminals located in most of the major buildings on campus. Elaborate publicity campaigns were conducted before and during the period of operations. A total of 349 persons registered in the program—most of them graduate students from psychology, education, and library science. During this period, 4388 searches were made. The participants tried the retrieval system (1) to review an area exhaustively (59%); (2) to survey the literature in general (39%); (3) to keep up to date in one or two content areas (32%); (4) to find several current references in an area (32%); and (5) to find a specific reference or abstract (22%). Most of the participants had no previous experience with computer terminals (66%) or computer-based retrieval systems (75%).

The Telephone Aid Service attached to the SUPARS was used rather extensively by the participants (a total of 551 inquiries were received during the operation period). In the in-depth interviews with 20 respondents in a stratified random sample of the participants (psychologists versus others), about half of them indicated that they successfully retrieved what they had wanted to find.

Although the experiment was short in duration and the in-depth interviews were few in number and did not include potential users who did not try the innovation, the project demonstrates that much can be gained from technical innovations when the user component is given consideration in the innovation design and when studies of user feedback are an integrated part of an innovation.

Another example of innovation-user interaction study was provided by an experiment of selective dissemination of information (SDI), conducted by the National Cancer Institute (Schneider, 87). About 100 scientists who had received research grants from the NCI participated in an experiment matching their research interests and 1396 articles published in 12 major cancer-research journals. During the one-year evaluation period, participating scientists received 6458 summaries of articles. An evaluation slip sent with each summary requested the scientist to indicate the extent of his interest in the article and its usefulness to his research. Nearly 82 percent of the evaluations (5278 slips) were returned.

The scientists indicated that 35 percent of the articles were of considerable interest to them, that 26 percent of the articles were related to the scientists' research and that 25 percent of the articles were very useful to them. Of the 1305 articles (25%) judged to be very useful, 76 percent were not known to the scientists before their publications. Furthermore, the summaries of 61 percent of the "very useful" articles provided the scientists their initial knowledge of the articles.

The experiment effectively demonstrated that an "information awareness" innovation for published data would be valuable for scientists, if some systematic matching between the information content of the data and the interests of scientists were arranged. Yet, few innovations in SIS even incorporate such a simple feedback mechanism. As Schneider lamented, ". . .it is incredible that so much money has been spent on the development and operation of scientific information systems before basic data on the comparative performance of various indexing methods have been gathered, analyzed, and confirmed by multiple investigators" (87, p. 307).

Also, it has become increasingly clear that any changes, especially implementations of new components, must be considered, not solely by their advantage or contribution to an information system, but by how they will work, along with the existing and other innovative components, as a whole (Garvey et al., 27). Implementation of a single innovation can have substantial effects on the functioning of other components—some of these effects being unanticipated and undesirable. The recent debates about the Single Article Service installed by the American Chemical Society and the early publication system developed by the American Psychological Association have been tense and real (Boffey, 9; Brayfield, 11; Clark, 15; Grant, 32; Holt, 42; Jenkins, 44; Miller, 69; Seashore, 88; Senders, 89). Should the professional socieites be chiefly responsive to quantity control in the information system or to quality control, or both? While most innovative efforts have been intended to alleviate the pressing problems related to quantity—availability and speed (Boutry, 10), the responses from within the existing information system have mainly been a genuine concern for the potential loss of quality control in the information system. The initial intention of an innovation may be addressed solely to one problem; and yet its interaction with existing components becomes so intertwined that, unless the users as well as the designers of the information are made aware of the specific functions and relationships among system components new and old, confusion and resistance about innovation will continue to arise whenever an innovation is initiated.

As more and more efforts are invested in innovations, the issue of feedback will also gain prominence as the major concern in the actual success and evaluation of the innovations. It is, therefore, quite disturbing in our review to find few innovations being implemented that have a built-in feedback component to provide information about the actual uses and responses of the potential users to the planners and administrators of the innovations. Researchers have repeatedly affirmed the necessity of such a component, and yet the actual development and operations of innovations time and again show an almost total lack of concern for a feedback component. How is the gap formed? It seems that the gap exists because of two factors: (1) the lack of cooperation between researchers and innovation developers and administrators and (2) the specific functions of innovations assigned by the financial sources of innovations. A lack of cooperation between the researchers on the one hand and developers and administrators of innovative techniques has existed a long time and has been the topic of numerous discussions. But there have been formal occasions for researchers, developers, and administrators to cooperate in the effort or even to exchange ideas. The experience gained from the Stanford, Public Information Retrieval System (Martin & Parker, 64; Parker, 74, 75) and the Syracuse University Psychological Abstracts Retrieval Service should be used in a "real" SIS system.

Another reason for the gap lies in the functional specifications of the financial sources of many innovations. The financial sources that support the development of the "hardware" do not see justification for investment in a "software" area such as a feedback component. The American Institute of Physics submitted a proposal in conjunction with its National Information System for Physics and Astronomy on a series of studies intended to examine if the innovations meet the specifications. The proposal was turned down by the institutional source that had invested substantially in the hardware developments on the grounds that such a "product improvement" project was inappropriate for the source to support.

CONCLUDING REMARKS

In summarizing the activities in the study of information needs and uses for the past year or so, it would be fruitful to discuss several crucial issues, the solutions of which may help direct our future efforts toward a more systematic understanding and use of research findings.

The first issue concerns the concept of the invisible colleges. We are approaching a phase in time where it has become clear that the concept of the invisible colleges must go under some theoretical scrutiny. We need to have a clearer definition. Does it mean to tap quantity, quality, and interaction (in documents as well as in interpersonal exchanges) simultaneously? Or, do these factors occur in sequence? For example, should we adhere to Price's contention that highest quality, small numbers and a great amount of cross-citations constitute the basic sequences for the construction of the invisible college? Or, since Price warned it would be difficult to reconstruct any invisible colleges from merely examining the indicators, should we study the invisible colleges only as historical events? In that case, should we proceed with our examinations of the formal and informal properties of science and technology without being concerned with the concept of the invisible colleges?

Another issue, still concerning information exchange, focuses on the communication stars in technological organizations. Allen and his associates have shown that, in the communication network in an office or department, a limited number of stars serve as the gatekeepers whose communication positions are such that they can relay information from the outside to their fellow workers. It would be interesting and important to ascertain whether the information relaying is indeed related to the function of the communication stars. A systematic series of studies tracing the actual flow of specific information from the outside to an office or department would lend substance to the importance of the communication stars in the technological transfer. Such studies would also dispel or confirm the alternative explanation that the communication star has a prestigious status and is one from whom reinforcement and support are needed to effectively perform the assigned tasks. It may well be that communication stars serve both functions. But until actual tracings of specific information incidents are conducted, different explanations are plausible.

The research-development-operation gap constitutes another important issue for our attention. There seems to be a tremendous communication gap between researchers and designers of scientific information systems. The researchers, on one hand, discuss and single out the crucial elements of exchange and feedback between an information system and the scientists and technologists (Garvey et al., 27; Paisley, 71; Parker, 74). The designers, on the other hand, seem to invest almost all their efforts in the technical soundness of the innovative information system. Given the present state of lack of communication, we may predict that cooperations between researchers, on one hand, and the developers and administrators of innovations, on the other, will continue to be few. Unless the funding agencies and policy-makers of innovations are made aware of the fact that the feedback component must be an integral part of any innovation in the information system, we may further predict that many innovations will fall far short of the use envisioned by scientists and technologists.

Finally, the issue that should most concern researchers is the conceptualization of information behaviors of scientists and technologists. Such conceptualization would be important if we were to depart from piecemeal studies and embark on a systematic analysis of the system of interactions between information and its actual and potential users. We are of the opinion that the communication model can be used to conceptualize the information-user interactions. Recent discussions (Chapanis, 14; Crane, 20; Lin, 54) all point to the potential effectiveness of this approach.

REFERENCES

(1) ALLEN, THOMAS J. Communication networks in R. & D. laboratories. R & D Management, 1:1 (October 1970) 14-21.

(2) ALLEN, THOMAS J.; GERSTBERGER, PETER G. Report of a field experiment to improve communications in a product engineering department: the non-territorial office. Massachusetts Institute of Technology, Alfred P. Sloan School of Management, Cambridge, Massachusetts, December 1971, (Working paper no. 579-71).
(3) ALLEN, THOMAS J.; PIEPMEIER, JAMES S.; COONEY, S. The international technological gatekeeper. Technology Review, 73:5 (March 1971) 2-9.
(4) AMERICAN INSTITUTE OF PHYSICS. PHYSICS INFORMATION DIVISION. The AIP program for physics information: a national information system for physics and astronomy 1972-1976. American Institute of Physics, New York, 1971, 74 p. (ED 051 849).
(5) AMERICAN INSTITUTE OF PHYSICS. PHYSICS INFORMATION DIVISION. A program for a national information system for physics and astronomy, 1971-1975. American Institute of Physics, New York, June 1970, 117 p. (PB 192 717. ED 033 731).
(6) ARCHIBALD, KATHLEEN A. Alternative orientations to social science utilization. Social Science Information, 9:2 (1970) 7-34.
(7) ATHERTON, PAULINE; ed. Large scale information processing systems Section IV-B: the user component of the system-B. Syracuse University, School of Library Science, Syracuse University Psychological Abstract Retrieval Service (SUPARS), Syracuse, New York, 1971, 116 p.
(8) BECHHOFER, F.; ed. Population growth and the brain drain. Edinburgh University Press, Edinburgh, Scotland, 1969, 236 p.
(9) BOFFEY, PHILLIP M. Psychology: apprehension over a new communication system. Science, 167:3922 (27 February 1970) 1228-1230.
(10) BOUTRY, G. A. Quantity versus quality in scientific research (II): the paper explosion. Impact of Science on Society, 20:3 (1970) 195-206.
(11) BRAYFIELD, ARTHUR H. Perspective on NISP. American Psychologist, 26:4 (April 1971) 337-338.
(12) BRITTAIN, JOHN MICHAEL. User studies in education and the feasibility of an international survey of information needs in education. Council of Europe, EUDISED Steering Group, Strasbourg, France, September 1971, 49 p.
(13) BROADUS, ROBERT N. The literature of the social sciences: a survey of citation studies. International Social Science Journal, 23:2 (1971) 236-243.
(14) CHAPANIS, ALPHONSE. Prelude to 2001: explorations in human communication. American Psychologist, 26:11 (November 1971) 949-961.
(15) CLARK, KENNETH E. A critical examination of the national information system for psychology. American Psychologist, 26:4 (April 1971) 325-348.
(16) COLE, JONATHAN R. Patterns of intellectual influence in scientific research. Sociology of Education, 43:4 (Fall 1970) 377-403.
(17) COLE, JONATHAN R.; COLE, STEPHEN. Measuring the quality of sociological research: problems in the use of the Science Citation Index. American Sociologist, 6:1 (February 1971) 23-29.
(18) COOK, KENNETH H. Large scale information processing systems. Section I: introduction and overview. Syracuse University, School of Library Science, Syracuse University Psychological Abstracts Retrieval Service (SUPARS), Syracuse, New York, July 1971, 11 p.
(19) CRANE, DIANA. Information needs and uses. In: Cuadra, Carlos A.; ed. Annual review of information science and technology, vol. 6. Encyclopedia Brittanica, Chicago, Illinois, 1971, 3-39.
(20) CRANE, DIANA. Invisible colleges: diffusion of knowledge in scientific communities. University of Chicago Press, Chicago, Illinois, 1972.
(21) CRANE, DIANA. Social structure in a group of scientists: a test of the "invisible college" hypothesis. American Sociological Review, 34:3 (1969) 335-352.
(22) CRANE, DIANA. Transnational networks in basic science. International Organization, 25:3 (1971) 585-601.

(23) CRAWFORD, ELISABETH T.; BIDERMAN, ALBERT D. Paper money: trends of research sponsorship in American sociology journals. Social Science Information, 9:1 (1970) 51-77.
(24) CRAWFORD, SUSAN. Informal communication among scientists in sleep research. Journal of the American Society for Information Science, 22:5 (September/October 1971) 301-310.
(25) CRAWFORD, SUSAN; ed. Informal communication among scientists: proceedings of a conference on current research. American Medical Association, Chicago, Illinois, 1971.
(26) FUNKHOUSER, RAY G.; MACCOBY, NATHAN. Communicating specialized science information to a lay audience. Journal of Communication, 21:1 (March 1971) 58-71.
(27) GARVEY, WILLIAM D.; LIN, NAN; NELSON, CARNOT E. Communication in the physical and social sciences. Science, 170:3963 (11 December 1970) 1166-1173.
(28) GARVEY, WILLIAM D.; LIN, NAN; TOMITA, KAZUO. Description of a machine-readable data bank on the communication behavior of scientists and technologists. Johns Hopkins University, Baltimore, Maryland, October 1971, 156 p. (JHU-CRSC report no. 20).
(29) GERSTBERGER, PETER G. The preservation and transfer of technology in research and development organizations. Massachusetts Institute of Technology, Alfred P. Sloan School of Management, Cambridge, Massachusetts, June 1971, 271 p. (Unpublished Ph.D. dissertation).
(30) GOLDBERG, ALEKSANDR L. Information needs of social scientists and ways of meeting them. International Social Science Journal, 23:2 (1971) 273-284.
(31) GOULDNER, ALVIN W. Theoretical requirements of the applied social sciences. In: Bennis, W. G.; Benne, K. D.; Chin, R.; eds. The planning of change. Holt, Rinehart and Winston, New York, 1962, 84 p.
(32) GRANT, DAVID A. Psychology: apprehension over a new communication system. American Psychologist, 26:4 (April 1971) 329-330.
(33) GREENBERG, DANIEL S. The new politics of science. Technology Review, (February 1971) 40-45.
(34) GRIFFITH, BELVER C.; JAHN, MARILYN J.; MILLER, JAMES A. Informal contacts in science: a probabilistic model for communication processes. Science, 173:4 (9 July 1971) 164-166.
(35) GUSHEE, DAVID. Problems of the primary journal. Journal of Chemical Documentation, 10:1 (February 1970) 30-32.
(36) HÄGERSTRAND, TORSTEN. Innovation diffusion as a spatial process. University of Chicago Press, Chicago, Illinois, 1967, 334 p.
(37) HAGSTROM, WARREN O. Inputs, outputs, and the prestige of university science departments. Sociology of Education, 44:3 (Fall 1971) 375-397.
(38) HALÁSZI, J. Reading and searching habits of agricultural scientists and students and motivation of agricultural scientists for buying scientific literature. Center for Agricultural Publishing and Documentation, Wageningen. The Netherlands, 1970, 64 p.
(39) HALL, EDWARD T. The hidden dimensions. Doubleday, Garden City, New York, 1966, 193 p.
(40) HAVELOCK, RONALD G. Planning for innovation through dissemination and utilization of knowledge. University of Michigan, Institute for Social Research, Center for Research on Utilization of Scientific Knowledge, Ann Arbor, Michigan, 1971, 533 p.
(41) HILLS, JACQUELINE. A review of the literature on primary communications. Aslib, London, England, 1970, 82 p.
(42) HOLT, ROBERT R. Some neglected assumptions and problems in psychology's information crisis. American Psychologist, 26:4 (April 1971) 331-334.

(43) JENCKS, C.; RIESMAN, D. The academic revolution. Doubleday, New York, 1968, 558 p.
(44) JENKINS, JAMES J. The NISP controversy: a version from the board of scientific affairs. American Psychologist, 26:4 (April 1971) 334-335.
(45) JOHNS HOPKINS UNIVERSITY. CENTER FOR RESEARCH IN SCIENTIFIC COMMUNICATION. The information-dissemination process associated with journal articles published by heating, refrigerating and air-conditioning engineers. Johns Hopkins University, Baltimore, Maryland, April 1971. (JHU-CRSC report no. 19).
(46) JOHNS HOPKINS UNIVERSITY. CENTER FOR RESEARCH IN SCIENTIFIC COMMUNICATION. The production, dissemination, and assimilation of information contained in journal articles in geography. Johns Hopkins University, Baltimore, Maryland, March 1971, 64 p. (JHU-CRSC report no. 18. ED 048 874).
(47) JOHNS HOPKINS UNIVERSITY. CENTER FOR RESEARCH IN SCIENTIFIC COMMUNICATION. Production, exchange and dissemination of information in journal articles on sociology. Johns Hopkins University, Baltimore, Maryland, January 1971, 70 p. (JHU-CRSC report no. 17).
(48) JOHNS HOPKINS UNIVERSITY. CENTER FOR RESEARCH IN SCIENTIFIC COMMUNICATION. The role of the national meeting in scientific and technical communication. Johns Hopkins University, Baltimore, Maryland, 1970, 455 p.
(49) JOHNS HOPKINS UNIVERSITY. SoGSIP STUDY GROUP. Some preliminary results from a survey of graduate students in psychology. American Psychological Association, Office of Communication, Washington, D.C., 1971, 93 p. (OC-3/71-TR no. 15).
(50) KAO, CHARLES H. C. Brain drain: a case study of China. Wisconsin State University, Department of Economics, River Falls, Wisconsin, 1970, 229 p.
(51) KATZER, JEFFREY. Large scale information processing systems. Section V: cost-benefits analysis. Syracuse University, School of Library Science, Syracuse University Psychological Abstracts Retrieval Service (SUPARS), Syracuse, New York, 1971, 85 p.
(52) LANGE, GLADYS ENGEL. Professionalism under attack: the case of the anthropologists. Social Science Information, 10:3 (1971) 117-132.
(53) LIBBY, MILES; ZALTMAN, GERALD. The role and distribution of written informal communication in theoretical high energy physics. American Institute of Physics, New York, 1967 (AIP/SDD-1. AFCNYO-3732).
(54) LIN, NAN. Comparisons between the scientific communication model and the mass communication model. In: Conference on psychology of technical communications. Philadelphia, Pennsylvania, 14-15 February 1972, Institute of Electrical & Electronics Engineers (IEEE), Group on Writing and Speech, New York, 1972, 24 p.
(55) LIN, NAN. The study of human communications. Bobbs-Merrill, Indianapolis, Indiana, (To be published 1973), 250 p.
(56) LIN, NAN; GARVEY, WILLIAM D. The formal communication structure in science. In: American Sociological Association. Annual Meeting. Denver, Colorado, August/September 1971. American Sociological Association, Washington, D.C., 1971, 45 p.
(57) LIN, NAN; NELSON, CARNOT E. Bibliographic reference patterns in core sociological journals, 1965-1966. American Sociologist, 4:1 (February 1969) 47-50.
(58) LINE, MAURICE B. The information uses and needs of social scientists: an overview of INFROSS. Aslib Proceedings, 23:8 (August 1971) 412-434.
(59) LINE, MAURICE B.; BRITTAIN, J. MICHAEL; CRANMER, FRANK A. The information needs of social workers. Investigation into information requirements of the social sciences. Bath University of Technology, University Library, Bath, England, February 1971, 17 p. (Research report no. 4. ED 049 776).

(60) LINE, MAURICE B.; BRITTAIN, J. MICHAEL; CRANMER, FRANK A. Information requirements of college of education lecturers and school teachers. Investigation into information requirements of the social sciences. Bath University of Technology, University Library, Bath, England, February 1971, 28 p. (Research report no. 3. ED 049 775).
(61) LINE, MAURICE B.; BRITTAIN, J. MICHAEL; CRANMER, FRANK A. Information requirements of researchers in the social sciences. Investigation into information requirements of the social sciences. Bath University of Technology, University Library, Bath, England, May 1971. (Research report no. 1. vol. 1: Text, 280 p. ED 054 806; vol. 2: Tables, 261 p. ED 054 807).
(62) LINE, MAURICE B.; BRITTAIN, J. MICHAEL; CRANMER, FRANK A. Information requirements of social scientists in government departments. Investigation into information requirements of the social sciences. Bath University of Technology, University Library, Bath, England, March 1971, 29 p. (Research report no. 2. ED 049 774).
(63) MacRAE, DUNCAN, JR. Scientific communication, ethical argument, and public policy. American Political Science Review, LXV:1 (March 1971) 38-50.
(64) MARTIN, THOMAS H.; PARKER, EDWIN, B. Designing for user acceptance of an interactive bibliographic search facility. Stanford University, Stanford, California, March 1971, 14 p.
(65) MAUERHOFF, GEORG R. Some aspects of Canada's highly qualified manpower resources with special reference to the CAN/SDI project. In: American Society for Information Science, Western Canada Chapter. Annual Meeting. Calgary, Canada, October 1971. Proceedings. 11-23.
(66) MENZEL, HERBERT. Formal and informal satisfaction of the information requirements of chemists. Columbia University, Bureau of Applied Social Research, New York; and New York University, Department of Sociology, New York, June 1970, 116 p.
(67) MERTON, ROBERT K. Priorities in scientific discovery: a chapter in the sociology of science. American Sociological Review, 22:6 (1957) 655-659.
(68) MERTON, ROBERT K; LEWIS, RICHARD. The competitive pressures (I): the race for priority. Impact of Science on Society, 21:2 (1971) 151-161.
(69) MILLER, GEORGE A. The real heart of NISP. American Psychologist, 26:4 (April 1971) 335-336.
(70) PAISLEY, WILLIAM J. Clustering scientific articles to form "minijournals"—preliminary considerations. Stanford University, Institute for Communication Research, Stanford, California, March 1971, 61 p.
(71) PAISLEY, WILLIAM J. Developing a "sensing network" for information needs in education. Stanford University, Institute for Communication Research, Stanford, California, September 1971, 34 p.
(72) PAISLEY, WILLIAM J. Improving a field-based "ERIC-like" information system. Journal of the American Society for Information Science, 22:6 (November/December 1971) 399-408 (Opinion paper).
(73) PAISLEY, WILLIAM J.; PAISLEY, MATILDA B. Communication at scientific and professional meetings. Stanford University, Institute for Communication Research, Palo Alto, California, April 1971, 74 p.
(74) PARKER, EDWIN B. Behavioral research in development of a computer-based information system. In: Nelson, Carnot E.; Pollack, Donald K., eds. Communication Among Scientists and Engineers. Heath Lexington Books, Lexington, Massachusetts, 1970, 281-292.
(75) PARKER, EDWIN B. On-line polling and voting. Stanford University. Institute for Communication Research, Palo Alto, California, 1971, 28 p.
(76) PRESCOTT, SUZANNE. Psychologist's interest in audiotapes and other audiovisual media: survey reports. American Psychological Association, Office of Communication Management and Development, Washington, D.C., 1970, 30 p. (OCMD-10/70-TR no. 10).

(77) PRESCOTT, SUZANNE. The value of postdoctoral institutes for practitioners. Professional Psychology, 2 (Summer 1971) 259-261.
(78) PRICE, DEREK J. de SOLLA. Is there a decline in big science countries and in big science subjects? In: International congress for the history of science. 13th, Moscow and Leningrad, 18-19 August 1971, 21 p.
(79) PRICE, DEREK J. de SOLLA. Little science, big science. Columbia University Press, New York, 1963.
(80) PRICE, DEREK J. de SOLLA. Principles for projecting funding of academic science in the 1970s. Science Studies, 1 (1971) 85-99.
(81) PRICE, DEREK J. de SOLLA. Some remarks on elitism in information and the invisible college phenomenon in science. Journal of the American Society for Information Science, 22:2 (March/April 1971) 74-75.
(82) PRICE, DEREK J. de SOLLA. Some theoretical studies in science and their practical implications. International Conference on Science and Society. 4th. Herceg-Novi, Yugoslavia, 3-10 July 1971, 35 p.
(83) PRICE, DON K. Science at a policy crossroads. Technology Review, (April 1971) 30-37.
(84) ROGERS, EVERETT M. Diffusion of innovations. Free Press, New York, 1962, 367 p.
(85) SABATO, JORGE A. Quantity versus quality in scientific research (I): the special case of developing countries. Impact of Science on Society, 20:3 (1970) 183-194.
(86) SASMOR, ROBERT M. National information system for psychology: support to informal communications. NISP/American Psychological Association, Washington, D.C., 1970, 13 p.
(87) SCHNEIDER, JOHN H. Selective dissemination and indexing of scientific information. Science, 173 (23 July 1971) 300-308.
(88) SEASHORE, STANLEY E. An alternate view. American Psychologist, 26:4 (April 1971) 330-331.
(89) SENDERS, JOHN. The hierarchy of publication forms. American Psychologist, 26:4 (April 1971) 336-337.
(90) SKELTON, BARBARA. Comparison of results of science user studies with "investigation into information requirements of the social sciences." Design of information systems in the social sciences. Bath University of Technology, University Library, Bath, England, July 1971, 44 p. (Working paper no. 1).
(91) SMITH, CLAGETT G. Scientific performance and the composition of research teams. Administrative Science Quarterly, 16:4 (December 1971) 486-495.
(92) SYRACUSE UNIVERSITY. SCHOOL OF LIBRARY SCIENCE. SYRACUSE UNIVERSITY PSYCHOLOGICAL ABSTRACTS RETRIEVAL SERVICE. Large scale information processing systems, Section IV-A: the user component of the system-A. Syracuse University, School of Library Science, Syracuse University Psychological Abstracts Retrieval Service (SUPARS), Syracuse, New York, 1971, 59 p.
(93) TAGLIACOZZO, RENATA; KOCHEN, MANFRED; EVERETT, WILLIAM. The use of information by decision-makers in public service organizations. American Society for Information Science. Annual Meeting. 34th, Denver, Colorado, 7-11 November 1971. Proceedings, vol. 8: Communication for decision-makers. Greenwood Publishing Corp., Westport, Connecticut, 1971, 53-57.
(94) VAN COTT, HAROLD P. Functions and forms of international congresses of psychology. American Psychological Association, Office of Communication, Management & Development, Washington, D.C., 1971, 12 p. (OC-5/71-TR no. 16).
(95) WOLTERS, PETER H.; BROWN, JACK E. CAN/SDI system: user reaction to a computerized information retrieval system for Canadian scientists and technologists. Canadian Library Journal, 28:1 (January/February 1971) 20-23.
(96) WOOD, D. N. User studies: a review of the literature from 1966 to 1970. Aslib Proceedings, 23:1 (1971) 11-23.

2 Costs, Budgeting, and Economics of Information Processing

JOHN H. WILSON, JR.
U.S. Atomic Energy Commission

INTRODUCTION

Early in 1971 the Director of Defense Research and Engineering directed that several information centers supported by the Department of Defense begin recovering at least half their costs from their customers —or close down. In this manner notice was officially given that the era had passed in which management accepted on faith that information services were to be supplied free, particularly in research and development. Cleverdon (26) believes that economic constraints are the most binding restriction currently governing the design and operation of retrospective search systems. Gushee (60), talking in a more general sense claims that economics is the key factor in information activities today.

But the literature still echoes with such statements as that of Bowman & Brown (14). Discussing their company's current-awareness service, they write: "Although the costs of operating our current-awareness service are high and tangible savings to the company elusive, we feel, as does our research management, that the service is invaluable to Dow." Since management is putting their money into the service, they acknowledge value received other than dollar value.

Thus, costs and benefits of information or any other social activity should not always be measured in terms of dollars. Most treatments of the benefits problem warn us that the total welfare of the community must be considered. Welfare economics considers benefits to the entire community, including the benefits derived from information (4, 9).

This chapter is concerned with costs, budgeting, and economics of information processing, primarily as these activities are required in planning. Let us define the many kinds of costs to be discussed. Our definitions need not be too rigid, so long as we are clear about our general purpose. We are not here concerned, as is classical economics, with marginal cost—the cost of producing one more unit of whatever we are producing. The costs that information specialists and managers are concerned with are working costs—total costs, unit costs, average costs, costs of particular operations. These are the costs used in controlling operations and in budgeting. Two important questions must be answered before any cost can be meaningful. First, do the costs include the cost of setting up in business (for instance in a computerized system, do they include the prorated purchase or rent of the computer and the programming expense)? Or are we talking about the cost of one particular operation? And, second, does the cost include vacation and sick pay, space, etc.—(overhead, the accountants call it)? It will usually add 25% to 100% to the bare costs of labor and material.

We are concerned with libraries, information centers, and storage and retrieval systems. We shall not, unfortunately, be able to delve into such intriguing aspects as the cost (and cost effectiveness) of scientific and engineering meetings (which may go as high as $750,000 per 1,000 persons attending), or the cost factors of publishing, printing, or reproducing books, journals, and reports. Our purpose is to introduce some current approaches to costs to those who haven't had to deal much with them and to bring up to date those who are more acquainted with cost trends and controversies.

Material is presented under headings into which the literature sorts quite easily: cost analysis and reporting—essentially accounting; cost effectiveness—how efficiently the job gets done; programming, planning, and budgeting systems—budgeting according to objectives rather than operations; cost benefits and marketing—concerning the value of information and how much you can charge for it. We will be concerned more with the techniques of costing and what costs and economic analysis can tell us, than in actual or comparative costs. Lack of full description in reported costs, and almost complete lack of standards as to what to report or how to report it, makes cost comparisons time-consuming and of questionable value. This is particularly evident in Bourne's surveys (11, 12, 13) and Olsen (136) makes the same point. One reason for a national system of statistics for libraries (Palmer, 138) is to establish standards. Reynolds (149) and Tesovnik & Dehard (166) had difficulty finding useful measurement data because of the wide disparity. Techniques, concepts, and approaches to the many problems of costs are increasingly available and many can be easily and quickly adapted to particular needs.

In earlier volumes of this series, discussions of costs, costing, and economics appeared as parts of chapters. In this first chapter on costs, references from earlier years are included. Much of the literature of the last several years is still valid, and there is more of it than might be expected.

COST REPORTING AND ACCOUNTING

Despite complaints about the lack of cost literature, plenty of it is being produced. Much unpublished material is accessible (136, 166). Little of it is as complete as the reader concerned about costing his operation would like.

Cost analyses of many operations are available, and they are useful for those still doing traditional budgeting (where funding is organized according to operations). They are also useful for one who is trying to compare costs as a measure of efficiency (cost effectiveness), or for one who is making a cost analysis in preparation for a price quotation.

If there is one operation on which there is sufficient cost and system analysis information for any serious inquirer or would-be user, it is for libraries. Bourne's surveys have compared costs nationwide, one of them for several decades (11, 12, 13). Systems analysis of libraries is a well-established discipline, particularly of university libraries: Morse (130); Leimkuhler & Cooper (107, 108); Leimkuhler (105, 106); Buckland et al. on the British University of Lancaster (18); Raffel & Shishko (148). Value of work-measurement studies is attested not only by their number, but by their being written primarily by librarians. Their titles make evident the concern of many librarians with rising costs unrelated to increase in production: "A time and motion study in library operations" (Kozumplik, 100); "Methods and procedures for measuring patron use and cost of patron services. . ." (Nelson Associates, 133); ". . .technical service time and costs. . ." (Tesovnik & Dehard, 166); "Measuring library output" (Palmer, 137); "Work sampling in library administration" (Poage, 143). Competent cost analyses have been performed for state and local library systems by Milliman & Pfister (127), Pfister & Milliman (141), Stocker (163), and Yocum & Stocker (179). The data contained in the referenced documents would have to be interpreted, clarified, adapted by whomever wanted to use them, but no manager can expect to find a cost system that he can apply "as is" to his own operation.

The most thorough presentation this year of cost reporting for an information activity is Price's *Collecting and Reporting Real Costs of Information Systems* (146). He tells how to design the costing system and how to implement it. Flow charts, forms, graphs—everything needed for accounting and control—are there. The document is a down-to-earth treatment of the overall concepts, as well as the nuts-and-bolts activities performed. It describes a cost system developed over five years that has been used in determining and controlling costs of two major federally supported systems: the NASA Scientific and Technical Information Facility and the Educational Resources Information Center (ERIC). Price is confident that, using this system, he could project costs with sufficient accuracy to accept a fixed-unit-price contract and make money. How many information managers would risk that?

In this reviewer's opinion, the fact that this accounting system was developed by a contractor to the federal government demonstrates that contracting out an information system greatly improves the chances of getting the costs of information analyzed and reported. The funding agency has to be very clear about what it wants, and the contractor has to establish a viable cost scheme to stay alive.

Cost-accounting systems applicable to library operations date back over 30 years (17, 126, 150), although Marron (119), as recently as 1969, found difficulty fitting information into the usual cost accounting structure. Current literature agrees that the different costs involved in information operations do have multiple interactions which make them difficult, but not impossible, to fit into workable accounting categories.

Helmkamp (68) gives a lengthy and detailed presentation of a system developed for NASA's Aerospace Research Applications Center (ARAC). Hemkamp's is an accountant's system, including a statistical costing and control subsystem that can be used by any information center. However, his system does not include the entire operation: job order and process costing methods are applied to only two processes—selective dissemination of information and retrospective searches. A technical information center's operation is, Helmkamp claims, highly analogous to that of a typical business firm in which management is dependent on reliable cost information for effective planning, controlling, and decision making.

Therefore many concepts applied to business operations can be applied to information activities—for example, depreciation schedules. The argument that library collections can't be depreciated is difficult to uphold. A collection of older reports will, in general, be of less value and use than a collection of newer reports, even though the value of specific reports may go up. Library insurance is now being widely purchased and requires estimation of the value of a collection. Rare books go up in value and that should be anticipated.

COST-EFFECTIVENESS ANALYSIS

Storage and Retrieval Systems

In any given situation it is possible that there will be several different system designs that, from the viewpoint of performance, would produce equally satisfactory results. In such circumstances, cost must be the determining criterion, Cleverdon (26) claims. Lancaster (102) lamented early in the year that "One barrier to the application of cost-effectiveness. . .to information systems is that realistic costing procedures for information products and services are generally lacking." The Helmkamp (68) and Price (146) presentations are widely applicable and help meet this need.

Cost studies almost invariably show how hard it is to set down precisely what the system is trying to achieve. But until that is done cost-effectiveness analysis is impossible. Once the objectives are clearly stated, the various ways of achieving them can be cost-compared.

The design of storage and retrieval systems has reached a state where Lancaster can summarize in a check-off list the items required for cost-effectiveness analysis (102). He relates *effectiveness* of the system (how well it satisfies its objectives) to *cost effectiveness* (how efficiently it satisfies them), and cost effectiveness to *cost benefits* (whether the system justifies its existence). He sets a modest goal for cost-effectiveness analysis of storage and retireval systems: to serve as a useful tool in the decision-making process. There are two major costs that are variable: one is a function of the number of transactions and the other a function of alternative modes of operating the system. Lancaster spotlights how critical it is that the user of a retrieval system be assisted to frame a good request and points out that this is an aspect of cost effectiveness that the designer of a storage and retrieval system may overlook in making sure that the system is rigorously designed—i.e., that the indexing is adequate, and relevance and recall nicely balanced.

Statistical treatment of costs for large, computer-based document-transfer systems reached the textbook stage with King & Bryant's *Evaluation of Information Services and Products* (89). They have done a great deal to show us how to quantify functions common to many information operations. They concentrate their analysis on the document identification subsystem, devoting three chapters to it. Indexing gets one chapter; screening, another; and user-system interface, another; composition, reproduction, acquisition, storage, and presentation are all tumbled together in one chapter! The authors identify six basic functions of document transfer: composition, reproduction, acquisition and storage, identification and location, presentation, and assimilation. They omit, as do most analyzers of information systems, the all-important initial activity—creating the information. This reviewer feels that, although this initial step might be accounted for under the heading of research and development, we should include it as a function within the overall information system, to get a complete view of the total costs of information.

In the opinion of many, writing a book, journal paper, or report is probably the most expensive step in the communication cycle. No other step in this cycle costs anything close to that, unless it is the user's putting the information to use. If a piece of information redirects the course of his research, he can spend many thousands of dollars in time and equipment. But it will be the rare journal article that will so drastically affect a researcher's efforts. Consequently, for overall improved cost effectiveness, the creation stage is the place to try to save money: can research results be data-banked, so that they don't have to be written up? (This question leads to such questions as how to overcome the "publish or perish" requirement, which we will not go into here.)

A simple cost-effectiveness model that can be applied easily for a storage and retrieval system is developed by King & Caldwell (90). The model uses the following equation:

$$\text{Total costs} = \text{fixed costs} + \text{costs related to input} + \text{costs related to output}$$

Eighteen variables related to input, output, and costs can be plugged into the equation and manipulated and the results tabulated for assessing various tradeoffs. In considering alternate subsystems, one might ask how many subsystems should be considered for a thorough cost-effectiveness analysis. King & Caldwell compared 36 subsystems for the American Psychological Association: three search modes at four levels of recall, and six screening alternatives. Most information managers think they have done a thorough job when they have compared two or three alternatives!

Bradford's distribution (Leimkuhler, 105; Price, 145) is one of several mathematical formulae applicable to cost-effectiveness studies. An example of simple random distribution, it states that for every item of great interest there are quite a few items of lesser interest, a far greater number of items of still lesser concern, and so on. Measurement can be in number of documents in the collection, circulation, or search terms. It is useful in the allocation of resources to be able to allow use of the core of materials that are most in demand. Chi-square test for goodness of fit is advocated by King & Bryant (89) as another useful test.

Computers and Improved Cost-Effectiveness

When to use computers, and what tasks to use them for—and whether to use them at all—with the pros and cons that related experience provides—are recurring themes in cost-effectiveness studies. The issue frequently focuses on book versus card catalogs. Once the data are mechanized, cards or books can be printed in multiple copies. Computerized book catalogs are coming on hard, as can be seen by scanning Waldron's bibliography (172), *Book Catalogs: Survey of the Literature on Costs*, and the lengthy analysis of computerized library catalogs by Dolby et al. (39). Kilgour (86) examines costs of computer-produced cards. Overall treatments of computer application to library activities include Fasana (46), Griffin (59), Hayes & Becker (64), and Jacob (78). Specialized applications include: circulation (99), acquisitions (116), budgeting (71), collection development (157), and costs of all technical processes (43).

The cost-effectiveness of computers for libraries is seen in a rosy glow by Warheit (173) in contrast to Locke's (111) more jaundiced view. Warheit tosses a challenge to librarians to meet the spectacular rise in costs by changing to computer operations. He presents his argument in terms of costs per character—$1.00 per character per year to store information in 1956 as compared with 0.008¢ per character in 1968. He states clearly what the librarian who is contemplating implementation of computer operations faces: (1) start-up and changeover costs; and (2) support of a parallel manual system until the computer can take over. The only alternative he sees is to stay with a manual system with the attendant rising costs and no increase in productivity. Unfortunately, Warheit's presentation is rather general and needs details of analysis and case histories of successful and unsuccessful application to make his case. One cost of computers that is often overlooked is the reprogramming, and consequent rebudgeting, that stems from constant change of computer systems. This is rarely taken into account in initial cost-effectiveness studies.

Locke's short, succinct presentation of the extremely high costs of computers for libraries is the one that should be pondered by the proponents of "computers now," although he bases his analysis almost entirely on experience at the Massachusetts Institute of Technology Library. Most computer installations for information use have been made with "soft money"—federal government funds—but the days of soft living are over. Have we achieved better services or new services with computers? Perhaps, but are they cheaper? Not necessarily.

Computers may be cost-effective for business functions of the library before they are for other functions. Costs will be comparatively low in implementing business operations because these operations are being automated for more and more applications all the time, and a system already in use can be easily adapted. But even here there is little literature to indicate cost effectiveness, particularly for small or medium-sized libraries. Computers may supply faster service or service that otherwise would not be provided; or the librarian may find he can pry funds for computer services out of his management when he can't get any to increase his staff. Cost effectiveness for the librarian may depend on whether he has to go to an outside computer service bureau and pay full charges, or use an in-house computer at a greatly reduced rate.

Axford (5) reports a phoenix-like operation of building a computer-assisted university library system by salvaging what was useful—mostly the business programs—from what had started out to be an all-computer system at Florida Atlantic University.

The question of whether or not to participate in an automated library network was explored by four California college libraries in a 13-week series of workshops (Montague, 129). The purpose of the workshop was to determine the costs and benefits involved in network use of the BALLOTS and SPIRES library automation and information retrieval systems being developed at Stanford University. Representatives of the working staffs of the libraries met one day a week at Stanford and spent at least one day a week at their home site analyzing their own operations in relation to potential use of the network. The study considered the network operating environment, assessed the impact on user-libraries, and determined both the operating costs of using the system (including computing, manual, and displaced costs) and the comparative costs of performing technical processing functions manually and in the network. Libraries were then free to determine whether they would join the network, if at all, and when. Three of the four participating colleges have expressed interest in joining, and so have four others.

For giant computerized on-line national systems such as MEDLARS, cost effectiveness emphasis is reflected in efforts to set up networks that achieve the cheapest transmission rates. Telecommunication costs can run several times—up to ten times—the computer costs for on-line systems (McCarn, 113). Multiplexing and use of already established commercial networks are expected to cut costs of these huge systems with a hundred or more user terminals planned from coast to coast.

Cost-Effectiveness Analysis of Libraries

One of the best cost-effectiveness studies yet made of a single operation is the Raffel & Shishko study (148) of the library of the Massachusetts Institute of Technology. They are little concerned with computers, but they *are* concerned with application of systems analysis techniques. Their use of Morse's work (130), that of Leimkuhler's pupils at Purdue (96), and readily available statistical techniques indicate that useful theoretical and mathematical groundwork has been laid for cost-effectiveness analysis. The Raffel & Shishko study was a graduate thesis sponsored by the Center for International Studies (!) at MIT with the unstinting cooperation of the director of MIT's libraries. Theoretical physicist Morse early fostered an interest at MIT in the systematic analysis and development of advanced library systems. Professor Leimkuhler and his graduate students have been applying industrial engineering to improve the cost effectiveness of libraries for several years at Purdue University.

In this reviewer's opinion, what is greatly needed is systematic application of cost-effectiveness techniques. For instance, in merely setting goals: it is really difficult to state Raffel's & Shishko's two basic objectives for a university library—support of study and required reading and support of research!

The astonishing discovery that the space used for the seating of patrons is the highest-costing item of the MIT library, while three out of four readers using this expensive space are probably not using library materials (Dainte & Gorman, 31), is a vivid illustration of the need for cost-effectiveness analyses. The point that space is a library's most costly aspect, but doesn't get the attention it deserves because it is buried in the overhead costs, was argued convincingly by Fremont Rider thirty years ago (Leimkuhler, 105). If providing study area is a function of libraries, funds should be provided, and librarians should have the responsibility to make the most cost-effective use of space.

Garfield (53) believes that cost-effectiveness of information systems has been largely ignored in the past because people have been preoccupied with achieving sophistication and complexity for their own sake. He would have us make such elementary information sources as telephone books and road and freeway signs more cost effective—and who wouldn't agree?

PLANNING, PROGRAMMING, AND BUDGETING SYSTEMS

Novick (134) presents convincingly the case for planning, programming, and budgeting systems (PPBS). Planning, programming, budgeting are three explicit, consecutive steps. PPBS was developed at the RAND Corporation by Charles Hitch and others and then applied in the Department of Defense, the source of all its subsequent wide application among federal agencies.

In information science as elsewhere, resources are rarely, if ever, equal to needs. It is the essence of decision making to choose among alternatives and to ration scarce means to their accomplishment step-by-step. This is true in profit and nonprofit, public and private organizations. Not only is the extent to which they pursue particular objectives influenced by the resources available, but the character of the objectives themselves is influenced by these resources.

PPBS meets these damands by projecting a *plan*, *programming* the steps by which it will be achieved, and *budgeting* to achieve that plan. Its revolutionary aspect—and its continuing difficulty for managers—lies in its cutting across operational lines. The program budget does not allocate funds for acquisitions, cataloging, and circulation, but for the outreach program for the handicapped, the cooperative integration of all county information activities, and the five-year plan to convert all high school libraries to branch libraries in the county system.

An organization can determine its policies most effectively if it chooses rationally among alternative courses of action, with as full a knowledge as possible of the implications of these alternatives. The PPBS budget design should be helpful in conducting meaningful measurements of the total money costs of accomplishing the defined objectives. Use of PPBS makes it easier to compare alternative ways of accomplishing a given objective and it clearly identifies the future cost implications inherent in near-term financial commitments. When related segments of a single program are administered by different management units, PPBS makes possible comparison of inputs and outputs. It delineates the objectives of spending commitments in such terms that significant cost-effectiveness analysis can be carried out. It makes possible aggregation of related expenditures wherever they occur in the administrative structure. Bromberg (16) has reduced the process to an elementary level in a didactic article aimed at the library school student and the beginning practitioner.

Munn's (131) urgent plea to academic librarians to adopt PPBS would be extended by this reviewer to the entire information fraternity. Such techniques as PPBS require a much more rigorous analysis of return against investment than has usually been applied. How can the claims of the library or information service for budget support be evaluated against those of the computer group, the analytical chemistry group, or the supply division? PPBS will assist information managers in arriving at their answers.

Buckman (19) suggests ways of obtaining such answers in a work that is intended primarily for libraries but is a good introduction to PPBS for all information people. Buckman is a humanist who, after ten years with two large university libraries, is convinced of the merits of PPBS for improved management of information systems. He gives credit for the introduction of the concept to the Hoover Commissions of 1947-1953; but Novick believes it was used as early as 1912 by the Taft Commission. At any rate, the concepts of program budgeting have been around for several decades. Clearly defined statistics and work units are needed because of PPBS's requirement that similar subactivities from various operations be combined to determine whether program goals are being achieved. He buttresses his argument with a summary of the analysis by Hamburg et al. (61).

Reporting and control are only possible when everybody working with a program budget agrees on terms, units, and measurements. If possible, the units measured and the approach to measurement should be such that the results can be grouped for use both with the PPBS budget and the accounting "line item" breakdown required by the controller or the accounting department. The effectiveness of a program budget as an instrument for analysis, planning, and control depends directly on the quality of the data fed into the total operation. Work measurement related to program budgeting is gone into in considerable depth by Schultz (154) and Jones (80) and less rigorously by Howard (73) and Jenkins (79).

Stitleman (162) and Sturtz (164) list several features that distinguish program budgeting techniques from traditional budgeting techniques: identification of objectives, identification of outputs, consideration of costs in a multiyear frame, and development of alternative ways to achieve objectives. They point out that PPBS also requires current operations to compete on an equal footing with new proposals.

PPBS appears to be used in Europe. Kanevsky (81) gives us a picture of how national library development is incorporated in overall planning in Soviet-bloc countries for up to 15-20 years ahead. He refers to the application of mathematical models and statistics but, unfortunately, does not give details or examples. De Vrieze & Ducarme (35) explain how PPBS was applied to the Royal Albert Library of Belgium, rendering the library's operations more visible and governable, helping to identify problems, and facilitating the disposition resources. They summarize succinctly the relative merits of PPBS and address the question of whether it's just a fad.

Background and introductory literature in PPBS is plentiful. The big picture of PPBS as applied to federal agencies is sketched by Dorfman (41) and Novick (134), in two established monographs in the field, and by Hinrichs & Taylor (69). Shorter treatments of PPBS written expressly for professionals in the information field are Ellis (45), Fazar (47), and H. Keller (84). Tudor (167, 168) and Young (180) have prepared extensive bibliographies on the subject.

THE VALUE OF INFORMATION

Marketing—Information for a Price

In the absence of easily defined demonstrable utility for information services, how do we measure their value? In our society the answer is clear—however unpalatable. We judge the value of information services based on what either organizations or individual users are willing to pay for them. Individual users have grown up in a society with a heritage of free information, and they are still surrounded by free services. If one institution decides to shift some of the cost to the user, instead of paying, the user may go elsewhere. Services which start charging often find their demand cut 50% or more. Free services tend to drive out pay services. Under such conditions it is obvious that information services are worth what is paid for them—their price. To the user who refuses to pay, they are worthless. If the user's company is paying, he may be unaware of the price.

What price will the market bear? That is a crucial question for the producer of information who can no longer supply it free.

Swanson (165) in a brief paper presents us with several provocative ideas, e.g.: (1) The marketplace is one place to determine the value of information services. (2) Present methods of paying for library services should be supplemented by a wider range of choices based upon willingness to pay. (3) Providing a minimum of free library service for everyone, as is done now, doesn't bar providing extra services for a price. Why is there, for instance, no widespread order-by-phone, home-or-office-delivery library or information service, such as is provided by the National Lending Library in Britain? Presumably it is thought too expensive, but the potential customer, who may be willing to pay, is not given a choice. The barrier, then, is both the cost and the lack of a scheme or system for recovering costs by passing them on to the customer. Technology may permit home delivery of unlimited amounts of information by hundreds of video-bandwidth electromagnetic channels that use coaxial cables. Slower home delivery could be achieved by means of telephone and delivery trucks. It might be worth finding out whether the demand exists.

On the other hand, to charge even a modest amount for information services might drastically reduce demand: at the Smithsonian's Science Information Exchange, it was discovered that when it began to charge $35 for previously free unscreened searches, demand dropped from 8,000 to 4,000 a year (3, 90).

Charging can be an advantageous policing move: casual inquiries that overload the staff may be eliminated. However, high prices do not necessarily scare off customers. Over 1,200 copies of guides to material properties have been sold by the Electronic Properties Information Center (EPIC) at $150 a volume (Veazie & Connolly, 171). An 8-year marketing case history of EPIC highlights what can be achieved and the obstacles that must be overcome. EPIC showed early in its history a tendency to market what it could not afford to produce and distribute free of charge. Plenum Press agreed to publish and sell some of EPIC's material, and EPIC itself put up other items for sale. The lessons revealed by the study are that marketing is a rocky road but is essential if the operation wants to stay alive. If an information product is useful, customers will pay; if it is a high-quality product that they cannot get elsewhere, they will pay a high price. EPIC's current marketing goal is stated as: ". . .the development of the right marketing mix. . . ."

There is no inherent difficulty in establishing total or partial cost-recovery procedures; it is resistance to the commerciality of such a practice that keeps people from establishing such procedures. After all, guidelines under which federal agencies can charge for information are a dozen years old (170). However, a difficulty in federal agencies charging includes problems of legislative authority for "revolving funds" so that recoverable costs are available to the recovering agency. A year-end report of information-center activities in the Department of Defense (Pebly, 139) indicates that many agencies are moving toward one of three ways for charging for at least part of their services: (1) making arrangements with commercial publishers; (2) letting the National Technical Information Service, which already has thousands of deposit accounts, handle the billing; or (3) handling all sales themselves.

Wills & Christopher (177) tackle another marketing-information question: How much money should an organization spend on information to optimize the marketing of a new product? They develop a marketing model and use as its inputs the estimates of the share of the total market in percent, the probable payoff in dollars for the total market, the probability of success, and the profit likely to be realized (% x payoff x probability of achievement). This simple probabilistic model can be applied to nonprofit organizations such as government agencies, who have to determine the cost/benefit values of their programmed products and services.

Marketing is a new activity for most federal agencies. But vendors and societies selling information services and products for a profit have learned to be adept at marketing, and government organizations must learn from them. Simulating a market environment may help to establish the price-value of information (Green et al., 58).

Cost Benefits

The benefits and value received from information are not, many insist, necessarily quantifiable in money terms (Arrow & Scitovsky, 4; Pigou, 142); other considerations have to be taken into account. But many benefits can be and should be tagged with dollars, and because resources are usually stated in dollars, stating benefits in dollars helps relate the two. No matter how great the benefits—in dollars, time saved, or psychological satisfaction—the drain on resources, stated in the same terms, for a proposed activity may be too great. Or, if the originator of the information sees benefits he is willing to support, he may be willing to supply it to the user at less than cost. Unfortunately, we know little about the benefits of information, but the pace of investigation into benefits is increasing. Study of benefits of public libraries has been applied in the U.S. by Kountz (97) for the Orange County, California, libraries, and by Consad Research (28) for those in the Baltimore area. Hogg (72), the Liverpool Institute of Information Scientists (110), and Durham University (44), Wills & Christopher (177), and Stern (161) consider the benefits problem in the United Kingdom. King & Lancaster (91) and Crum (30) compare cost benefit and cost effectiveness.

A pertinent question related to benefits might be: Does the user receive twice the benefits from twice the amount of information produced and made available? By no means, says Price (145): "An information system has to be doubled in size—perhaps more in cost—for every 5 percent increase in value. . . ." Strong control measures would increase benefits in relation to size—but these are a part of the cost of the system.

The value of public libraries must be estimated in the context of their forming a subnetwork of the local urban or suburban information system (Hearle, 65; Howard, 73). Goddard (56) concludes that the public library could allocate resources more efficiently in a social sense by concentrating on educational activities for patrons of all ages, on programs for deprived persons (poor, black, handicapped, aged), and on service to government agencies. He maintains that the overlap between school libraries and public libraries is critical and that costs created by inadequate school libraries are borne by public libraries. The combination of inputs for school and public library services must be found that will minimize total public cost in supplying library services.

Raffel & Shishko (148) point out that only 40 percent of the expenditure for required student reading at the Massachusetts Institute of Technology is library expenditure. They ask what community benefits could be achieved if the amounts that students spend a year for books (estimated at $100 each) plus what the professors spend ($130) could be combined with the library's in one operating fund (adding $850,000 to the library's $2,280,000, an increase of better than 37 percent).

For calculating benefits of a specific activity, King & Bryant (89) give a simple formula:

$$\text{Excess benefit value} = \text{benefits} - \text{costs}.$$

Where the activity has benefits worth their costs, the excess benefit value is zero and benefits equal costs. They derive benefits by assuming probabilities that certain consequences take place, plotting curves where they are helpful, and then applying appropriate actual costs of operations or the best cost-effectiveness figures available. The technique is very subjective, except where prices determine the minimum benefit value—the price at which the product or service is sold. Yet subjectivity does not make the benefit calculations less useful, since all planning is subjective and has to compete with the reality that is disclosed by future events. In this vein, several writers point out that benefit calculations, as do program budgeting and systems analysis, help to formulate sound judgment but do not substitute for it (16, 41, 47, 69, 134, 153).

Stern (161) defines cost benefit as the ratio of the amount of money collected from customers to the total funding for the information service. He assumes at least a token charge for most services, which would make the user more likely to demand what he really needs. The ratio of total sales to total funding will give the cost benefit of the entire operation, while the ratio of receipts for one subsystem to the costs of running it will give the cost benefit of that subsystem. If the entire system is to be self-supporting, what is collected must equal costs, and the overall ratio will be at least unity. Ratios of subsystems can be set higher or lower, depending on which services management thinks should be supplied below cost and which above cost to support the others.

Lancaster (102) lists criteria for measuring benefits of a storage and retrieval system: actual hard dollar cost savings; loss of productivity if the information is not available; improved decision making (decisions that couldn't be made or would be wrongly or badly made without the appropriate information); avoidance of duplication of effort; and stimulation of invention. Carlson (23) also asks, what is the cost of the worker's not knowing information?

Figures that could serve as the basis for a cost-benefit analysis are found in many cost analyses but frequently are not exploited. For example, Bowman & Brown (14) note an instance in which 73 people saved time when they found new research leads to pursue. How much time was saved at what rate per hour? The accounting office probably has an average professional hourly rate it uses. Bowman & Brown also report that ". . .20% indicated that their literature searching had been reduced by 75% and 13%. . .felt that their time had been reduced by about 50%. About 5% said they were now completely dependent on the current awareness service for their literature needs. . . ." Certainly, one could put some dollar benefit values on these by expending a little further effort to establish the number of hours saved and the rates per hour. Kramer (101) does make these types of calculations as a means of surviving in industry.

A reasonable, brief, explicit approach to calculating cost benefits resulting from an information center's answering questions and issuing data compilations is expounded by Maranchik (118) in a 5-year study of the Air Force Machinability Data Center. He reports estimates that $800 was saved for each question answered and $300 was saved for each use made by readers of suggestions contained in the center's publications. These totaled a surprising $40,000,000 for the years 1965-1969, or $8,000,000 per year. An estimate of the multibillion-dollar metal chip removal industry gives an overall economic view of the industry that the center serves. The technique is simple and generally applicable.

The national benefit that would accrue from wider application of the results of one activity—Library of Congress cataloging—is projected by Kochen & Segur (95). They predict that wider use of Library of Congress cataloging would cost $0.88 million a day, compared to the $1.07 million for cataloging per day that is now being spent. Policy indications are clear: unless the $0.19 million a day being spent for other cataloging is justified, a concerted effort should be made to increase usage of Library ofCongress cataloging, which could achieve a saving of $40,000,000 a year ($0.19 million per day for 250 working days). This study demonstrates the ambiguity of benefit analyses. The Library of Congress is months behind in cataloging. What would be the cost to libraries of developing systems to find their monographs while they are being cataloged? What would be the cost to users of lack of access?

The search for a definition of cost benefits may prove as unrewarding as the search of 19th century economists for "utility." But until we can better define and trace the uses and effects of information—its value, price, utility, whatever we want to call them—the idea of benefit, whether measured in dollars or other units, is at least forcing us to search out the purposes that information serves in our society.

ECONOMICS OF INFORMATION

The Information Industry

Economic analysis of information has, after a decade of development, reached at least the stage where a bibliography of documents on the economics of information has been published (Olsen, 136). Much of the material listed provides a general background in economics as it can be related to information, so there isn't much that is directly pertinent to the issues in this chapter.

The first book devoted to the economics of information, and so far the only one, is Machlup's *The Production and Distribution of Knowledge in the United States* (114), published in 1962. Machlup's easily read analysis credits 29% of the gross national product to the knowledge industry. Machlup does not specifically break out scientific and technical information activities, and undoubtedly most technical information specialists and managers will feel a little discomfited to realize that their profession—or "industry," as Machlup calls it—takes up but a tiny corner of the vast territory Machlup maps out as the knowledge industry. Professional economists have begun to follow Machlup's lead in giving information activities formal economic treatment. Marschak (121) concludes after a rigorous mathematical analysis that there is nothing that sets information outside the bounds of activities to which the most rigorous econometric analysis may be applied.

The Newer Economics

Less rigorous but equally provocative is the treatment of information in the new affluent-society economics of Galbraith (51) (see his *The Affluent Society*). In this reviewer's opinion, we have too many automobiles, and we have too much information. As an example of the latter, a study for the American Psychological Association several years ago (3) showed that one project was reported on 31 times, frequently to the same people—in local and national colloquia, preprints, progress reports, final reports, and journal articles. Information activities, however, have traced an economic path that is the reverse of from-hungry-to-affluent: after an affluent quarter century, as a peripheral activity growing fat off the billions poured into nuclear, aerospace, and defense research and development, technical information is now on hard times as research money dries up (Wilson, 178). While there is some irrigation of the desert, money is not, in the foreseeable future, going to flow to make things bloom as it once did.

Galbraith's analysis of the new industrial state (52) raises information to a primary role. Power in the corporation, Galbraith claims, has passed to the group, which draws on specialized scientific and technical knowledge, on the accumulated information of many professionals using highly sophisticated techniques. The efficiency of the group and the quality of its decision depend on the quality of the information provided and the precision with which it is tested.

Welfare Economics

One of the major tenets of welfare economics, the branch of economics in which economists categorize nonprofit information activities, is that costs can be social costs as well as dollar costs. Welfare economics is concerned with the conditions that determine the total economic welfare of a community (Arrow & Scitovsky, 4; Pigou, 142). Benefits to one individual can be increased without diminishing the benefits for anybody else. Baumol (8), in his discussions of welfare economics, presents the basic difficulty—that of stating all input and output data in terms of dollars: "The cost to society of producing some item may contain elements which can never be expected to show up in the books of the producing firm. . . Similarly, the production of the item may provide social benefits such as improved technology. . .and other advantages which are not reflected in the revenues of the firm."

The interaction between economists and information specialists, that Olsen (136) notes as desirable but heretofore lacking, is beginning to take place, as seen in the literature and in the participation of several economists in a panel "The Economics of Information" at the Denver meeting of the American Society for Information Science in November 1971. One hopes that Olsen's prophecy will come true—that economists will apply their techniques to information activities in the 1970's with stimulating consequences.

TRENDS, QUESTIONS, AND PROBLEMS

Briefly, what are the trends, questions, and problems of information as they are reflected in the recent literature? Techniques for reporting and analyzing costs are being developed and are available to those who want to apply them, although both gathering the data and manipulating them are hampered by lack of standards. Cost effectiveness—how well resources are being applied to getting the job done—is presented at great length and with considerable mathematical sophistication. For most practitioners in the information field, these equations will be difficult to apply, but they are available and mark a significant advance in application of systems analysis. Computers are being used more and more for information chores, although their cost effectiveness is difficult to tie down. The question is less "to computerize or not to computerize" than what subsystem to computerize first, or what computerized services to take advantage of—when or if the money is available. The benefits and value of information along with pricing and marketing present new and thorny problems. And the thorniest is to decide which values to attach a dollar sign to.

Controversy continues between programming, planning, and budgeting (PPBS)—budgeting by objective and ongoing projects—and conventional budgeting by type of operation. PPBS may not be as rigorously practiced now as during the MacNamara-Hitch days in the Pentagon. But requiring budgets to show the programs upon which hard-to-come-by funds are expended and to project what they are going to cost in the future is not an unreasonable demand and is here to stay.

Finally, economics of information is in its infancy. But there is some indication that the 1970's may see considerable development in application of formal economic techniques.

REFERENCES

(1) AMERICAN CHEMICAL SOCIETY. COMMITTEE ON CORPORATION ASSOCIATES. Cost effectiveness of information systems; a report by the Subcommittee on the Economics of Chemical Information of the Committee on Corporate Associates. American Chemical Society, Washington, D.C., May 1969, 15 p. (ED 047 753).

(2) AMERICAN LIBRARY ASSOCIATION. STATISTICS COORDINATING PROJECT. Library statistics: a handbook of conceptions, definitions and terminology. Edited by Joel Williams. American Library Association, Chicago, Illinois, 1966, 176 p.

(3) AMERICAN PSYCHOLOGICAL ASSOCIATION. Reports of the American Psychological Association's project on scientific information exchange in psychology, vol. 1, overview report and reports no. 1-9. American Psychological Association, Washington, D.C., December 1963. (PB 164 496).

(4) ARROW, K. J.; SCITOVSKY, T.; eds. Readings in welfare economics, selected by a committee of the American Economic Association. Richard D. Irwin, Homewood, Illinois, 1969, 734 p.

(5) AXFORD, H. WILLIAM. An approach to performance budgeting at the Florida Atlantic University Library. College & Research Libraries, 32:2 (March 1971) 87-104.

(6) AXFORD, H. WILLIAM. The economics of a domestic approval plan. College & Research Libraries, 32:5 (September 1971) 368-375.

(7) BAKER, DALE B. Comments on UNISIST recommendation 18, pricing policies. Information, 3:3 (May/June 1971) 128.

(8) BAUMOL, WILLIAM J. Economic theory and operations analysis. Prentice-Hall, Englewood Cliffs, New Jersey, 1965.

(9) BAUMOL, WILLIAM J. On the economics of library operation. Mathematica, Princeton, New Jersey, 1967, 168 p. (ED 022 525. Also in: Libraries at large. R. R. Bowker Company, New York, New York, 1969).

(10) BOSE, ANINDYA. Information system design methodology based on PERT/CPM networking and optimization techniques. Pittsburgh University, Graduate School of Library and Information Sciences, Pittsburgh, Pennsylvania, 1970, 230 p. (AD 711 670).

(11) BOURNE, CHARLES P. Cost analysis of library operations. 1971. (In manuscript).

(12) BOURNE, CHARLES P. Data collection and cost modeling for library circulation systems. U.S. Department of Health, Education, and Welfare; Office of Education; Bureau of Research. Washington, D.C., November 1970, 90 p. (ED 046 445).

(13) BOURNE, CHARLES P.; NORTH, JEANNE B.; KASSON, MADELEINE S. Abstracting and indexing rates and costs: a literature review. University of Minnesota, Educational Resources Information Center, Clearinghouse for Library and Information Sciences, Minneapolis, Minnesota, May 1970, 68 p. (ED 043 798).

(14) BOWMAN, CARLOS M.; BROWN, MARILYN T. The development, cost, and impact of a current awareness service in an industrial organization. Journal of Chemical Documentation, 11:2 (1971) 72-75.

(15) BRAUDE, ROBERT M.; HOLT, NANCY. Cost-performance analysis of TWX-mediated interlibrary loans in a medium-sized medical center library. Bulletin of the Medical Library Association, 59:1 (January 1971) 65-70.

(16) BROMBERG, ERIK. Simplified PPBS for the librarian. Prepared for: Dollar Decision Pre-Conference Institute, sponsored by the Library Adminstration Division of the American Library Association, Dallas, Texas, 17-19 June 1971. 13 p. (ED 047 751).

(17) BRUTCHER, CONSTANCE; et al. Cost accounting for the library. Library Resources and Technical Services, 8:4 (Fall 1964) 413-431.

(18) BUCKLAND, M.K.; HINDLE, A.; MACKENZIE, A.G.; WOODBURN, I. Systems analysis of a university library: final report on a research project. Occasional papers no. 4. University of Lancaster, Lancaster, England, 1970, 100 p. (ED 044 153).

(19) BUCKMAN, THOMAS R. PPBS in university, national and large public libraries in the United States. (Available from the author at Northwestern University, Evanston, Illinois).

(20) BURCK, GILBERT. Knowledge: the biggest growth industry of them all. Fortune (November 1964) 128-132, 269-270.

(21) BURKHALTER, BARTON R.; ed. Case studies in systems analysis in a university library. Scarecrow Press, New York, 1968.

(22) CARLSON, WALTER M. The economics of information transfer. In: Transactions of New York Academy of Sciences, November 1969, 803-812.

(23) CARLSON, WALTER M. What is the cost of not knowing? In: Proceedings of Air Force Second Scientific and Technical Information Conference, 28-30 April 1965, 5-10. (AD 621 800).

(24) CAWKELL, A. E. Real cost of information systems. Journal of the American Society for Information Science, 21:1 (January/February 1970) 100.

(25) CHARTRAND, ROBERT L.; JANDA, KENNETH; HUGO, MICHAEL; eds. Information support, program budgeting, and the Congress. Spartan Books, New York, New York, 1968, 231 p.

(26) CLEVERDON, CYRIL W. Design and evaluation of information systems. In: Cuadra, Carlos A.; ed. Annual review of information science and technology, vol. 6, Encyclopaedia Britannica, Chicago, Illinois, 1971, 41-73.

(27) COMMITTEE ON SCIENTIFIC AND TECHNICAL INFORMATION. progress in scientific and technical communications, 1970 annual report. U.S. Federal Council for Science and Technology, Committee on Scientific and Technical Information, Washington, D.C., 1971, 155 p. (COSATI-71-1).

(28) CONSAD RESEARCH CORPORATION. Baltimore metropolitan area library study: recommended long-range work program, final report. CONSAD Research Corporation, Pittsburgh, Pennsylvania, 15 January 1970, 51 p. (ED 045 171).

(29) COOK, J. Financing a library/information service by operating a cost recovery system. In: Conference of Aslib Electronics Group, 13th, Cambridge, England, 9-11 July 1971. Aslib Electronics Group, London, England, 1971.

(30) CRUM, NORMAN J. Cost-benefit and cost-effectiveness analysis: a bibliography of applications in the civilian economy. General Electric Tempo, Santa Barbara, California, April 1969, 28 p. (Report 69 TMP 30. ED 047 715).

(31) DAINTE, ROBERT J.; GORMAN, KENNETH A. A statistical sampling of book readership at a college library. Rider College, Trenton, New Jersey, January 1970, 52 p. (ED 045 149).

(32) DAMMERS, H. F. Computer use in information and data handling: an appraisal of its economic aspects. Information Storage and Retrieval, 6:1 (May 1970) 17-28.

(33) DAVID, EDWARD. Communications on computers: a look at the opportunities. EDUCOM, 6:3 (Fall 1971) 2-3.

(34) DENSMORE, GLEN; BOURNE, CHARLES P. A cost analysis and utilization study of the Stanford University Library System. Stanford Research Institute, Stanford, California, 1965, 38 p. (ED 026 080).

(35) De VRIEZE, FRANS; DUCARME, JEAN-PAUL. Le PPBS à la bibliotheque royale Albert ler de Belgique. Presented at: International Federation of Library Associations, Liverpool, England, August 1971.

(36) DINKA, TESFAYE; OKUTCU, DAVUT. An analysis of book storage and transportation requirements of the Five Associated University Libraries. Five

Associated University Libraries, Syracuse, New York, August 1970, 38 p. (ED 049 767).

(37) DITTBERNER, DONALD. Telecommunications equipment and costs. In: Interlibrary Communications and Information Networks. Sponsored by American Library Association and U.S. Office of Education, 28 September-2 October 1970.

(38) DOLBY, JAMES L.; FORSYTH, V. J. An analysis of cost factors in maintaining and updating card catalogs. Journal of Library Automation, 2:4 (December 1969) 218-241.

(39) DOLBY, JAMES L.; FORSYTH, V. J.; RESNIKOFF, H. L. Computerized library catalogues: their growth, cost, and utility. Massachusetts Institute of Technology Press, Cambridge, Massachusetts, 1969, 176 p.

(40) DONBITO, P. A. Annotated bibliography on systems costs analysis. Rand Corporation, Santa Monica, California, March 1967, 80 p.

(41) DORFMAN, ROBERT; ed. Measuring benefits of government investments. Presented at: A Conference of Experts, 7-9 November 1963. The Brookings Institution, Washington, D.C., n.d.

(42) DOUGHERTY, RICHARD M.; HEINRITZ, FRED J. Scientific management of library operations. Scarecrow Press, New York, 1966, 258 p.

(43) DOUGHERTY, RICHARD M.; LEONARD, LAWRENCE. Management and costs of technical processes: a bibliographical review 1876—1969. Scarecrow Press, Metuchen, New Jersey, 1970.

(44) DURHAM UNIVERSITY. Project for evaluating the benefits from university libraries. Durham University, Durham, England, October 1969, 244 p. (ED 051 824).

(45) ELLIS, ARTHUR E. Influence of PPB on capital budgeting. Presented at: Institute on Program, Planning, and Budgeting Systems for Libraries, Wayne State University, Detroit, Michigan, Spring 1968. Wayne State University, Department of Library Science, Detroit, Michigan, 1968, 21 p. (ED 045 123).

(46) FASANA, PAUL J. Determining the cost of library automation. Bulletin of the American Library Association, 61 (June 1967) 656-671.

(47) FAZAR, WILLARD. Application of PPB to certain federal programs. Presented at: Institute on Program Planning and Budgeting Systems for Libraries, Wayne State University, Detroit, Michigan, Spring 1968. Wayne State University, Department of Library Science, Detroit, Michigan, 1968, 14 p. (ED 045 117).

(48) FAZAR, WILLARD. The importance of PPB to libraries. Presented at: Institute on Program Planning and Budgeting Systems for Libraries, Wayne State University, Detroit, Michigan, Spring 1968. Wayne State University, Department of Library Science, Detroit, Michigan, 1968, 26 p. (ED 045 114).

(49) FAZAR, WILLARD. Program planning and budgeting theory: improved library effectiveness by use of the planning-programming-budgeting system. Special Libraries, 60:7 (September 1969) 423-433.

(50) FREEMAN, MONROE E. Determining costs of information systems. Journal of Chemical Documentation, 7:2 (1967) 101-106.

(51) GALBRAITH, JOHN KENNETH. The affluent society. New American Library, New York, New York, 1958.

(52) GALBRAITH, JOHN KENNETH. The new industrial state. New American Library, New York, New York, 1967.

(53) GARFIELD, EUGENE. Information science and the information-conscious society. Journal of the American Society for Information Science 22:2 (March/April 1971) 71-73.

(54) GILCHRIST, ALAN. Cost-effectiveness. Aslib Proceedings, 23:9 (September 1971) 455-464.

(55) Glossary for systems analysis and planning-programming-budgeting. U.S. General Accounting Office. Washington, D.C., U.S. Government Printing Office, 1969.

(56) GODDARD, HAYNES C. An economic analysis of library benefits. Library Quarterly, 41:3 (July 1971) 244-255.

(57) GORES, HAROLD B.; WEINSTOCK, RUTH. Library facilities and the money crunch. Library-College Journal, 4:3 (Summer 1971) 22-28.

(58) GREEN, PAUL E.; et al. Experiments on the value of information in simulated marketing environments. Allyn and Bacon, Boston, Massachusetts, 1967, 194 p.

(59) GRIFFIN, HILLIS L. Estimating data processing costs in libraries. College & Research Libraries, 25 (September 1964) 400-403, 431.

(60) GUSHEE, DAVID E. Factors affecting dissemination of chemical information. Journal of Chemical Documentation, 11:4 (November 1971) 201-204.

(61) HAMBURG, MORRIS; et al. A systems analysis of the library and information science statistical data system: the preliminary study. Interim report. University of Pennsylvania, Philadelphia, Pennsylvania, July 1969, 55 p. (ED 035 421).

(62) HAMBURG, MORRIS; BOMMER, MICHAEL R. W.; RAMIST, LEONARD E. The development of a statistical information system for university and large public libraries. In: Operations Research Society of America Meeting, 39th, Purdue University, Industrial Engineering, Lafayette, Indiana, 7 May 1971.

(63) HARGROVE, THOMAS L.; STIRLING, KEITH H. California State Library Processing Center design and specifications. University of California, Institute of Library Research, Berkeley, California, 1970, 94 p. (ED 043 356).

(64) HAYES, ROBERT M.; BECKER, JOSEPH. Handbook of data processing for libraries. Becker & Hayes Inc., Bethesda, Maryland, 1970, 997 p.

(65) HEARLE, EDWARD F. R. Designing urban information systems. Nation's Cities, (April 1970) 16-19.

(66) HEINRITZ, FRED J. Quantitative management in libraries. College & Research Libraries, 31:4 (July 1970) 232-238.

(67) HELMKAMP, JOHN G. Managerial cost accounting for a technical information center. American Documentation, 20:2 (1969) 111-118.

(68) HELMKAMP, JOHN G. Managerial cost accounting for a technical information center. Indiana University Foundation, Bloomington, Indiana, January 1968, 308 p. (N68-15502. ED 034 557).

(69) HINRICHS, H. H.; TAYLOR, G. M.; eds. Program budgeting and benefit-cost analysis: cases, text, and readings. Goodyear Publishing, Palisades, California, 1969, 420 p.

(70) HIRSHLEIFER, JACK. Notes on the private and social value of information. University of California, Los Angeles, Western Management Science Institute, Los Angeles, California, March 1967, 22 p. (AD 650 256).

(71) HOFFMAN, WALTER. Data processing applied to library budgets. Presented at: Institute on Program Planning and Budgeting Systems for Libraries, Wayne State University, Detroit, Michigan, Spring 1968. Wayne State University, Department of Library Science, Detroit, Michigan, 1968, 5 p. (ED 045 122).

(72) HOGG, FRANK N. Cost-benefit analysis: the cost of the public library service in relation to value given. In: Dublin Conference, 27 September 1967. Papers and Discussion.

(73) HOWARD, EDWARD N. Toward PPBS in the public library. American Libraries, 2:4 (April 1971) 386-393.

(74) HYSLOP, MARJORIE R. The economics of information systems: observations on development costs and nature of the market. In: American Society for Information Science. Annual Meeting. 31st, Columbus, Ohio, 20-24 October 1968. Proceedings, vol. 5. Greenwood Publishing Corp., Westport, Connecticut, 1968, 301-306.

(75) INTERINSTITUTIONAL COMMITTEE OF BUSINESS OFFICERS. A model budget analysis system for program 05 libraries. c/o Evergreen State College, Office of Interinstitutional Business Studies, Olympia, Washington, March 1970, 30 p. (ED 051 866).

(76) ISRAEL SOCIETY OF SPECIAL LIBRARIES AND INFORMATION CENTRES. Economics of information systems (several papers). In: International Conference on Information Science. Tel Aviv, Israel, 29 August-3 September

1971. Israel Society of Special Libraries and Information Centres, Tel Aviv, Israel, 1971.
(77) JACKSON, W. CARL. Telefacsimile at Penn State University: a report on operations during 1968-1969. Library Resources and Technical Services, 15:2 (Spring 1971) 223-228.
(78) JACOB, MARY ELLEN L. Standardized costs for automated library systems. Journal of Library Automation, 3:3 (September 1970) 207-217.
(79) JENKINS, HAROLD R. The ABC's of PPB. Library Journal, 96:17 (1 October 1971) 3089-3093.
(80) JONES, ARTHUR. Criteria for the evaluation of public library services. Journal of Librarianship, 2:4 (October 1970) 228-245.
(81) KANEVSKY, B. P. Elaboration of programmes, plans and budgets of the nationalist libraries in socialist countries. Presented at: International Federation of Library Associations, 37th, Liverpool, England, August 1971.
(82) KATTER, ROBERT V. Design and evaluation of information systems. In: Cuadra, Carlos A.; ed. Annual review of information science and technology, vol. 4. Encyclopaedia Britannica, Chicago, Illinois, 1969, 47-51.
(83) KAZLAUSKAS, EDWARD JOHN. A shelflist conversion for multi-library uses. Library Resources and Technical Services, 15:2 (Spring 1971) 229-240.
(84) KELLER, HARRY. Development and history of the concept of PPB. Presented at: Institute on Program Planning and Budgeting Systems for Libraries, Wayne State University, Detroit, Michigan, Spring 1968. Wayne State University, Department of Library Science, Detroit, Michigan, 1968, 22 p. (ED 045 113).
(85) KELLER, JOHN E. Program budgeting and cost benefit analysis in libraries. College & Research Libraries, 30:2 (1969) 156-160.
(86) KILGOUR, FREDERICK G. Costs of library catalog cards produced by computer. Journal of Library Automation, 1:2 (June 1968) 121-127.
(87) KING, DONALD W. Design and evaluation of information systems. In: Cuadra, Carlos A.; ed. Annual review of information science and technology, vol. 3. Encyclopaedia Britannica, Chicago, Illinois, 1968, 69-70.
(88) KING, DONALD W.; BROWN, A. M. Some comments on marketing AIP information products and services. Westat Research Inc., Rockville, Maryland, July 1970, 137 p.
(89) KING, DONALD W.; BRYANT, EDWARD. The evaluation of information services and products. Information Resources Press, Washington, D.C., 1971, 306 p.
(90) KING, DONALD W.; CALDWELL, NANCY W. Cost effectiveness of retrospective search systems. American Psychological Association, Washington, D.C., 1971, 34 p. (ED 051 837).
(91) KING, DONALD W.; LANCASTER, F. WILFRID. Costs, performance, and benefits of information systems. In: American Society for Information Science. Annual meeting. 32d, San Francisco, California, 1-4 October 1969. Proceedings, vol. 6. Greenwood Publishing Corp., Westport, Connecticut, 1969, 501-505.
(92) KING, DONALD W.; NEEL, PEGGY W. Cost effectiveness of on-line retrieval systems. Westat Research, Inc., Rockville, Maryland, February 1971, 13 p. (ED 046 460).
(93) KING, DONALD W.; WIEDERKEHR, ROBERT V.; BJORGE, SALLY E.; URBACH, PETER F. Experimentation, modeling, and analysis to establish a new pricing policy at CFSTI. In: American Society for Information Science. Annual meeting. 31st, Columbus, Ohio, 20-24 October 1968. Proceedings, vol. 5. Greenwood Publishing Corp., Westport, Connecticut, 1968, 311-314.
(94) KLINTOE, KJELD. Cost analysis of a technical information unit. Aslib Proceedings, 23:7 (July 1971) 362-371.
(95) KOCHEN, MANFRED; SEGUR, BERTRAND A. Effects of cataloging volume at the Library of Congress on the total cataloging costs of American research li-

braries. Journal of the American Society for Information Science, 22:2 (March/April 1971) 133-139.

(96) KORFHAGE, ROBERT R.; DELUTIS, THOMAS G. A basis for time and cost evaluation on information systems. Purdue University, School of Industrial Engineering, Lafayette, Indiana, 1969, 45 p. (PB 188 946).

(97) KOUNTZ, JOHN. Cost-benefit and cost studies performed at Orange County Public Library, 1969-1971. (Request from the author).

(98) KOUNTZ, JOHN. Library cost analysis: a recipe. Orange County Public Library, California. (Request from the author).

(99) KOZUMPLIK, WILLIAM G. Circulation mechanized. Special Libraries, 62:7/8 (July/August 1971) 287-288.

(100) KOZUMPLIK, WILLIAM G. A time and motion study in library operations. Special Libraries, 58:8 (1967) 585-588.

(101) KRAMER, JOSEPH. How to survive in industry - cost justifying library services. Special Libraries, 62:11 (November 1971) 487-489.

(102) LANCASTER, F. WILFRID. Cost-effectiveness analysis of information retrieval and dissemination systems. Journal of the American Society for Information Science, 22:1 (January/February 1971) 12-27.

(103) LANDAU, HERBERT B. Cost analysis of document surrogation: a literature review. American Documentation, 20:4 (October 1969) 302-310.

(104) LANDAU, HERBERT B. Document dissemination. In: Cuadra, Carlos A.; ed. Annual review of information science and technology, vol. 4. Encyclopaedia Britannica, Chicago, Illinois 1969, 243-246.

(105) LEIMKUHLER, FERDINAND F. Mathematical models for library systems analysis. Purdue University, School of Industrial Engineering, Lafayette, Indiana, September 1967, 17 p. (ED 028 783).

(106) LEIMKUHLER, FERDINAND F. Storage policies for information systems. Purdue University, School of Industrial Engineering, Lafayette, Indiana, June 1969, 18 p. (ED 053 778).

(107) LEIMKUHLER, FERDINAND F.; COOPER, MICHAEL D. Analytical planning for university libraries. University of California, Office of the Vice President - Planning and Analysis, Berkeley, California, January 1970, 57 p. (ED 040 729).

(108) LEIMKUHLER, FERDINAND F.; COOPER, MICHAEL D. Cost accounting and analysis for university libraries. University of California, Berkeley, California, 1970, 47 p. (ED 040 728).

(109) LINTON, W. D. The economics of microfilm in libraries and information centres. In: Plumb, Philip W.; ed. The economics of microfilming and document reproduction: papers given at seminars held by the Microfilm Association of Great Britain, Cambridge, 27th September 1968, and Edinburgh, 8th November 1968. Microfilm Association of Great Britain, 52 High Street, Buntingford, Herts, England, 1969, 4-14.

(110) LIVERPOOL INSTITUTE OF INFORMATION SCIENTISTS. The value of technical information to national and industrial economic development in Britain. In: Conference held in the Adelphi Hotel, Liverpool, England, 3 March 1969. Proceedings, 66 p.

(111) LOCKE, WILLIAM. Computer costs for large libraries, Datamation, 16:2 (February 1970) 69-74.

(112) LORE, HOWARD. A better look at budgets. School Library Journal, (15 March 1971) 93-94.

(113) McCARN, DAVIS B. Networks with emphasis on planning an on-line bibliographic access system. Presented at: Cranfield International Conference on Mechanized Information Storage and Retrieval Systems. 3d, Cranfield, England, 20-23 July 1971. Cranfield Institute of Technology, Cranfield, Bedford, England.

(114) MACHLUP, FRITZ. The production and distribution of knowledge in the United States. Princeton University Press, Princeton, New Jersey, 1962.

(115) MACKENZIE, A. GRAHAM; STUART, IAN M.; eds. Planning Library Services; Proceedings of a Research Seminar (University of Lancaster 9-11 July 1969). University of Lancaster Library, Bailrigg, Lancaster, England, 1969, 238 p.

(116) McKINLEY, MARGARET; comp. A computer-assisted job cost accounting report for the acquisitions department. University of California, Davis, California, July 1970, 40 p.

(117) MAIER, JOAN M.; et al. A cost study of the center's present operations. Bibliographical Center for Research, Rocky Mountain Region, Denver, Colorado, 1969, 89 p. (ED 045 161).

(118) MARANCHIK, JOHN, JR. Cost savings resulting from the operation of the Air Force Machinability Data Center, October 1, 1964 - January 31, 1969. Cincinnati, Ohio, 1 February 1969.

(119) MARRON, HARVEY. On costing information services. In: American Society for Information Science. Annual meeting. 32d, San Francisco, California, 1-4 October 1969. Proceedings, vol. 6. Greenwood Publishing Corp., Westport, Connecticut, 1969, 515-520.

(120) MARSCHAK, JACOB. Economics of information systems. Journal of the American Statistical Association, 66:33 (March 1971) 192-219.

(121) MARSCHAK, JACOB. Economics of inquiring, communicating, deciding. American Economic Review, 58 (May 1968).

(122) MARVIN, KEITH E. PPB as a tool in legislative planning. Presented at: Institute on Program Planning and Budgeting Systems for Libraries, Wayne State University, Detroit, Michigan, Spring 1968. Wayne State University, Department of Library Science, Detroit, Michigan, 1968, 16 p. (ED 045 125).

(123) MATHEMATICA. A cost benefit approach to evaluation of alternative information provision procedures. Mathematica, Princeton, New Jersey, January 1971.

(124) MENKHAUS, EDWARD J. Microfilm: a new survey report. Business Automation, 18:7 (May 1971) 38-42.

(125) MILES, HERMAN W. Technical information - availibility vs. selectivity vs. cost. U.S. Defense Documentation Center, Alexandria, Virginia, September 1969, 14 p. (AD 713 200).

(126) MILLER, ROBERT A. Cost accounting for libraries: acquisition and cataloging. Library Quarterly, 7:4 (October 1937) 511-536.

(127) MILLIMAN, JEROME W.; PFISTER, RICHARD L. Economic aspects of library service in Indiana. Indiana Library Studies, report no. 7. Indiana University, Bloomington, Indiana, 1970, 147 p.

(128) MLYNARCZYK, FRANK, JR. Measuring library costs. Presented at: Institute on Program Planning and Budgeting Systems for Libraries, Wayne State University, Detroit, Michigan, Spring 1968. Wayne State University, Department of Library Science, Detroit, Michigan, 1968, 13 p. (ED 045 120).

(129) MONTAGUE, ELEANOR. Summary of a feasibility study on the participation of four colleges and universities in a Stanford University library automation project. Stanford University, Stanford, California, November 1971, 72 p.

(130) MORSE, PHILIP M. Library effectiveness: a systems approach. Massachusetts Institute of Technology, Cambridge, Massachusetts, 1968, 224 p.

(131) MUNN, ROBERT FERGUSON. The bottomless pit or the academic library as viewed from the administration building. College & Research Libraries, 29:1 (January 1968) 51-54.

(132) NATIONAL LIBRARY OF AUSTRALIA. Ninth annual report 1968-1969. Canberra, Australia, June 1970, 37 p. (ED 049 780).

(133) NELSON ASSOCIATES. Methods and procedures for measuring patron use and cost of patron services for the Detroit Metropolitan Library project. Nelson Associates, New York, New York, 1967, 106 p. (ED 032 084).

(134) NOVICK, DAVID; ed. Program budgeting: program analysis and the federal budget. 2d ed. Holt, Rinehart & Winston, New York, New York, 1969.

(135) NUSSBAUM, HARVEY. Operations research applied to libraries. Presented at: Institute on Program Planning and Budgeting Systems for Libraries, Wayne State University, Detroit, Michigan, Spring 1968. Wayne State University, Department of Library Science, Detroit, Michigan, 1968, 7 p. (ED 045 121).

(136) OLSEN, HAROLD ANKER. The economics of information: bibliography and commentary on the literature. Educational Resources Information Center, Clearinghouse on Library and Information Sciences, Washington, D.C., January 1971, 30 p. (ED 044 545).

(137) PALMER, DAVID C. Measuring library output. Presented at: Institute on Program Planning and Budgeting Systems for Libraries, Wayne State University, Detroit, Michigan, Spring 1968. Wayne State University, Department of Library Science, Detroit, Michigan 1968, 17 p. (ED 042 462).

(138) PALMER, DAVID C. Planning for a nationwide system of library statistics. U.S. Department of Health, Education, and Welfare, Office of Education, National Center for Educational Statistics. Washington, D.C., 1970. (Superintendent of Documents Catalog No. HF 5.215:1507. OE 15070).

(139) PEBLY, HARRY E., JR. Department of Defense Information Analysis Center activity 1971, submitted to COSATI Panel 6. (Available from the author at Plastics Technical Evaluation Center, Picatinny Arsenal, Dover, New Jersey).

(140) PENNER, RUDOLF J. The practice of charging users for information services: a state of the art report. Defense Research Board, Ottawa, Ontario, Canada, 1971, 21 p. (AD 702 262).

(141) PFISTER, RICHARD L.; MILLIMAN, JEROME W. Economic aspects of library service in Indiana. Indiana University, Graduate Library School, Bloomington, Indiana, 1970, 151 p. (ED 044 136).

(142) PIGOU, A. C. Economics of welfare. 4th ed. Macmillan, New York, 1960.

(143) POAGE, S. T. Work sampling in library administration. Library Quarterly, 30:3 (1960) 213-218.

(144) PRICE, BRONSON. Library statistics of colleges and universities. Analytic report, Fall 1968. U.S. Department of Health, Education, and Welfare, Office of Education, National Center for Educational Statistics, 1970, 85 p. (ED 039 888).

(145) PRICE, DEREK J. de SOLLA. Some remarks on elitism in information and the invisible college phenomenon in science. Journal of the American Society for Information Science, 22:2 (March/April 1971) 74-75.

(146) PRICE, DOUGLAS S. Collecting and reporting real costs of information systems. American Society for Information Science, SIG/CBE, Washington, D.C., 1971, 160 p. (ED 055 592).

(147) Project INTREX, semiannual activity report, September 15, 1970-March 15, 1971. INTREX PR-11. Massachusetts Institute of Technology, Cambridge, Massachusetts, 15 September 1971.

(148) RAFFEL, JEFFREY A.; SHISHKO, ROBERT. Systematic analysis of university libraries: an application of cost-benefit analysis to the M.I.T. Libraries. M.I.T Press, Cambridge, Massachusetts, 1969, 107 p.

(149) REYNOLDS, ROSE; comp. A selective bibliography on measurement in library and information services. Aslib, London, England, April 1970, 20 p. (ED 052 787).

(150) RIDER, FREMONT. Library cost accounting. Library Quarterly, 6:4 (October 1936) 331-381.

(151) ROGERS, RUTHERFORD D.; WEBER, DAVID C. University library administration. H. W. Wilson Company, New York, 1971, 454 p.

(152) SCHIEBER, WILLIAM D.; SHOFFNER, RALPH M. Telefacsimile in libraries: a report of an experiment in facsimile transmission and an analysis of implications for interlibrary loan systems. University of California. Institute of Library Research, Berkeley, California, February 1968, 137 p.

(153) SCHLESINGER, JAMES R. Uses and abuses of analysis. In: Hinrichs, Harley H.; Taylor, Graeme M. Program budgeting and benefit-cost analysis, cases, text, and readings. Goodyear, Pacific Palisades, California, 1969, 346-358.
(154) SCHULTZ, JON S. Program budgeting and work measurement for law libraries. Law Library Journal, 63 (August 1970) 353-362.
(155) SESSIONS, VIVIAN S. The cost and costing of information storage and retrieval. Information Storage and Retrieval, 6:2 (June 1970) 155-170.
(156) SESSIONS, VIVIAN S. URBANDOC: a bibliographic information system. Demonstration report. New York City Planning Commission and U.S. Department of Housing and Urban Development, Washington, D.C., 1971, 173 p. (ED 051 821).
(157) SIMMONS, PETER. Collection development and the computer. A case study in the analysis of machine readable loan records and their application to book selection. University of British Columbia, Vancouver, Canada, 1971. (ED 054 817).
(158) SPENCER, CAROL C. Random time sampling with self observation for library cost studies: unit costs of interlibrary loans and photocopies at a regional medical library. Journal of the American Society for Information Science, 22:3 (May/June 1971) 153-160.
(159) SPENCER, MILTON. Projecting program cost over an adequate time horizon. Presented at: Institute on Program Planning and Budgeting, Wayne State University, Spring 1968. Wayne State University, Department of Library Science, Detroit, Michigan, 1968, 18 p. (ED 045 119)
(160) STANDERA, OLDRICH. COMPENDEX/TEXT-PAC: current information service. Calgary University Data Center, Alberta, Canada, August 1970, 94 p. (ED 044 120).
(161) STERN, B. T. A cost benefit technique for R&D based information. The Wellcome Foundation Ltd., Langley Court, Beckenham, Kent, BR 3 BS, England, August 1970, 7 p. (ED 054 818).
(162) STITLEMAN, LEONARD. Cost utility analysis applied to library budgeting. Presented at: Institute on Program Planning and Budgeting Systems for Libraries, Wayne State University, Detroit, Michigan, Spring 1968. Wayne State University, Department of Library Science, Detroit, Michigan, 1968, 15 p. (ED 045 126).
(163) STOCKER, FREDERICK D. Financing public libraries in Ohio. Ohio State University, Center for Business, Columbus, Ohio, March 1971, 83 p. (ED 048 892).
(164) STURTZ, CHARLES. The difference between conventional budgeting and PPB. Presented at: Institute on Program Planning and Budgeting Systems for Libraries, Wayne State University, Detroit, Michigan, Spring 1968. Wayne State University, Department of Library Science, Detroit, Michigan, 1968, 12 p. (ED 045 115).
(165) SWANSON, DON R. Should present methods for financing library and information services survive? In: Association for Computing Machinery. Annual Conference. Chicago, Illinois, 3-5 August 1971. Proceedings. Association for Computing Machinery, New York, New York, 1971, 568-569.
(166) TESOVNIK, MARY E.; DEHARD, FLORENCE E. Unpublished studies of technical service time and costs: a selected bibliography. Library Resources and Technical Services, 14:1 (Winter 1970) 56-67.
(167) TUDOR, DEAN. Planning-programming-budgeting-systems. Council of Planning Librarians, Monticello, Illinois, March 1970, 20 p. (Exchange bibliography 121).
(168) TUDOR, DEAN. Planning, programming, budgeting systems. (A supplemental to exchange bibliography no. 121 of March 1970). Council of Planning Librarians, Monticello, Illinois, April 1971, 6 p. (Exchange bibliography 183).
(169) U.S. DEFENSE DOCUMENTATION CENTER. A DDC bibliography on cost/benefits of technical information services and technology transfer. U.S. Defense Documentation Center, Alexandria, Virginia, July 1968, 297 p. (DDC-TAS-68-29. Supplement is DDC-TAS-68-29A).

(170) U.S. EXECUTIVE OFFICE OF THE PRESIDENT. Circular no. A-25, To the Heads of Executive Departments and Establishments. Subject: user charges. U.S. Executive Office of the President, Bureau of the Budget, Washington, D.C., 23 September 1959. (Issued by Maurice Stans).

(171) VEAZIE, WALTER H., JR.; CONNOLLY, THOMAS F. The marketing of information analysis center products and services. Educational Resources Information Center, Clearinghouse on Library and Information Sciences, Washington, D.C., June 1971, 33 p. (ED 050 772).

(172) WALDRON, HELEN J. Book catalogs: survey of the literature on costs. Rand Corporation, Santa Monica, California, May 1971, 26 p. (ED 053 775).

(173) WARHEIT, I. A. Automation of libraries—some economic considerations. Presented to: Canadian Association for Information Science, Ottawa, Ontario, Canada, 27 May 1971.

(174) WEIL, BEN H. Document access. Journal of Chemical Documentation, 11:3 (August 1971) 178-185.

(175) WESSEL, CARL J.; et al. Criteria for evaluating the effectiveness of library operations and services. Phase 1: Literature search and state of the art, 1967. (AD 649 468). Phase 2: Data gathering and evaluation, 1968, 120 p. (AD 676 188). Phase 3: Recommended criteria and methods for their utilization, 1969, 104 p. (AD 682 758). J. I. Thomas and Co., Washington, D.C.

(176) WILLIAMS, GORDON; et al. Library cost models: owning versus borrowing serial publications. Center for Research Libraries, Chicago, Illinois, 1968, 166 p. (PB 182 304).

(177) WILLS, GORDON; CHRISTOPHER, MARTIN. Cost/benefit analysis of company information needs. UNESCO Bulletin of Libraries, XXIV:1 (January/February 1970) 9-22.

(178) WILSON, JOHN H., JR. Major trends and portents related to information costs. In: American Society for Information Science. Annual meeting. 33d, Philadelphia, Pennsylvania, 11-15 October 1970. Proceedings, vol. 7: The information conscious society, Greenwood Publishing Corp., Westport, Connecticut, 1970, 249-252.

(179) YOCUM, JAMES C.; STOCKER, FREDERICK D. The development of Franklin County Public Libraries, 1980. Prepared for Columbus Public Library and Advisory Council of Franklin County Public Libraries, Ohio State University, Center for Business and Economic Research, Columbus, Ohio, 1970, 258 p. (ED 044 160).

(180) YOUNG, HELEN A. Performance and program budgeting: an annotated bibliography. American Library Association Bulletin, 61:1 (January 1967) 63-67.

II

Basic Techniques and Tools

Richmond's chapter addresses the status of document description, including descriptive analysis of documents (bibliographic analysis) and descriptive representation of documents (subject analysis), and reviews the studies and advances—or lack of them—made in 1971.

The description of documents (book, serial, or non-book materials) must satisfy the librarian's need to distinguish the document from all other documents, and must simultaneously satisfy the need of the user to easily decide from the description whether or not the document is the one he seeks. Because the needs served by document description vary greatly, the descriptions themselves tend to vary in form and complexity, the lack of uniformity posing problems for their users. Some progress has been made recently in bringing out more uniform document description; economic pressures and the related pressures to centralize and automate have forced greater acceptance of the idea of uniformity.

Although significant progress is beginning to be made in standardizing book description, not as much is being made in solving the growing problem of the description of non-book materials such as microforms, reprints, audio-visual aids, and computer tape data bases. Richmond feels that the only significant advances have been in the bibliographic control of audio-visual materials. She recognizes the dangers of premature standardization but pleads for information scientists to end what she feels is a shameful duplication of efforts in document description and representation.

Prywes and Smith address themselves to the problems of organizing information in information systems with large and complex data bases. They believe that the organization of information can and should be mechanized and that, in order to facilitate the mechanized organization of information, it is necessary to create a Data Description Language (DDL) capable of describing every aspect of data organization and helping to facilitate inter-computer communication of data and the conversion of data from one organization to another. Such DDLs are now being developed as a result of recognition of the importance of these uses.

Prywes and Smith review the current literature related to DDL development and discuss a prototype DDL using, as a recurring example, the *Annual Review*. They argue that the components of the prototype DDL should be able to describe logical organization of data (fields, groups, records, files, files of files), physical organization of the data, and mapping of the data. They should also provide automatic aids, such as locators and directories of standardized names for data items, to enable the user to cope with the problems of search, browsing, and maintenance. The development of DDLs that meet these requirements would facilitate the mechanization of data conversion from a current organization to a new one.

In his chapter on the user interface in interactive systems, Bennett focusses sharply on an area of growing importance in information science, the relationship between user behavior and the design of the interface facility in interactive computer systems. The designer of interactive systems must analyze four major system components (task, user, terminal type, and display) to create an interactive facility that can support the user effectively in his decision-making activities. To date, no highly workable procedures have been developed for task analysis, and the user—the person directly interacting with the terminal—has largely been neglected by system designers. Current user studies reveal that both user and designer will benefit when designers better understand the user's needs, skills, and motivations. A number of useful studies have recently been made of the two major types of terminals (typewriter and cathode ray tube) and of other possible media for man-computer communication, such as automatic speech recognition. Clearly, users need clear displays of information at the terminal; they would also be helped by having standardized input and output formats.

Designers of interactive systems must be prepared not only to adapt systems to user needs but to train the users so that they can fully exploit system capabilities. Although we are beginning to see controlled experiments, case studies and field trials of interactive systems, there is still much to learn. For example, little if any data have yet been gathered on how users are affected by the time lapse between completion of input to the terminal and output from the terminal. However, progress is being made in designing interface languages that take into account the user's natural language habits.

User behavior is known to change with experience in using interactive systems. Therefore, interactive systems should be designed with flexibility for change. Users of interactive systems are presently confronted with a bewildering array of user-interface conventions. Obviously, they would benefit greatly from the adoption of common user-interface conventions.

The chapter by Kletter and Hudson provides the first discussion of video cartridges and cassettes to appear in the *Annual Review*. They regard video cassettes ("cartridge television") as the newest communication tool, a particularly important one because it provides the user with great control over specific topic, time, and place of viewing. Large private and public institutions that need to instruct new employees have long needed inexpensive well-packaged lessons. The video cassette, which encourages such methods as student-controlled pacing, may provide a better way of teaching new skills. It may prove to be as useful in the classroom as in the industrial world and become a necessary supplement to and enrichment of formal education.

Disappointingly, most of the current literature on video cassettes is on technical and marketing aspects, rather than on potential uses and social impact. Kletter and Hudson discuss each of the major systems, many of which appear to be incompatible with each other in one or more respects. (As with most areas that are heavily concerned with hardware, much of the literature consists of brochures and newsletters, and precise descriptions are not always available.) If standardization does not occur, perhaps natural selection will eliminate the least effective systems.

Kletter and Hudson feel that economic factors should not continue to dominate the literature and that the individual user and the potential influence of the new technology on society should be closely examined. For example, the management and distribution of such video-cassette instructional media must be carefully considered. Perhaps public libraries could become access centers for the distribution of audio-visual materials, including cassettes, to the community. Used in the home, especially, the video cassette could contribute effectively to the creation of a better-informed society. With abundant cable television channels, the video cassette could make television broadcasting itself a victim of natural selection.

3 Document Description and Representation

PHYLLIS A. RICHMOND
Case Western Reserve University

INTRODUCTION

The complementary areas of descriptive analysis and representative or subject analysis of documents will be covered in this chapter. The preceding six versions of the chapter (19, 130, 146, 55, 8, 162) have leaned very heavily on the side of document representation, with only minimal attention to document description (55, p. 73; 8, pp. 143, 148-149). This omission will be remedied here. As with previous reviews it has been necessary to read much that cannot be included in such a short chapter, and undoubtedly pearls of wisdom have eluded the reviewer's attention. Errors of omission and commission, of course, are the reviewer's responsibility.

In document description there are two equally important obligations. One is to treat each document as a member of the total document population. Each must be differentiated from all the others. The second obligation is to the users. They must be able to tell from the description whether the document is the one they seek or whether it might potentially be useful to them. Of course, to do this, they must be able to find the document among the total population. This latter feature, usually termed "bibliographic control," is partly a matter of document representation as well. "Document" here includes books, serials, and nonbook materials forming the collection of a library or information center.

Ideally, all documents should be described uniformly so that the users can learn the system and use it anywhere. Standardization and codification attempt to achieve this objective. Most of the section on document representation will be concerned with this aim and its accomplishment.

In document representation, there is a dichotomy of sorts between primary emphasis on structure and primary emphasis on terminology. Both have venerable antecedents in philosophy and practice. Because of the need to keep up with constant changes in subject content, the area of document representation does not lend itself very happily to standardization and codification, though there is no shortage of attempts in this direction. The section on document representation will be concerned with such attempts as well as with activity directed toward developing greater flexibility in response to change.

DOCUMENT DESCRIPTION

General Remarks on the Descriptive Analysis of Documents

Document description covers the decision-making process, called *entry*, used in determining authorship, or, without an author, the title to be used as the chief identifying characteristic of a work.[1] It also includes a physical description. While the amount of descriptive material varies with the document, essentially it includes enough data to differentiate one physical document from another. A coded standardization of form and format follows choice of entry. Document description is designed to render authors, titles, series, and other bibliographic elements distinctive from each other and among themselves. For example, one form of an author's name is chosen to represent all the variants (other than pseudonyms) that he may have used. The purpose of document description is bibliographic control of a continuum of books, serials, and non-book materials. The book part of this continuum in the world to date is estimated by Asleson to be 30 million works (9). Works or collections of works coming out in microform or as reprints or both compound the problem of description because of their format and content. Bibliographic control of serials is complex, with *content* control being displayed through abstract journals, indexes, and bibliographies in the subject literatures, while *identification* control treats them as books.

Document description comes in several levels of completeness. Rare books, manuscripts, and books that are of unusual interest receive

[1] "Work" is used here in the sense established by Lubetsky (90). A single "work" can have many editions, varying titles, translations, abridgments, editors, etc.

special attention. Analytic and descriptive bibliography (51, 93, 28) represents the apex of scholarship in this respect, in that it is a minute examination of descriptive matters of interest to the critic. At the lowest level are simple title-a-line catalogs designed as fast indexes to a collection (117). Most document description lies somewhere between these two extremes and is variable as to content.

Descriptive Analysis of Books

For books and for identification of serials, the methodology of description as it is conceived today was begun in the 19th century by Panizzi (111) of the British Museum, Cutter (46) of the Boston Public Library, and Jewett (78) of the Smithsonian Institution. Their pioneering efforts have been updated by Lubetsky (90), formerly of the Library of Congress, whose work has been characterized by attention to logic in the formulation of a more easily used set of rules governing decisions required for entry.

In the early 1950's, when Lubetsky began his study aimed at improving the system, there had been two Anglo-American codes for document description, one in 1908 (2), and a second in 1949 (151, 3) divided between physical description and rules for entry. Neither was an ideal tool. Lubetsky's new draft code (90) laid the foundation for the present *Anglo-American Cataloging Rules* (AACR), which are published in two texts, North American (6) and British (7), that represented seemingly irreconciliable views when the code was published in 1967.

Descriptive rules of any kind seem to generate controversy, especially at conferences and institutes on code revision (137, 72, 73, 74, 75). None of the basic differences have actually been settled and they crop up over and over again. For example, is uniformity in entry possible? If so, how can it best be achieved? What is the most logical method for choice of entry and form of name? Is corporate entry the best solution for non-distinctive titles? What is the justification for its use since at least one-fifth of users reject it out of hand? What is the justification for using the vernacular in foreign corporate names and not for classical authors? What are the most logical methods for handling pseudonymous, anonymous, and classical works? Is uniform title a workable solution to the problems of indeterminate or variable title entry or translated titles? How do we achieve standardized descriptive terms whose interpretation is clear? Are the present forms too rigid in interpretation? What is the justification for successive entry versus entry under earliest or latest title for serials? What kind of users need each? What compromises between legalism and permissiveness must be made so that clarity to the users is paramount? Is a combination of logic and users' behavior desirable? or possible? Or should we develop a logical base that can be taught to users? Will such a base always require a middleman at the interface between users and system? How can users usefully supply feedback necessary for continuous reaction and change as the knowledge base changes?

These problems represent some objective realities that confront those who deal with the descriptive analysis of some 30 million books. Lubetsky has made a *logical* analysis of the problems and their solutions to date, but what is needed is a *scientific* analysis. If natural scientists, as Kuhn (84) has pointed out, made "critically important advances in the understanding of nature" by studying "what the craftsmen had already learned how to do," surely, in respect to the questions given above, information scientists can do as well. This kind of research is urgently needed.

Some of the 1971 authors continue analysis of the questions, in such studies as Blanken's discussion of international name indexes (21), a well-done review of *form of name* problems; Maxwell's discussion (100) of what goes into the description (more than the administration wants to pay for and less than the user needs); studies by Diefenbach (50) and Isa (77) on handling Indonesian materials; Wang's work (165) on cataloging pirated Chinese books; and many others. Since filing rules strongly affect catalog usage, standardized rules are available (4, 154), but these are often abused in practice.

A bibliographic description is taken from the title page and incorporates other matter from elsewhere in the work. For instance, the author's name and parts of the imprint are not always on the title page; the form of the author's name may change from opus to opus; edition statements may be well hidden; and the series inclusion is almost never on the title page.

Where does documentary behavior leave off and bibliographic behavior begin? Obviously, this occurs the minute the title page ceases to have all the necessary information on it. But "necessary" is a loaded term. While Lubetsky (91) calls for a purification of current rules by deleting compromises made between logic and practice (in favor of logic), others such as Massonneau (97) and Kieffer (81) point out that needs for descriptive information differ between book and card catalogs. One may also add that the sheer number of books makes a difference. The needs of the little 250,000-volume library bear almost no relation to those of the Library of Congress, but if the little library is going to accept centralized cataloging it automatically becomes part of the continuum. Furthermore, the little library may have the only surviving copy of a work, which would demand that the work be part of a central catalog.

Where differences of opinion on physical description become too acrimonious, heat can be taken out of the argument by the Judgment of Solomon, as is the case with the Ohio College Library Center (OCLC), which tailors the format of cards to suit each library's specifications (82, 107, 69). Yet this method can be dangerous, as witnessed by all the correction procedures as to entry that have had to take place before the National Union Catalog depository could be printed.

The factor of centralization as a force encouraging more uniform document description has been mentioned. More and more libraries are recognizing that they are part of one single global entity. Not only does each have a share in the data base of 30 million or more works, but the communication base for any kind of cooperation is comparably extensive. This is true whether the cooperation is in cataloging, cooperative or at least non-competitive purchasing, interlibrary loan, or photoduplication at a distance by photocopying, facsimile transmission, or other process.

Another important factor, besides the one-big-happy family concept, is the availability of machine-readable cataloging via the MARC II program at the Library of Congress or British MARC from the *British National Bibliography*. This has provided a potential means of getting data copy cheaper and faster than previously. The MARC II program, ably discussed by Avram (15) in the preceding volume, continues to make progress. Ristow & Carrington (120) outline MARC processes for maps. A serials format has been developed (153). A special program for automatic recognition of descriptive elements in MARC has been devised (152); its algorithms are given by Maruyama (96), and its implications by Shoffner (131). The pilot project of RECON (Retrospective Conversion of Library of Congress records to MARC format) is being continued, and Avram & Maruyama (16) report that various input devices, such as optical character recognition equipment, are being considered. Three groups from the American Library Association have formed a joint committee "to review and recommend action on standards for the representation in machine-readable form of bibliographical information, with a view to the development of standards which would make possible the effective exchange of machine-readable bibliographic data" (42). Here is a case in which automation forces standards by necessity.

At least two major projects are using MARC tapes as input: the Ohio College Library Center (82, 69) and the Stanford University time-shared project BALLOTS (for Bibliographic Automation of Large-

Library Operations On Time-Sharing) (54). The OCLC became operational just before the fall semester of the 1971/72 academic year. BALLOTS ended a nine-month operational experiment with a prototype system. Descriptions of other uses of MARC may be found in almost every issue of the *Journal of Library Automation*.

MARC has continued to arouse international interest. A conference on automation was held in Regensberg, Germany, in 1970, the results of which fill almost the whole year's volume of *Libri* (148). At this meeting, Coward (45) suggested that three things are necessary for satisfactory international use of MARC: a standard for communicating bibliographic material in electronic form, similar to the one adopted by British and American users (156); the adoption of *Anglo-American Cataloguing Rules* British version (7); and the addition of the Universal Decimal Classification numbers. Chauveinc (35, 36, 37) described a processing format in use at the Université de Grenoble, based on a combination of MARC II and British MARC, adapted for French usage.

The MARC success is one more link in a chain of national bibliographic aids. Centralization—in the production and distribution of Library of Congress document descriptions in card form, in the cooperative creation of these descriptions, and in forming and using the National Union Catalog depository—has long existed, but without much impression being made on uniformity in document description itself. Even the addition of computerized publication methods might not have had very much impact without the National Program for Acquisitions and Cataloging (NPAC)—Shared Cataloging—authorized under Title IIC of the Higher Education Act of 1965. This program, founded with the goal of developing a means of once-and-for-all cataloging, is discussed in several 1971 publications, notably those by Budington (30), Pfeifer (112), and Schrader & Orsini (129), and its progress is outlined each year in the *Annual Report* of the Librarian of Congress (150). Among other things, this program has helped to initiate the attempt, described by Anderson (5) and Sullivan (140), to reunite the British and American texts of the Anglo-American code according to the international Paris Principles (76), and also to develop compromises that may be necessary to apply *internationally uniform* rules to all national bibliographies to create acceptable cataloging at the point of origin for much documentation.

In 1971, the Council on Library Resources granted funds to the Permanent Secretariat of the International Federation of Library Associations so that their Committee on Cataloging might "serve as a center for the international coordination and standardization of cataloging rules and practices'' (62). One may note that wider acceptance and stricter application of uniform rules for document description would make searching far more productive than it is now, and the use of these rules should lessen redundancy caused by using many different types and forms of entry for an identical document. It would not cut down on the redundancy caused by multiple publications of the same work, for example, as a report, an article, a book, a sourcebook, a reprint, and/or a microform, as discussed by London (89), Voos (164), and others, who claim that the various literature ''explosions'' are actually paper explosions. White (168) gives guidelines for avoiding the purchase of ''information which is duplicated too heavily to do the collection any good.''

As part of the perennial arguments over how best to describe books, studies are made of users. Tagliacozzo et al. (143, 144, 145) at the University of Michigan, have examined catalog usage. Their conclusions suggest that authors' names are preferred elements used in searching, even when other forms of entry are easier to find. Lipetz's work at Yale (87, 88) confirms the Michigan studies. Maltby (94), in a survey of user studies in general, views more accurate memory of titles as occurring only among scientists. In a different approach, Chervenie (38) considers how much training is required to find one's way through the card catalog using the *Anglo-American Cataloging Rules*. He concludes that ''to attain the minimum level of efficiency takes an average of sixty hours instruction and 200 hours of practice.'' This reviewer believes that this a reasonable estimate. The complexity of document description satisfactory to critical users makes such description self-defeating when it comes to making it clear to the same users. In other words, the demands of users are almost impossible to meet when one is confronted by the *materia bibliographica* (the information about itself given on and in a document). This complexity is not limited to the card catalog; it also appears in subject bibliographies. The argument may be made that this shows that the Anglo-American code is futile, but such an argument begs the question. How does one do justice to the almost infinite variety in ways of indicating authors, titles, editions, editors, series, and so on *actually found in the books themselves*? How far dare one go in departing from the title page? Surely any deviation must be recorded; and this is how codes begin.

It is interesting at this point to note that report literature is the stepchild in international codification plans. An existing code for U.S. government documents (149) does not jibe with any international codes for reports. There is an unfortunate tendency, in citations, to treat reports as journal literature, which makes them exceptionally hard to find.

Because they are generally held in low opinion and are often ephemeral in nature, there has not been much pressure for action on standardization.

One final matter in document description remains. Cataloging-in-publication (CIP) has been re-introduced as a somewhat less ambitious successor to the ill-fated Cataloging-in-source experiment of 1958-59 (33). Articles by Wheeler (167), Clapp (39), and Welsh (166) discuss the various factors involved in putting cataloging data in every book. Descriptively, this will include author, brief title, series notes, and added entries. The Library of Congress has received grants of $200,000 each from the National Endowment for the Humanities and the Council on Library Resources to support the program for two years.

Finer details and other topics of document description may be found in the "Year's work" article by Massonneau (98) in *Library Resources & Technical Services*.

Descriptive Analysis of Non-Book Materials

In contrast to the generally optimistic outlook for book description in both the physical and intellectual sense, problems of non-book materials continue to pose major obstacles. Microforms, reprints, audio-visual aids, and computer tape data bases demand serious attention. These kinds of materials, before they began to proliferate, were usually described, if at all, outside the main catalog to a collection. There were problems, not only with description, but with storage, servicing, circulation, and consultation that led librarians to consider these materials something of a nuisance. A few libraries or information centers have existed just to handle special media (maps, pictures, engineering drawings, etc.).

The whole subject of micropublishing, and its problems—which are based in part on what is called "Product invisibility"—is well covered by Veaner (160). "Product invisibility," which is caused by the fact that the buyer cannot check his purchase without considerable expense,[2] is a result of bibliographic control so poor that Veaner can cite academic institutions that are being pressured by their faculty *to buy in hard copy what has already been bought in microform*. Some standards are urgently needed to lead publishers to supply adequate bibliographic data for the contents of the microform. Veit (161) has given a detailed

---

[2]It takes time to read the whole reel, fiche, etc. to determine whether he has the right item, what is in it, whether the contents agree with the publisher's list (if there is one), whether the photography is good throughout, and so on.

summary of microforms that is less critical than that of Veaner. Arthur D. Little, Inc. (71) is completing a "forecast of business growth in information-imaging markets" including "microimage systems and publishing." We may hope that some attention will be paid to user resistance based on inaccessibility[3] and unreliability[4] of the product.

Various committees of national organizations (42, p. 533) have been formed with the avowed purpose of improving the situation. A most important study to discover an effective method of bibliographic control of microforms has been undertaken by Reichmann & Tharpe (116) for the Association of Research Libraries. Their interim report recommends that no microform unit be produced unless it is accompanied by adequate cataloging copy. The final report is in press and will appear in 1972. At a meeting of the Special Advisory Group to this project (95), it was agreed that full description was desirable but not likely to be achieved; recommendations were made for some kind of brief listing. Since a large proportion of the material in micropublishing consists of items already cataloged, another possibility is to expand the *National Register of Microform Masters* (104) into a *National Union Catalog of Microforms* (103).

The large number of new academic libraries established in the past fifteen years has helped the reprinting field to become much larger, adding serious problems in document description. Whether the reprints are facsimiles, in microform or hard print, or new issues of unchanged old material, bibliographic control is inadequate. The Rare Book Libraries Conference (135, 136) is having a list of standards drawn up, for publication in 1972. The most serious difficulty is inadequate information about contents. For hard copy one can usually tell a facsimile reprint by inspection, but it may bear no mention of who reprinted it and when. Reprints of recent books can be deceptive, leading the buyer to think he has an updated version or even a new edition of something that is already in his collection.

A special meeting at the American Library Association Conference in 1970 produced a group of interesting papers on reprints by Dunlap (52), Nemeyer (106), Rappaport (115), Garrett (60), Sullivan (139), and

---

[3]The user has to go to a special place, at stated hours only, and use special equipment.

[4]Publishers have listed contents inaccurately, either omitting what is in a fiche (reel, etc.) or listing what is not there. In many cases, the bibliographic descriptions supplied are insufficient to identify items included. The photographic reproduction may be out of focus or incomplete (margins, etc.). Interested readers should consult the report of Reichmann & Tharpe (116).

Devlin (49) discussing all facets of the reprint field. Nemeyer (106, p. 46) best summarized the descriptive viewpoint as follows:

> The current state of bibliographic controls imposed upon reprints is both chaotic and penurious. Reprint publishers must find ways to make certain that their titles are either consistently recorded as "regular" books in standard book trade reference sources, or they must spearhead a search for alternative bibliographic control methods.

She suggests that librarians and publishers should work together on this score, and some publishers already have hired bibliographers for their staffs. As noted above, Veaner has indicated that microform purchases are being duplicated in hard copy because no one can get at the texts. This reviewer asks, why not buy only hard copy in the first place? An alternative solution to microtext is University Microfilms' *OP Books*. The initial cost may seem high, but it is lower than that of a collection of unusable microforms.

Somewhat different problems exist with audio-visual materials, which have been used as teaching aids for a long time. Some things, such as slides, music scores, films, and phonorecords, are common in all kinds of educational institutions. The three latter categories have been cataloged by the Library of Congress for years, but the newer media are not. Until the last five years or so, the handling of many types of media tended to be hit-or-miss. Bibliographic control has now become available in several forms, represented by the revised edition of standards put out by the Association for Educational Communications and Technology (AECT) (10), and an excellent compilation by Riddle et al. (119) in consultation with the Canadian Library Association. Various branches of the American Library Association are joining with their Canadian counterparts and the AECT to produce an international cataloging standard for A-V material (140).

An absorbing report by Firschein & Fischler (58) describes a methodology for handling visual materials, such as aerial photographs, that have no central themes—in other words, no distinctive parts such as author, title, or even subject. Firschein & Fischler are concerned with pattern recognition for descriptive purposes. This work is important because some A-V material cannot be described by categorizations that are adequate for other materials; yet libraries must assume responsibility for its housing, control, and dissemination.

Another kind of material that requires completely new means of handling in a library or information center is the computer tape data base. Material that used to come only in codex book form, such as U.S. Census data, or in abstract journal form, as with *Chemical Abstracts*, now comes on magnetic data tapes as well, and is threatening to come, as with MEDLINE, to local terminals from a central computer location. There is some doubt as to whether such material belongs in a library at all. A very strong argument for a study of the feasibility of including all or much of this material in a research library's collection has been made by Hayes (64), speaking at the 76th meeting of the Association of Research Libraries in 1970. Among other things, he called for "an examination of how data bases should be cataloged," which, of course, opens a major new document description field with no past experience to help (or hinder). Apparently the challenge has been accepted by Byrum & Rowe (31), who have devised a computerized system for bibliographic control of data banks in machine-readable form. The system combines what is usable from standard AACR codes with new physical description required for this special medium.

In all areas, it becomes apparent that standards are a basic necessity in document description, and yet, adherence to standards is a significant issue in document description at present. With the growth of networks, consortoria, cooperative ventures, centralized cataloging, centralized storage and distribution, and centralized dissemination of computerization results, it is imperative that the records be interchangeable so that the disgraceful waste of effort that has been identified with all kinds of information handling can be cut to the minimum. To this reviewer, it is ridiculous for each library or information center to do original cataloging or listing of the same material. It is equally ridiculous for each computer center to operate in such a way that programs from other centers have to be rewritten to be operated on a center's computer. It is also ridiculous that machines are not standardized and that one has to have a separate reader-printer for each brand or type of microform, or a separate terminal for each computer service. It is ridiculous for microforms to be issued wholesale with bibliographic control that is weak, spurious, or non-existent. All of these things make document description unduly expensive. The use of document description depends on adequate availability and reasonable intelligibility, and without bibliographic control, the item is as good as thrown away. On the other hand, standardization, at least in theory, interferes with further development towards more ideal methods, especially if a system is standardized too soon. In descriptive work with books, we have had sixty-four years of standards and seem hardly nearer uniformity than in 1908. Equipment is a nightmare of idiosyncrasies. Perhaps the future will be kinder than the past in observance of standards, as cooperation in sharing resources renders communication mandatory.

DOCUMENT REPRESENTATION

General Remarks on Subject Analysis of Documents

Document representation is concerned with what the document is about. It refers to a multitude of kinds of document subject analyses. It has been customary to divide the field of document representation into two major parts: one part includes systems that are based on classification according to various theories and structured with formats that usually lend themselves to a brief code for manipulation, and the other part includes systems that deal primarily with words and word strings. In actual practice, the two are so intertwined that the use of one without the other is almost impossible. Unindexed classification schemes are cumbersome and frustrating, and unstructured indexing systems are ambiguous and indeterminate. The comments on the following pages under the heading of either "classification" or "indexing" mean that the system discussed is primarily one or the other; it is rarely exclusively so.

Some very interesting things have gradually come to light in the sector of document representation. In classification, there is a significant difference between systems composed of semantic classes and those composed of mathematical classes[5] that do not bear distinct names. In indexing, there are sets of terms for use by specialists and others for use by the general public. The interests of the two groups hardly coincide. The system needed by subject specialists—historians, say—is too detailed for ordinary users. Even worse, there is another factor of magnitude in the system required by input specialists, catalogers and others, who cover all subject specialties and all at the subject specialist's level of detail. This latter difference gives rise to the claim that the library catalog is made for librarians, especially in university research

[5]"Mathematical" includes the postulated classes of mathematics and mathematical logic (such as, "Let (symbol) be the class of all. . . ."), as well as the "classes" discovered by statistical and other applied mathematical methods (such as, the end-products of clumping, clustering, factor analyzing, etc.).

libraries. It certainly is. Who else deals with the global continuum of which book titles alone comprise 30 million items? Abstracting and indexing services and certain information centers handle equally large numbers but in relatively homogeneous fields where they are not required to be all things to all men.

The mention of specialists is a reminder that document representation calls for help from many sources. In what direction are we going at present? The rest of this chapter covers semantic classification, mathematical classification, and indexing.

Semantic Classification

The traditional classification systems continue to be heavily used in libraries. The 18th edition of the Dewey Decimal Classification has been applied all year by the Decimal Classification Division of the Library of Congress and in the *British National Bibliography*, although, at the end of December, the schedules themselves still were not published (99). Bruin (29) tells of problems encountered by application of the system thousands of miles apart geographically and sometimes also in interpretation. Canadian and British members have been added to the Dewey Decimal Classification Editorial Policy Committee in an attempt to increase standardization in development and application of the system (32). The report of this Committee indicates that work has already begun on the 19th edition, which is to be computerized (48). There has been no decline of study in depth of individual parts of the classification, the most notable being that of the 800's by Chan (34).

At least two new parts of the full English edition of the Universal Decimal Classification (UDC) were published this year: 616 *Pathology*, and 655 *Graphic industries, Printing, Publishing, Book trade* (57), both British Standard, B S 1000. This system is widely used in Europe because it transcends language barriers. Dahlberg (47), however, is dissatisfied with its present format and suggests that it needs a major update and rearrangement to bring it in line with modern advances in each subject. She suggests also that for an index it needs an alphabetical thesaurus similar to the *Thesaurofacet* (1), and a uniform array of special auxiliaries "attached to the fields through the technique of interrupted subdivision," and expressing the following categories: (1) theory; (2) objects; (3) processes; (4) attributes; (5) [free]; (6) order, organization; (7) relation; (8) determination; (9) evaluation. Two papers from the Regensberg Conference were concerned with the mechanization of UDC: Koch (83) discussed the feasibility, while Barnholdt (18) described a finding-list type of book catalog, arranged in classified order by UDC and made by computer at the Danmarks Tekniske Bibliotek, Copenhagen. These catalogs are distributed all over Denmark. Somewhat in line with one of the Dahlberg recommendations, Stueart (138) attempted a merger of UDC class description terminology with descriptors from the *Thesaurus of Engineering and Scientific Terms* for similar topics. He concluded that UDC could be used for a term system by itself, but the merger with the *Thesaurus* produced more satisfactory results than with either one by itself.

UDC schedules appear at irregular intervals, topic by topic, as full editions are slowly completed, language by language. In contrast, the Library of Congress (LC) Classification publishes corrections and updates quarterly so that complete new editions appear only at lengthy intervals. In 1971 a fifth edition of *Class T: Technology* appeared (155), comprehending all corrections to date. (Working copies had begun to look like accordians because of all the insertions.)

Comparisons between treatment of subjects in Dewey and LC are almost standard for library school students, but an interesting new version was made by Auld (11), using KWOC (Keyword out of context) indexing and vocabulary comparisons. In the Dewey and LC schedules he examined, he found that only two fifths of the words co-occurred in the two systems. From this he assumed that choice and use of vocabulary are an editorial function. This reviewer would suggest that this may be due to the fact that editors must keep a running check on changes in vocabulary in each subject, and differences could be caused by one system's catching up faster than the other. This reviewer's study along the same line suggests that a merger of terminology could benefit the user (118).

The Colon Classification has undergone major expansion during the last few years. Neelameghan (105) outlines the significant changes coming in the seventh edition, to be published in 1972. The new main subjects ("classes" in other systems) number 85 (105, p. 319). Probably this is the most radical revision ever made of any used bibliographic classification of similar scope. It means almost a revolutionary revamping for institutions using Colon. New ideas are presented, such as the comprehensive "subject bundle," and common isolates are vastly expanded. Another important feature in the application of the Colon system is the development of depth classification schedules (86). This reviewer very strongly recommends that before making a thesaurus, an index, or a special classification scheme for any of the subjects in the depth schedules, or before adopting or adapting any existing scheme including the UDC, persons in need of a *detailed* method for document representation should take the time to study the depth schedules of the Indian school. While *faceted* classification of this type may not suit the collection at hand or may be too complex for general users, the display of terms and relationships cannot help but improve understanding of the full ramifications of the subject.

In the area of special classification schemes, the one for physics and astronomy (113) of the American Institute of Physics is worth mentioning. It is a four-level, hierarchical system with an index of permuted class descriptions and a simple notation. In medicine, Muench (102) has made an English and Spanish "correlation index" of five classification systems (National Library of Medicine, Dewey Decimal, Cunningham, Boston Medical, and Library of Congress), compared with each other and with Medical Subject Headings (MeSH) as a common denominator, an ambitious project that probably could not have been made very easily without a computer. The permutations that make up the tables are variations of the following (simplified) format, with appropriate conversion lists for codes used:

term	NLM	Dewey	LC	Cunn	Boston
abattoirs	WA707	614.31	RA578.H6	R3d3	32B

Special classification systems are always in demand for special collections. However, despite its difficulty, universal classification is needed in those libraries that must handle the whole universe of knowledge. The search continues for a system that is better than any that exists now.

Journal articles about semantic classification in general were not plentiful, but two should be mentioned: one by Foskett (59) on bias in classification, and an unusually lucid exposition by Rubin (123) on the "sovereignty of language and its effects upon our classification and indexing methods." All in all, it was a comparatively quiet year.

Mathematical Classification

In the past, both Hillman (66, 67) and Fairthorne (56) have suggested applying mathematical processes of the Intuitionist School—Brouwerian algebras and the like—to classification. Goffman (61) has developed a mathematical model by which classes of words are identified within an ordered collection of words. Class membership is determined by certain strengths of positional relationships amongst the members, and the size of the class depends on a selected threshold—the "critical probability." Class inclusion is entirely unrelated to intuitive interpretation of the words. No question of meaning arises during the procedure. Methodologies used for this type of classification are based on mathematical logic, statistical inference, or other probabilistic means.

An ambitious, unique, and quite advanced monograph in the field is that of Sparck Jones (132), *Automatic Keyword Classification for Information Retrieval.* The reviewer found this a fascinating book, more for the questions it raised, many unanswerable in the light of present knowledge, than for the experiments described. After the failure of clumping methods (133) as a means of producing automatic classes "untouched by human hands," Sparck Jones developed other means of creating the "non-ordered" (i.e. non-hierarchical) structures based on lattices that she conceived as necessary for classification by co-occurrence of words in documents. Elemental forms of strings, stars, cliques, and clumps were introduced, sets of words being "brought together by their subject connections, and not by any systematic semantic relations like synonymy" (132, p. 238). Her article with Barber (134) enumerates the more positive results described in Chapters 2, 3, and 9 of the book. Sparck Jones is to be commended in having the courage to "lay it on the line" in hard print by publishing one of the few monographs in this area of document representation.

Little more will be said about automatic classification. Its utility as a satisfactory means of *document* representation has not been demonstrated except for small, homogeneous collections in well-defined subjects of narrow scope. While we await the ultimate outcome of experimentation, it is advisable in reading each report to look carefully at the input material and method for conscious or unconscious human selectivity or bias. The automatic systems discussed here start from scratch —with words in documents. Wojciechowski (171, p. 12) has the last word on any system of classification based on words: "The question which in the case of such classification will remain open, is the problem of the relation of this classification to the objective reality, and its value for the study of that reality," the latter, of course, being the realm of the philosopher.

Indexing

The major research effort in document representation has been in indexing, rather than classification. This is partly because classification requires patterns of relationships and rather strong structure, and partly because classification is used in most American libraries only for shelf arrangement. Indexing is freer and can be almost structureless. It has long been used in library catalogs for the subject analysis of documents.

Indexing does not have the translingual advantages of classification, but at first glance it also does not have the intellectual and philosophical problems that beset classification. Second and third glances have shown that the latter is not entirely true. With deeper analysis, problems with definition, syntax, grammar, and other difficulties with words have turned out to be remarkably similar to some of the problems in classification. Thus the perplexing questions that halted much of the research in machine translation are basically the same as those that hold classification within limits set by determinants of relationships. The Colonel's lady and Molly O'Grady are indeed sisters under the skin (101).

Several generalized articles about difficulties in indexing were published this year. Vickery (163), in making an analysis of structure and function, distinguished between an indexing and a search language, a dictionary converting one language to another, and a thesaurus linking semantically related words within a particular language. One wonders whether this definition makes an English-English dictionary also a thesaurus. The task of determining which factors in indexing are comparable and suitable for evaluation studies was set for himself by Bloomfield (22, 23, 24, 25, 26). He arrived at the conclusion that there are six factors: breadth of vocabulary, depth of vocabulary, use of general or specific terms, use of *see* and *see also* cross-references, indexing format, and inclusion of titles or other qualifying phrases (26, p. 97). The Eighth Annual Information Retrieval Colloquium (53) included a panel on implementation of information systems, discussing the various factors involved in the formation of surrogates for documents.The panelists pointed out that:

> . . .human judgmental factors also enter into surrogate presentation; not only judgments in indexing, but communication between the supplier and the user of the service. Research of factors affecting performance of how well surrogates do, in fact, substitute for documents has been inconclusive to date.

Research continues on indexing factors affecting system search performance. In fact, it is almost an article of faith to end a report by indicating that more research is needed, which, of course, is the case. Inadequate depth control and weaknesses in vocabulary have been faulted by Lancaster (85) as producing less-than-desirable results with

MEDLARS. Studies of structured and unstructured vocabularies have been made by Pickford (114), Townley (147), Rosenberg (121), Hersey et al. (65), and Corbett (44). This problem of whether to structure or not is currently being debated in England more than on this side of the Atlantic.

Mathematical and statistical efforts in studies by Rush & Russo (124), Avramescu (17), Cooper (43), and Rosenberg (122); computer-assisted indexing by Bernhardt (20), Blum (27), Hines et al. (68), and Palmer (110); and problems with compound words in post-coordinate retrieval systems delineated by Jones (79) all form an ongoing attempt to improve indexing. In all of these cases, the depth of thought is not that of Sparck Jones, nor are the vital questions asked. One study, however, will bear comparison in that respect. This is the McAllister (92) attempt to answer the question: "To what extent do machine-recognizable textual clues account for human indexer behavior?" This is a fundamental question that must be answered if we are to be satisfied with automatic indexing. The two models that McAllister used did not match human indexing at all and the conclusion reached was that there is insufficient evidence as yet to tell exactly how the subject content of a document affects indexing. Sparck Jones (132, p. 146) approached the problem with a different question: ". . .what is it that makes a document relevant to a request though they do not coincide verbally, where a document which is verbally closer to it is not relevant to the request?" This sounds like the old immunity puzzle that Osler (109) so effectively illustrated with the Parable of the Sower in discussion of the communication of tuberculosis.

Various different kinds of indexing have commanded attention. The most impressive this year has been chain indexing (indexing by every word in a hierarchy, at the same time including each higher level in a word's family tree), originally a side-effect of Ranganathan's Colon Classification. Wilson (170) has produced a programmed text for self study, while Immroth (70) has made available his intriguing dissertation on vocabulary control for the Library of Congress classification and subject headings. He demonstrates that a chain index can be a good tool to improve both, and he develops twenty-six rules for chain indexing in the process. The chain index was found to be superior to subject headings or class descriptions or the index terms used in classification schedules. Moreover, Immroth believes he has discovered a major process for improving the composition of all three so that each may be made more effective in the future. This certainly is an experiment that should be repeated and verified.

A new machine approach called BROWSER has been worked out by Williams (169), who declares that machine retrieval systems have reached a plateau of effectiveness—a most interesting observation considering that few of them has even begun to touch the volume of subject matter encountered daily in manual systems. BROWSER features an interactive terminal arrangement, non-Boolean freeform queries, and a pattern for data responses that Williams hopes will bridge the gap between indexing as a recognition procedure and searching as a recall one.

Two major indexes were introduced in 1971. First the URBANDOC Information System's final report appeared (157, 158, 159). This program was specifically aimed at "the improvement of bibliographic services in urban affairs." Its thesaurus is the second major one to appear in the social sciences, the first being that of the Organization for Economic Cooperation and Development (108). The URBANDOC thesaurus is quite elaborate. The usual thesaurus terms are enhanced by the addition of "opposite term," "prohibited entry," and two self-cross-referencing "modified terms." Obviously the thesaurus terms fit a preconceived pattern, introduced presumably, to enhance successful retrieval.

The second accomplishment was the success of the PRECIS method of making subject headings for the *British National Bibliography*. These can be seen by examining any issue of the Bibliography since March. Three new and clearer descriptions of the process are now available, written by Austin (12, 13, 14). As a replacement for chain indexing, which could no longer be used in its usual form when the 18th edition of the Dewey Decimal Classification was adopted, it is a welcome, functioning addition to indexing methods of universal subject scope. Original input is manual, but results are computerized for production.

A revival of interest in aspects of the methodology of the Cranfield II experiment has led Swanson (142) and his student Harter (63) to discover that the methodology used in experimentation missed a considerable number of documents in the search results, thus casting doubt upon many conclusions drawn from the experiment. Svenonius (141), another student, studied indexing specificity using Cranfield data for testing. She arrived at the same conclusions as Sparck Jones on specificity—that results are of greater pertinence with highly specific terms, but of less breadth—but by entirely different means. Salton (125), using the same Cranfield package as these four, concluded that the addition of "bibliographic citation codes" to "standard content indicators" enhanced retrieval. This makes sense because anything that adds clues for the search effectively adds "hooks" for fishing in the grand pool of knowledge.

The five projects discussed above (142, 63, 141, 125, 132) have used a special "package" of 200 documents on aerodynamics and 42 genuine questions from the Cranfield II project (40, 41), developed for testing various parts of Salton's SMART system (126, 127, 128, 80). These documents were indexed in 33 different ways, based on five major indexing "languages." Each document in the package, therefore, has 33 indexing approaches (each with at least one input entity[6] and usually more than one). When the 200 documents are tested, using a single query, at least 6600 index entities are involved, or for all 42 queries, a total of 277,200 entities minimum. Swanson and Harter suggest that the ideal means of testing the 33 input methods has yet to be discovered and, further, that all studies that compare their own methods against the Cranfield "norm" are probably inaccurate.

Finally, problems of latent classification occur in structuring index term lists and deliberate classification is added for definition of words. The problems of homonyms, homographs, the use of metaphor, treatment of synonymy, analogy, and similar matters when moving toward total (general, universal) coverage by either words or classification are unsolved. How simple are "simple concepts?" This question is as bad as the specificity question studied by Svenonius. Are titles descriptive? This is a devastating problem outside of science and engineering. Indexing based on abstracts instead of full documents is another snare. The sum of what has been discussed in this section suggests that the human brain's capacity for making order out of chaos is still needed to devise new workable systems and to continue to improve present systems empirically.

CONCLUSION

At this point it is appropriate to ask, "Where are we?" and "Where do we go from here?" The long list of basic unsolved problems in the decision-making (entry) aspect of document description haunts us. Codes and standards exist as a result of decades of logical argument combined with solutions reached by trial and error. Now we have mushrooming numbers of audio-visual materials, microforms, reprints, and

---

[6]"Entity" is used here to cover the various products of the five indexing languages: single terms, simple concepts, controlled terms, titles, and abstracts.

computer data bases, with minimal bibliographic control. Our catalog access system takes at least 200 hours to learn.

We also have scientific, experimental, and quantitative methods for studying and solving our problems. Somehow we need to bring the two together. But aside from the impressive beginnings made by Tagliacozzo et al., how many have made the attempt? How many with the needed methodological capabilities are even aware of the problems? How many of those with such expertise have had enough experience with descriptive analysis on the scale necessary to feel the full pressure of the problems?

In document representation, our problems are also of heroic proportions. How do we describe an infinitely changing objective reality? Our systems are hardly out of the nineteenth century; we need an underlying, organizational philosophy for the late twentieth century. Where is it? How do we change to it when we have found it? How do we build into our systems a continuous reaction and adjustment to change?

In indexing, especially with automatic indexing, how do we deal with imagery, variety in vocabulary, synonymy, and other features that make up good English? (Or good French or good any other language?) How do we handle metaphor, analogy, allusion, and the other means by which new ideas are introduced? Indexing must cut to the core of meaning in spite of many kinds of literary styles. Svenonius, McAllister, Immroth, and Austin have all broken new ground. Sparck Jones' thoughtful questions deserve answers.

In fine, we end virtually where we began. We have some promising starts. We need more, much more.

REFERENCES

(1) AITCHISON, JEAN; GOMERSALL, ALAN; IRELAND, RALPH. Thesaurofacet: a thesaurus & faceted classification for engineering & related subjects. English Electric Co. Ltd., Whetstone, Leicester, England, 1969, 491 p.

(2) AMERICAN LIBRARY ASSOCIATION. Catalog rules; author and title entries. American ed. A. L. A. Publishing Board, Boston, Massachusetts, 1908, 88 p.

(3) AMERICAN LIBRARY ASSOCIATION. DIVISION OF CATALOGING AND CLASSIFICATION. A. L. A. cataloging rules for author and title entries. 2d ed. Edited by Clara Beetle. American Library Association, Chicago, Illinois, 1949, 265 p.

(4) AMERICAN LIBRARY ASSOCIATION. SUBCOMMITTEE ON THE ALA RULES FOR FILING LIBRARY CARDS. ALA rules for filing catalog cards, prepared by the ALA Editorial Committee's Subcommittee on the ALA Rules for Filing Catalog Cards. 2d ed. American Library Association, Chicago, Illinois, 1968, 260 p.

(5) ANDERSON, DOROTHY. International standards in cataloguing. International Library Review, 3:3 (June 1971) 241-249.

(6) Anglo-American cataloguing rules. North American text. American Library Association, Chicago, Illinois, 1967, 400 p.
(7) Anglo-American cataloguing rules. British text. The Library Association, London, England, 1967, 327 p.
(8) ARTANDI, SUSAN. Document description and representation. In: Cuadra, Carlos A.; ed. Annual review of information science and technology, vol. 5. Encyclopedia Britannica, Chicago, Illinois, 1970, 143-167.
(9) ASLESON, ROBERT F. Microforms: where do they fit? Library Resources & Technical Services, 15:1 (Winter 1971) 57-62.
(10) ASSOCIATION FOR EDUCATIONAL COMMUNICATIONS AND TECHNOLOGY. Standards for cataloging nonprint materials. Rev. ed. Association for Educational Communications and Technology, Washington, D.C., 1971, 56 p.
(11) AULD, LARRY. KWOC indexes and vocabulary comparisons of summaries of LC and DC classification schedules. Journal of the American Society for Information Science, 22:5 (September/October 1971) 322-325.
(12) AUSTIN, DEREK. A conceptual approach to the organization of machine-held files for subject retrieval. In: Ottawa University. Faculty of Philosophy. Ottawa Conference on the Conceptual Basis of the Classification of Knowledge. 1st, Ottawa, Ontario, Canada, 3 October 1971, 38 p. (Preprint. Commentary by Jean Perreault).
(13) AUSTIN, DEREK. PRECIS indexing. Information Scientist, 5:3 (September 1971) 95-113.
(14) AUSTIN, DEREK. Two steps forward . . . In: Palmer, B. I. Itself an education. The Library Association, London, England, 1971, 69-111.
(15) AVRAM, HENRIETTE D. Library automation. In: Cuadra, Carlos A.; ed. Annual review of information science and technology, vol. 6. Encyclopedia Britannica, Chicago, Illinois, 1971, 171-217.
(16) AVRAM, HENRIETTE D.; MARUYAMA, LENORE S. RECON pilot project: a progress report, April-September 1970. Journal of Library Automation, 4:1 (March 1971) 38-51.
(17) AVRAMESCU, AUREL. Probabilistic criteria for the objective design of descriptor languages. Journal of the American Society for Information Science, 22:2 (March/April 1971) 85-95.
(18) BARNHOLDT, B. The computerization of the UDC-classed library catalog of Danmarks Tekniske Bibliotek, Copenhagen. Libri, 21:1-3 (1971) 234-245.
(19) BAXENDALE, PHYLLIS. Content analysis, specification and control. In: Cuadra, Carlos A.; ed. Annual review of information science and technology, vol. 1. Interscience Publishers, New York, New York, 1966, 71-106
(20) BERNHARDT, RÜDIGER. Erstellung von Registern. Libri, 21:1-3 (1971) 215-225.
(21) BLANKEN, ROBERT R. The preparation of international author indexes, with particular reference to the problems of transliteration, prefixes, and compound family names. Journal of the American Society for Information Science, 22:1 (January/February 1971) 51-63.
(22) BLOOMFIELD, MASSE. Evaluating indexing. 1. Introduction. Special Libraries, 61:8 (October 1970) 429-432.
(23) BLOOMFIELD, MASSE. Evaluating indexing. 2. The simulated machine indexing experiments. Special Libraries, 61:9 (November 1970) 501-507.
(24) BLOOMFIELD, MASSE. Evaluating indexing. 3. A review of comparative studies of index sets to identical citations. Special Libraries, 61:10 (December 1970) 554-561.
(25) BLOOMFIELD, MASSE. Evaluating indexing. 4. A review of the Cranfield experiments. Special Libraries, 62:1 (January 1971) 24-31.
(26) BLOOMFIELD, MASSE. Evaluation of indexing. 5. Discussion and summary. Special Libraries, 62:2 (February 1971) 94-99.

(27) BLUM, FRED. Two machine indexing projects at the Catholic University of America. Journal of the American Society for Information Science, 22:2 (March/April 1971) 105-106.
(28) BOWERS, FREDSON THAYER. Bibliography and textual criticism. Clarendon Press, Oxford, England, 1964, 207 p.
(29) BRUIN, JOYCE E. The practice of classification: a study towards standardization. Journal of Librarianship, 3:1 (January 1971) 60-71.
(30) BUDINGTON, WILLIAM S. Access to information. In: Advances in librarianship, vol. 2. Seminar Press, New York, New York, 1971, 1-43.
(31) BYRUM, JOHN D., JR.; ROWE, JUDITH S. An integrated user-oriented system for the documentation and control of computer-readable data files. Library Resources & Technical Services, 16:2 (Spring 1972. In press).
(32) Canadian and British librarians to serve on Dewey Decimal Classification Editorial Policy Committee. Library Resources & Technical Services, 15:1 (Winter 1971) 95.
(33) Cataloging in publication. American Libraries, 2:8 (September 1970) 874.
(34) CHAN, LOIS MAI. The form distinction in the 800 class of the Dewey Decimal scheme. Library Resources & Technical Services, 15:4 (Fall 1971) 458-471.
(35) CHAUVEINC, MARC. Automation of the catalog at the University of Grenoble. Libri, 21:1-3 (1971) 188-192.
(36) CHAUVEINC, MARC. MONOCLE. Journal of Library Automation, 4:3 (September 1971) 113-128.
(37) CHAUVEINC, MARC. MONOCLE; projet de mise en ordinateur d'une notice catalographique du livre. Bibliothèque Universitaire, Grenoble, France, 1970, 156 p.
(38) CHERVENIE, PAUL. Library catalogs in American academic libraries. Drexel Library Quarterly, 7:1 (January 1971) 56-64.
(39) CLAPP, VERNER. CIP in mid-1970. Library Resources & Technical Services, 15:1 (Winter 1971) 12-23.
(40) CLEVERDON, CYRIL W.; KEEN, MICHAEL. Factors determining the performance of indexing systems, vol. 2: Test results. College of Aeronautics, Cranfield, Bedfordshire, England, 1966, 377 p. (Aslib Cranfield Research Project).
(41) CLEVERDON, CYRIL W.; MILLS, JACK; KEEN, MICHAEL. FACTORS DETERMINING THE PERFORMANCE OF INDEXING SYSTEMS, VOL. 1: Design. College of Aeronautics, Cranfield, Bedfordshire, England, 1966, 377 p. (Aslib Cranfield Research Project).
(42) COOK, C. DONALD. Resources and Technical Services Division: Annual reports 1970/1971. President's report. Library Resources & Technical Services, 15:4 (Fall 1971) 532-534.
(43) COOPER, WILLIAM S. On deriving design equations for information retrieval systems. Journal of the American Society for Information Science, 21:6 (November/December 1970) 385-395.
(44) CORBETT, LINDSAY. Controlled versus natural language: a report on the great debate. Information Scientist, 5:3 (September 1971) 114-120.
(45) COWARD, RICHARD E. MARC International, lecture notes for the Regensburg Seminar. Libri, 21:1-3 (1971) 130-134.
(46) CUTTER, CHARLES AMMI. Rules for a dictionary catalog. 4th ed. Government Printing Office, Washington, D.C., 1904, 173 p. (Reissued by the Library Association, London, England, 1953).
(47) DAHLBERG, INGETRAUT A. Possibilities for a new Universal Decimal Classification. Journal of Documentation, 27:1 (March 1971) 18-36.
(48) Decimal Classification Editorial Policy Committee report. Library Resources & Technical Services, 15:4 (Fall 1971) 545-546.
(49) DEVLIN, ELEANOR. Public service librarians and reprints. Library Resources & Technical Services, 15:1 (Winter 1971) 72-75.

(50) DIEFENBACH, DALE ALAN. Conference on Southeast Asian Research Materials, Puntjak, Indonesia, April 21-24, 1969. Library Resources & Technical Services, 15:1 (Winter 1971) 76-91.

(51) DUNKIN, PAUL. How to catalog a rare book. American Library Association, Chicago, Illinois, 1951, 85 p.

(52) DUNLAP, CONNIE R. Reprinting: problems, directions, challenges. Library Resources & Technical Services, 15:1 (Winter 1971) 34-35.

(53) Eighth Annual Information Retrieval Colloquium, May 6-7, 1971. Information Systems—Panel on Implementation. In: News from Science Abstracting and Indexing Services, Philadelphia, Pennsylvania, 1971, 15.

(54) EPSTEIN, A. H.; et al. Bibliographic automation of large library operations using a time-sharing system. Phase I. Final report. Stanford University Libraries, Stanford, California, 1971, 303 p. (ED 049 786).

(55) FAIRTHORNE, ROBERT A. Content analysis, specification and control. In: Cuadra, Carlos A.; ed. Annual review of information science and technology, vol. 4. Encyclopedia Britannica, Chicago, Illinois, 1969, 73-109.

(56) FAIRTHORNE, ROBERT A. Toward information retrieval. Butterworths, London, England, 1961, 126, 171.

(57) FID Publications. English full edition of UDC. FID News Bulletin, 21:2 (February 1971) 14.

(58) FIRSCHEIN, O.; FISCHLER, M. A. Describing and abstracting pictorial structures. Lockheed Missiles & Structure Company. Lockheed Palo Alto Research Laboratory. Information Sciences Laboratory, Palo Alto, California, 1970, 45 p. (LMSC 6-80-70-37A).

(59) FOSKETT, ANTHONY C. Misogynists all; a study in critical classification. Library Resources & Technical Services, 15:2 (Spring 1971) 117-121.

(60) GARRETT, DANIEL C. The ethics of reprint publishing. Library Resources & Technical Services, 15:1 (Winter 1971) 53-56.

(61) GOFFMAN, WILLIAM. An indirect method of information retrieval. Information Storage and Retrieval, 4:4 (December 1968) 361-373.

(62) Grant enabling IFLA to establish a permanent secretariat for cataloging activities. Library Resources & Technical Services, 15:4 (Fall 1971) 550 (News note).

(63) HARTER, STEPHEN P. The Cranfield II relevance assessments: a critical evaluation. Library Quarterly, 41:3 (July 1971) 229-243.

(64) HAYES, ROBERT M. Research libraries and machine-readable information. In: Association of Research Libraries, Minutes of the 76th meeting, 27 June 1970, Detroit, Michigan. Association of Research Libraries, Washington, D.C., 1970, 16-26.

(65) HERSEY, DAVID F.; et al. Free text word retrieval and scientist indexing: performance profiles and costs. Journal of Documentation, 27:3 (September 1971) 167-183.

(66) HILLMAN, DONALD J. Mathematical classification techniques for non-static document collections, with particular reference to the problem of relevance. In: International Study Conference. 2d, Elsinore, Denmark, 1964. Proceedings, Classification research. Munksgaard, Copenhagen, Denmark, 1965, 503-523.

(67) HILLMAN, DONALD J. On concept-formation and relevance. In: American Documentation Institute, 1964. Proceedings, vol. 1, 23-29.

(68) HINES, THEODORE C.; et al. Experimentation with computer-assisted indexing: American Documentation, vol. 20. Journal of the American Society for Information Science, 21:6 (November/December 1970) 402-405.

(69) HOPKINS, JUDITH. Manual for OCLC catalog card production. Rev. & enl. Ohio College Library Center, Columbus, Ohio, February 1971, 69 p. (ED 046 471).

(70) IMMROTH, JOHN PHILLIP. Analysis of vocabulary control in Library of Congress classification and subject headings. Libraries Unlimited, Littleton, Colorado, 1971, 172 p. (Research studies in library science, no. 3).

(71) Information-imaging under study. Special Libraries, 62:10 (October 1971) 451 (News note).
(72) INSTITUTE ON CATALOG CODE REVISION, MCGILL UNIVERSITY, MONTREAL, JUNE 13-17, 1960. Summary of proceedings. American Library Association, Chicago, Illinois, 1960, 93 p.
(73) INSTITUTE ON CATALOG CODE REVISION, MCGILL UNIVERSITY, MONTREAL, JUNE 13-17, 1960. Working papers. American Library Association, Chicago, Illinois, 1960, 1 v. (Various pagings).
(74) INSTITUTE ON CATALOG CODE REVISION, STANFORD UNIVERSITY, JULY 9-12, 1958. Summary of proceedings. [n.p.] 1958, 62 p.
(75) INSTITUTE ON CATALOG CODE REVISION, STANFORD UNIVERSITY, JULY 9-12, 1958. Working papers. Stanford, California, 1958, 1 v. (Various pagings).
(76) INTERNATIONAL CONFERENCE ON CATALOGUING PRINCIPLES, PARIS, 1961. Report. [A. H. Chaplin, Dorothy Anderson, eds. Organizing Committee of the International Conference on Cataloguing Principles, National Central Library] London, England, 1963, 293 p.
(77) ISA, ZUBAIDAH. The entry-word in Indonesian names and titles. Library Resources & Technical Services, 15:3 (Summer 1971) 393-398.
(78) JEWETT, CHARLES COFFIN. On the construction of catalogues of libraries, and their publication by means of separate, sterotyped titles. With rules and examples. 2d ed. Smithsonian Institution, Washington, D.C., 1853, 96 p. (Publication no. 47).
(79) JONES, KEVIN P. Compound words: a problem in post-coordinate indexing. Journal of the American Society for Information Science, 22:4 (July/August 1971) 242-250.
(80) KEEN, E. MICHAEL. Test environment. In: Information storage and retrieval. Scientific report no. ISR-13 to the National Science Foundation. Reports on evaluation procedures and results 1965-1967. Cornell University, Department of Computer Science, Ithaca, New York, 1967, p. I-1-48. (PB 177 812).
(81) KIEFFER, PAULA. Book catalog—to have or not to have. Library Resources & Technical Services, 15:3 (Summer 1971) 290-296.
(82) KILGOUR, FREDERICK G. A regional network—Ohio College Library Center. Datamation, 16:2 (February 1970) 87-89.
(83) KOCH, KARL-HEINZ. Die Maschinengängigheit der Dezimalklassifikation. Libri, 21:1-3 (1971) 226-233.
(84) KUHN, THOMAS S. The relations between history and history of science. Daedalus, 100:2 (Spring 1971) 284-285. (Issued as Proceedings of the American Academy of Arts and Sciences).
(85) LANCASTER, F. WILFRID. Aftermath of an evaluation. Journal of Documentation, 27:1 (March 1971) 1-10.
(86) Library Science with a Slant to Documentation. 1:1-8:4 (January 1964-December 1971) 8 v.
(87) LIPETZ, BEN-AMI. Catalog use in a large research library. Library Quarterly, 42:1 (January 1972) 129-139.
(88) LIPETZ, BEN-AMI. User requirements in identifying desired works in a large library. Yale University Library, New Haven, Connecticut, 1970, 121 p. (ED 042 479).
(89) LONDON, GERTRUDE. The publication inflation. American Documentation, 19:2 (April 1968) 137-141.
(90) LUBETSKY, SEYMOUR. Code of cataloging rules: author and title entry. An unfinished draft for a new edition of cataloging rules prepared for the Catalog Code Revision Committee. With an explanatory commentary by Paul Dunkin. American Library Association, [n.p.], 1960, 86 p.

(91) LUBETSKY, SEYMOUR. 1976 minus 6....5.... Library Journal, 96:3 (1 February 1971) 450-451.

(92) McALLISTER, CARYL. A study and model of machine-like indexing behavior by human indexers. International Business Machine Corporation. Advanced Systems Development Division, Los Gatos, California, 1971, 139 p. (Laboratory report).

(93) McKERROW, RONALD BRUNLEES. An introduction to bibliography for literary students. Clarendon Press, Oxford, England, 1927, 358 p.

(94) MALTBY, ARTHUR. Measuring catalogue utility. Journal of Librarianship, 3:3 (July 1971) 180-189.

(95) MARTIN, LOUIS E. Summary of the meeting of the Special Advisory Group to Task I of the Microform Project, Brookings Institution, Washington, D.C., March 4, 1971. Association of Research Libraries, Washington, D.C., 15 April 1971, 3 p.

(96) MARUYAMA, LENORE S. Format recognition: a report of a project at the Library of Congress. Journal of the American Society for Information Science, 22:2 (July/August 1971) 283-287.

(97) MASSONNEAU, SUZANNE. The main entry and the book catalog. Library Resources & Technical Services, 15:4 (Fall 1971) 499-512.

(98) MASSONNEAU, SUZANNE. The year's work in cataloging and classification. Library Resources & Technical Services, 16:2 (Spring 1972. In press).

(99) MATTHEWS, WINTON F. Dewey 18: a preview and a report to the profession. Wilson Library Bulletin, 45:6 (February 1971) 572-577.

(100) MAXWELL, MARGARET. A cataloger's view. RQ, 10:2 (Winter 1970) 148-149.

(101) MONTGOMERY, CHRISTINE A. Automated language processing. In: Cuadra, Carlos A.; ed. Annual review of information science and technology, vol. 4. Encyclopedia Britannica, Chicago, Illinois, 1969, 145-174.

(102) MUENCH, EUGENE V. A computerized English/Spanish correlation index to five biomedical library classification schemes based on MeSH. Bulletin of the Medical Library Association, 59:3 (July 1971) 404-411. (Spanish translation, 412-419).

(103) MUMFORD, L. QUINCY. Letter to Felix Reichmann. 5 April 1971.

(104) National register of microform masters. Library of Congress, Washington, D.C., 1965-date.

(105) NEELAMEGHAN, A. Colon Classification. In: Encyclopedia of library and information science, vol. 5. Marcel Dekker, New York, New York, 1971, 316-340.

(106) NEMEYER, CAROL A. Scholarly reprint publishing in the United States: select findings from a recent survey of the industry. Library Resources & Technical Services, 15:1 (Winter 1971) 35-48.

(107) OHIO COLLEGE LIBRARY CENTER. Instruction manual for catalog production. Ohio College Library Center, Columbus, Ohio, February 1970, 26 p.

(108) ORGANISATION FOR ECONOMIC COOPERATION AND DEVELOPMENT. DEVELOPMENT CENTRE. Liste commune des descripteurs. Aligned list of descriptors. Organisation for Economic Cooperation and Development, Paris, France, 1969, 5 v.

(109) OSLER, WILLIAM. The principles and practice of medicine . . .Rev. Henry A. Christian. 13th ed. Appleton-Century, New York, New York, 1938, 1424 p.

(110) PALMER, FOSTER M. Automatic processing of personal names for filing. Journal of Library Automation, 4:4 (December 1971) 185-197.

(111) PANIZZI, ANTHONY; et al. Rules for the compilation of the catalogue. In: Catalogue of printed books in the British Museum, vol. 1. Printed by Order of the Trustees, London, England, 1841, v-ix.

(112) PFEIFER, RUTH ANN. Shared cataloging. Catholic Library World, 42:10 (July/August 1971) 650-653.

(113) Physics and astronomy classification scheme; a service of the National Information System for Physics and Astronomy. American Institute of Physics, Information Division, New York, New York, 1971, 110 p. (AIP-ID-71 B).

(114) PICKFORD, A. G. A. Some problems of using an unstructured information retrieval language in a co-ordinate indexing system. Aslib Proceedings, 23:3 (July 1971) 133-136.

(115) RAPPAPORT, FRED. The changing philosophy of reprint publishers. Library Resources & Technical Services, 15:1 (Winter 1971) 48-52.

(116) REICHMANN, FELIX; THARPE, JOSEPHINE M. Determination of an effective system of bibliographic control of microform publications. Interim report. Association of Research Libraries, Washington, D.C., November 1970, 51 p. (ED 046 404).

(117) RICHMOND, PHYLLIS A. Book catalogs as supplements to card catalogs. Library Resources & Technical Services, 8:4 (Fall 1964) 359-365.

(118) RICHMOND, PHYLLIS A. LC and Dewey: their relevance to modern information needs. ALA Preconference on Subject Analysis of Library Materials, Atlantic City, New Jersey, 19 June 1969, 28 p. + appendices. (In press).

(119) RIDDLE, JEAN; LEWIS, SHIRLEY; MacDONALD, JANET. Non-book materials: the organization of integrated collections. Prelim. ed. Canadian Library Association, Ottawa, Ontario, Canada, 1970, 58 p.

(120) RISTOW, WALTER W.; CARRINGTON, DAVID K Machine-readable map cataloging in the Library of Congress. Special Libraries, 62:9 (September 1971) 343-352.

(121) ROSENBERG, VICTOR. Comparative evaluation of two indexing methods using judges. Journal of the American Society for Information Science, 22:4 (July/August 1971) 251-259.

(122) ROSENBERG, VICTOR. A study of statistical measures for predicting terms used to index documents. Journal of the American Society for Information Science, 22:1 (January/February 1971) 41-50.

(123) RUBIN, JUDITH G. Language, classification and indexing. Special Libraries, 62:4 (April 1971) 189-194.

(124) RUSH, JAMES E.; RUSSO, PHILIP M. A note on the mathematical basis of the SLIC index. Journal of the American Society for Information Science, 22:2 (March/April 1971) 123-125.

(125) SALTON, GERARD. Automatic indexing using bibliographic citations. Journal of Documentation, 27:2 (June 1971) 98-110.

(126) SALTON, GERARD. Automatic information organization and retrieval. McGraw-Hill, New York, New York, 1968, 514 p.

(127) SALTON, GERARD. Automatic text analysis. Science, 168:3929 (17 April 1970) 335-343.

(128) SALTON, GERARD; comp. The SMART retrieval system: experiments in automatic document processing. Prentice-Hall, Englewood Cliffs, New Jersey, 1971, 556 p. (Prentice-Hall series in automatic computation).

(129) SCHRADER, BARBARA; ORSINI, ELAINE. British, French and Australian publications in the National Union Catalog: A study of NPAC's effectiveness. Library Resources & Technical Services, 15:3 (Summer 1971) 345-353.

(130) SHARP, JOHN R. Content analysis, specification and control. In: Cuadra, Carlos A.; ed. Annual review of information science and technology, vol. 2. Interscience Publishers, New York, New York, 1967, 87-122.

(131) SHOFFNER, RALPH M. Some implications of automatic recognition of bibliographic elements. Journal of the American Society for Information Science, 22:4 (July/August 1971) 275-282.

(132) SPARCK JONES, KAREN. Automatic keyword classification for information retrieval. Archon Books, Hamden, Connecticut, 1971, 253 p.

(133) SPARCK JONES, KAREN. Clumps, theory of. In: Encyclopedia of library and information science, vol. 5. Marcel Dekker, New York, New York, 1971, 208-224.

(134) SPARCK JONES, KAREN; BARBER, E. O. What makes an automatic keyword classification effective? Journal of the American Society for Information Science, 22:3 (May/June 1971) 166-175. Standards for reprint publishing. Special Libraries, 62:11 (November 1971) 498 (Interim report for comment). Standards proposed. American Libraries, 2:11 (December 1971) 1131 (News note).

(135) Standards for reprint publishing. Special Libraries, 62:11 (November 1971) 498 (Interim report for comment).

(136) Standards proposed. American Libraries, 2:11 (December 1971) 1131 (News note).

(137) STROUT, RUTH FRENCH. Toward a better cataloging code. University of Chicago, Graduate Library School, Chicago, Illinois, 1957, 116 p.

(138) STUEART, ROBERT D. An analysis of the Universal Decimal Classification as a term system for nuclear science and technology. Library Resources & Technical Services, 15:3 (Summer 1971) 399-411.

(139) SULLIVAN, HOWARD A. Reprints and the technical services, or, "The age of happy problems." Library Resources & Technical Services, 15:1 (Winter 1971) 67-72.

(140) SULLIVAN, THOMAS E. Cataloging and Classification Section report. Library Resources & Technical Services, 15:4 (Fall 1971) 537-539.

(141) SVENONIUS, ELAINE. The effect of indexing specificity on retrieval performance. University of Chicago, Chicago, Illinois, 1971, 418 p. (Dissertation. ED 051 863).

(142) SWANSON, DON R. Some unexplained aspects of the Cranfield tests of indexing performance factors. Library Quarterly, 41:3 (July 1971) 223-228.

(143) TAGLIACOZZO, RENATA; KOCHEN, MANFRED. Access and recognition: from users' data to catalogue entries. Journal of Documentation, 26:3 (September 1970) 230-249.

(144) TAGLIACOZZO, RENATA; KOCHEN, MANFRED. Information-seeking behavior of catalog users. Information Storage and Retrieval, 6:5 (December 1970) 363-381.

(145) TAGLIACOZZO, RENATA; SEMMEL, DOROTHY; KOCHEN, MANFRED. Written representation of topics and the production of query terms. Journal of the American Society for Information Science, 22:5 (September/October 1971) 337-347.

(146) TAULBEE, ORRIN E. Content analysis, specification and control. In: Cuadra, Carlos A.; ed. Annual review of information science and technology, vol. 3. Encyclopedia Britannica, Chicago, Illinois, 1968, 105-136.

(147) TOWNLEY, HELEN M. A look at natural language IR systems. Information Scientist, 5:3 (March 1971) 3-15.

(148) UNESCO-Seminar Elektronische Datenverarbeitung in Bibliotheken. UNESCO-Seminar Electronic Data Processing in Libraries. Regensburg Universitätsbibliothek, April 1970. [Proceedings] In: Libri, 21:1-3 (1971) 297 p.

(149) U. S. FEDERAL COUNCIL FOR SCIENCE AND TECHNOLOGY. COMMITTEE ON SCIENTIFIC INFORMATION. Standard for descriptive cataloging of government scientific and technical reports. Rev. no. 1, Washington, D.C., October 1966, 50 p. (PB 173 314. AD 614 092).

(150) U. S. LIBRARY OF CONGRESS. Annual report of the Librarian of Congress for the fiscal year 1966-1970. U. S. Library of Congress, Washington, D.C., 1967-1971. 5 v.

(151) U. S. LIBRARY OF CONGRESS. DESCRIPTIVE CATALOGING DIVISION. Rules for descriptive cataloging in the Library of Congress. (Adopted by the American Library Association). U. S. Library of Congress, Washington, D.C., 1949, 141 p.

(152) U. S. LIBRARY OF CONGRESS. INFORMATION SYSTEMS OFFICE. Format recognition process for MARC records; a logical design. American Library Association, Information Science and Automation Division, Chicago, Illinois, 1970, 150 p. + appendices.

(153) U. S. LIBRARY OF CONGRESS. INFORMATION SYSTEMS OFFICE. Serials: a MARC format. U. S. Library of Congress, Washington, D.C., 1970, 72 p.

(154) U. S. LIBRARY OF CONGRESS. PROCESSING DEPARTMENT. Filing rules for the dictionary catalogs of the Library of Congress. U. S. Library of Congress, Washington, D.C., 1956, 187 p.

(155) U. S. LIBRARY OF CONGRESS. SUBJECT CATALOGING DIVISION. Library of Congress Classification. Class T. Technology. 5th ed. U. S. Library of Congress, Washington, D.C., 1971, 370 p.

(156) USA Standard Code for Information Interchange. USAS X3.4-1967. Revision of X3.4-1965. Approved July 7, 1967, United States of America Standards Institute [now American National Standards Institute] New York, New York, 1967, 15 p.

(157) URBANDOC: a bibliographic information system: demonstration report. City University of New York, Graduate Division, New York, 1971, 79 p. & appendices. (URBANDOC-71-1).

(158) URBANDOC: a bibliographic information system. Technical supplement 1/general manual. City University of New York, Graduate Division, New York, 1971, 136 p. & appendix, 120 p. (URBANDOC-71-2).

(159) URBANDOC: a bibliographic information system. Technical manual 2/operations manual. City University of New York, Graduate Division, New York, 1971, 243 p. (URBANDOC-71-3).

(160) VEANER, ALLEN B. Micropublication. In: Voigt, Melvin J.; ed. Advances in librarianship, vol. 2. Seminar Press, New York, New York, 1971, 165-186.

(161) VEIT, FRITZ. Microforms, microform equipment and microform use in the educational environment. Library Trends, 19:4 (April 1971) 447-466.

(162) VICKERY, BRIAN C. Document description and representation. In: Cuadra, Carlos A.; ed. Annual review of information science and technology, vol. 6. Encyclopedia Britannica, Chicago, Illinois, 1971, 113-140.

(163) VICKERY, BRIAN C. Structure and function in retrieval languages. Journal of Documentation, 27:2 (June 1971) 69-82.

(164) VOOS, HENRY. The information explosion: or, redundancy reduces the charge! College & Research Libraries, 32:1 (January 1971) 7-14.

(165) WANG, SZE-TSENG. Cataloging pirated Chinese books. Library Resources & Technical Services, 15:3 (Summer 1971) 385-392.

(166) WELSH, WILLIAM J. Report on the Library of Congress plans for cataloging in publication. Library Resources & Technical Services, 15:1 (Winter 1971) 23-27.

(167) WHEELER, JOSEPH L. Cataloging in/at source. Why we must have cataloging in publication. Library Resources & Technical Services, 15:1 (Winter 1971) 6-12.

(168) WHITE, CARL. How to avoid duplicated information. RQ, 10:2 (Winter 1970) 127-137.

(169) WILLIAMS, J. H., JR. Functions of a man-machine interactive information retrieval system. Journal of the American Society for Information Science, 22:5 (September/October 1971) 311-317.

(170) WILSON, T. D. An introduction to chain indexing. Shoe String Press, Hamden, Connecticut, 1971, 85 p.

(171) WOJCIECHOWSKI, JERZY A. The philosophical relevance of the problems of the classification of knowledge. In: Ottawa University. Faculty of Philosophy. Ottawa Conference on the Conceptual Basis of the Classification of Knowledge. 1st, Ottawa, Ontario, Canada, 1 October 1971, 13 p. (Preprint).

4 Organization of Information

NOAH S. PRYWES
and
DIANE PIROG SMITH
The Moore School of Electrical Engineering
University of Pennsylvania*

INTRODUCTION

This chapter describes *formal* and *automatic* tools that help designers and users to organize and exchange information in large and complex data bases and to improve processing efficiently.

The chapter includes a review of computer languages that have been developed to specify in a clear and unambiguous manner an organization of information. A data description language (DDL) is described, with illustrations of how it is used to specify an existing or desired organization of information. The DDL also serves as a basis for the automatic conversion of data bases from one organization of the information to another one, that can be processed more efficiently. With very large data bases, appropriate ordering of the data can reduce search times and storage requirements greatly. The determination and communication of such organizational schemes to designers and users cannot be done comprehensively by manual means, and there is a need for automatic aids to perform these functions. These major methodologies are described.

The developments described in this chapter are a natural sequel to the intense activity of the past five years in developing hardware and software to handle data in information systems. These software systems have been variously called "data management systems (DMSs),"

*The research upon which this chapter was based has been supported in part by the Office of Naval Research, Information Systems Program, Contract N00014-67-A-0216-0014.

"data base management systems (DBMSs)," and "file systems." Recently emphasis has been on handling data on random-access devices, especially magnetic discs, and increasingly on on-line interactive use from remote terminals. Every major computer hardware manufacturer and several independent software companies have developed such systems. Currently, a new user, who starts from scratch and has a relatively small file (consisting typically of up to 10,000 records or up to 10 million characters), can expect an adequate set of hardware and software to handle his data at a reasonable cost, as cost can be measured by the benefits from similar applications. However, for application areas that include very large data bases, large numbers of users, use different computers or use computer networks, there are severe problems. The primary problem in designing an information system for such an application is cost of design and use of computer services that may make the entire application economically impractical. There are also problems of ease of use and browsing, reliability, backup and recovery, and finally the problem of security and protection of the information.

While efforts are being directed specifically to these problems, in the opinion of the authors, their root is the organization of information and the cure for them is its mechanization. While the title of the corresponding chapters in previous volumes of the *Annual Review* was "File Organization, Maintenance, and Search" (27), we have decided to limit the scope of the chapter to "Organization of Information" and to exclude direct discussion of the problem areas enumerated in the previous paragraph because of space limitation. In another sense, however, we have not restricted the scope because it covers two methodologies that are used to attack the problems at the root. We review in this chapter the techniques needed to obtain mechanized organization of the information. These techniques can contribute dramatically toward practical and economic solutions to the problems enumerated above.

RESEARCH AND REPORTS ON DATA DESCRIPTION LANGUAGES

There are no texts dealing with data description languages (DDLs) specifically. However, several texts and surveys that include sections on DDLs for programming languages and data base management systems (DBMSs) have been published in the last few years. Lefkovitz (51) has written a classic text on data organization for information systems. A new text by Bertziss (8) describes data organizations mathematically and specifies different storage structures for processing these organizations on computerized storage. Flores is the author of two texts: the first (38) is similar in content to the Bertziss text relative to data description but is not as well organized or written. The second (39) includes a detailed description of the data organizations provided by IBM OS/360 and the JCL statements used to describe these organizations. A general text by Kent (47) fits data organizational concepts into the framework of information retrieval systems.

There are several surveys of particular interest. One is produced by the CODASYL[1] Committee and is called *Feature Analysis of Generalized Data Base Management Systems* (26). This work includes an analysis of the data organization options provided by eleven DBMSs, some of which are widely used. The survey presents a list of data organization features that it defines and describes for each system. Although one may not agree with the organization or completeness of the list, its value cannot be disputed. At the very least, it can serve as a basis for testing whether a generalized DDL can be used to describe each of these features. A second survey (21) is a collection of papers that analyze and criticize the DDL developed by the CODASYL Data Base Task Group (DBTG). Finally, a recent symposium has dealt with the problems of DMSs, file organization, and optimizing methods (2).

Many of the recent publications relating to DDLs are directed towards the analysis and improvement of data description capabilities in programming languages and in DBMSs. Others describe existing data organizations. We will only examine work that is of special relevance because of the description statements being investigated, or because of the approach taken in describing the data organization. These will be discussed relative to the appropriate component of our DDL.

Early work on developing DDLs appeared as part of research on extensible languages. Standish's dissertation (92) presents a powerful data definition language designed to provide programming languages with a means for extending their data organizational capabilities. In 1969, Olle (70) published an interesting study of the different types of DDLs that already existed and that might be developed in the future. He developed a taxonomy for DDLs that has stimulated CODASYL and its efforts in DDL research.

In fact, the next significant research undertaken to develop a generalized DDL was sponsored by CODASYL. A Data Base Task Group

[1]CODASYL is an organization of industry affiliated representatives whose purpose is to design and develop techniques and languages to assist systems analysis, design, and implementation. It is primarily noted for its development of COBOL.

(DBTG) was formed and set to the task of developing a DDL that could be used as a common input language for DBMSs. In effect, the scope of this language was restricted to the *logical* organization of data as distinct from the *physical* storage organization but the DDL was meant to be general within these limits. A report on the language (24) was first published in October 1969 and a revised version (25) was published in April 1971. This DDL has been the center of considerable controversy having been criticized as much for its lack of generality as for its excessive generality. The latter criticism was made by those concerned with the implementation of the DBTG's DDL. The final version of the language, however, took a middle path whereby it could describe the data organizations provided by DBMSs as described in the CODASYL *Feature Analysis of Generalized Data Base Management Systems* (26) but excluding less common data organizational features considered difficult to implement.

CODASYL also set up a task group to study the design of a DDL to use for data conversion. This group (called the Storage Structure Definition Language Task Group (SSDLTG)) has published a study (3) of the design problems for developing such a language. It decided to restrict its efforts to a subset of the storage structures into which logical organizations of data can be mapped. However, this subset was selected to include most commercially used storage structures. An outgrowth of this work is the dissertation of Taylor (98). He has developed a DDL which is strongly oriented to the description of those data organizations provided by DBMSs.

Simultaneously with CODASYL's related efforts, work was also being done on DDLs at the Moore School of Electrical Engineering, University of Pennsylvania, by one of the authors (87). This work was also an outgrowth of research on DBMSs (44, 58, and 76) but was more strongly oriented towards the problem of data conversion.

DATA DESCRIPTION LANGUAGES

We begin by discussing what data description languages (DDLs) are and why their development is important. Simply speaking, a DDL is a language which enables a person to describe every aspect of a data organization from the interrelation among elements of the organization to its representation as a linear string and its positioning on a specific storage medium. Such descriptions can serve as a basis for organizing or converting the respective data bases automatically. Every programming language and DBMS or DMS contains data description statements for specifying some aspects of data (e.g., the Data Division of COBOL or a call to the Indexed Sequential Access Method (ISAM) of the IBM/360 operating system). The data description parts of programming languages, DBMSs and DMSs are used to evoke the creation and maintenance of the data organizations provided by these systems. Therefore, they need only be descriptive enough to distinguish between the organizational options provided. Thus, none of these DDLs permits the description of every aspect of a data organization nor do they provide for conversion from one organization to another.

The first generalized DDLs that describe all aspects of data organizations have appeared during the past year, and a conversion processor using one such language is being tested (79, 87, and 98).

The importance of developing such DDLs, independent of any DMS, can be best understood in terms of their projected uses: (a) to communicate data organizations between humans (b) to communicate the organization of data to computers to permit processing, and (c) to convert data from one organization to another.

A DDL should allow the creator of a data base to describe its data organization explicitly and completely. Such a description will then provide users with all the information necessary to understand and use this organization. Such a DDL relieves the user of the burden of extracting this information from the variety of programs maintaining the data base. Hence, a DDL provides a means of communication between users.

The complete separation of the description of procedures or algorithms from the description of data organization (data independence) is considered highly desirable (Meadow & Meadow, 61, p. 177). Such independence allows a user to describe his entire data organization on one occasion only. Subsequently, each time he wants to write a program using data in that organization, he can reference the data simply by using its name in the data description. Under a wide range of conditions the same program can work together with data descriptions of the same or even different data, thereby permitting generality. In this way a DDL permits communication between the user and the computer.

A DDL that could describe the entire organization of data down to the details of the medium on which it is stored can be applied to the problem of mechanizing the conversion of data from an existing organization to a more useful new organization. Marden (59) has documented the cost of not being able to provide this capability and has thereby established the importance of devoting research to it. And indeed this capability is a major feature of current DDLs.

A practical approach for using a DDL for data conversion requires the development of a processor that can accept three inputs: the data itself, a DDL description of its current organization, and a DDL description of its new organization (including a description of the relation of elements in one organization to the other). The proposed processor would then produce a file that would conform to the specification of the new organization. Such a generalized conversion utility would free programmers from the need to write special conversion programs for each set of data to be converted.

A conversion utility could be used to solve a wide range of data interchange problems that arise in dealing with computerized data. In particular, it could be used: (a) to interface data between programs; (b) to interface data organizations across programming languages; (c) to interface them across operating systems; (d) to interface them across hardware; (e) to move data organizations from one device to another; (f) to extract small amounts of data from large organizations to form smaller ones; (g) to integrate many small data organizations to form; more useful larger ones; and thereby (h) to create and maintain data bases.

The importance of these uses has led to the development of two generalized DDLs (87, 98). In the remainder of this section, we will review their design and the work contributing to it. Because the concept of such DDLs is so new and may be unfamiliar to many readers, we will review these works by discussing them in the context of the design of DDLs. That is, we will survey the design of a prototype DDL and relate research contributions to its component parts. The survey itself will be clarified by the use of a running example which illustrates the ability of the DDL to describe a data organization common to all of the readers—that of the *Annual Review of Information Science and Technology* (ARIST).

REVIEW OF THE DEVELOPMENT OF DATA DESCRIPTION LANGUAGES

The components of our prototype DDL can be partitioned into three distinct classes. This is because the three aspects of data organizations that they describe are created at distinct times and by distinct processes. Briefly, in organizing data, the individual elements are related one to another by the user of the data, to reflect his concept of the data and how the data and the relations between the data are represented as a string of characters. One class of DDL components describes this logical organization of data. The user must also take into consideration the physical storage media on which the data are to be kept, and how the data are to be organized. This forms the physical organization (or storage structure) of the data. One class of DDL components describes this physical organization. Finally, the user must determine how the representation of his logical organization is to be placed in its storage structure. A final class of DDL components describes such mappings. Thus, we can see that DDLs must include statements for describing these three aspects of data organization.

LOGICAL ORGANIZATION OF DATA

The aspects of logical data organization and the DDL components that describe them can also be partitioned into meaningful groupings that reflect the different levels of complexity possible in a data organization. The simplest level is that of a *field*; fields can be combined to form organizations called *groups*; groups form *records* and records form *files*, as these terms are understood in data processing. In addition, files themselves may be combined to form *files of files* where the access relation between files (the ability to access one file from another) forms a hierarchy. This may be illustrated by the example of the ARIST organization. First, we note that each ARIST volume consists of: (a) the table of contents, (b) the individual chapters, (c) the reference lists following each chapter, and (d) the indexes following the set of chapters and their reference lists. Second, we identify the relations between these components in terms of their use to access one component from another:

(a) The table of contents is used to locate individual chapters and the indexes.
(b) Each chapter can be accessed directly from the chapter preceding it.
(c) The chapters provide references to entries in their adjoining reference lists.
(d) The indices are used to locate information in the chapters and in the reference lists.

If we call each of the components (the table of contents, each chapter, each reference list, and the indexes) *files*, then the entire ARIST volume forms a hierarchy of files (where the table of contents may be considered a file of files). Further, if we examine any one of these files, say for example a reference list, we can discern that it too has a hierarchic nature. We note first that each reference list is composed of a set of similar reference entries, each describing a differ nt book or paper. We can refer to each such entry as a *record*. Each of these entries consists of a grouping of data which provide information about authors, titles, publishers, etc. Each of these can be called a *group*. These groups consist of sets of smaller groups and/or of individual pieces of data such as a name for an author and a date of publication. We call these pieces of data *fields*. Thus, we can see that the relation "consists of" between components of a file forms a hierarchy. This hierarchic structuring of files and sets of files is illustrated in Figure 1 in terms of the concepts of file, record, group, and field, and in terms of the example of the ARIST organization. This partitioning is similar to that developed by Smith (87). Taylor (98) further refines the file level into additional partitions.

It is necessary to have a means of describing each component of a file in terms of those components from which it is formed. The prototype DDL does this by referring in the description of each component to those components organized to form it. The statements for describing each component are presented below, beginning with the field statement (at the bottom of the hierarchy) and ending with the statement for describing the interrelation of files. The examples of ARIST components illustrated in Figure 1 are used throughout.

Describing Items of Data (Fields)

Items of data (or data elements) such as an author's name or title form the basic units of meaningful information in an organization, such as the reference list following each ARIST chapter. Conceptually, a data item is a string of characters and a name that indicates how the string is to be interpreted or understood. For example, the title *Handling chemical compounds in information systems* forms a data item in an ARIST reference list. Only the italicized string of characters appears in the list itself. However, its interpretation as a title can be identified by the position of the string in the reference list entry. These items have a format or structure in which they appear throughout the chapter. For example, each title is followed by a period, and each author's name is given in capital letters. In the terminology of our DDL, such data items are called *fields*. The concept of fields was developed in papers such as those by Mealy (62) and Chapin (18). Hsiao & Harary (46) developed a mathematical model of a field that was the basis of a model of records developed by Hsiao (45).

Components of structures such as punctuation marks (delimiters) and the encoding alphabet are called *structural characteristics*. A list of the structural characteristics for fields and their options is given in Table 1 together with the specific options for the title field in the ARIST reference list. Explanation of a few of these characteristics will further illustrate their use in describing fields.

Characteristic 1, field name, is the name by which the field can be referred to in describing its inclusion in more complex organizations.

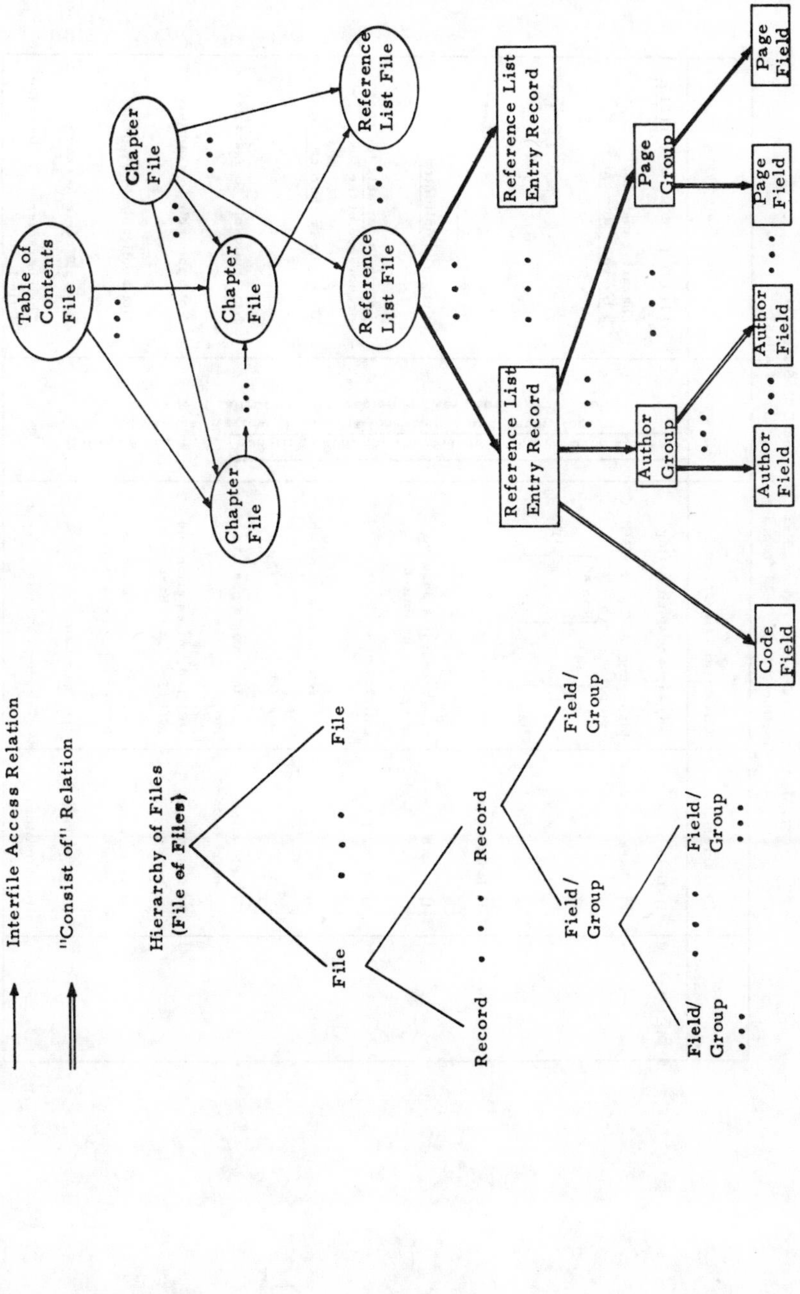

Figure 1. The Hierarchic Structuring of Data Organization

Table 1. Field Characteristics, Example, and DDL Statement for the TITLE Field from Reference List of ARIST

Name of Component	Characteristic	Characteristic Option	Example	DDL Statement
FIELD	1) field name	any alphanumeric string	(130) TATE, F.A. Handling chemical compounds in information systems. In: Annual Review of Information Science and Technology, Carlos A. Cuadra, ed. Interscience New York 1967, Vol. 2, p. 285-309.	FIELD: field name is TITLE
	2) character code	bit string, ASCII or EBCDIC computer codes {5, 5 1/2, :, 14} point {Roman, Boldini, :} type ...		character code is 5 1/2 point Roman
	3) length type	character or bit		Length is given in number of characters
	4) length	n, where n is a positive integer or unlimited		Length is unlimited
	5) uniformity	uniform or variable		Length is variable for each occurrence of the field
	6) data type	character string or number where base, sign and scale is given for numbers		Data type is character string
	7) field alignment factor*	n, where n is a positive integer		Not applicable to example
	8) field alignment*	{LEFT, RIGHT} orientation and pad character		Not applicable to example
	9) value alignment*	{LEFT, RIGHT} orientation and pad character		Not applicable to example
	10) criterion*	criterion name		Not applicable to example
	11) delimiters*	delimiting character string		The character '.' follows the Title field.

* optional characteristics

Characteristic 5, uniformity, specifies whether each occurrence of a field in a file will have the same length. Titles, for instance, may be expected to be of different lengths.

Characteristics 7 and 8, field alignment factor and field alignment, specify whether a field is to be aligned to the left or right with respect to some physical boundary such as a word in computer storage or a column on a page, and how preceding or trailing positions are to be filled (e.g., with blanks). For example, the code number field (see Figure 2) in each reference list entry is aligned to the right of a column that is five character positions wide and preceded with blanks when the code number is less than five characters in length.

Characteristic 9, value alignment, specifies whether the value is aligned to the left or right of a fixed number of positions that do not coincide with some physical boundary.

Characteristic 10, criterion, specifies conditions that must be met for a particular string to be the value of a field. The form of such criteria is discussed in connection with link implementation characteristics in the section entitled "Describing Files."

Describing Groups and Records

We can see that fields in each reference list entry are *grouped* together to form meaningful collections of data. For example, in some entries, a title field is grouped together with a second title field. This occurs whenever a paper being referenced is part of a book. The two title fields are separated by the word "In:" which serves as a delimiter. In a group like this the appearance of the second field is optional, depending on the data.

Groups can also be grouped together. Our entire example of a reference list entry can be considered as a group of different types of information, specifically: a code number field, an author group consisting of one or more author's name fields, a title group, an optional editor field, a publisher group consisting of publisher, city and year fields, an optional volume group consisting of volume and perhaps number fields and a page count field. This structure is illustrated in Figure 2.

A group that is to be used (retrieved or stored) as a single entity is called, in the terminology of our DDL, a *record*.

In our example of an ARIST volume there are many organizational entities which could be classed as records: (a) the entries in the reference lists, (b) the sections of each chapter, (c) the entries in the indices, and (d) the entries in the table of contents.

The structure of a record is exactly the structure of the group that is to be treated as a record. Thus, to describe a record, one must

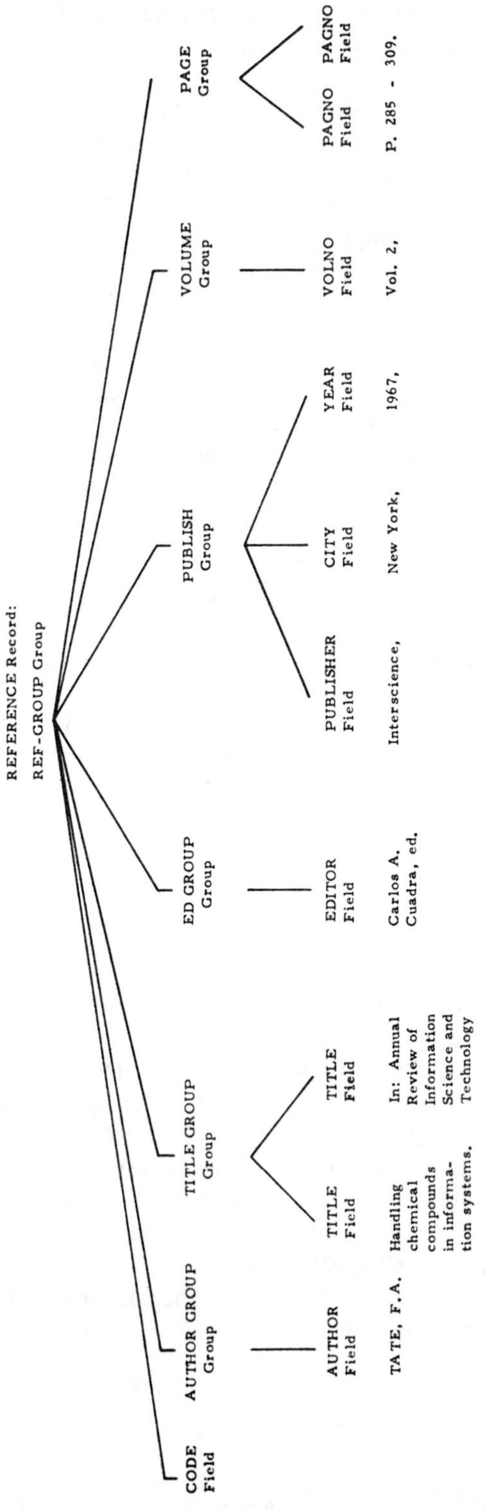

Figure 2. Group Structure of REFERENCE Record

describe the group and declare it to be a record. COBOL was the first programming language to provide such an organizational capability explicitly. Since then, all business-oriented programming languages and computer systems provide their users with record organizations. The CODASYL report (26) describes in detail the record structures provided by the 11 DBMSs it analyzes, and a paper by Maclaren (56) discusses some of the record features in PL/1.

A list of the structural characteristics for records, groups and their options is given in Table 2, together with the specific options for the title group of our example.

Characteristic 7, repetition uniformity, is used in specifying groups containing subordinate groups or fields that are to occur more than once. It is used to indicate whether the subordinate group or field is always to occur the same number of times (it is uniform) whenever the group occurs or whether the number of occurrences may vary. Characteristic 6, number of repetition, gives the maximum number of times the subordinate group or field may occur when characteristic 7 is variable and the fixed number times it may occur when characteristic 7 is uniform.

Characteristic 8, criterion, specifies conditions under which an optional field or subordinate group must occur.

Describing Files

Having developed a means of describing records in terms of their organization, we now consider how to describe the organizing of records into files.

First, let us examine the different ways in which records can be organized. The concept of a record corresponds to the notion of a set of information about one of a collection of similar objects. For example, entries (or records) in an ARIST reference list provide information about individual books or papers. However, given a set of such records, a user may need to represent relations among them. These relations are included in the organization to facilitate the storage, retrieval, and interpretation of the information. They can be thought of as "access paths" between records in the sense that, given one record, there is some means of getting from it to another record. The first record we call the head record of the path and the second record the tail record. For example, the entries in a reference list are used to obtain information published by a particular author. Thus, the entries should be arranged (should be accessible) relative to each other so that the publications of an author can be easily found. This is accomplished in the ref-

Table 2. Group Characteristics, Example, and DDL Statements for the Title Group from Reference List of ARIST

Name of Component	Characteristic	Characteristic Option	Example	DDL Statement
GROUP	1) group name	any alphanumeric string	(130) TATE, F.A. Handling chemical compounds in information systems. In: Annual Review of Information Science and Technology. Carlos A. Cuadra, ed. Interscience, New York, 1967, Vol. 2, p. 285-309.	GROUP: group name is TITLE GROUP.
	2) record status	RECORD or NOT A RECORD		TITLE GROUP is NOT A RECORD.
	3) order of subordinate groups or fields within group	any order, or ordered as named		**Fields** within TITLE GROUP are ordered as they are named below.
	4) **sub**ordinate group or field name	any alphanumeric string		1st field name is TITLE.
	5) occurrence	mandatory, or optional		TITLE is mandatory in TITLE GROUP.
	6) Number of repetitions	n, where n is a positive integer or unlimited		TITLE appears 1 time as the first component of TITLE GROUP.
	7) repetition uniformity	variable or uniform		The number of repetitions of TITLE is uniform.
	8) criterion*	criterion name		Not applicable to the example.
	9) delimiters*	delimiting character string		No delimiters are used in the example.
	characteristics 4) - 9) are specified for each subordinate group or field in the group			2nd field name is TITLE. TITLE is optional in TITLE GROUP. TITLE appears at most 1 time as the 2nd component of TITLE GROUP. The number of repetitions of TITLE varies. Criterion is not applicable. The characters ' IN: ' precede TITLE.

* optional characteristics

erence list by arranging the entries in alphabetical order by author. Thus, there is an access path from a head record in this file to a tail record if, and only if, the author's name in the head record comes alphabetically before the author's name in the tail record and there are no other records with an author's name falling between these two. This condition, or *criterion*, on the value of the author's name determines when two records are to be linked by an access path.

One way to specify such a relation would be to list as pairs each two records that are to be linked. However, in a large file this approach is impractical. A more concise way to specify a linking relation is to describe the *criterion* that determines the linkage. Such a criterion can be specified over values in records, over structural characteristics, and over other linkage relations. The statement for describing a criterion is given in Table 3, together with an example of the use of the statement to describe the criterion for linking the records of an ARIST reference list. (The criterion statement in the last column of Table 3 has been spelled out in the previous paragraph in English.) The options of the statement in Column 3 provide the expressive power of an applied predicate calculus.

Option 1 allows arithmetic tests over values of fields and characteristics to be specified. In our example, the following parts of the criterion statement specify arithemetic criteria over values:

(1) (author's name of HEAD reference record) ≤ (author's name of TAIL reference record)

(2) (author's name of HEAD reference record) ≤ (author's name of any other reference record X1)

(3) (author's name of reference record X1) ≤ (author's name of TAIL reference record)

Option 2 allows tests on the membership of a value or characteristic in a set of other values or characteristics to be specified. There are no such criteria in our example. However, if we wanted to test if the value of the author's name field was one of a set of allowable values (such as JONES, BOND, . . .) it would be specified as follows:

author's name MEM (JONES, BOND,. .)

Option 3 allows criterion over arbitrary records to be quantified (i.e., the criterion in question must be true for all records or at least one record before a link can be created). In our example the arithmetic criteria (2) and (3) listed above must be true for all records. This is specified in our example as follows:

ALL (X1) (. . .criterion (2) . . . criterion (3) . . .)

Option 4 allows new criteria to be specified in terms of other criteria by negating them or by combining them with the connectives AND and

Table 3. Criterion Components, Example, and DDL Statement for Describing Reference List File

Name of Statement	Criterion Components	Options	Example:	DDL Criterion Description
CRITERION	criterion name	a character string	Reference list	CRITERION: criterion name is Criterion 1
	criterion expression	1) arithmetic criterion : (arithmetic expression) relation symbol (arithmetic expression) where the relations are: ≤ greater than or equal to = equal to < greater than ≥ less than or equal to > less than ≠ not equal to	(1) AVRAM H. D. . . 1967 p. (2) BOND, . . . 77 p. . . .	((author's name of HEAD reference record) ≤ (author's name of TAIL reference record) AND (ALL (X1) (NOT ((author's name of HEAD reference record) ≤ (author's name of any other reference record X1)) AND ((author's name of reference record X1) ≤ (author's name of TAIL reference record))))
		2) set criterion : reference name MEM set		
		3) quantified criterion : ALL (X integer)(criterion) SOME (X integer) (criterion)	(13) DODD, . . . 133 p.	
		4) logical criterion : NOT (criterion) (criterion) AND (criterion) (criterion) OR (criterion)	(54) WILLIAMS, . . . 350 p.	

OR. In our example, a criterion is formed by negating the arithmetic criterion (2) listed above and connecting this new criterion to arithmetic criterion (3). This is specified in our example as follows:

(NOT (criterion (2))) AND (criterion (3))

Much research effort has been expended on this aspect of data organization and description. Graph theory has been used to analyze and describe relations between records by Earley (36), Rosenberg (81), Hsiao & Harary (46), and Zunde (108). The notion of describing relations between records by means of a relational notation has aroused a great deal of interest. One of the first papers developing this notion was by Codd (22). Several DDLs have since been studied and implemented for use with DBMSs based on them by Kuhns (48), Minker & Sable (63), Chang (17), DiPaola (32), and Goldstein & Strand (42). Attempts were also made to use a set-theoretic notion for describing file relations. Childs (20) introduced the basic idea, and Fillat & Kraning (37) implemented a DDL and DBMS based on it. Zilles (107) used a functional notation to extend the programming language PAL to allow the specification of data organization. This latter report is particularly well written in that the data descriptive features of the language are formally defined and illustrated by a series of examples. A report by Sandewall & Makila (84) describes a language designed for a DBMS and used for expressing binary relations. Biss et al. (9) present a formal description of a data organization based on a first-order calculus that, they claim, allows the representation of natural language information.

Although these research efforts were all directed to solving problems relating to programming languages and DBMSs, the ideas and techniques that were developed provided the basis for the generalized DDLs of Smith (87) and Taylor (98).

Having specified the file relation for a set of records, it remains to specify the manner in which the access paths of the relation are implemented. An access path between two records can be implemented in one of three ways. The tail record may be stored directly after the head record of the path; there may be a pointer to the tail record stored (or embedded) in the head record; or a pointer to the tail record may be stored after the pointer to the head record in a table of pointers (or directory). The reference list of our example in Table 3 is implemented by sequential storage. For an example of an organization implemented by pointers we can look to the table of contents of an ARIST volume. This is a table of pointers to chapter files. The page number in each entry in the table is the pointer. This organization is illustrated in Figure 3.

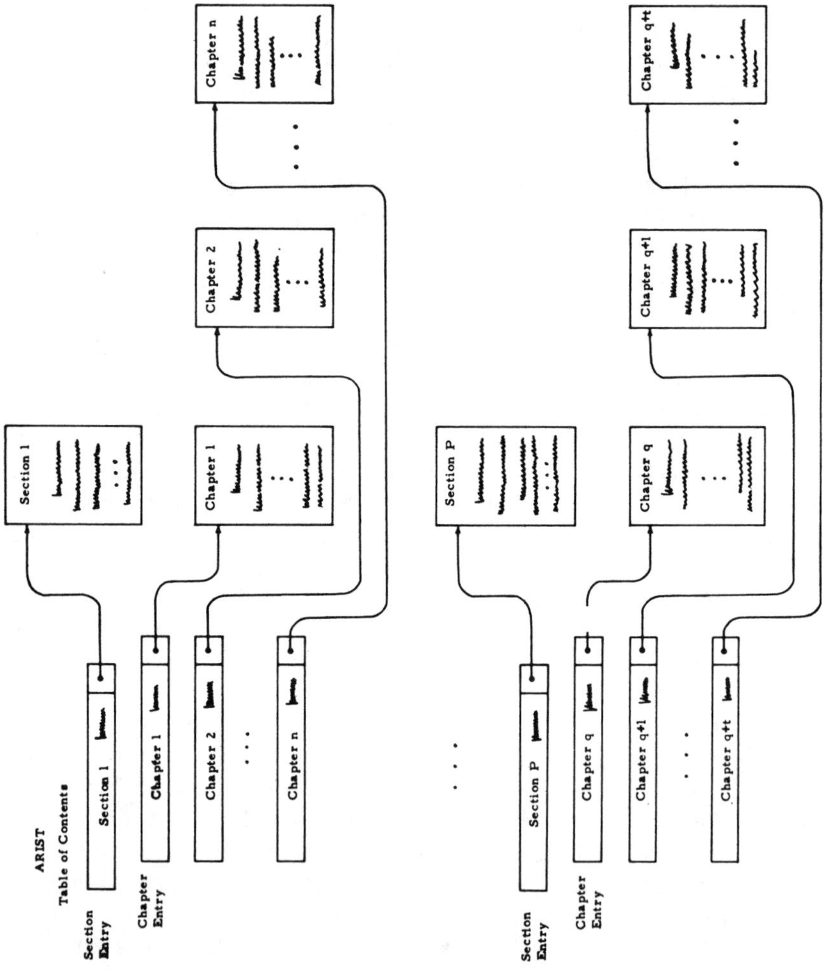

Figure 3. The Table of Contents Used as a Directory in an ARIST Volume

To describe a sequential implementation, it is sufficient merely to indicate that the relations are implemented sequentially, whereas, to describe an implementation using embedded pointers or tables of pointers, the form of the pointers and the structure of the table must be specified. Because the form of the pointer may depend on the storage device used for the data organization, we will defer our discussion of this until the section on storage structures. However, assuming the form of the pointer has been described, it is then only necessary to specify that the pointers are embedded to describe this type of implementation. When the pointers are to be stored in tables, the table itself must be described as another file (i.e., its records [entries], relations between records, and their implementation must be described). Hsiao & Harary (46) investigate the different ways that embedded pointers and tables of pointers can be used to implement file relations.

The declarations and specifications that must be made to describe each type of implementation of a file relation are listed in Table 4. The use of a DDL statement to describe the implementation of the relation between chapters (ordering by chapter number) is also demonstrated in the table. Explanation of a few of these characteristics will further illustrate their use:

> Characteristics 1 and 2 specify the types of records that are to be linked if the criterion named by characteristic 3 is satisfied.
>
> Characteristic 4 specifies the actual implementation.
>
> Characteristics 5 and 6 put restrictions on the number of tail records that can be linked to any particular head record.

Together the LINK statement and the CRITERION statement referred to in it describe the access paths of a file relation.

Records in one file can be linked by access paths to records in other files. This is the case in an ARIST volume that can be easily thought of as a number of interlinked files consisting of: (a) the table of contents file; (b) each chapter making up a file; (c) each reference list, following each chapter, forming a file; and (d) the indexes at the end of each volume forming a file. These files are interlinked. There are pointers from the table of contents to the beginning of each chapter. There are pointers from each chapter to entries in the reference list following that chapter, and there are pointers from the index to pages in the chapters and in the reference lists. The pointers are in fact from records in one file to records in another file. In that sense, table of contents entries are the records of the table of contents file; sections form records in the chapter files; indexes form records in the index file; and reference entries form records in the reference list files. This is illustrated in Figure

Table 4. Link Implementation Characteristics, Example, and DDL Statement for Describing the Table of Contents

Name of Component	Characteristics	Characteristic Options	Example	DDL Description
LINK	link name	any character string	Table of Contents for ARIST Volume 5:	LINK: link name is Chapter Order.
	1) head record name	character string which is the name of a record	I. Planning Information Systems and Services 1.	Head record is Main Chapter Record.
	2) tail record name	character string which is the name of a record	1. Information needs and uses 3.	Tail record is Main Chapter Record.
	3) criterion name	character string which is the name of a criterion	2. Design . . .	Criterion is Criterion 2.
	4) implementation	SEQUEN EMBED, pointer name DIREC, pointer name, file name	⋮ 13. Library and Information Center Management 353.	Implementation is DIREC. Pointer name is pointer 1, file name is Table File.
	5) link number	integer or NO LIMIT		Link number = 1
	6) link uniformity	fixed or variable		Link uniformity is fixed.

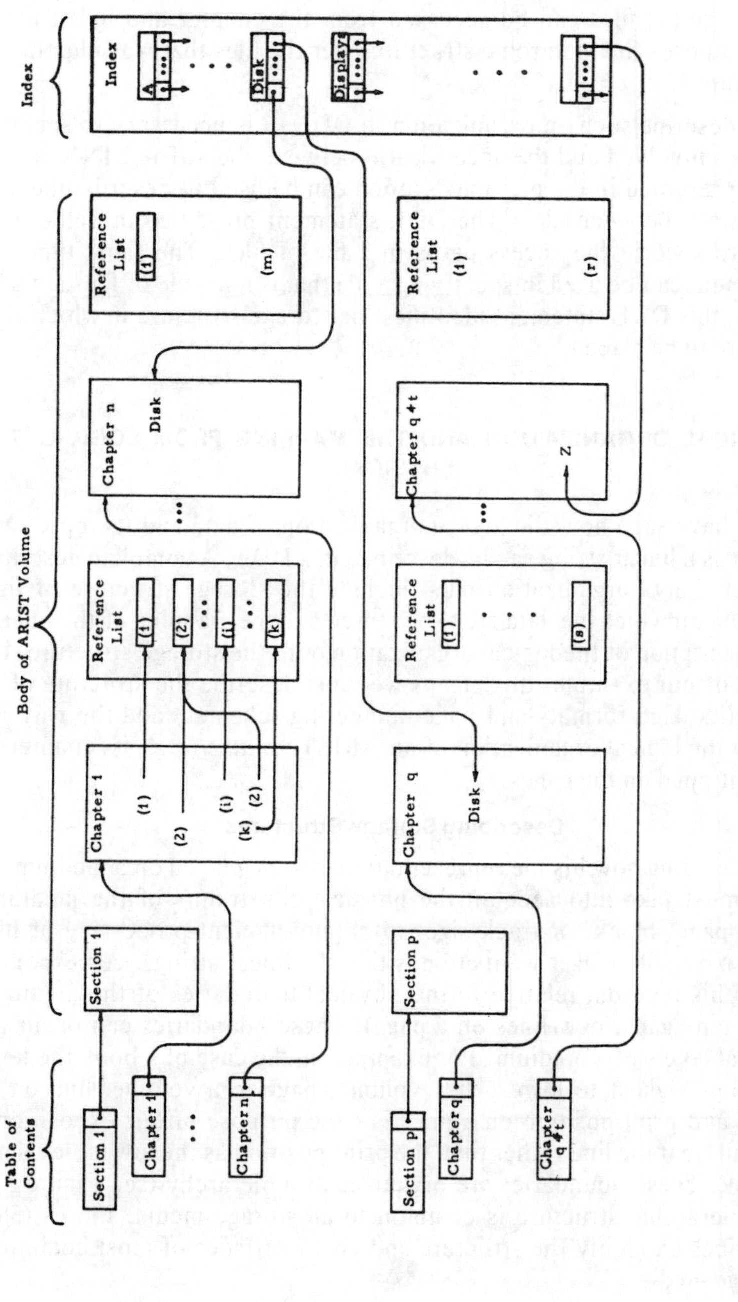

Figure 4. An Example of Hierarchical Files: The Data Structure of an ARIST Volume

4. Thus, it can be seen that the chapter file can be entered by way of access paths from the table of contents and index files. Similarly, the reference list files can be accessed from the chapter and index files. This imposes the hierarchic structure over the files that was illustrated in Figure 1.

To describe such an organization in DDL, it is necessary to specify the files involved and the access paths between them. The LINK statement presented in the previous section can be used to describe the access paths between files. The DDL statement presented in Table 5 is used to specify the access paths in a file of files. The same type of statement can be used in specifying a file that is not a file of files. In addition, this DDL statement identifies the storage structure in which the files are to be placed.

PHYSICAL ORGANIZATION AND THE MAPPING FROM LOGICAL TO PHYSICAL

We have seen how the logical organization of data and its representation as a linear string can be described in a DDL. A complete description of a data organization must include the storage structure of the medium on which the data are to be stored and the mapping of the linear representation of the logical organization onto the storage structure. In terms of our example, this means we must describe the structure of a book (its page formats and page-numbering schemes) and the way in which the logical organization of an ARIST volume (e.g., its chapters) is positioned on the pages.

Describing Storage Structures

In deciding how his file representation is to be placed on a medium, a user must take into account the physical constraints of the medium (e.g., page, block, or track size) to obtain efficient processing of his data. Normally a user wants to position the linear strings, corresponding to his records, relative to the physical boundaries of the medium (e.g., tape gaps, new lines on a page). These boundaries can occur at several levels of a medium. For example, in the case of a book the levels from highest to lowest are: volume, page in a volume, line on a page, and print position on a line. For the purpose of our exposition, we will treat the line rather than the print position as the lowest level of a book. These boundaries are organized as a hierarchy (see Figure 5). The hierarchic structure is common to all storage media. Flores (38) describes explicitly the structure and characteristics of most common storage media.

Table 5. File Characteristics, Example, and DDL Statement for Describing an ARIST Volume

Statement Name	Characteristic	Characteristic Option	Example	DDL Statement
FILE	1) file name	a string of characters	The ARIST Volume consisting of the files and the relations between their records as illustrated in Figure 6.	FILE: file name is ARIST Volume.
	2) link name	a name that refers to the LINK statement specifying a relation between records in the files		Link name 1 is Table of Contents to Chapter Link.
				Link name 2 is Table of Contents to Indices Link.
	.			Link name 3 is Chapter Order.
	.			Link name 4 is Index to Chapter Link.
	.			
	link name			Link name 5 is Index to Reference List Link.
				Link name 6 is Chapter to Reference List Link.
				Link name 7 is Reference List Link.
				Link name 8 is Index Order.
	3) storage structure name	a name that refers to the specification of a storage structure by means of a BLOCK statement (see Table 8)		Storage structure name is ARIST Storage Structure.
	4) device name : device name	a name that refers to the specification of the devices used to store the logical structure (see Table 9)		Device name is ARIST Book.

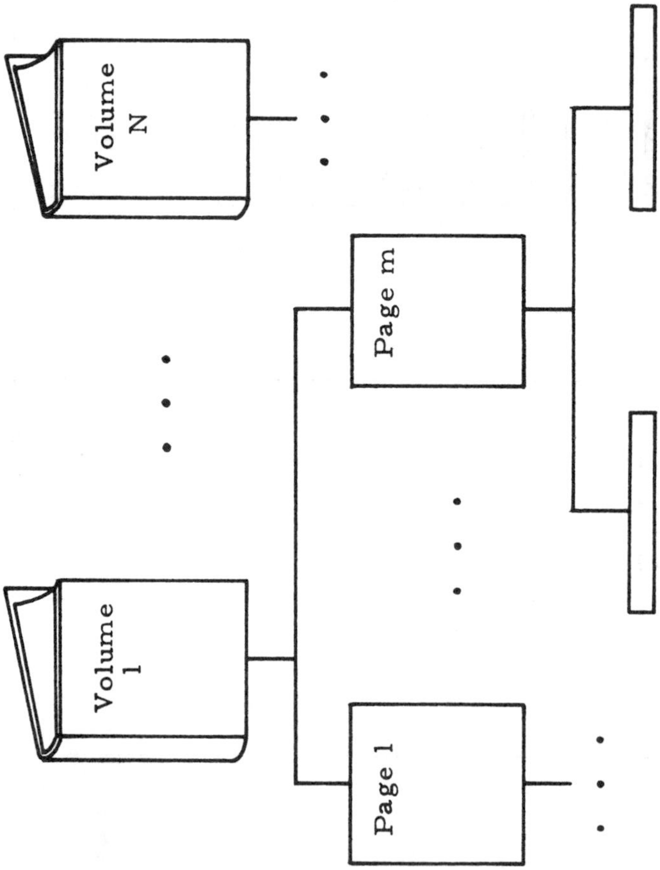

Figure 5. The Hierarchic Storage Structure of a Book

To be general, we will call the unit of storage at the lowest level (line, in our example) a *basic block*, and the units of storage at the higher level *blocks*. This organization of blocks forms the *storage structure* of a medium.

Within a block, the basic blocks or subordinate blocks (often called "subblocks") may have many different formats. These formats take the form of size, structure of subblocks, addressing schemes, and labels used to indicate the beginning and end of blocks. For example, in an ARIST volume there are five types of pages:

(1) the pages that contain the table of contents: these pages have only blank lines at top and bottom as labels to create margins and no addressing scheme (they are not numbered);
(2) the first pages of chapters and sections: these pages have only the blank lines at top and bottom as labels but are numbered in sequence with pages of types 3, 4 and 5;
(3) the left-hand pages of the book that contain the contents of the section and chapters: these pages, in addition to the blank lines at top and bottom, contain the authors' names and the page number as headers. They are numbered in sequence with pages of types 2, 4 and 5;
(4) the right-hand pages of the book that contain the contents of the sections and chapters: these pages, in addition to the blank lines at top and bottom, contain the title of the section or chapter and the page number as headers. They are numbered in sequence with pages of types 2, 3 and 5;
(5) the index pages: these pages are split into two columns, each one of which contains the records of the index file. In addition to the blank lines at top and bottom, they contain the string "Index" and the page number as headers, and are numbered in sequence with pages of types 2, 3 and 4.

The organization of these pages to form the ARIST storage structure is illustrated in Figure 6. Each of these page types is in turn composed of lines having particular structures. For example, the pages in the section/chapter blocks are composed of lines containing 100 character positions of which the first and last 10 are blanks determining the left and right margins.

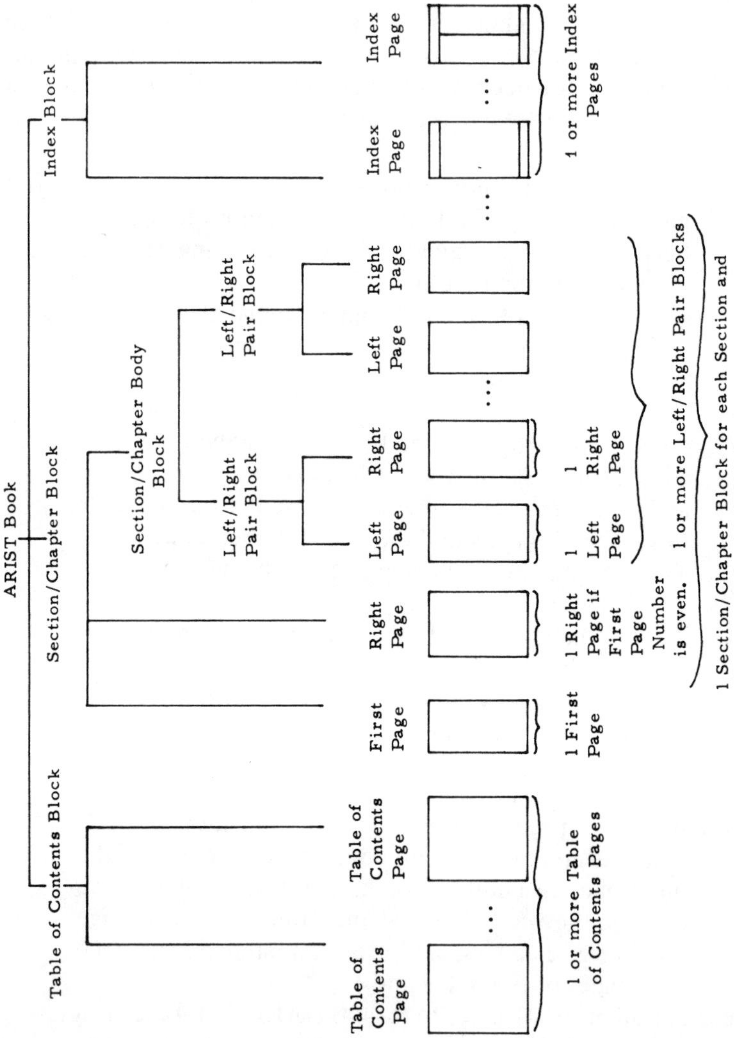

Figure 6. The Storage Structure of an ARIST Book down to the Page Level

The different blocks and basic blocks of a storage structure are implemented on a storage medium in terms of such characteristics as labels, block or basic block size, and addressing scheme. Thus, to describe a storage structure, it is necessary to have a means of describing the hierarchic nature of the structure and the implementation of the blocks and basic blocks within it. This is accomplished by using statements analogous to the FIELD and GROUP statements used in describing the logical organization of data. These are the BBLOCK, and BLOCK statements, respectively.

The implementation of basic blocks is described in terms of the characteristics given in Table 6. These characteristics are described by Smith (87). The example of lines in a chapter block is taken to illustrate the use of these characteristics to describe a basic block.

Characteristics 3-6 are used to describe how records in a logical organization of data are positioned in a basic block. Their use will be discussed in the following subsection.

The structure of a block (its subblock and basic block component) and its implementation are described in terms of the characteristics given in Table 7. The example of a right page is taken to illustrate the use of these characteristics.

Characteristic 2 is used to describe how addresses are assigned to subblocks and basic blocks contained in the block being described. Since the lines of a page are not individually addressed (numbered) this characteristic is not specified in the example. Rosenberg (81) has been studying the problem of addressing, relative to graph structures.

Characteristic 3 is used to indicate the different types of subordinate blocks and basic blocks that may occur in the block being specified. In our example a page consists of 45 of the same type of lines. This is specified in the statement.

Mapping the Logical Organization into Physical Structures

The mapping of the logical organization of the ARIST volume into the storage structure of a book is illustrated in Figure 7. It shows the additional specifications needed to indicate the positioning of records and files relative to the basic blocks in the storage structure. For example, each chapter file should start on a new page, and if a chapter does not fit on a single page it may be spread over a number of pages. Also, any pointers contained in the file are to be interpreted in terms of such characteristics as addressing schemes. The characteristics that determine the positioning of a user's records relative to basic blocks are indicated in Table 6 by means of the symbol "†."

Table 6. Basic Block Description, Example, and DDL Statement for Describing a Line in an ARIST Volume

Name of Statement	Characteristic	Characteristic Option	Example	DDL Description
BBLOCK	1) block name	a character string	information systems. Richteritsch (36) reviews, in particular, the building of data bases and file handling programs that will interface with applica- tion programs in MIS. In spite of these contribu- tions, we remain without a symbolic language that is capable of describing all known file structures in	BBLOCK: block name is <u>Chapter Line</u>
	2) length	n, where n is an integer or NOLIM		Length is 100 character positions
	3) record count: basic block count ratio †	n : n NOLIM : NOLIM where n is an integer		Record count: block count ratio is 1: NOLIM
	4) count uniformity †	fixed or variable		Count uniformity is variable
	5) Split record set †	SPLIT: record name, ..., record name		SPLIT: Chapter Record, Main Chapter Record
	6) Start record set †	START: record name, ..., record name		
	7) header label* ⋮ header label	HDR: character string		HDR: ␣␣ ··· ␣␣ (10 blanks)
	8) trailer label* ⋮ trailer label	TLR: character string		TLR: ␣␣ ··· ␣␣ (10 blanks)

* optional characteristics

† characteristics used to describe the mapping of logical to physical structure for each basic block

Table 7. Block Characteristics, Example, and DDL Statements for Describing a Page in a Volume

Name of Statement	Characteristic	Characteristic Option	Example	DDL Description
BLOCK	1) block name	a character string	A right page in an ARIST chapter: 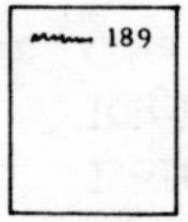	BLOCK: block name is Right Page
	2) addressing scheme:			
	address length*	n, where n is an integer		
	address order	ascending or descending		
	base	n, where n is an integer		
	first address	character string		
	3) subordinate blocks or basic blocks:			Subordinate basic block: Block name is Chapter Line
	block or basic block name	a character string		
	occurrence	mandatory or optional		Occurrence is mandatory.
	repetition number	n, where n is an integer or NOLIM		Repetition number is 45 (45 lines/page).
	uniformity	fixed or variable		Uniformity is variable (i.e., 45 lines/page is the actual repetition number and not a maximum).
	address level*	current level or next level		
	address scope*	with other block types or within this block type only		
	Characteristic 3) is specified for each subordinate block or basic block in the block being specified			
	4) header label* : header label	HDR: character string		HDR: ⊔ ... ⊔ blank line HDR: blank line HDR: blank line HDR: blank line HDR: chapter name, page address HDR: blank line
	5) trailer label : trailer label	TLR: character string		TLR: blank line ... TLR: blank line } 6 trailers

* optional characteristics

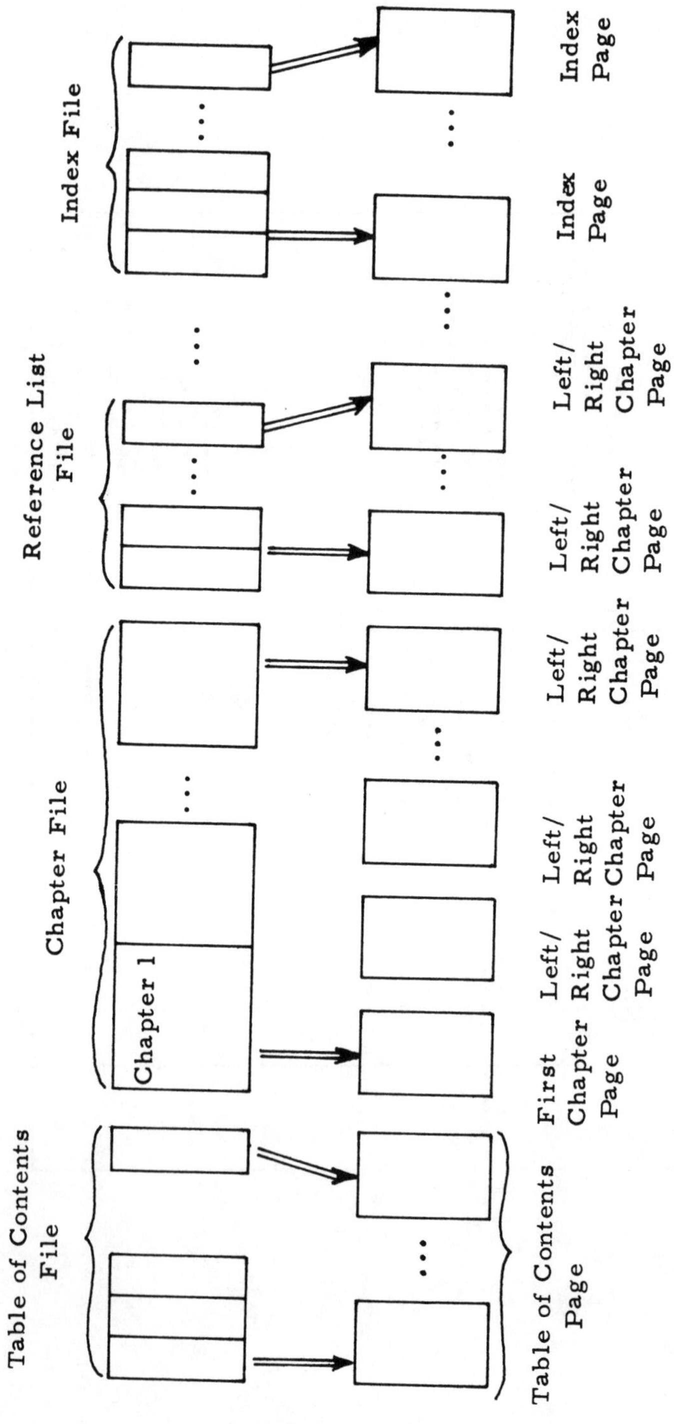

Figure 7. Mapping the Logical Organization of an ARIST Volume Into Its Storage Structure

Finally, it is further necessary to relate the storage structure to a specific medium to complete the description of the total data organization. This is done by identifying which blocks in the storage structure correspond to actual levels on the medium for each type of device that has been specified. In Figure 6 we can see that there are levels of the hierarchy that do not correspond to physical levels of the medium. For example, the left/right pair blocks do not correspond to a physical level. One way that this relation between levels in the storage structure and physical levels of a particular device can be described is to have a separate statement for each kind of media used. In our example, the only medium used is a book. Therefore, the statement for relating a storage structure to a book is described in Table 8. Similar statements would be used for tapes, discs, and other storage media.

Data Conversion and Integration

As indicated earlier, one of the major motivations for the development of DDLs is the mechanization of data conversion from a current organization (source structure) to a new organization (target structure). A conversion processor would accept, as input, the data, a DDL description of the data organization, a DDL description of a new desired organization for the data, and a description of the relation between elements in one organization and those in the other. By interpreting and processing these inputs, the conversion processor would output the data in its new organization.

The literature relating to data interchange and conversion discusses either the problems of interchange or strategies for avoiding the problem. Papers on the problems involved have been authored by Gold (41) and Dennis (31). On the other hand Tell et al. (99), White (104), Anderson et al. (1), Shtefanik et al. (86), and Stevens (94) have reported on strategies for reducing data interchange problems. Acceptance of industry-wide standards minimizes the problem; it does not cure it. Thus, the announcement of a standard for recorded magnetic tape (73) is worth noting.

However, it is already too late to prevent data interchange problems for existing systems and we must look to the development of generalized data-conversion utilities for their cure. One of the early efforts devoted explicitly to the design of a generalized DDL for use in data conversion was that of Gabrini (40). He designed a DDL that was very powerful at the record level. Anderson et al. (1) have developed a processor for use in the ARPA network that converts character sets, adds

Table 8. Storage Device Characteristics, Example, and DDL Statement for Describing a Book

Name of Statement	Characteristics	Characteristic Option	Example	DDL Description
BOOK	name	character string	The type of book containing an ARIST Volume (see Figure 7)	BOOK: book name is <u>ARIST Book</u>
	Volume level blocks	VOL: block name, ..., block name		VOL: <u>ARIST Volume</u>
	Page level blocks	PAGE: block name ..., block name		PAGE: Table of content pages First chapter page Left chapter page Right chapter page
	Line level blocks	LINE: block name, ... block name		LINE: <u>Chapter Line</u> (see Table 7)

or deletes messages, inserts message counters and flags, and transposes fields. However, attempts to create a data converter that can convert stored data from one organization to another (involving changes in field, record, file and storage organization) awaited the design of the necessary DDL.

To use a DDL for data conversion it must be augmented by a description facility for specifying the relation between the source and target structures. Such a facility can take the form of an association list that identifies, for each field in the target structure, the source of a value for that field in the source structure. Such an association list is described in Table 9 and is illustrated by specifying the creation of a combined index file for an ARIST volume from index files of previous volumes.

In the target file there is to be a record for each different index term in the index files. Each such record will contain page number fields whose values are to be obtained from records in the index files for the respective index term. This conversion results in the integration of the index files into the combined index file. The conversion is illustrated in Figure 8. Assuming there are four index files to be used as source files, volume numbers in the respective volumes precede the respective page numbers.

Each entry in the ASSOCIATE statement identifies a field in the target structure and the source of the value for that field in the source structure by giving the name of the source file, the name of the source file containing this type of record (if there is more than one), a means of specifying a criterion for selecting a particular occurrence of the source record, and a means of selecting a particular group or field when one is referred to that repeats within the record. Such criteria may have the same form as the criteria presented in Table 4 or they may simply indicate that the record or group to be selected is simply one already used for the source of target field already converted. This is expressed by the phrase SOURCE (target field name). Smith (87) developed the concept of the association list to its present form.

Presently, a data conversion utility using such a DDL is being developed at the Moore School of Electrical Engineering, University of Pennsylvania, where the implementation of a subset of Smith's DDL (87) is underway, and at the University of Michigan where the implementation, a subset of Taylor's DDL (98), is being designed.

These implementations are based on the concept of syntax-directed compilation. That is, the converter reads and interprets the description of a source file as if it were a syntax description and uses it to "parse" the source to obtain its component data item. In a similar fashion, it uses the description of the target file to organize the

Table 9. Associate Characteristic Example, and DDL Statement for Integrating Index Files to Form Combined Index File

Name of Statement	Characteristics	Characteristic Option	Example	DDL Description
ASSOCIATE	(association entry) . . . (association entry)	target field name, source field name, criterion for selecting source record,* criterion for selecting source group or field*	Conversion from Index Records to Records for Combined Index (see Figure 7)	ASSOCIATE (Index Term, Index Term in Index Record) (Volume 1 Page Number, Page Number in Index Record of ARIST Volume 1 File, record criterion: index term = index term in SOURCE (index term)) . . (Volume 5 Page Number, Page Number in Index Record of ARIST Volume 5 File, record criterion: index term = index term in SOURCE (index term))

* optional characteristic options

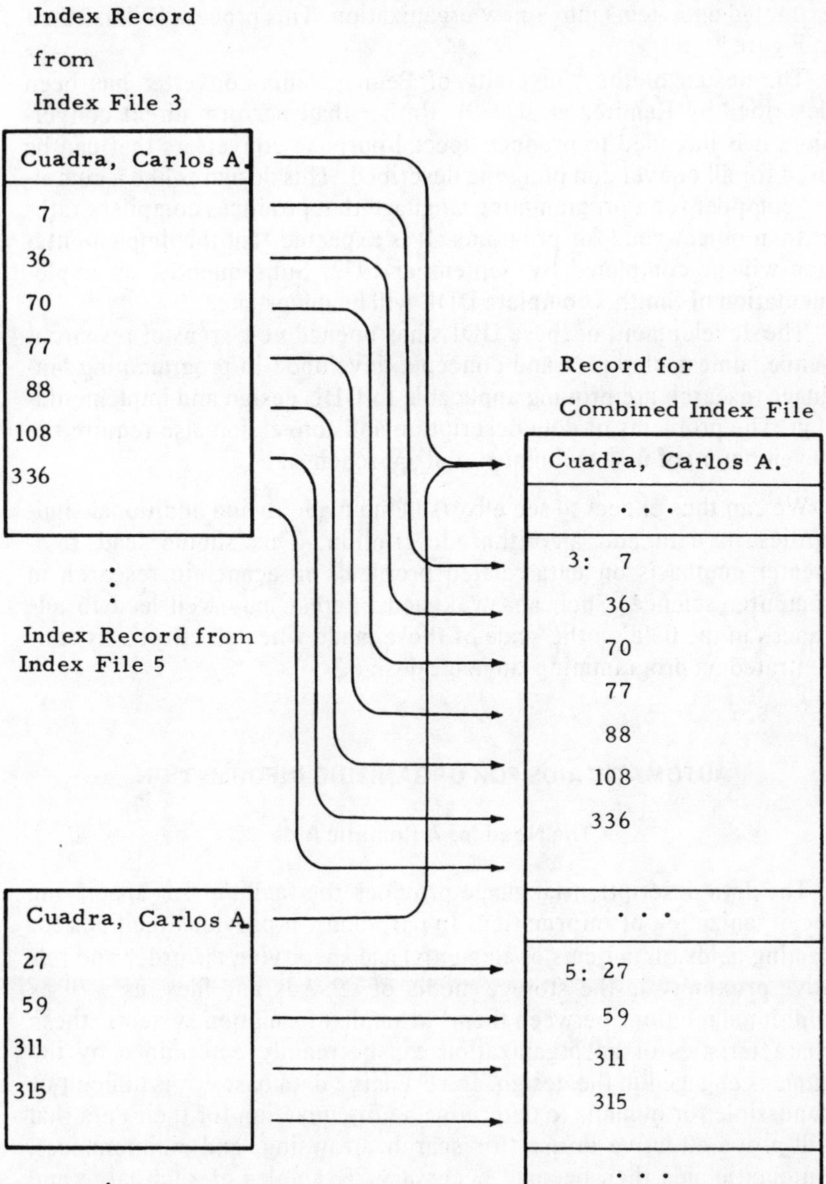

Figure 8. Creation of Combined Index File from Index Files for the ARIST Volumes

extracted data items into a new organization. This process is illustrated in Figure 9.

The design of the University of Pennsylvania converter has been described by Ramirez et al. (79). Rather than perform direct conversion, it is intended to produce special-purpose converters that can be used for all conversion of a type described. This design is like a compiler-compiler for a programming language that produces compilers rather than object code for programs. It is expected that this implementation will be completed by September 1972. Subsequently, an implementation of Smith's complete DDL will be undertaken.

The development of these DDLs has opened new areas of research. While some techniques and concepts developed in programming language research are proving applicable to DDL design and implementation. The problems of data description and conversion also require the development of new techniques and approaches.

We can thus expect to see efforts being made to find additional similarities in data and algorithm description. This should lead to a greater emphasis on data related problems in academic research in computer science. Such an awakened interest may well lead to advances in the field on the scale of those made when all effort was concentrated on programming language design.

AUTOMATIC AIDS FOR ORGANIZING INFORMATION

The Need for Automatic Aids

The data description language provides the facilities for specifying the organization of information. In particular, it provides facilities for naming fields (data items or elements) and specifying the order and relative proximity in the storage media of records and files, as well as additional relations between them. In small information systems, these characteristics of an organization can be readily determined by the humans engaged in the design. In very large data bases, it is difficult or impossible for humans to determine an organization for their data that will prove effective in use (for search, browsing, and maintenance). Automatic aids then become necessary. Examples of such large and complex data bases abound. They include the files with millions of citations of the Library of Congress and the National Library of Medicine and the files of hundreds of millions of income tax returns of the U.S. Internal Revenue Service. Specifying data organization is even more complicated in management information systems where diverse kinds

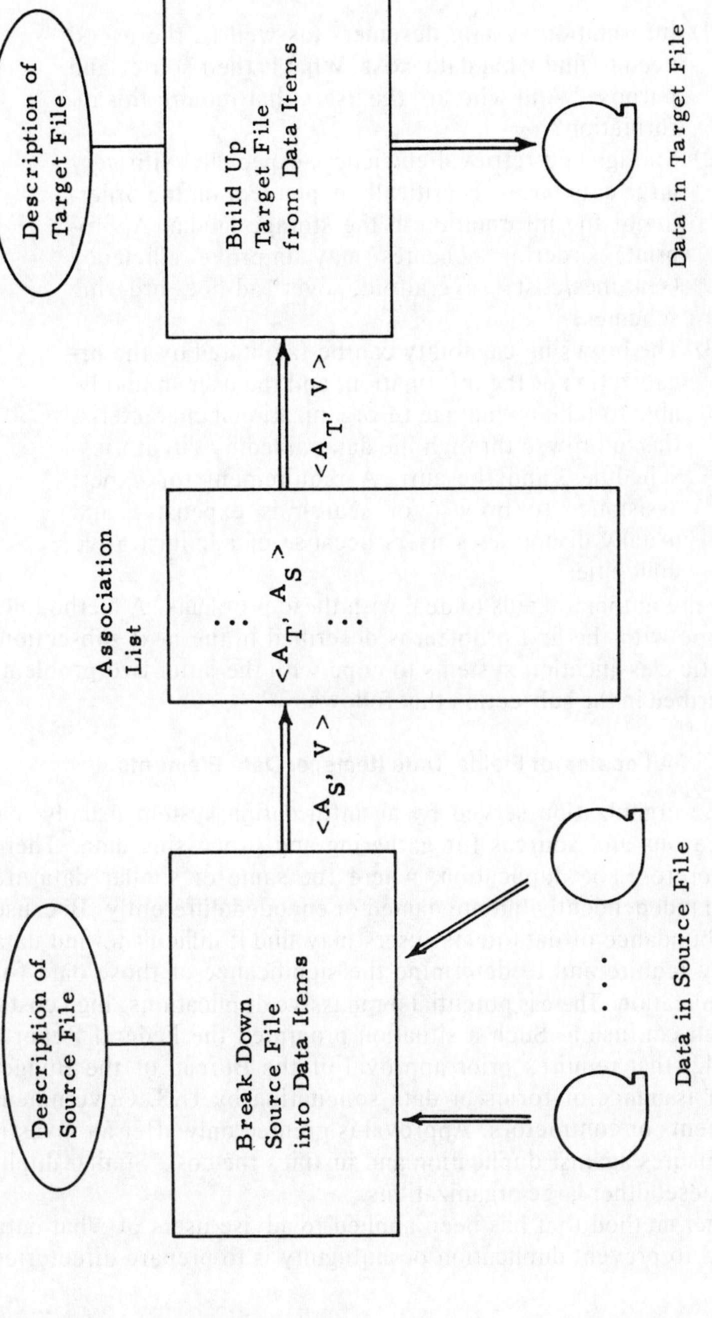

Figure 9. The Conversion Process

of information are gathered for lage business, industrial, or governmental organizations. The problems that arise fall into three categories:

(1) Information system designers (as well as the users) need to find what data exist. What is their source and purpose? And who are the users that require this information?

(2) Storage and retrieval efficiency, especially with very large data bases, is critically dependent on the ordering of the information in the storage media. Appropriate ordering schemes may improve efficiency (searches/cost) severalfold, over ad-hoc ordering schemes.

(3) The browsing capability can be facilitated by the organization of the information, and the user should be able to take advantage of organizational characteristics to browse through the data, aided by directories, schedules, and thesauri. A requirement for expert assistance to browse or search is expensive and usually discourages users because of administrative difficulties.

There are automatic aids to deal with these problems. A methodology to cope with the first problem is described in the next subsection. Automatic classification systems to cope with the latter two problems are described in the subsection that follows.

A Locator for Fields, Data Items, or Data Elements

A large organization served by an information system usually has many reasons and sources for gathering and processing data. There may, therefore, be duplication, where the same or similar data are gathered independently but are named or encoded differently. Because of the abundance of data items, users may find it difficult to find data that they require and to determine the significance of those data for their application. There is potential for massive duplications, high costs, and much confusion. Such a situation prompted the Federal Reports Act (1942) that requires prior approval of the Bureau of the Budget (100) for issuance of forms or data solicitation by U.S. Government departments or contractors. Approval is granted only after an investigation ensures against duplication and justifies the cost. Similar duplications beset other large organizations.

Another method that has been applied to advise users of what data exist and to prevent duplication or ambiguity is to prepare directories of standardized names for data items. An example of such a directory is the *Manual for Standard Data Elements* produced by the Department of Defense (101). It not only lists the data elements, but also, in some instances, specifies all the *values* that these data elements have. The result is an extremely voluminous manual that has been very expensive to compile and is only of questionable use.

A more effective approach to this problem has been to organize the directories in accordance with classification systems by which data elements are also to be indexed. The data elements are assigned index terms based, for instance, on the sources of the data, reasons for gathering the data, the budget items that support the gathering of the data, the missions of the organization for which the data are gathered, the users, etc. Classified schedules are produced by computers that list the data elements for each index term. This approach has been called the locator system by McDonough and is described in his book *Centralized Systems—Planning and Control* (55). Such locator systems were suggested by Nisenoff (68) for a police information system and by the Computer Command and Control Company (23) for an information system for the Office of the Secretary of U.S. Department of Transportation. Similar activities have been described by Schruben (85) as applied at the Emerson Electric Company and by Stevens (95) as applied in the field of banking. In all these examples, computers are used to produce reports of names of data elements, ordered by the indexes of the various classification systems described above, in linear fashion as in a directory or in multidimensional matrix form. These reports indicate to the users the significance and function of the data and allow them to trace the cause and effect sequence, starting with the reasons for gathering the data and ending with the missions of the organization that the data support.

AUTOMATIC CLASSIFICATION

What Automatic Classification Is and How It Works

The basic definition of a classification system preceded the development of modern computers. Quoting Margaret Mann, "Classification is, in simplest statement, the putting together of like things, or, more fully described, it is the arranging of things according to likeness or unlikeness" (57).

The arranging or ordering of "things" together can be applied to any one of the levels in the hierarchy of information described in this chapter. This includes fields, records, files, and files of files. For convenience, we will refer only to the ordering of records, but the extension can be made readily to other levels.

The criterion of "likeness" for grouping of records may vary in breadth. If a criterion is judged to be too broad in the sense of covering too many records, it may be subdivided by applying a number of narrower subcriteria. The broader group divides into several narrower groups. Thus, the idea of a classification system is also that of a tree as illustrated in Figure 10. If a notational system with decimal numbers is used to name files at the nodes, it is called a *decimal classification system*. The terminal nodes in the classification tree are files with information records stored in cells in memory or shelves in a library.

Automatically generated classification systems do not have theory of breakdown of information by concept; only a criterion of being "satisfactory in use" is applied. Such a criterion can be determined only after the collection of records has been assembled and examined. Therefore, we refer to a manmade classification system based on a preconceived theory of breakdown of information as being a priori. Automatic classification systems are by contrast a posteriori.

There is, then, a two-step process. In the first step, the values of specified fields in each record are extracted and become the index terms which that index records. Another product of this first step is a vocabulary of the index terms from several records. In the second step, records that are considered to be "alike" in the sense that they have index terms in common are grouped in the storage media. The terms assigned to the records in such a group form a subdivision in the classification schedule. The vocabulary of index terms is thus repeatedly subdivided, thereby forming a classification schedule.

The automatic classification process determines an organizational scheme by specifying the ordering of fields, records, and files. Once the ordering information is produced automatically, it can be readily restated using the DDL. One can envisage that combining the DDL description and the automatic classification will reduce the work of specification of the organization required of the information system designer, and facilitate the reorganization of the files automatically.

The organization of this volume of ARIST can be used here to illustrate conventional manual and automatic classification systems. In the preface to Volume 6 of ARIST (27), Cuadra describes a classification system for the series of ARIST volumes, which is illustrated in Figure 11. This is a manual classification system created a priori for each volume. The respective authors of ARIST follow a generally similar classification system each year in preparing their contributions on a specific chapter topic that was assigned to them. However, they need to describe new developments, which very likely cannot be constricted by

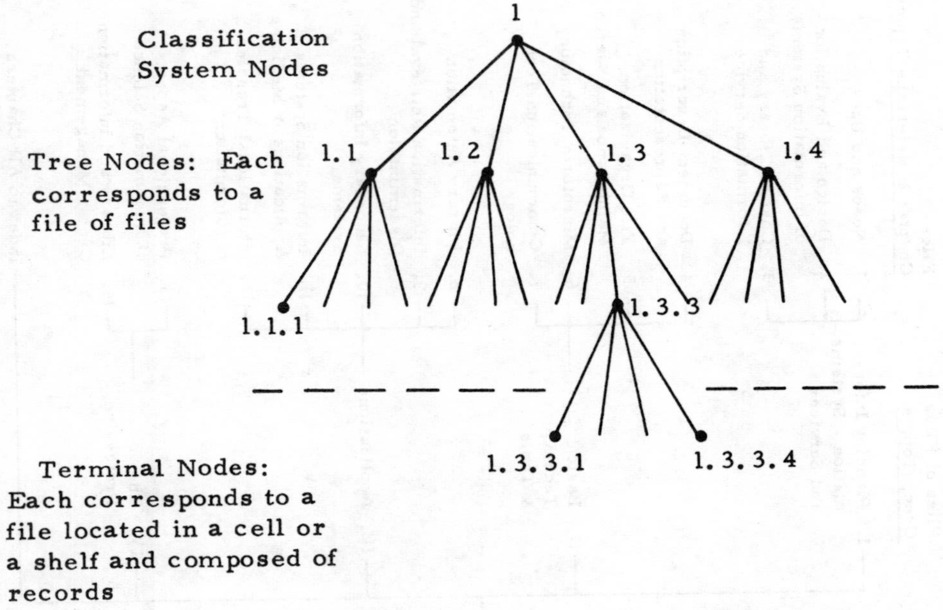

Figure 10. The Tree as an Illustration of a Classification

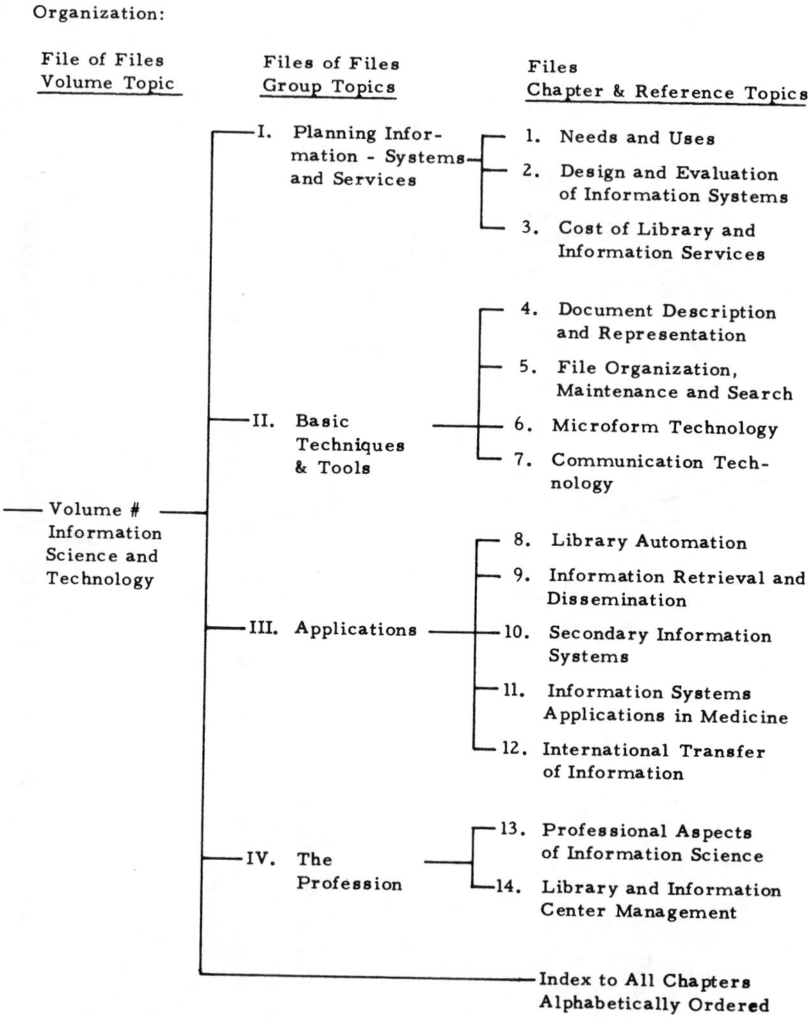

Figure 11. Illustration of an A Priori Manually Created Classification System for ARIST (24)

the same set of chapter topics. Therefore the material, as well as the references, usually cover other topics. Also chapter material by the various contributors may overlap. The current solution to this problem is to continue some topics from year to year, rotate other chaper topics, and occasionally add and delete chapter topics. If an automatic classification process is to be applied to ARIST, it would automatically generate groups and subgroups of index terms. The index of ARIST could then be ordered accordingly, rather than ordered by the present alphabetical system. This classification system could also be applied to the references producing bibliographies for the automatically generated new classification numbers (instead of the I through IV and 1 through 14 notes in Figure 11). Finally, the automatically generated classification system may serve for guidance in preparing future volumes of ARIST.

Improving Search Efficiency with Automatic Classification

A major reason for employing automatic generation of classification systems is the potential dramatic reduction in processing times involved in the storage and retrieval functions. This is well illustrated by the results of experiments conducted by Litofsky (54, summarized in 78). Litofsky employed a program named "CLASFY," which automatically generated a classification and organized the data base accordingly. The file was composed of 46,821 *Nuclear Science Abstracts*, and he measured the processing work involved in searches of the file to respond to 165 requests. He compared the search-processing load with that needed for a randomly ordered file and a file ordered on a manually indexed a priori classification. As shown in Figure 12, a severalfold reduction of the number of cells searched results from ordering the records in the file in accordance with the classification produced by CLASFY, over a randomly ordered file. Furthermore, the CLASFY-ordered file results in fewer cell searches than a file ordered by a manually generated classification. While reconstructing a manually created classification is extremely laborious and the result can be easily outdated, with the aid of CLASFY, a completely new classification can be automatically reprocessed and maintained up to date. The changes from the old classification schedule to the new can be reported as well, and the changes may give an indication of developments in the subject area. Research, on how meaningful such developments would be is underway by one of the authors.

In addition to the reduction in the numbers of cells searched, when a file is ordered by a classification scheme, the search times are even

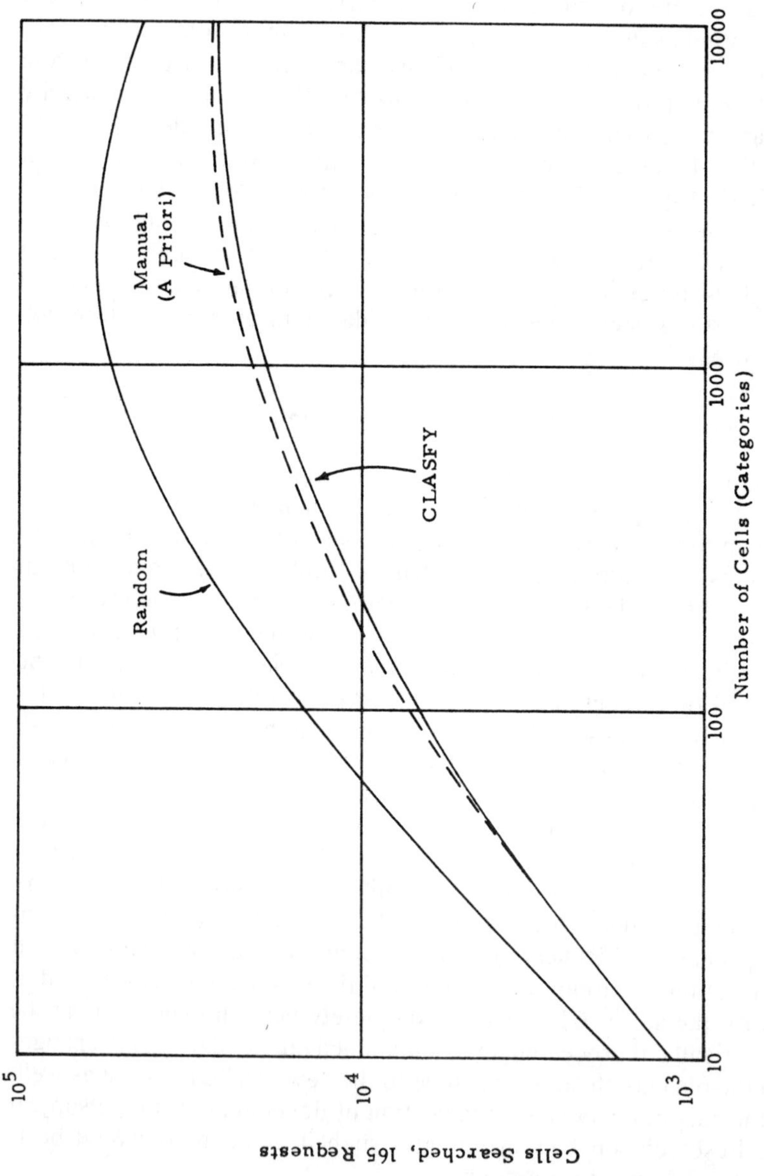

Figure 12*. Cells (Categories) Searched, 46821 Records

* From Litofsky (53). Used with permission of the author.

more dramatically reduced. The computer time required to perform a search is highly dependent on the size of the file (number of records) and the size of the directories (number of index term entries). Examples worked out in (54) and (77) show that the directory size is greatly reduced through stratifying the directory in accordance with an automatically generated classification system. This results in search times that are an order of magnitude shorter than when the methodology of an inverted-file directory is used. The search time improvements become significant for very large and complex data bases only. The examples cited above involve files with over a million records, over 10,000 index terms, and over 10 terms used on the average for indexing each record in the file.

Browsing Aids Provided by the Automatic Classification

The browse capability should be an essential portion of complex information systems. Many times a user has only a vague idea of the data he desires and, by browsing, he may find the information that he desires.

Effectiveness of browsing can be greatly aided by two features provided by automatic classification: (a) hierarchical sets of categories, whereby one can start with broad categories and work towards specifics, and (b) ordering of records (documents) and groups that can be used for broadening searches.

Naturally, automated browsing can be most effective with on-line computer systems through man-machine interaction. The user can key-in nodes (classification numbers) or terms. The computer system then displays the nodes, showing the respective parts of the node-to-term classification schedule as well as statistics, such as how many records there are beneath each node. When the user selects branches and new nodes, the cycle repeats with the new nodes. If desired, one would backtrack up the hierarchy or jump to completely different portions. Once the user has narrowed his search, he can demand retrieval of some or all of the records.

Another way of browsing is to start at the very bottom. Assume one has a specific query in mind and upon submitting it to the system, obtains only one record. If this is insufficient one could broaden the search by requesting the display of other records that are stored near the one retrieved. Since these records have been classified as being close in content to the original, they might also satisfy the query or they might suggest new index terms for the user to use in expanding his query in order to reference other nodes and retrieve other records of interest. (Minker, et al. (64) were unsuccessful in broadening the searches. However they did not use the hierarchical and ordering aspects of a classification. They broadened queries only to clusters.)

An on-line computer is not an absolute necessity for browsing. An automatically generated *classification schedule* could be made in book form, and the browsing could then be done by hand turning of pages. The procedures would be similar to those outlined above but somewhat slower because of the page turning.

These methods of browsing are strikingly similar to those employed in traditionally organized libraries. They do not require users to be familiar with a thesaurus, its structure, or with relations between terms. They do not require formulation of query formulas and understanding computerized processing of such formulas. In short, these methods do not require a highly trained staff to interpret user queries, but they allow user-direct browsing along traditional browsing patterns.

Review of Automatic Classification Experiments

Lance & Williams (50) have divided a posteriori classification strategies into hierarchical and clustering types. They have further subdivided hierarchical strategies into agglomerative and divisive types. In agglomerative strategies, the hierarchy is formed by combining records and groups of records until all—the entire collection—is in one large group. Experiments using such methods were performed by Doyle (35) using the Ward & Hook grouping program (103).

With divisive techniques, the entire collection is successively subdivided, until appropriately sized cells (or shelves) are obtained. Doyle (34) has proposed a system of this type [see Dattola (30) for preliminary experiments]. Another classification algorithm of the divisive hierarchical type is that of CLASFY (54) described earlier.

Table 10 presents an updated summary of automatic classification experiments reported originally by Litofsky (54). Note especially the progress in corpus size, which is most important because of the contributions of this methodology to efficiency of processing in very large data bases.

More recently, a number of large-scale automatic classification experiments have been conducted but reports on them are not available. Efforts of this type are currently underway at the U.S. Patent Department.[1] Large improvements in search times due to use of automatic classification are obtained only for very large data bases. Therefore, organizations that require on-line processing of very large data bases are interested in the use of this technique.

---

[1]Private communication to Dr. B. Litofsky from Harold Pfeffer, The Office of Research and Development, U.S. Department of Commerce, Patent Office, August 1971.

Table 10.* Survey of Automatic Classification Experiments

Source	Maron [59]	Borko [11] Borko and Bernick [14, 15]	Williams [105]	Bonner [9]	Doyle [34]	Dale and Dale [27]	Atherton and Borko [3]	Rocchio [80]	Perriens and Williams [71]	Sparck Jones and Needham [90]	Lefkovitz and Angell [51]	Litofsky [53]	Augustson and Minker [4]
Year of Publication	1961	1962-4	1963	1964	1964-5	1965	1965	1966	1967	1968	1966	1969	1970
Related Pubs. [1]	--	[15]	--	--	[32, 33, 103]	--	--	[52, 82, 83]	[105]	[64, 65, 67, 91]	[50]	[78]	
Corpus Size [2]	247/85	618, 243/372, 654/987	300/83	350	100	260	77, 350	405	1022/89, 673	165	2500, 4000	46821, 46942	2267
Number of Keywords	90	90, 150	30?	18	?	90	96, 145	4041	180	641	500, 6000	8044, 13302	3950
Number of Groups	32	4, 10, 18 21, 11	20	3, 4	1-100	8, 19	5, 8	20, 30, 40	6	?	1-49, 70	1-1284	?
A Posteriori?	NO	YES	NO	YES	YES	YES	YES	YES	NO	YES	YES	YES	YES
Hierarchical?	--	NO	--	NO	YES	NO	NO	NO	--	NO	YES	YES	NO
Name of Classification	--	Factor Analysis	Discriminant Method	Clustering	Word Grouping	Clumping	Factor Analysis	Clustering	Discriminant Method	Clumping	CLASFY	CLASFY	Clustering
Main Concept in Classification	statistical	matrix	statistical	graphical	comparative	graphical	matrix	graphical	statistical	graphical	multi-pass, comparative	multi-pass, comparative	matrix
Corpus Topic	Computers [3]	Psychology Computers [3]	Computers [3]	Medical symptoms	German affairs Time Ordered Items	Computers [3]	Nuclear	Computers [3]	Broadcast items, News articles	Aeronautics	(artificial surrogates) [5] Aerospace	Nuclear	misc.
Criterion [4]	(b)	(c), (b)	(b)	(d)	(d)	(a)	(d)	(a)	(b)	(a)	description redundancy vs. random categories	(c)	(b), (d)
Automatic Indexing	YES	YES	YES	NO	NO	YES	?	YES	YES	NO	--	NO. Yes	NO
Indexed Text	Abstracts	Abstracts	Abstracts	--	--	Abstracts	Description of work, Search requests	Abstracts	Items	--	--	--	--

From Litofsky (53). **Used with permission of the author.**

NOTES FOR TABLE 10

1. These experiments expand the theory, present partial results, or are extensions of the described experiments.
2. Number of records actually used. Where A/B is shown
   A = number of records used to set up categories or to obtain criteria for a priori categories, and
   B = number of records automatically classified.
3. Used same basic corpus of 405 abstracts from IRE PGEC, March, June, and September, 1959.
4. Classification was evaluated by measurements using one or more of the following criteria:
   (a) relevance assessments of records in categories with respect to a few search requests,
   (b) whether records were placed into the same categories a human classifier would have placed them,
   (c) whether a posteriori categories are the same as a priori, human-organized categories,
   (d) whether the categories "look good" (subjective criterion), and
   (e) comparison with four other classification schemes (plus variants) (including a priori) for each file with respect to minimizing keywords in categories and, via 165 search requests, minimizing categories looked at and documents searched.
5. Produced by random-number generation.

To be of practical use, the classification algorithm must do its task for large collections in a reasonable period of time. In automatic classification systems, classification times can be proportional to the square, or even the cube, of the number of records. This is because of the need to compare every record with every other record or to generate and manipulate matrixes whose sides are proportional to the number of records and/or the number of discrete terms in the system (Doyle, 33). This means that the cost of classification per document would go up at least linearly with the number of documents. Considering collections numbering in the tens of millions of records, it is evident that systems with the above characteristics are unacceptable.

There are two systems that are known to break this N^2 effect (N records in the collection). These are the algorithms described by Doyle (33) and CLASFY. In both, the time proportionality factor is approximately $N \log_n N$, where the logarithmic base n is the number of branches at each node of the hierarchy. With appropriate selection of this node stratification number, the classification time (and hence cost) per record can be held to a constant. Using CLASFY, Litofsky (54) has estimated classification times, using third-generation computers, of about .04 seconds per record, independent of the number of documents in the collection.

A wide variety of classification techniques have been proposed that seek to group records with high association factors together into clusters (5, 10, 80, and 83), clumps (28, 64, 65, 67, and 86) or factors (13, 15, and 16) without trying to obtain a hierarchy or an ordering essential in an information system. Also, these methods require matrix manipulation, which makes them impractical because of long processing times when used for large files.

CONCLUSION

We have discussed the many problems that plague the designers and users of large information systems of complex and large organizations. These range from the problems of dispersion of the users, remote use, and use of many different computers to problems of efficiency of processing and protecting the integrity of the information. We are on the verge of announcements by major computer manufacturers of new hardware and new software that will offer better facilities, and perform faster and at a lower cost. But even when this is achieved, the problems of placing massive amounts of information into the computers, exchanging information between computers, and processing efficiently will still pose an enormous obstacle to progress. The methodologies described in this chapter were addressed to these latter problems that can be solved through automatic data conversion, better ordering of information, and providing automatic aids to organizing information. These will have to be applied before overall progress is obtained.

The methodologies that we have described, having passed the research stage, are in the development stage.

The work to be done before there can be widespread use of DDLs includes the following: experience must be gained in operating with prototypes like those now under development at the University of Pennsylvania and the University of Michigan. Then a data description-language must be standardized that will serve as a standard for utility programs for data conversion for specific computers.

As for automatic aids, locator systems have been applied to approximately a dozen very large and complex organizations. The methodology has been determined and reported in McDonough's textbook (55).

As for automatic classification, the next step would be to provide a new access method in data management systems (similar to the way that present systems provide ISAM or SAM) that will use automatic classification storage strategy. Search and browsing facilities could then be provided as well. At the same time experience with larger files, with millions of records, will be very necessary because this is the file size range at which benefits of automatic classification become significant.

REFERENCES

(1) ANDERSON, R. H.; CERF, V.; HARSLEM, E. F.; HEAFNER, J. F.; MADDEN, J.; METCALFE, B.; SHOSHANI, A.; WHITE, J. P.; WOOD, D. The data reconfiguration services—an experiment in adaptable, process/process communication. July 1971, 23 p. (RAND publication P-4673).

(2) ASSOCIATION FOR COMPUTING MACHINERY; NATIONAL AERONAUTICS AND SPACE ADMINISTRATION. Symposium on Information Storage and Retrieval. College Park, Maryland, 1-2 April 1971. Proceedings. Edited by Jack Minker and Sam Rosenfeld. University of Maryland. Conference and Institute Division. College Park, Maryland, 1971, 291 p. (ED 049 796).

(3) ASSOCIATION FOR COMPUTING MACHINERY. SPECIAL INTEREST COMMITTEE ON FILE DESCRIPTION AND TRANSLATION. STORAGE STRUCTURE DEFINITION LANGUAGE TASK GROUP. Storage structure definition language, SSDL. Record of the 1970 Association for Computing Machinery SICFIDET Workshop on Data Description and Access. Rice University, Houston, Texas, 17-19 November 1970. Association for Computing Machinery, New York, New York, 1970.

(4) ATHERTON, PAULINE; BORKO, HAROLD. A test of the factor-analytically derived automated classification method applied to descriptions of work and search requests of nuclear physicists. American Institute of Physics, Documentation Research Project, New York, New York, January 1965, 1-15. (Report no. AIP/DRP65-1, SDC/SP1905).

(5) AUGUSTSON, J. G.; MINKER, JACK. An analysis of some graph theoretical cluster techniques. Journal of the Association for Computing Machinery, 17 (October 1970) 571-588.

(6) BAKER, FRANK B. Information retrieval based upon latent class analysis. Journal of the Association for Computing Machinery, 9:4 (October 1962) 512-521.

(7) BAKER, FRANK B. Latent class analysis as an association model for information retrieval. In: Stevens, Mary E.; et al.; eds. Statistical association methods for mechanized documentation. National Bureau of Standards, Washington, D.C., 1965, 149-155. (NBS mis. pub. 269).

(8) BERTZISS, A. T. Data structures—theory and practice. Academic Press, New York, 1971, 442 p.

(9) BISS, K. O.; CHIEN, R. T.; STAHL, F. A. A data structure for cognitive information retrieval. Illinois University, Coordinated Science Lab., Urbana, Illinois, October 1970, 22 p. (AD 713 432).

(10) BONNER, RAYMOND E. On some clustering techniques. IBM Journal, 8:1 (January 1964) 22-32.

(11) BORKO, HAROLD. The construction of an empirically based mathematically derived classification system. In: American Federation of Information Processing Societies. Spring Joint Computer Conference. San Francisco, California, 1962. Proceedings, vol. 21. National Press, Palo Alto, California, 1962, 279-289.

(12) BORKO, HAROLD. Indexing and classification. In: Borko, Harold; ed. Automated language processing. John Wiley & Sons, Inc., New York, New York, 1967, 99-125.

(13) BORKO, HAROLD. Measuring the reliability of subject classification by men and machines. American Documentation, 15:4 (October 1964) 268-273.

(14) BORKO, HAROLD. Research in automatic generation of classification systems. In: American Federation of Information Processing Societies. Spring Joint Computer Conference. Washington, D.C., 1964. Proceedings, vol. 25. Spartan Books, Inc., Washington, D.C., 1964, 529-535.

(15) BORKO, HAROLD; BERNICK, MYRNA D. Automatic document classification. Journal of the Association for Computing Machinery, 10:2 (April 1963) 151-162.

(16) BORKO, HAROLD; BERNICK, MYRNA D. Automatic document classification. Part II. Additional experiments. Journal of the Association for Computing Machinery, 11:2 (April 1964) 138-151.

(17) CHANG, YEAN-HSI. The implementation of a relational document retrieval system. Illinois University, Coordinated Science Lab., Urbana, Illinois, September 1970, 56 p. (AD 713 319).

(18) CHAPIN, NED. A deeper look at data. In: National Conference of the Association for Computing Machinery. 23d, Las Vegas, Nevada, 27-29 August 1968. Proceedings. Brandon Systems Press, Princeton, New Jersey, 1968, 631-638.

(19) CHIEN, R. T.; PREPARATA, F. P. Search strategy and file organization in computerized information retrieval systems with mass memory. Illinois University, Coordinated Scientific Lab., Urbana, Illinois, 1967, 1-11.

(20) CHILDS, DAVID L. Feasibility of a set-theoretic data structure. A general structure based on a reconstituted definition of relation. In: Congress of the International Federation for Information Processing (IFIP). 4th, Edinburgh, Scot-

land, 5-10 August 1968. Proceedings. North-Holland Publishing Co., Amsterdam, The Netherlands, 1968, 420-430. (Booklet I, 162-172).

(21) CODASYL Symposium. Collected papers and discussion notes of the British Computer Society Symposium on CODASYL Data Base Task Group report, October 1970. British Computer Society, London, England, 1971, 59 p.

(22) CODD, E. F. A relational model of data for large shared data banks. Communications of the ACM, 13:6 (June 1970) 377-387.

(23) COMPUTER COMMAND AND CONTROL COMPANY. A management information system for the Office of the Secretary of Transportation, vol. 1. Computer Command and Control Company, Washington, D.C., January 1970. (Report 136-5).

(24) CONFERENCE ON DATA SYSTEMS LANGUAGES. DATA BASE TASK GROUP. Report to the CODASYL Programming Language Committee. Association for Computing Machinery, New York, New York, October 1969, 191 p.

(25) CONFERENCE ON DATA SYSTEMS LANGUAGES. DATA BASE TASK GROUP. Report to the CODASYL Programming Language Committee. Association for Computing Machinery, New York, New York, April 1971.

(26) CONFERENCE ON DATA SYSTEMS LANGUAGES. SYSTEMS COMMITTEE. Feature analysis of generalized data base management systems. Association for Computing Machinery, New York, New York, May 1971, 511 p.

(27) CUADRA, CARLOS A. Preface. In: Cuadra, Carlos A.; ed. Annual review of information science and technology, vol. 6. Encyclopaedia Britannica, Chicago, Illinois, 1971.

(28) DALE, ALFRED G.; DALE, N. Some clumping experiments for associative document retrieval. American Documentation, 16:1 (January 1965), 5-9.

(29) DALE, N. Automatic classification system user's manual. University of Texas, Linguistics Research Center, November 1964. (Report no. LRC 64 TTM-1).

(30) DATTOLA, R. T. A fast algorithm for automatic classification. Information storage and retrieval, scientific report no. ISR-14, section V to the National Science Foundation. Cornell University, Department of Computer Science, Ithaca, New York, October 1968.

(31) DENNIS, JACK B. On the exchange of information. In: Association for Computing Machinery-SICFIDET Workshop on Data Description and Access. Houston, Texas, 15-16 November 1970. Proceedings. Association for Computing Machinery, New York, New York, 1970, 41-67.

(32) DiPAOLA, R. A. The relational data file and the decision problem for classes of proper formulas. RAND Corporation, Santa Monica, California, February 1971, 28 p. (Report no. R-661-PR. AD 719 752).

(33) DOYLE, LAUREN B. Breaking the cost barrier in automatic classification. System Development Corp., Santa Monica, California, 1 July 1966, 62 p. (SP-2516. AD 636 837).

(34) DOYLE, LAUREN B. Is automatic classification a reasonable application of statistical analysis of text? Journal of the Association for Computing Machinery, 12:4 (October 1965) 473-489.

(35) DOYLE, LAUREN B. Some compromises between word grouping and document grouping. In: Stevens, Mary E.; et al.; eds. Statistical association methods for mechanized documentation. National Bureau of Standards, Washington, D.C., 1965, 15-24. (NBS misc. pub. 269).

(36) EARLEY, JAY. Toward an understanding of data structures. In: Association for Computing Machinery-SICFIDET Workshop on Data Description and Access. Houston, Texas, 15-16 November 1970. Proceedings. Association for Computing Machinery, New York, New York, 1970, 1-40.

(37) FILLAT, A. I.; KRANING, L. A. Generalized organization of large data-bases; a set-theoretic approach to relations. Massachusetts Institute of Technology,

Department of Electrical Engineering, Cambridge, Massachusetts, June 1970, 248 p. (AD 711 060).
(38) FLORES, IVAN. Data structure and management. Prentice-Hall, Inc., Englewood Cliffs, New Jersey, 1970, 400 p.
(39) FLORES, IVAN. JCL and file definition. Prentice-Hall, Inc., Englewood Cliffs, New Jersey, 1971, 288 p.
(40) GABRINI, PHILIPPE J. Automatic introduction of information into a remote-access system: a physics library catalog. University of Pennsylvania, Moore School of Electrical Engineering, Philadelphia, Pennsylvania, 1 November 1966, 79 p. (T.R. 67-09. AD 641 564).
(41) GOLD, MICHAEL M. A total system view of conversion—what questions must be asked before strategies are determined. USC Inc., Pittsburgh, Pennsylvania, February 1971, 84 p. (AD 721 122).
(42) GOLDSTEIN, ROBERT C.; STRAND, ALOIS J. The MacAims Data Management System. Massachusetts Institute of Technology, Cambridge, Massachusetts, April 1971, 32 p. (AD 721 620).
(43) GRAUER, ROBERT T.; MESSIER, MICHAEL. An evaluation of Rocchio's clustering algorithm. Information storage and retrieval, report no. ISR-12, section VI, to the National Science Foundation. Cornell University, Department of Computer Science, Ithaca, New York, June 1967, 39 p.
(44) HORTON, MICHAEL; et al. The Extended Data Management Facility (EDMF). Reference manual. University of Pennsylvania, Moore School of Electrical Engineering, Philadelphia, Pennsylvania, March 1972, 125 p.
(45) HSIAO, DAVID K. A generalized record organization. IEEE Transactions on Computers, C20:12 (December 1971) 1490-1495.
(46) HSIAO, DAVID K.; HARARY, FRANK. A formal system for information retrieval from files. ACM, 13:2 (February 1970) 67-73.
(47) KENT, ALLEN. Information analysis and retrieval. John Wiley & Sons, New York, New York, 1971 367 p.
(48) KUHNS, JOHN L. Interrogating a relational data file: remarks on the admissibility of input queries. RAND Corp., Santa Monica, California, November 1970, 57p. (Report no. R-511-PR. AD 721 671).
(49) LANCE, G. N.; WILLIAMS, W. T. A general theory of classificatory sorting strategies. I. Hierarchical systems. Computer Journal, 9:4 (February 1967) 373-380.
(50) LANCE, G. N.; WILLIAMS, W. T. A general theory of classificatory sorting strategies. II. Clustering systems. Computer Journal, 10:3 (November 1967) 271-277.
(51) LEFKOVITZ, DAVID. File structures for on-line systems. Spartan Books, New York, March 1969, 215 p.
(52) LEFKOVITZ, DAVID; ANGELL, THOMAS. Experiments in automatic classification. Computer Command and Control Company, Philadelphia, Pennsylvania, December 1966. (Report no. 85-104-6).
(53) LESKE, MICHAEL E. Performance of automatic information systems. Information Storage and Retrieval, 4:2 (June 1968) 201-218.
(54) LITOFSKY, BARRY. Utility of automatic classification systems for information storage and retrieval. University of Pennsylvania, Philadelphia, Pennsylvania, 1969, 185 p. (Doctoral thesis).
(55) McDONOUGH, ADRIAN M. Centralized systems—planning and control, chapter 1. Thompson Book Company, Wayne, Pennsylvania, 1969.
(56) MACLAREN, M. D. Data matching, data alignment, and structure matching in PL/1. Association for Computing Machinery SIGPLAN Notices, 5:12 (December 1970) 30-43.

(57) MANN, MARGARET. Introduction to cataloguing and the classification of books, 2d ed. American Library Association, Chicago, Illinois, 1943, 288 p.

(58) MANOLA, FRANK A. An extended data management facility for a general purpose time sharing system. University of Pennsylvania, Moore School of Electrical Engineering, Philadelphia, Pennsylvania, May 1971. (Moore School report no. 71-24), 152 p.

(59) MARDEN, ETHEL C. Statement of need for a data descriptive language. Statement prepared for USA Standards X3 Ad Hoc Committee, 1969.

(60) MARON, M. E. Automatic indexing: an experimental inquiry. Journal of the Association for Computing Machinery, 8:3 (July 1961) 404-417.

(61) MEADOW, CHARLES T.; MEADOW, HARRIET R. Organization, maintenance and search of machine files. In: Cuadra, Carlos A.; ed. Annual review of information science and technology, vol. 5. Encyclopaedia Britannica, Chicago, Illinois, 1970, 169-191.

(62) MEALY, GEORGE H. Another look at data. In: American Federation of Information Processing Societies. Fall Joint Computer Conference. Anaheim, California, 1967. Proceedings, vol. 31. Thompson Books, Washington, D.C., 1967, 525-534.

(63) MINKER, JACK; SABLE, JEROME D. Relational data system study. Auerbach Corp., Philadelphia, Pennsylvania, September 1970, 264 p. (AD 720 263).

(64) MINKER, JACK; WILSON, G.; ZIMMERMAN, B. An evaluation of query expansion by addition of clustered terms for a document retrieval system. Maryland University, Computer Science Center, College Park, Maryland, October 1971. (TR-172).

(65) NEEDHAM, ROGER M. Applications of the theory of clumps. Mechanical Translation, 8 (June/October 1965) 113-127.

(66) NEEDHAM, ROGER M. Automatic classification in linguistics. December 1966. (AD 644 961).

(67) NEEDHAM, ROGER M.; SPARCK JONES, KAREN. Keywords and clumps: recent work in information retrieval at the Cambridge Language Research Institute. Journal of Documentation, 20:1 (March 1964) 5-15.

(68) NISENOFF, NORMAN. The use of management information systems for police operation. In: American Conference of the Institute of Management Science. 12th, Detroit, Michigan, 1 October 1971. Proceedings.

(69) O'CONNOR, JOHN. The possibilities of document grouping for reducing retrieval storage size and search time. In: Advances in Documentation and Library Science, vol. III, pt. 1. Interscience Publishers, New York, 1960, 237-279.

(70) OLLE, T. WILLIAM. A taxonomy of data definition languages. FDT, Bulletin of ACM-SICFIDET, 1:1 (August 1969) 24-28.

(71) PERRIENS, M. P.; WILLIAMS, J. H., JR. Computer classification of intelligence-type documents. September 1967, 1-92. (AD 820 801).

(72) PRICE, NANCY; SCHIMINOVICH, SAMUEL. A clustering experiment: first step towards a computer-generated classification scheme. Information Storage and Retrieval, 4:3 (August 1968) 271-280.

(73) Proposed American National standard: recorded magnetic tape for information interchange (1600 CPI, phase encoded). Communications of the Association for Computing Machinery, 13:11 (November 1970) 679-685.

(74) PRYWES, NOAH S. Browsing in an automated library through remote access. In: Sass, Margo A.; Wilkinson, William D.; eds. Computer augmentation of human reasoning. Spartan Books, Washington, D.C., 1965, 105-130.

(75) PRYWES, NOAH S. An information center for effective research and development management. In: Information systems sciences. (Proceedings of the 2d congress.) Spartan Books, Washington, D.C., 1965, 109-116.

(76) PRYWES, NOAH S. Man-computer problem solving with Multilist. Proceedings of IEEE, 54 (December 1966) 1788-1801.

(77) PRYWES, NOAH S. Structure and organization of very large data bases. In: Symposium on Critical Factors in Data Management. University of California, Los Angeles, California, March 1968. Proceedings. Edited by Fred Gruenberger. Prentice-Hall, Englewood Cliffs, New Jersey, 1969, 127-146.

(78) PRYWES, NOAH S.; LITOFSKY, BARRY. All-automatic processing for a large library. Session S70BB—Information Management Systems—Foundation and Future. In: American Federation of Information Processing Societies. Spring Joint Computer Conference. Atlantic City, New Jersey, 1970. Proceedings, vol. 36. AFIPS Press, Montvale, New Jersey, 1970, 323-331.

(79) RAMIREZ, JESUS A.; SOLOW, HAROLD; PRYWES, NOAH S. Design of the Data Description Language Processor. University of Pennsylvania, Moore School of Electrical Engineering, Philadelphia, Pennsylvania, December 1971, 212 p. (M.S. 72-19).

(80) ROCCHIO, JOSEPH J., JR. Document retrieval systems—optimization and evaluation. Harvard University, Division of Engineering and Applied Physics, Cambridge, Massachusetts, 1966. (Doctoral thesis).

(81) ROSENBERG, ARNOLD L. Data graphs and addressing schemes. Journal of Computer and System Sciences, 5 (June 1971) 193-238.

(82) SALTON, GERARD. Progress in automatic information retrieval. IEEE Spectrum, 2 (August 1965) 90-103.

(83) SALTON, GERARD; ed. The SMART retrieval system, experiments in automatic document processing. Prentice-Hall, Englewood Cliffs, New Jersey, 1971, 556 p.

(84) SANDEWALL, E.; MAKILA, K. A data base structure for a question-answering system. Research Institute of National Defense, Stockholm, Sweden, November 1970, 35 p. (PB 197 621).

(85) SCHRUBEN, LEE. The information system model. Datamation, 15:7 (July 1969) 93-101.

(86) SHTEFANIK, V.; VITKOVA, G.; VOLNYI, Y. Data retrieval, processing, and exchange procedures. JPRS-52674, 19 March 1971, 30 p. (Translation of Nauchno-Tekhnicheskaya Informatsiya. Seriya 1: Organizatsiya i Metodika Informatsionnoi Raboty, no. 10, 1970, 18-23, 28-29).

(87) SMITH, DIANE P. An approach to data description and conversion. University of Pennsylvania, Philadelphia, Pennsylvania, 1971, 309 p. (Doctoral thesis).

(88) SOERGEL, DAGOBERT. Mathematical analysis of documentation systems. An attempt to a theory of classification and search request formulation. Information Storage and Retrieval, 3 (July 1967) 129-173.

(89) SOKAL, R. R. Numerical taxonomy. Scientific American, 215 (December 1966) 106-116.

(90) SPARCK JONES, KAREN; JACKSON, DAVID M. Current approaches to classification and clump-finding at the Cambridge Language Research Unit. Computer Journal, 10 (May 1967) 29-37.

(91) SPARCK JONES, KAREN; NEEDHAM, ROGER M. Automatic term classifications and retrieval. Information Storage and Retrieval, 4:2 (June 1968) 91-100.

(92) STANDISH, THOMAS A. A data definition facility for programming languages. Carnegie-Mellon University, Pittsburgh, Pennsylvania, 1967, 292 p. (Doctoral thesis).

(93) STEVENS, MARY ELIZABETH. Automatic indexing: a state-of-the-art report. National Bureau of Standards, Washington, D.C., March 1967, 1-220. (NBS monograph no. 91).

(94) STEVENS, MARY ELIZABETH. Standardization, compatibility and/or convertibility requirements in network planning. National Bureau of Standards, Washington, D.C., May 1970, 339 p. (PB 194 179).

(95) STEVENS, WILLIAM B. The concept of the "Data Analysis and Control Catalogue" for management information systems. Computers and Automation, 17:4 (April 1968) 40-42.
(96) STONE, DON C. Word association experiments—basic consideration. August 1966, 2-15. (AD 660 085).
(97) TAULBEE, ORRIN E. Classification in information storage and retrieval. In: Association for Computing Machinery. National Conference. 20th. Cleveland, Ohio, 24-26 August 1965. Proceedings. Association for Computing Machinery, New York, 1965, 119-137.
(98) TAYLOR, ROBERT WALKER. Generalized data base management system data structure and their mapping to physical storage. University of Michigan, Ann Arbor, Michigan, July 1971, 278 p. (ISDOS Project working paper no. 49).
(99) TELL, BJORN V.; LARSSON, R.; LINDH, R. Information retrieval with the ABACUS program—an experiment in compatibility. In: International Atomic Energy Agency. Handling of Nuclear Information, Vienna, Austria, 16-20 February 1970. Proceedings. International Atomic Energy Agency, Vienna, Austria, 1970, 183-200. (IAEA-SM-128/21. Available from UNIPUB Inc., P. O. Box 433, New York, New York. Also available from IAG Journal, 3:4 (December 1970) 323-341).
(100) U. S. BUREAU OF THE BUDGET. Circulars numbers A17, A40 and A46 (Revised). Also, Standard form 83. U.S. Bureau of the Budget, Office of Statistical Policy, Washington, D.C., July 1968. (GPO 1962-0-627181).
(101) U. S. DEPARTMENT OF DEFENSE. Manual for standard data elements. U.S. Department of Defense, Office of the Secretary of Defense, Comptroller, Washington, D.C., 1 March 1970. (500.12M).
(102) WALSTON, CLAUDE E. Information retrieval. Advances in Computers, vol. 6. Academic Press, New York, 1965, 1-30.
(103) WARD, J. H., JR.; HOOK, M. E. Application of a hierarchical grouping procedure to a problem of grouping profiles. Education and Psychological Measurement, 21 (1963) 69-92.
(104) WHITE, D. Information processing of medical records. In: Information processing of medical records, 1970, 387-400.
(105) WILLIAMS J. H., JR. Computer classification of documents. Annual progress report. IBM Federal Systems Division, Gaithersburg, Maryland, June 1967, 25 p. (AD 663 178).
(106) WOLFBERG, MICHAEL S. Determination of maximally complete subgraphs. University of Pennsylvania, Moore School of Electrical Engineering, Philadelphia, Pennsylvania, May 1965. (Report no. 65-27), 58 p.
(107) ZILLES, STEPHEN N. An expansion of the data structuring capabilities of PAL. Massachusetts Institute of Technology, Cambridge, Massachusetts, October 1970, 203 p. (AD 720 761).
(108) ZUNDE, PRANAS. Structural models of complex information sources. Information Storage and Retrieval, 7:1 (June 1971) 1-18.

5 The User Interface in Interactive Systems

JOHN L. BENNETT
IBM Research Laboratory

INTRODUCTION

The digital computer has been used as a problem-solving tool for only two decades. During most of this time, computer scientists have concentrated on learning how to build the tool: applying electronic technology, arranging for data flow between components, and manufacturing the hardware. Now we are entering a new stage in which computing power is made available through interactive terminals to people who are not computer scientists. This is possible on a large scale only because design and marketing innovators now have confidence in their ability to provide reliable, cost-effective service to less sophisticated users. In this new stage, the natural behavior patterns of users become an important element in the design of the interface to the tool.

Serving new users through terminals also introduces new training considerations. While designers may have clear ideas on effective ways of using the tool they have provided, this same insight is not automatically shared by people who were not involved in tool design. R. Miller (69) is especially telling on the requirement for training: "The best way—or even an effective way—for using a tool is not usually evident to users. . . .The design of a tool implies a procedure [for its use], and in fact it makes sense to think of the design of the procedure as part of the tool design itself."

In this review we focus on what has been learned as people use computer-based information systems to solve significant problems. By observing what goes on at the interface between the user and the terminal, we can identify the impact that design decisions have on user performance. However, the lack of significant, directly applicable theory to serve as a basis for design forces the reader to provide his own interpretive framework as he studies the literature on the emerging interface-design technology.

Our goal, therefore, is to review and interpret literature that can be of benefit to designers who are responsible for (1) synthesizing the interactive facility provided for the user and (2) planning for its effective use. We hope the review will enable information science students to identify those authors who have stated well the challenges to be met in the solution of user-interface problems. Further, a general description of user experience may assist the non-expert to judge for himself how well designers have succeeded in providing useful problem-solving tools.

Earlier *Annual Review* chapters addressed man-computer interaction from a different point of view. In the 1966 review by Davis (23) the dominant focus was on interactive programming and the software techniques of time-sharing, the vehicle for making interactive programming feasible. Applications oriented toward non-programmers were reported, but they were in an early stage of development. Mills (72) emphasized activities on the computer side of the user interface. In the last *Annual Review* chapter to cover all aspects of man-computer communication, Licklider (56) expressed disappointment that the lack of significant material precluded a review of "man-computer interaction techniques and on-line problem solving and decision making." Though high-quality reports of user experience with interactive information systems are still scarce, there are now enough to support a review emphasizing activities on the user side of the interface; that is, the impact that system components, design decisions, and user expectations can have on user performance.

Over 1000 items relating to some aspect of the user interface in interactive systems have been published during 1971. This reviewer has scanned over 500 items, read over 250, and chosen to use about 100. Four points should be made at the outset. First, much of the published literature contains what might be called "application descriptions": a report on the system environment followed by a list of the functions provided for the user at the terminal. The items selected for inclusion here either provide some description of user experience or give an explanation of why the designer chose to offer particular functions. Second, much of the reported work is directed toward assisting the user to accomplish relatively specific tasks in a relatively narrow application area. Items in this class are included because their authors have touched on issues that are important to designers seeking to serve the needs of users in other applications. Third, while not all new applications have been included, the items discussed give a cross-section of representative activities. Fourth, we have excluded items dealing solely with computer hardware design, data storage internal to the computer, or computer-oriented details that a user need not know in order to make effective use of the interactive facility.

Many of the publications reviewed describe work in bibliographic search. This is due, in part, to the reviewer's familiarity with this body of literature and, in part, to the fact that vigorous search for literature that focused on the user interface in other applications was often fruitless. For example, one might expect to find the design rationale for user-oriented features in high-level interactive programming languages, but information appears to be available only through personal communication. The items which were found tend to confirm an impression that issues of general importance are well-illustrated by work in bibliographic search. It is hoped that enough bridging material is presented to enable the reader to recognize the wider applicability of the results reported in specific applications.

The organization of the chapter is as follows. We first outline the components of the system in which a problem-solving tool is to be used. (We reserve the term "system" for this larger context and refer to that which is provided by the designer as the "interactive facility.") In the next two sections, we discuss how the designer synthesizes an interactive facility to meet the requirements of the user and how evaluation techniques enable the designer to determine if he has met his goal. In a fourth section, we review human engineering developments and the pressure for user interface commonality that together can have significant impact on interactive facility design.

THE COMPONENTS OF INTERACTIVE SYSTEMS

In planning an interactive facility, the designer must take into account the properties of (1) the task to be performed, (2) the user, (3) the terminal, and (4) the computer-stored information content. These information-system components are strongly interdependent, but the task, in a sense, governs the others. Task characteristics determine the behavior required of the user at the terminal, suggest the nature of the data that will flow between the user and the computer store, and indicate the logical structure of information to be shown on the terminal. The designer's analysis of the components prepares him to provide a user interface that supports the interactive problem-solver.

The Task

R. Miller (68) cuts across applications in his delineation of task archetypes found in man-computer problem-solving. The information that a user needs to guide his decision-making determines an "information domain." Miller's conceptual models for problem-solving activities may be summarized as follows: (1) Simple Inquiry—e.g., looking up the telephone number of a known person; (2) Status Briefing and Exception Detection—the comparison between information displayed and an expected situation; (3) Diagnosis—testing to determine the source of an identified problem; (4) Discovery—e.g., browsing, hypothesis formation, and hypothesis testing; (5) Planning—allocation of resources as guided by a model in order to achieve a desired goal; and (6) Designing and Constructing—translation of ideas into actuality. As he observes, these activities are not mutually exclusive. All information is interrelated, but there is a discoverable statistical generality: "A given user. . .is likely to work nearly all of the time within a bounded domain." Miller offers no recipe for good task analysis. It is up to the designer of the problem-solving tool, through his study of actual and projected usage, to define information domains. While somewhat more specific to the business decision-making environment, the frameworks for task analysis offered by Morton (75) and Gerrity (39) are also useful.

The User

No one should be surprised at the inclusion of the user—the person actually involved in the interaction at the terminal—as a component in the interactive system. Since the goal of interaction is to improve the user's task performance, it is clear that we must understand his needs, his skills, and his motivation as he uses the terminal. What should be surprising is that design descriptions seldom give more than superficial attention to the actual or intended user. The explanation may be that, although the user is a crucial component in the system, he is the one least under the designer's control.

Katter (47) provides an excellent in-depth discussion "identifying those characteristics of potential users. . .important for successfully introducing and developing on-line bibliographic searching facilities." Although the anticipated users were medical personnel in the National Library of Medicine Biomedical Communications Network, the report is a model for the analysis that will be profitable whenever an interactive tool is introduced to non-programmer users. In taking a human-engineering approach to the tradeoff of design and usage alternatives, he identifies factors that bear on user acceptance: (1) immediate terminal feedback may "bully" the user into moving at a faster than optimum rate, (2) typewriter limitations may cause a "peephole effect" as the user tries to gain insight into data base content by scanning very limited subsets, and (3) visibility of his interaction to colleagues (and to mysterious people back at the computer) may lead to a "fishbowl effect." In surveying the literature, this reviewer has found numerous instances where user rejection can be linked to neglect of one or more of the observed factors. Katter introduces the concept of a "line of credit" which the user extends to the designer, and the facility must deliver expected benefits before the designer's credit is exhausted. The paper also contains an interesting examination of the experience of others with search facilities and makes cogent suggestions for on-line experimentation.

Martin & Parker (64) make a plea for "study of the information needs and information-seeking habits of the target population to ensure that design goals are plausible." A general survey of anticipated users may reveal predictors of behavior that would be overlooked in a narrower focus on the user at a particular interface. On the other hand, "It is very difficult to assess how people will react to a new technology before they have experienced it." The prospective user often has an unclear picture of the proposed interactive facility. Therefore, his opinion is of limited value in helping the surveyor predict the impact of the tool on problem-solving behavior.

One message is clear from user studies at all levels: the introduction of an effective tool will cause a change in user habits. The designer is well advised to continuously collect data that will help him to change the system to the user's advantage.

The Terminal

The typewriter terminal is by far the most widely used device for man-computer interaction. Dolotta (28) has written functional specifications for typewriter-like units suitable for office use and for interfaces to a computer. The paper is "aimed at the needs of the users," and Dolotta believes that "none of the features described presents any major technological or manufacturing problems." The report would seem to lay the groundwork for a standard. It is based on a three-year collaboration of seven workers, and it was reviewed by over 100 experienced users before publication. But progress is slow. Ancona et al. (2) offer two (!) standards for keyboard layout of special characters.

Dolotta (27) replies to Ancona and emphasizes changes he would recommend if the criterion for placement were "ease of operation" rather than "cheaper to implement."

There are over one hundred different cathode ray tube (CRT) display devices on the market today. They differ from typewriter terminals chiefly in the absence of hard copy and in their potential for display of patterns limited only by device and human-eye resolution. The technological possibilities have led to a bewildering variety in both input and output formats offered to the user. In a U.S. National Bureau of Standards conference (105), Swarthe & Little report issues to be resolved in achieving "standardization from the standpoint of the user." Current discussions are still at the level of delineating functions—for example, whether to say "clear screen" or "erase screen." They observe that (1) display design is much more application-dependent than typewriter design, and (2) the functional interface between the terminal hardware and the computer software is not yet well defined. One sensible suggestion they report is to accept as a standard the overlap with whatever basic keyboard layout is adopted for typewriter devices. A user-oriented, definitive set of specifications for display terminals such as that provided by Dolotta for typewriters seems to be a long way off.

A trio of articles by Vartabedian (109, 110, 111) provides what may be a partial answer to our question, "By what means will order follow from all this display-option chaos?" He reports on experimentation at the Bell Laboratories leading to a proposed graphic character set for the American Standard Code for Information Interchange (ASCII). After first describing tests for comparing character-set legibility and readability, he gives an overview of how this work fits in with Bell System plans "for the development of a general-purpose terminal for use, to the maximum extent possible, in different applications." The third and most recent article presents the 96 graphic characters, generated in a 7x9 dot matrix, and discusses how to handle letters without using descenders (g, j, etc.) "if some loss in aesthetic appearance can be tolerated." "A communications display terminal incorporating the proposed symbol set. . .is now being built by the Teletype Corporation for use in a variety of Bell System operations. The font has also been incorporated into the Four Phase System IV/70 [terminal]."

S. Miller (71) provides an excellent description of how currently available display stations fall short of matching man's visual capability. After describing the characteristics of current applications where terminals are or would be useful, he concludes, ". . .the psychological necessity of having the eye rather than the display be the limiting element in the channel from computer processor to human brain requires a great deal more study." His arguments for the eye as a limiting criterion are convincing because of his demonstrated awareness throughout the paper of the production-oriented, cost/benefit requirements placed on hardware designers. As for the current state of the art, Dreyfus (31) gives a brief informative survey of user-oriented developments in CRT's. Sutherland (97) provides a clear overview of the technology necessary to "paint" pictures on the screen. The current display capability, the direction for prospective developments that will have impact on the user interface, and the tradeoffs between hardware and software function are ably outlined by this imaginative engineer who is well-grounded in practical experience.

What about other media for man-computer communication? Clapper's survey (17) of progress in automatic speech recognition brings us up to date. Individual non-connected words chosen from a vocabulary of sixteen words and spoken by an operator with one-half hour of training can be recognized with an error rate of about one word in twenty. He concludes that new solutions are required for recognition of words in normal speech. Automatic speech generation is an easier problem. Smith & Goodwin (94) discuss the role of TOUCH-TONE® input and audio-response for man-computer interaction in a sample medical information dialog. While limited applications are clearly feasible, the authors comment on the lack of "human engineering data on the use of speech output as an auditory display." They point out that there is no capability to convey graphic information, no way to provide simultaneous display of multiple alternatives, and no convenient memory aid.

The Information Content

The information structure and content displayed by the computer should appear clear and natural to the problem-solver so that he may effectively exercise his decision-making capability. This reviewer has not found a general discussion of alternatives for logical information structures analogous to that found for task archetypes. The Conference on Data Systems Languages (CODASYL) Systems Committee report (19) provides a start in this direction in its tutorial discussion of the data structure features available to the non-programmer in present-day data management systems. Van Dam (107), in his tutorial survey, observes that the information structure required for conversational manipulation in interactive graphics is fundamentally different from the information structure that is adequate for off-line plotting. Neither report suggests, however, under what problem-solving circumstances a network information structure, for example, is more advantageous than a hierarchical information structure.

Just as the introduction of the interactive facility can lead to changes in problem-solving habits, so the presentation of information content on-line can lead to new ways for the user to think of logical structure. In an example drawn from library applications, McAllister (59) suggests that present cataloging rules are designed to serve the serial structure of the card catalog; in an on-line catalog, each access-point file—title, descriptor, author—can provide a parallel path to the document file, and each can have its own user-oriented logical structure. If we carry her line of reasoning further, the terminal can permit the user to think of a logical information structure through which he can progress naturally from search word to title to bibliographic entry to document text.

Some applications make use of analytic models to transform information content from one state to a new state under user control. Such models are clearly application-dependent. Morton (75) describes the impact that a new logical structure for forecast data can have on the business decision-maker.

SYNTHESIS OF THE INTERACTIVE FACILITY

The Framework for Design

The user's concept of a problem-solving tool has an important influence on his subsequent usage patterns. The designer can provide an interface language that will support effective usage patterns. If design decisions are made to be consistent with a user-oriented "conceptual framework," subsequent transfer of the framework to the user's mind can strongly assist his acceptance and use of the tool.

G. Miller (67) suggests that designers take advantage of "the human tendency to locate information spatially." He observes that "computer-based systems do not necessarily assign any unique role to spatial tags," and so system designers overlook "a feature of considerable importance for the organization of the user's memory." Treu (101) responds to Miller's challenge with a proposed multichannel interface that displays information on different surfaces during search. Using the spatial concept as an organizing principle, he gives a thorough discussion of why he chooses each function which he would provide for the user. Bennett (8), also strongly influenced by G. Miller, describes design features of the Negotiated Search Facility that enable the searcher to formulate a query satisfying his information need. He draws upon the spatial concept to encourage the searcher to think of information as located in different functional "areas." Instead of using multiple surfaces, the Negotiated Search Facility gives the user a command language to bring any desired area to one screen. Though both designs are applied to bibliographic search, they serve to illustrate the general principle of how the conceptual framework to be provided for the user can guide design decisions in building problem-solving tools.

Some argue that it is up to the designer to discover, through his analysis of system components, what is already in the mind of the user. Gerrity (39) cautions against the limitations of a "descriptive modeling which [can] lock an analyst into a certain set,. . .inhibiting his ability to think freely about 'what should be'." A worthwhile problem-solving tool will inevitably lead to new user behavior. Indeed, as Gerrity observes, the most creative part of the design process comes in bridging the gap between current practice and projected use. This reviewer notes that software designers have been justly criticized for providing tools that force users to behave in nonproductive modes. While designers have been correct in foreseeing new modes, either they did not anticipate new use patterns accurately (poor design) or they did not effectively transfer to the user's mind the conceptual framework that guided the design (poor training). In any event, the impact on system performance of the user's concept of the tool is too important to be left to chance.

The designer seeks to provide an interface language that will reinforce the user's image of the problem-solving tool and help him to know what action is expected of him next. The options provided in the interface language require the designer's judgment on the user's capability to understand and use them effectively and on the power of the interactive facility to support the conceptual framework that they help create in the user's mind. Adams (1) suggests an achievement criterion for interface language design:

> The effectiveness of [an interface language] depends on the extent to which a person can immerse himself in it, accept the conventions, symbolizations, codes of the [language], and by adopting a proper 'set', send and receive messages at higher levels than can be explicitly represented. Thus, what is at stake. . .is the *level of communication* itself; poor [language] techniques restrict communication to the most literal and mechanical level.

We observe that the dialogue scenarios now being reported for some interactive facilities often reveal that the user must cope with language details that are extraneous to his task and that therefore interfere with communication.

The question of economic tradeoff can be a decisive constraint for system components and interface language alternatives. As Katter & Blankenship (48) observe in their excellent comparison of interactive file-search systems, "Costs incurred by the features described are not usually dealt with explicitly. Undoubtedly this is often because the problem of clearly defining costs and benefits is a difficult one, but in some cases it is only because an explicit system-analysis approach was not taken in writing the document." Selection of a typewriter terminal in spite of task characteristics that make a display terminal more appropriate is an example of a component constraint. However, the perceptive designer, alert to factors important in user acceptance of an interactive tool, can help overcome some cost constraints by finding inexpensive alternatives leading to interface language improvements. An example is the design of improved error messages that alert the user to the nature of a problem and help him to take corrective action.

Response Time

The time between user completion of input to the terminal and response from the terminal is a quantity important to the user during conversational interaction. R. Miller (70) discusses response time requirements for 17 categories of user input ranging from mechanical keystroke action to a "run my problem" command. Performance acceptable to the user is strongly dependent upon the event; "faster" is not necessarily "better" if the criterion is demonstrably better system usage. However, as delay increases beyond an acceptable range, he suggests that human efficiency drops until a point of discontinuity is reached. Beyond this point, problem-solving interaction ceases to be conversational. His concept of a nominal response time and a permissible range of variation is important; it suggests the need for experimental work conducted in application environments to fill in values for various categories. Carbonell et al. (15) make similar terminal response-time observations in the narrower context of interactive programming.

When the user has alternative problem-solving strategies available, constraints on terminal response time can help him make wise and economical use of computer resources. Doherty (26) offers an interesting example where a control program forces terminal response time to be proportional to resources employed.

The time between terminal output and user input can also have significant effects on a user's problem-solving performance. Nickerson et al. (78) suggest how his awareness of how he is being charged can press a user into rapid response—in effect, making him reply without thinking through the implications of his last interaction. Sackman (85) has also identified this as a behavioral factor in interactive programming. He indicates that a large part of the user's time is spent away from the terminal, apparently in preparation for the next rapid-fire session. Boehm et al. (10) report improvement in the quality of solution when users are "locked out" for a fixed period of time after each terminal output. Significantly, users objected to even mild restraint, but, as the authors observe, quantitative data on problem-solving processes is far too scant for the results to be considered conclusive.

Ease of Use

There is hardly an instance of an interface language that is not characterized (by its designer) as "easy to use." R. Miller (69) again provides the keynote for an overview of one dimension on this often used but seldom defined catch phrase. He begins by relating ease of use to the task that the user is performing and gives stipulations for valid measurement. Primary ease-of-use criteria can be summarized as follows: (1) length of time for user population to learn to reach a level of competence; (2) proportion of relevant population which can learn to use the tool in a given time; (3) time required to reach "communication" level—user frustration responses ("oh, damn") as well as the number and the kind of errors can give evidence of non-attainment; and (4) user attitude toward employment of the tool. He continues with an exposition of secondary variables that should be used in measurement and tradeoff variables that can be manipulated in interface language design. This is a rich source of ideas for the designer seeking to understand factors in user acceptance.

There is another, more dynamic dimension to "ease of use." Success in introducing problem-solving power is related to the user's readiness to accept responsibility for its exercise. Katter & McCarn (49) report experience suggesting that a user passes through phases of development. During an "uncertainty phase" he overcomes hesitancy and anxiety to attain relaxed confidence in his ability to control the tool and avoid disaster. During an "insight phase" he begins to see underlying principles and decides, if he finds the tool helpful, how best to use it for his special needs. If he judges it serves his needs, he enters an "incorporation phase" where the mechanics of the tool become second nature and its use becomes a part of his information-seeking behavior.

While the observations are particular to bibliographic search, this reviewer considers them appropriate for applications where a non-captive user employs the interactive facility as one of many problem-solving tools. Further, the conceptual model for studying user behavior suggests that a user may be ready for added problem-solving power only after he has become familiar with a previous level of complexity. Since this kind of perceived ease of use changes with user experience, the designer may want to plan his introduction of the conceptual framework in such a way that the user can match interface language features to his current level of sophistication.

English as an Input Language

In a philosophical discussion of the challenges in using English for the man-computer interface, Watt (113) points out that a "habitable" language should enable a person to address the computer without being exasperated by failure of the device to handle language that he feels is appropriate. The person using English will inevitably carry over his habits, and a "habitable" interface language must be perceived as natural by the person; he should not have to take into account constraints on the designer due to limitations in processing power.

The major trend is toward a pragmatic resolution of input language problems through reference to data base content. Dostert & Thompson (29, 30) describe progress with Rapidly Extensible Language (REL), wherein natural language inputs are "disambiguated by context." In both papers concentration is on grammatical issues to be solved for REL English. Though there are no reports from users, the authors believe communication levels in interactive REL are "just barely beyond [the] threshold [where]. . .the user feels that he does indeed have natural English at his disposal." Carbonell (12, 13) provides a progress report on very ambitious computer-assisted instruction systems where artificial intelligence techniques are applied to support "a true mixed-initiative man-computer dialogue on a given topic." His method relies on a highly structured data base to provide tests of contextual relevance. Kellogg et al. (50) describe current research "to develop and implement an expressive and extendable subset of ordinary English" for "on-line communication with complexly structured data bases." They conclude with a "cautious, qualified optimism" that "some of the major stumbling blocks are gradually being overcome."

Progress in these outstanding systems is very important to those who hope to see man-to-computer English used in a commercial environment. The issue is not one of desirability but of practicality: can the designer support user expectations? English-like languages encourage users to submit instructions or questions which programs cannot interpret. Designers sometimes do not want to admit that their programs are as limited as they indeed are. Minker & Rosenfeld (73), in a succinct overview of information storage and retrieval progress in the last decade, identify "fundamental gaps in our intellectual knowledge of syntactic and semantic analysis of natural language" as one reason why no operational systems which handle full natural language input "have been developed, nor are any expected to be developed in the near future."

In spite of this sobering picture, there is reason to believe that the prospects for effective man-computer interactive problem-solving are very bright. Meadow (66) concludes his chapter on Natural Language Communication by suggesting that while it is vital to supply an interface language that the user finds natural for man-computer interaction, the language need not be the one that he uses for person-to-person communication. Until a designer can construct a computer program able to consult stored information and respond to the user as would a person, "telling a computer how to perform an intricate function in detail may best be done by using a precisely defined vocabulary and syntax suitable to the function." Following this line of reasoning, we observe that the choice of a verb-like vocabulary to represent commands and a noun-like vocabulary for labels does have proven value both for establishing an easy-to-teach conceptual framework and for aiding memory during use. This highly desirable practice, drawing on a user's language habits, can be productive even though it stops far short of the full natural language exchanges envisioned by some.

Design Alternatives Illustrated in Application Studies

The references cited so far have not contained guidelines to help the designer test interface language choices during his design process. The criteria that have been discussed have had the virtue of being application-independent, but they require that the interactive facility be implemented and then tested for performance. We now examine literature that, because it is related to particular application tasks, may be useful in helping the designer choose between specific alternatives.

The proceedings of an invitational workshop on the user interface in interactive bibliographic search are available in a book edited by Walker (112). It includes a challenge paper by Bennett (6), which uses the traditional card catalog as an example of an existing conceptual framework. A series of discussion topics urges authors to report interface language design decisions that could lead to a new conceptual framework for interactive search. The twelve papers prepared for the workshop give a cross section of issues that have an impact on users. At the workshop, participants identified "problems in and prospects for more effective design." Carefully edited critical minutes present a condensation of information yet preserve the character of the discussion. An accurate picture of the state of the art in design is given by the "feature lists, showing the variety of alternatives available to the designer." There is still considerable terminological confusion and lack of agreement on the relative importance of various features. Participants nevertheless rated the workshop as a worthwhile way of gaining valuable perspective on interface issues.

Without the emphatic insistence on interface issues provided by a challenge paper and a focused workshop format, it appears that designers are reluctant to report their reasons for design choices. First, those guidelines that are available tend to appear commonplace unless related to specific decisions. Secondly, many designers seem to recognize, at least implicitly, the gap between the intended and actual effect of their decisions on user performance. Hansen (42) reports a set of principles that he employed while designing a facility for program construction and text editing. He is refreshingly candid in revealing that he is thus far both designer and user and in pointing out his oversights in adhering to his own principles. Hansen is to be commended for his approach; other system reports would be far more valuable to the field if they followed a similar plan.

Seldom are user interface issues addressed explicitly or are task archetypes identified clearly in reports of new applications. Within the scope of this review we can only identify a few representative sources that do a particularly good job of exposition or that present experience valuable to designers.

Meadow (66) includes perceptive comments on all aspects of man-computer interaction as he surveys representative applications. His rare ability to describe issues from the perspective of impact on the user while giving readers the benefit of his extensive and varied design experience makes this a valuable book. One of the tasks that Meadow identifies as basic to interactive systems is text editing. In their well-written survey, Van Dam & Rice (108) present many stimulating ideas as they describe 15 representative text manipulation systems. Though they are responsive to "user engineering" considerations, they do not identify experimental work that would indicate which features are better for which operations. They do occasionally offer comments bearing on ease of use.

One class of applications is the storage and search of data. As examples of personal use programs, Glantz (40) in his description of SHOEBOX and Linn & Reitman (57) in their description of AUTONOTE report research in applications where the user who is responsible for input and retrieval is knowledgeable about the logical information structure and content in the files. While both papers provide rationale for design choices, no specific user experience is reported. Astronomers and medical personnel have used DIRAC to access files of research records, and Vallee et al. (106) describe results observed by system managers. This reviewer believes that personal-use programs have immediate prospects for important expansion; designers would benefit now from reports on the experience of users, even though the service is still in the experimental stage.

The next step beyond personal-use programs is the team-augmentation concept where multiple users have access to shared files in a project environment. So far, most progress has appeared in the context of system programming; Engelbart et al. (34) gives a visionary description of "the on-line office," illustrating the power of the NLS (oN-Line System) through examples of use by software designer, manager, and report-writing team. The project is reaching a challenging new stage where techniques that have become familiar to the project staff through a total immersion process must now be organized for transfer of the conceptual framework to other teams of software developers in the Advanced Research Projects Agency (ARPA) Network who did not share in the design experience.

Most familiar, and perhaps of most interest, to readers of this *Annual Review* series are applications serving a broader community of users. Bibliographic search in a library environment is a prime example. Marcus et al. (63) report on INTREX, which has become "operational in an experimental mode." Their experience tends to highlight the need to teach searchers how to make effective use of the tool even in a carefully designed facility. Summit (96) considers "the terminal operator [to be] an intelligent decision-maker" and describes the features through which "the user completely controls the search process." Wente (114) presents a system manager's view of experience with RECON (the government's acronym for DIALOG). The older but still pertinent anecdotal case study of Timbie & Coombs (100) completes the triangle by illustrating the terminal user's view. Fried (38) describes BASIS-70, a new commercial entry into the field providing moderate flexibility.

In query formulation during bibliographic search, the set-combining power given by Boolean operators must be balanced against the fact that set concepts are unfamiliar to many searchers. Kugel (52) suggests that the often observed confusion in the meaning of union ('OR'), intersection ('AND'), and relative complement ('NOT') is caused by the choice of operators and their names; he recommends PLUS, OVER, and MINUS. Clarke (18) describes alternative interactive facility designs that involve tradeoffs of flexibility against ease of use. In the design he chooses, the user controls union by placing "equivalent" search terms in one list and intersection by the "combination" of lists. Though Thompson (99) provides an interesting survey of literature on pre-coordination, he sidesteps the issue of post-coordination during query formulation by relying on a hierarchical classification tree to be explored by the user; his research system makes no provision for coordinate search.

A second class of applications serving a community of users is order control and inventory maintenance. Typically these applications (1) are found in an industrial or business environment, (2) have proven to management's satisfaction to be cost-justifiable, (3) are designed to serve multiple clerical users, and (4) include a limited process-model that can support aids to the user and some consistency checking. The desired end result is often so well defined that the designer can plan to lead the operator through a series of steps necessary to complete the transaction.

Since some of these interactive facilities have been in operation for a number of years, one would expect to find reports on training programs, operational experience, and effectiveness tests. Not so. While there is clearly a wealth of potential experience, remarkably little appears in generally accessible printed form. Though this is regrettable from the viewpoint of the designer who wishes to sharpen his perception by drawing on significant experience of others, it is not really surprising. A company's operational experience can reveal to outsiders more about internal processes than the company desires. Further, good techniques developed through expensive empirical trial and error might be used by competitors to gain an economic advantage. This situation is not likely to change. Much useful information, a sort of "industrial iceberg," will remain submerged beneath a sea of "company confidential" proprietary labels, available only to the designer alert to its existence and authorized to seek it.

The IBM Advanced Administrative System (AAS) has been supporting order processing at branch offices since 1969. Wimbrow (115) gives an overview of the five years of system development required to design a system which provides "conversational continuity" to 5000 users in 320 different geographic locations. Two points are significant. First, there was early recognition of the need for training to achieve effective use of the system. O'Dea (79) gives a general account of the AAS computer-assisted-instruction training program which is administered on the same terminal used for transactions. While the idea of teaching the use of an interactive facility under computer control is often mentioned by designers, this appears to be the largest-scale instance in operation. Second, the early testing of realistic and complete simulation mock-up of full AAS transactions as seen by the operator was of paramount importance in achieving today's operational success.

A discussion of design alternatives for constructing interface languages suitable for use with an alphanumeric display terminal is available in an IBM publication (45) based on the AAS experience. In this "designer's handbook" guidelines for display content, display format, and operating modes are stated, illustrated, and compared. Note, however, that the experimental evidence that led to the formation of the guidelines is not reported. Further, the authors caution that the guidelines "are not intended to be applicable under all circumstances." The influence of this publication can be seen in another kind of order control and inventory management application. McAllister & Bell (60) provide a clearly written exposition of user-oriented features in the Experimental Library Management System. Here the operator tends to exercise more control over the facility than in AAS transactions. The authors observe, "Complex procedures can be made intelligible by good organization and careful display formatting."

A third class of applications serving a community of users is directed to support of decision-making by operational experts skilled in a technology. As an example, Beardsley (5) offers a survey of 21 commercially available computer-based aids for design of semiconductor integrated circuitry. These, he concludes, have now been proven cost-effective in operation. While Beardsley does not report specific user experience, he cites enough examples to give a clear idea of the kind of interaction made possible. Of interest to designers would be comparative or case-study reports of customer reaction to some of the strikingly different interfaces provided.

The last class of applications discussed here is decision-making by strategic management. Here the results are negative, but some lessons have been learned along the way. Dunlop (32) gives an interesting account of his observations at IBM Corporate Headquarters. He characterizes the executive self-image as one of dignity in exercise of power and control over people. The executive also has a negative reaction toward keyboard operation. Dunlop concludes that this helps explain why executives do not use information-oriented interactive facilities that require typed input. Supporting this conclusion, he describes a more successful information center wherein the executive interacts with an information specialist through a closed-circuit television monitor. Thus the use of the tool is delegated to the specialist, who "chauffeurs" the executive to the desired information. Feeney (36) has a more direct explanation of why the executive delegates interaction. "When we get to the point where terminals are useful [to them], executives will type up a storm." He speaks with authority, being both a terminal user and General Manager of the General Electric Information Services Division. Head (43) reports that large companies, for various reasons, are generally abandoning (at least temporarily) the idea of manager-computer interaction. He mentions the need for an improved user interface and a "new generation of managers more comfortable with computer technology."

EVALUATION FOR SYSTEM REDEVELOPMENT

In his review chapter devoted to "Design and Evaluation of Information Systems," Katter (46) has identified a "system redevelopment cycle" including analysis, synthesis, and evaluation. He terms it *re*-development because design is directed to "replacement of an older interactive [facility] by one that is newer, usually more expensive, and presumably more effective." This concept of redevelopment is especially appropriate to user interface design in interactive systems, where it has been amply demonstrated that the user's behavior *will* change as he exploits new problem-solving power. Thus Martin & Parker (64) are justified when they exhort, "plan from the beginning for multiple design iterations," and "the interface design should include an elaborate facility for gathering information. . .by unobtrusive monitoring." The computer thus becomes both the basis for the interactive facility provided to the user and the instrument through which data is gathered to support redevelopment.

Controlled Experiments

The methods of experimental design have been successfully applied by experimental psychologists, but the results are generally limited to a special context, are often controversial, and are occasionally suspect because of the unknown effect of uncontrolled variables on experimental subjects. Experiments in man-computer problem-solving must thus be appraised in a special light: just as there are as yet no validated theoretical models for predicting the effect of interactive facility alternatives on user performance, so there are few, if any, theoretical models for guiding the isolation of experimental variables. The mathematical model provided by Carbonell et al. (14) still represents an accurate picture of the art. We are immediately struck by the current lack of numerical values for his conceptual boxes "utility evaluation" and "results evaluation." For this reason, classical controlled experiments involving all the components in a system environment are impractical, if not impossible, at this time.

Controlled experiments on isolated system components as used in the performance of narrow, specialized tasks do provide interesting, if limited, results. However, few of the 1971 reports in this area offer much of value to the practical interface designer, as they are typically directed toward clarification of terminal hardware parameters or exploration of possible new hardware features. Vartabedian (110) reports the experimental setting for the task of finding a five-letter word among other words on the face of a display screen. He used character-generation method as his experimental variable and found that no significant search differences resulted. Smith & Goodwin (93) attack the same kind of problem and report that search time for a particular four-character item in a target class was 50% faster when a three-cycle-per-second blink was imposed on items in the target class. As often happens in such constrained laboratory tests, they question, "whether the present results would hold up over extended periods of display use." Mahood (62) discusses user performance and preferences in several experiments with TOUCH-TONE® data entry to a computer: "People tend to prefer the method they thought was faster rather than the method which was actually faster."

Fetter & Carlisle (37) describe experimental use of the Mead Data Central system by 12 Yale Law School students who had the task of searching a full-text Ohio Bar Association data base. Use of a typewriter terminal as compared with use of a video display terminal was the independent variable. While six hypotheses were tested, the generalizability of any specific result is clouded by extraneous factors, all fully reported. The discussion of planning for the experiment, subject behavior, and anomalies in performance make this an excellent and worthwhile paper. It offers a good example of exploratory work where the experimenters use statistics to illuminate relevant factors but are able to look beyond the constraints of experimental design to benefit from observation of the problem-solving process. Thus we gain from their experience, even though the effect of uncontrolled variables swamps the independent variable in the experiment.

Using 18 experienced decision makers from industry, Prokop & Brooks (83) investigated the effect of displaying the output of inventory control data on a display terminal or on printed computer listings. They report that when the display terminal was used, inventory policy decisions could be made significantly earlier and were more consistent with policy decisions made after all of the data were available. We observe that use of a dynamic bar graph on the display device without any counterpart on paper may account for the results. While their focus on results—rather than on observation of individual participant behavior—is in the generally accepted scientific methodological tradition, this makes the paper less valuable to the designer who wants to understand *why* the reported results were obtained.

One significant question that always arises in laboratory tests with people is the relation of the laboratory results to results that could be expected in field experience. Erdmann & Neal (35) describe the differences observed when a computer-based airline ticket vendor terminal was moved from a controlled environment to the Chicago airport. The experimenters report that they were able to establish test conditions in which laboratory users who operated the terminal served as reasonable predictors of actual customer performance. Work of this kind seems strongly needed to help establish the link between laboratory and operational use of more general problem-solving interfaces.

The cost-effectiveness controversy over interactive programming vs. batch programming has led to its becoming the most thoroughly studied interactive facility application. Sackman (85) provides a portrait of the needs and habits of the interactive programmer and presents an overview of five different experiments. Experimental results have not settled the controversy. While interactive problem-solvers tend to use more computer time and less man time to complete a task, individual differences in programming skill tend to overshadow any other experimental parameters. His observation that almost all problem-solving insight tends to come while the user is away from the terminal suggests that qualitative changes in behavior will occur when cost considerations permit the user to integrate the tool into his work habits. The interactive programming theme, supported by much more detail, is extended in a book by Sackman (86). Ten studies are covered, including his own recent work at the Air Force Academy. This wealth of experimental data gives us an appreciation for the complexity and number of process variables. The significance of what is still unknown should caution anyone who anticipates an imminent analytical model that predicts user performance.

Case Studies and Field Trials

There is a significant body of evaluative literature that examines the use of an interactive facility in a particular problem-solving environment. While the mass of admittedly uncontrolled variables makes it impossible to attribute the nature of the results to any one variable, these "case studies" are valuable precursors to eventual controlled experiments.

Sackman (87) kept a careful log of his progress at the on-line teletype as he learned the TINT programming language by following self-tutoring exercises in the TINT User's Guide. He draws on his experimental design experience to identify and give results for some 16 performance variables, but he is quick to point out: "The orientation of the study was exploratory and open-ended rather than a test of. . .preconceived hypotheses. Subjective responses were collected. . .to extend the base of the study and to provide independent qualitative checks on the quantitative findings." Though behavioral studies where subject and experimenter are the same person are risky, the Sackman study shows that a perceptive and trained observer can provide the designer with valuable information. The quality of the statistical measures applied, the open-ended attitudinal comments, and the error analysis all illuminate problems that can be remedied by the designer once they are recognized.

A preview by Cook (20) provides a good introduction to a massive report by Cook et al. (21). The latter gives the results of an 11-week field trial at Syracuse University, where a collection of 35,000 "full-text" titles and abstracts from *Psychological Abstracts* was available on-line. Access was provided to a total of 349 people via 75 typewriters located around the Collendale Campus. An undisclosed fraction of the registrants conducted at least one search during the trial period for a total of 4,388 searches. The findings of the experimenters corroborate the observation made by others that ways are needed to aid the searcher who wants to discover the variety of words that authors may have used to express a single concept of interest to the searcher. While the program searched on a full-text concordance, that list was not made available to the user at the interface. The experimenters describe operational experience during the trial, and they stress the value of both a telephone service that enables a user to get instant human aid when he encounters problems and a statistical program that collects data on searches as they are performed.

A well-organized book by Morton (75) describes the impact of an on-line economic model on a decision-making process in industry. A clear and exhaustive picture of how planning managers function gives a basis for reporting the operational results: the computer model, run under the control of the managers, enabled them to reach agreement on production schedules in a half day rather than the 20 days formerly required. This occurred even though the interactive model, replacing an earlier off-line model, enabled them to try many more alternatives in seeking a better solution. Morton stresses the importance of involving the managers in the design of the interactive facility; this has the effect both of ensuring that a useful and natural tool is provided and of minimizing the training required for the managers to realize the full power of the tool.

The Biomedical Communications Network Papers

This reviewer has found one set of reports that gives an unusual overview of an entire redevelopment cycle from analysis through evaltion. While the series provides different viewpoints on many aspects of an important problem-solving process—bibliographic search—as it is conducted in biomedical communications networks (BCN), it also offers a most satisfying continuity.

The State University of New York (SUNY) network, a good example of a regional BCN, went into service at Syracuse in October, 1968. Egeland (33) reports design considerations and operational experience gained in providing 16 medical centers with typewriter-access to 1,300,000 journal citations from the Medical Literature and Retrieval System (MEDLARS). The program asks the user a preplanned series of questions in order to formulate a query for him; this procedure makes the interactive facility easy to use but limited in flexibility. A more flexible "direct search method" provides more power but requires use of a computer-oriented format. In presenting a user-group evaluation of the SUNY service, Rae (84) underscores the need for "education of the user, both in the mechanics of operating the terminal and in the logic of indexing/searching." He is dismayed because misunderstanding of the interface language and of the user's role in search iteration caused users to leave the terminal "unaware that they did not have optimum results" and "unaware of the great assistance which the system could have given [them]" in satisfying their information need.

Davis (24) describes the analysis necessary for planning a nationwide BCN interfacing with particular customer groups. As she observes, "The [National Library of Medicine (NLM)] Biomedical Communications Network is a relevant model of the national networks considered and recommended during these last ten years." The paper documents the rationale for the NLM-BCN, the fundamentals of design, and the key prototype activities within a cost-benefit framework. This analysis lays the groundwork for expansion as hardware, communications, and user interface technologies permit. The Abridged Index Medicus search facility (AIM-TWX) is one example of a service provided by the NLM-BCN.

In preparation for AIM-TWX implementation, Seiden (89) analyzed 26 general purpose and 11 bibliographic interactive retrieval systems. Though discussion is directed to NLM-BCN requirements, the survey contains information of broad interest and serves as a useful model for others who wish to add later systems. Turning to analysis of the interface to be supported by the AIM-TWX computer programs, Katter & Blankenship (48) survey over 150 papers to identify 16 primary requirements. Their discussion for each follows an outline of definition, cost criteria, effectiveness criteria, need for additional fact finding, and specific features. We have already discussed at length a third paper by Katter (47) addressing the characteristics of potential BCN users. While other such series of papers representing work done under contract may exist, the particular set (89, 48, 47) demonstrates the wealth of informative planning data that can be compiled by a skilled and knowledgeable design team.

Katter & McCarn (49) describe user experience at the interface during the first few months of AIM-TWX operation in the NLM-BCN. The service, accessing a data base of over 150,000 citations, has been available on an experimental basis to over 33 different institutional users since May 1970. Katter's perceptive categorization of the phases a user passes through as he learns the interface language was referenced earlier. Two papers report evaluations by one class of users for whom the system was designed. Moll (74) gives an account of training in preparation for "working the system" during a two-week trial period at the University of Virginia. The key problem in system use was formulating search statements that made appropriate use of the controlled Medical Subject Headings (MESH) vocabulary. He observes that the best results were achieved when medical practitioners were present "when the search was run and could overview the citations as they came off the machine." This allowed immediate feedback to the operator for search iteration. The reader gains the impression that the trial was a "crash program" (e.g., two operators present to keep the teletype going), and the time press induced by limited availability heightened some of the "bullying" aspects of terminal usage anticipated by Katter (47). In the second paper, Stiller (95) compares and contrasts differences in search methods observed in her AIM-TWX and SUNY-BCN experience. These differences are in turn compared with the search power available to a knowledgeable information specialist using the off-line MEDLARS-I system. She concludes that the AIM-TWX interface is indeed an improvement over the SUNY-BCN interface and that it offers worthwhile service "to the user who does not have the time or interest to learn the vagaries of [MeSH] indexing or [MEDLARS] system usage."

From McCarn and Cuadra we learn the viewpoints of two leaders in the management of the AIM-TWX project. McCarn (61), responsible for working with contractors to install services in accordance with the NLM-BCN plan, offers advice on the need to "reduce the uncertainties and fears associated with the new system and move to avoid excessive expectations" on the part of the operating staff. Cuadra (22), head of the SDC contractor staff, illustrates problems leading to possible (and in some cases actual) user disenchantment. He echoes McCarn's observations: "We need to think hard. . .about the way in which we are going to successfully engineer acceptance once we have finished engineering the system itself."

Evaluations of search effectiveness in two facilities serve as a kind of postscript to the survey of BCN literature. Lancaster (55) devotes the bulk of his report on AIM-TWX to a recall and precision analysis of 48 searches. Of interest to the interface designer are his numerous suggestions for the kind of added features that the biomedical practitioner would find beneficial. Many problems would be solved by "a well constructed network of cross-references and an adequate entry vocabulary" to lead the researcher (as contrasted with the trained analyst) to more sophisticated search strategies.

Though the Epilepsy Abstracts Retrieval System (EARS) is not organizationally part of the NLM-BCN, it is clearly directed to the same kind of user. A brief paper by Porter et al. (82) serves as an overview of the user environment and of the interface to full text provided by Mead Data Central. Lancaster (54) employs the same evaluation framework used in his AIM-TWX study to examine 47 searches by 16 different users at 6 separate centers. At the time of the trial, the interactive facility provided 8-hour/week access to full bibliographic citations, abstracts, and index terms for 8,000 items. As in the AIM-TWX evaluation, searches in the sample were to be by practitioners, but there is strong circumstantial evidence that some, if not most, of the EARS searches were delegated. While Lancaster believes that a full-text facility has great potential for enabling practitioners to conduct effective searches, he faults the current facility that "requires perfection of entry, makes little or no allowance for common human errors, is confusing and inexplicit in some of its responses, and sometimes appears to behave in an idiosyncratic way." Ten pages of examples provide much of value for the designer responsive to the challenge of the redevelopment cycle.

DEVELOPMENTS INFLUENCING DESIGN OF THE INTERACTIVE FACILITY

Two developing trends have potential for impact on the resources available to the designer and on the expectation of the user at a terminal. First, the human-engineering discipline is an important though relatively untapped source of personnel who are trained in applying technology to aid people in task performance. Increased use of human-engineering skills can lead to more effective interface designs. Second, the imminent growth in problem-solving power offered through computer networks is leading to pressure for common user interface conventions. In addition to benefiting users, a broader base of common operations will permit designers to concentrate resources on the analysis necessary to bring problem-solving tools into operational use in major new applications areas.

The Challenge to Human Engineering

In 1969 Nickerson (77) identified "the increasing heterogeneity of the community of computer users" as the development that should "pose a challenge to psychologists and human factors researchers." After a careful search of the major human factors and applied psychology journals, he concluded ". . .there is remarkably little evidence of research undertaken for the express purpose either of increasing our understanding of man-computer interaction or of providing information that will be useful in the development of systems that are optimally suited to user's needs." While freely conceding the difficulty of such work, he invited further investigation by reviewing progress in three areas that would benefit from human-engineering expertise: (1) conversational languages, (2) the effects of computer system characteristics on user behavior, and (3) the problem of describing, or modeling, man-computer interaction. A 1970 paper by Parsons (81) provides another resume of human-engineering opportunities. He identifies terminal design as "what human factors people have dealt with in electromechanical and electronic systems." The man-computer interface is set apart as a "special breed" because "function is established not in the design of the equipment but in how the computer is programmed." He discusses the challenges in on-line languages, task description, training, and manning.

Is there current work in the human-engineering discipline that might lead to improved effectiveness and acceptability of the interactive facility? While there is a large body of literature in experimental psychology that could be stimulating if wisely interpreted, most of these items will be incomprehensible to designers untrained in the discipline of psychology.

One activity reported in the human-engineering literature is model building, and papers by Schrenk (88), Baker (3), and Teichner (98) are a representative cross-section. Without getting into a detailed analysis, this reviewer finds very little in these papers that would benefit a pragmatic system designer. The distance between the symbolic concepts and real-world data is just too great.

The impact of human-factors people on design procedures is much more hopeful. Singleton (92) gives an interesting discussion of different approaches to user interface design: (1) design intuitively and check systematically against a checklist, (2) use standard procedures for formal design, or (3) adapt a design to a situation on the basis of established theory. His illustrations show how the approaches overlap, and he warns: ". . .recommendations. . .tend to be an inextricable mixture of common sense, data from laboratory experiment, and field experience." Shackel & Shipley (90) have prepared an extensive review of ergonomic literature on terminal input-output alternatives. While they warn that it is "not intended as a design guide or handbook," the compilation will be useful to interactive facility designers.

The most direct contributions of people trained in behavioral sciences tend to be reported in the information science literature. The speculative writings of G. Miller (67) and R. Miller (68) help give perspective on issues. Treu (101) and Carlisle (16) propose frameworks in which man-computer interaction can be studied; their familiarity with the necessary computer-based resources makes their plans feasible though still extremely challenging. The evaluation studies reported by Sackman (85) on interactive programming and by Boehm et al. (10) on the effect of limited accessibility during problem solving draw on the methods of experimental psychology. Probably the strongest benefits have been realized when people trained in behavioral sciences and knowledgeable in computer technology have become leaders or members of interface design teams (Katter, 47; Cuadra, 22; Fetter & Carlisle, 37).

An extensive search through the current human-factors literature indicates to this reviewer that the challenge posed by Nickerson (77) and Parsons (81) is only beginning to be accepted. Grace (41) gives an indication of what must happen to increase the impact of the human engineering discipline on interactive facility design. The fact that "logic for operation exists both inside the machine and inside the head of the [operator]" is the "single characteristic which most clearly differentiates the information processing system from traditional man-machine systems" familiar to human factors people. She urges that "human factors people. . .master the computer discipline" in order to provide needed guidance to a field "which has not yet clearly understood human factors requirements." In summary, it appears that an interface technology will be most expeditiously advanced if those already trained in human engineering join the design team rather than if software people attempt to learn human engineering. While some progress along the latter lines is possible and has occurred, it is probably limited by a truth that McCarn (61) has observed: "The people who are experts in . . .computers. . .see well-bounded problems with great precision." They have difficulty in accepting the idea "that human communication is much more complex, and its context more extensive, than was initially conceived by computer programming staffs."

The Pressure for User Interface Commonality

For a decade computer scientists have been projecting computer-based utilities as a means for bringing problem-solving power to a wide segment of the populace. Kemeny (51) believes costs of operating computer networks will soon drop to where, for example, "Sitting in our homes we could have at our fingertips all the reference materials of the entire world. The impact on research and the ability of the average man to keep himself informed is beyond imagination." He observes that standards at the user interface should enable a user ". . .to switch from one national time-sharing network to another as easily as he now switches from CBS to NBC on a TV set."

In addition to cost, the communications equipment required for networks has been another barrier to network development. A widely quoted report prepared under the auspices of the National Academy of Engineering (76) envisions two-way networks based on existing cable television systems that would permit "viewing the city as a large information processing system" for "moving information rather than men or materials." The report suggests that the network for a city of 500,000 could be built for less than the cost of 10 miles of superhighway. Hughes & Campbell (44) explore the technical considerations and human engineering requirements for a two-way terminal based on a color-television-with-keyboard in the mass-produced $500-$750 range. Their discussion of customer wait-time suggests that system planning would benefit from an increased awareness of the existing response-time and task-requirement literature.

Agreement on user interface conventions necessary to support generalized access to computing networks has not kept up with progress in equipment. Little & Mooers (58) identify "elemental control actions which are of crucial importance to the user" in starting interaction and in keeping him in meaningful communication. Control actions suggested for standardization are: dialogue signals (how to get the attention of the program), string commands (simple editing, help request), system control commands (e.g., restart), and stop. They suggest that given a set of commands common to all programs, the user can explore the specialized problem-solving power available from a particular program. They also discuss the need for a machine-independent information representation that the user can "picture in his mind when he operates on (edits, selects, or rearranges) the stored data." An improved understanding has been achieved in this latter area since their 1968 paper [see, for example, CODASYL (19)].

It is useful to consider an analogy between a terminal user and an automobile driver. Agreement on conventions for driver controls has enabled the automobile industry to provide the customer with variety in styling, power, and load-carrying capability within a standard framework. A driver can rent a car and, after a few seconds of orientation and practice with controls, he can operate the car even though he may never have driven that model before. Further, the driver need not understand the inner workings of the automobile in order to make effective use of it. Berkeley (9) has used the analogy to develop an operational definition of understanding a computer: "You can derive conclusions,. . .[apply them] in the real world,. . .adopt means to ends,. . .and [can avoid] many kinds of trouble and mistakes." Little & Mooers challenge the computer utility industry to provide a user interface commonality that allows the user to concentrate on understanding the problem he wishes to solve rather than on understanding the inner workings of the computer.

Davis (25) outlines current Federal Government standards efforts to provide a marketplace that is better for both industry and user. She observes: "Once I've dialed up on a telephone line and been connected with a large computer, there's really nothing I can do between any two of these systems. . .because I don't know which button to press on the keyboard." In contrast with the telephone network, no standard protocol has been established. Perhaps the stimulus for user interface standards is best summarized by R.M. Fano as reported in Kemeny (51): "Standards begin to take effect when people are interested in working together,. . .there [is] incentive to collaborate. . . [and]. . .people gain more from cooperation than [from] competition."

Within application areas we can see first steps toward identifying common user interface characteristics and common problem-solving functions. At the 1971 Fall Joint Computer Conference Panel led by Bennett (7), six designers discussed interactive search subtasks (information seeking in response to "where is. . ." questions) that are found in problem-solving tasks (information seeking in response to "what if. . ." questions). Four Federal Government agencies sponsored a two-day "Forum on Interactive Bibliographic Systems" at which the goal was to enable managers of search systems to share experiences that suggest improvements to system capabilities. The proceedings (Meadow, 65) should contain valuable reports of user experience. Olle (80) draws on his experience as Chairman of the CODASYL Systems Committee to provide an initial comparison of common functions in generalized data management systems and interactive bibliographic search systems. Boulden & Buffa (11) suggest that while modeling and use costs in interactive systems are coming down, the step toward "development of standard industry [operational] models which can be used by a number of companies. . .would spread costs [. . .and enable usage by] companies with sales under $5 million." Steps toward sharing interactive programs add to the pressure for user interface commonality.

Several reports offer insight on the kind of user behavior that can be expected in new applications made feasible by forthcoming computer utilities. Sheridan (91) describes how a "computer-aided feedback and participation system" can be used to sample public opinion. He points out that the participant must understand (or be able to find out) the background of a question in order to understand the meaning of his answer. Turoff (102) has conducted Delphi Conferences in which the computer serves as "a real-time accountant" to maintain the anonymity of the participants. He observes the need for "establishment of a 'meaningful' group communication structure" in which an individual can respond to an agenda of questions and modify his initial estimates in interaction with other participants. In a second report, Turoff (103) describes a Delphi Conference held with 20 people during a 13-week period. His critique of the user interface will be of interest to designers. Umpleby (104) describes pilot demonstrations in which users "explore the future" through interaction with a computer-based model. He reports user comments indicating the richness of information required on the one hand and the demand for a structure for the interaction on the other hand.

In position papers prepared for an ACM '71 panel, Lancaster (53) and Baxendale (4) discuss the future of user-oriented access to information resources. Lancaster suggests that the computer will be used more advantageously if designers provide programs that are "capable of being queried in English language form without the need to use either controlled terms or formal Boolean search logic," and that "provide positive assistance to the user by guiding him along paths likely to lead to relevant documents." Baxendale envisions a "system of referral centers" with "a direct consumer interface" to a kind of "grand consumer's guide on where and how to become informed." Though both agree on the need for an interface usable in a non-delegated search mode, Lancaster tends to place relatively more automatic decision-making responsibility with the program while Baxendale points to experimental work directed toward helping designers "capitalize on [the consumer's] unique powers for learning, for inference making, and for integrating his experiences with information into his own framework of knowledge." These contrasting viewpoints symbolize the important tradeoff between perceived ease of use and flexibility to respond to individual demands. This issue is especially important as designers plan for new facilities that accommodate growth in user capability and in system power.

CONCLUSIONS

We have seen significant progress in the design of interactive facilities that effectively support the user's problem-solving task. This progress can be contrasted with earlier designs in which computer efficiency considerations were often paramount. However, the experience that makes optimum usage patterns obvious to the designer rests on a computer-oriented lore unknown to people who are not computer professionals. The designer is continually challenged to provide an interactive facility that compensates for this user inexperience.

The new public visibility of network terminals in stock quotation, reservation, and financial applications, coupled with demonstrated problem-solving successes by initiated specialists, is leading to requests for service in new applications. This high level of demand comes at a time when industry can support the mass production and heavy usage necessary to drive the computer hardware and communication service costs down. Further, a vigorous computer industry accustomed to explosive expansion must actively seek and exploit new applications in order to maintain growth.

The task characteristics in many of these new applications will require that the user and the computer play truly complementary roles. The user must recognize that the computer-based facility enables him to amplify his own problem-solving abilities, and he must overcome any false expectation that the computer will solve problems for him without intellectual effort on his part. This requirement for active participation, recognized by increasingly astute customer managements, will force the computer industry to supply user interfaces that are judged effective by knowledgeable users. In the long run, enhanced human capability to accomplish important results will provide the motivation for continued use.

There are several requirements for further development of the emerging user-interface technology. First, it is imperative to cut through the mass of inessential, application-specific detail and to overcome confusion in terminology so that the basic similarity of user services required in many applications becomes clear. The concentrated interchange which took place at the AFIPS Workshop (Walker, 112) illustrates both the existing problem and an example of a constructive first step toward solution. Second, observers of the computer scene have decried the tendency of software designers to produce each system as if others did not exist. To be successful in projecting interactive facilities into new applications, designers must learn to build on the work of others and stop dissipation of resources on unnecessary duplicated effort. Third, adoption of a tool-design approach—provision of a training protocol as well as the provision of problem-solving functions—will make it obvious where human-engineering skills and computer-assisted-instruction experience can help provide improved interface languages and training techniques.

Because the theoretical basis for incorporating user problem-solving characteristics into analytical models is so rudimentary, the resulting user interface technology will take the form of procedural rules used by designers to guide their creative judgement. Indeed, the challenge for research is to transform the current art of design into an engineering discipline by developing an agreement on ways for characterizing user tasks, for allocating interface resources to meet task requirements, and for evaluating user effectiveness in task performance.

REFERENCES

(1) ADAMS, EDWARD N. The computer in academic instruction. IBM Corporation, Yorktown Heights, New York, 14 September 1970, 18 p. (Research report, RC 3063).

(2) ANCONA, JOSEPH P.; GARLAND, STUART M.; TROPSA, JOHN J. At last: standards for keyboards. Datamation, 17:5 (1 March 1971) 32-36.

(3) BAKER, J. D. Quantitative modelling of human performance in information systems. Ergonomics, 13:6 (December 1970) 645-664.

(4) BAXENDALE, PHYLLIS B. The need for consumer-mediation with information resources: the prospect for graphic display techniques. In: Association for Computing Machinery. Annual conference. 26th, Chicago, Illinois, 1971. Proceedings. Association for Computing Machinery, New York, 1971, 569-573.

(5) BEARDSLEY, CHARLES W. Computer aids for IC design, artwork, and mask generation. IEEE Spectrum, 8:9 (September 1971) 63-79.

(6) BENNETT, JOHN L. Interactive bibliographic search as a challenge to interface design. In: Walker, Donald E.; ed. Interactive bibliographic search: the user/computer interface. AFIPS Press, Montvale, New Jersey, 1971, 1-18.

(7) BENNETT, JOHN L. A panel session—the user interface for interactive search. In: American Federation of Information Processing Societies. Fall Joint Computer Conference. Las Vegas, Nevada, 1971. Proceedings, vol. 39. AFIPS Press, Montvale, New Jersey, 1971, 197.

(8) BENNETT, JOHN L. Spatial concepts as an organizing principle for interactive bibliographic search. In: Walker, Donald E.; ed. Interactive bibliographic search: the user/computer interface. AFIPS Press, Montvale, New Jersey, 1971, 67-82.

(9) BERKELEY, EDMUND C. Not understanding a computer. Computers and Automation, 20:2 (February 1971) 6.

(10) BOEHM, BARRY W.; SEVEN, M. J.; WATSON, R. A. Interactive problem-solving—an experimental study of "lockout" effects. In: American Federation of Information Processing Societies. Spring Joint Computer Conference. Atlantic City, New Jersey, 1971. Proceedings, vol. 38. AFIPS Press, Montvale, New Jersey, 1971, 205-210.

(11) BOULDEN, JAMES B.; BUFFA, ELWOOD S. Corporate models; online, real-time systems. Harvard Business Review, 48:4 (July/August 1970) 65-83.

(12) CARBONELL, JAIME R. AI in CAI: an artificial-intelligence approach to computer-assisted instruction. IEEE Transactions on Man-Machine Systems, MMS-11:4 (December 1970) 190-202.

(13) CARBONELL, JAIME R. Artificial intelligence and large interactive man computer systems. Bolt, Beranek and Newman, Inc., Cambridge, Massachusetts, 12 July 1971, 17 p. (AD 726 441).

(14) CARBONELL, JAIME R. On man-computer interaction: a model and some related issues. IEEE Transactions on Systems Science and Cybernetics, SSC-5:1 (January 1969) 16-26.

(15) CARBONELL, JAIME R.; ELKIND, JEROME I.; NICKERSON, RAYMOND S. On the psychological importance of time in a time sharing system. Human Factors, 10:2 (March/April 1968) 135-142.

(16) CARLISLE, JAMES H. An experimental framework for man computer interaction research. Yale University, Department of Administrative Sciences, New Haven, Connecticut, August 1971, 53 p.

(17) CLAPPER, GENUNG L. Automatic word recognition. IEEE Spectrum, 8:8 (August 1971) 57-69.

(18) CLARKE, D. C. Query formulation for on-line reference retrieval: design considerations from the indexer/searcher viewpoint. In: American Society for Information Science. Annual meeting. 33d, Philadelphia, Pennsylvania, 11-15 October 1970. Proceedings, vol. 7: The information conscious society. Greenwood Publishing Corp., Westport, Connecticut, 1970, 83-86.

(19) CONFERENCE ON DATA SYSTEMS LANGUAGES. SYSTEMS COMMITTEE. Feature analysis of generalized data base management systems. Association for Computing Machinery, New York, May 1971. 520 p.

(20) COOK, KENNETH H. An experimental on-line system for psychological abstracts. In: American Society for Information Science. Annual meeting. 33d, Philadelphia, Pennsylvania, 11-15 October 1970. Proceedings, vol. 7: The information conscious society. Greenwood Publishing Corp; Westport, Connecticut, 1970, 111-114.

(21) COOK, KENNETH H.; TRUMP, LYNN H.; ATHERTON, PAULINE; BROWNING, SANDRA; FRIERSON, ELEANOR; FORSE, CINDI; KATZER, JEFFREY. Large scale information processing systems, sections I-VI. Syracuse University, School of Library Science, Syracuse, New York, July 1971, 415 p.

(22) CUADRA, CARLOS A. On-line systems: promise and pitfalls. Journal of the American Society for Information Science, 22:2 (March/April 1971) 107-114.

(23) DAVIS, RUTH M. Man-machine communication. In: Cuadra, Carlos A.; ed. Annual review of information science and technology, vol. 1. Interscience, New York, 1966, 221-254.

(24) DAVIS, RUTH M. The national biomedical communications network as a developing structure. Bulletin of the Medical Library Association, 59:1 (January 1971) 1-20.

(25) DAVIS, RUTH M. Serious compatibility problems in computer networking challenge NBS, industry. An interview by Samuel Stafford. Government Executive, 3:7 (July 1971) 64-66.

(26) DOHERTY, WALTER J. The effects of adaptive reflective scheduling. IBM Thomas J. Watson Research Center, Yorktown Heights, New York, 1 September 1971, 19 p. (Research report, RC 3672).

(27) DOLOTTA, T. A. Datamation, 17:11 (1 June 1971) 11-13. (Letter to editor).

(28) DOLOTTA, T. A. Functional specifications for typewriter-like time-sharing terminals. Computing Surveys, 2:1 (March 1970) 5-31.

(29) DOSTERT, BOZENA H.; THOMPSON, FREDERICK B. How features resolve syntatic ambiguity. In: Association for Computing Machinery. Symposium on Information Storage and Retrieval. College Park, Maryland, 1-2 April 1971. Proceedings. University of Maryland, Conference and Institute Division, College Park, Maryland, 1971, 19-32.

(30) DOSTERT, BOZENA H.; THOMPSON, FREDERICK B. Syntactic analysis in REL English. To appear in Proceedings, 1971 International Meeting on Computational Linguistics, Debreceu, Hungary, September 1971, 34 p. (California Institute of Technology report, REL report 1).

(31) DREYFUS, PATRICIA. CRTs (cathode ray tubes). Industrial Design, 18:3 (April 1971) 32-34.

(32) DUNLOP, ROBERT B. Some empirical observations on the man-machine interface question. In: Kriebel, Charles H.; Van Horn, Richard L.; Heames, J. Timothy; eds. Management information systems: progress and perspectives. Carnegie Press, Carnegie-Mellon University, Pittsburgh, Pennsylvania, 1971, 219-252.

(33) EGELAND, JANET. User-interaction in the State University of New York (SUNY) biomedical communication network. In: Walker, Donald E.; ed. Interactive bibliographic search: the user/computer interface. AFIPS Press, Montvale, New Jersey, 1971, 105-120.

(34) ENGELBART, DOUGLAS C.; et al. Advanced intellect-augmentation techniques. SRI Project 7079, Stanford Research Institute, Menlo Park, California, July 1970, 198 p. (Final Report, NAS1-7897).

(35) ERDMANN, ROBERT L.; NEAL, ALAN S. Laboratory vs. field experimentation in human factors—an evaluation of an experimental self-service airline ticket vendor. Human Factors, 13:6 (November/December 1971) 521-531.

(36) FEENEY, GEORGE. A three-stage theory of evolution for the sharing of computer power. An interview by Robert C. Haavind. Computer Decisions, 3:11 (November 1971) 42-45.
(37) FETTER, ROBERT B.; CARLISLE, JAMES H. Man-computer interaction in a decision-making environment. Yale University, Dept. of Administrative Sciences, New Haven, Connecticut, March 1971, 56 p. (AD 722 336).
(38) FRIED, JOHN B. BASIS-70 user interface. In: Walker, Donald E.; ed. Interactive bibliographic search: the user/computer interface. AFIPS Press, Montvale, New Jersey, 1971, 143-158.
(39) GERRITY, THOMAS P., JR. Design of man-machine decision systems: an application to portfolio management. Sloan Management Review, 12:2 (Winter 1971) 59-75.
(40) GLANTZ, RICHARD S. SHOEBOX—a personal file handling system for textual data. In: American Federation of Information Processing Societies. Fall Joint Computer Conference. Houston, Texas, 1970. Proceedings, vol. 37. AFIPS Press, Montvale, New Jersey, 1970, 535-545. (ED 041 612).
(41) GRACE, GLORIA L. Preface to special issue on information processing systems. Human Factors, 12:2 (March/April 1970) 161-164.
(42) HANSEN, WILFRED J. User engineering principles for interactive systems. In: American Federation of Information Processing Societies. Fall Joint Computer Conference. Las Vegas, Nevada, 1971. Proceedings, vol. 39. AFIPS Press, Montvale, New Jersey, 1971, 523-532.
(43) HEAD, ROBERT V. SMIS in Denver; a conference report. Datamation, 17:22 (15 November 1971) 57.
(44) HUGHES, WILLIAM L.; CAMPBELL, SAMUEL O. Some design considerations for home interactive terminals. IEEE Transactions on Broadcasting, BC-17:2 (June 1971) 37-41.
(45) INTERNATIONAL BUSINESS MACHINES CORPORATION. Display design guidelines for the IBM 2260 display station. IBM, Technical Publications Department, 112 East Post Road, White Plains, New York, 1971, 53 p. (Form no. G420-0146).
(46) KATTER, ROBERT V. Design and evaluation of information systems. In: Cuadra, Carlos A.; ed. Annual review of information science and technology, vol. 4. Encyclopedia Britannica, Chicago, Illinois, 1969, 31-70.
(47) KATTER, ROBERT V. On the on-line user of remote-access citation retrieval services. System Development Corporation, Santa Monica, California, 8 January 1970, 30 p. (Technical memo no. (L) 4494/000/00).
(48) KATTER, ROBERT V.; BLANKENSHIP, DONALD A. On-line interfaces for document information systems; considerations for the biomedical communications network. System Development Corporation, Santa Monica, California, June 1969, 59 p. (Technical memo no. (L) 4320).
(49) KATTER, ROBERT V.; McCARN, DAVIS B. AIM-TWX: an experimental on-line bibliographic retrieval system. In: Walker, Donald E.; ed. Interactive bibliographic search: the user/computer interface. AFIPS Press, Montvale, New Jersey, 1971, 121-142.
(50) KELLOGG, CHARLES; BURGER, JOHN; DILLER, TIMOTHY; FOGT, KENNETH. The converse natural language data management system: current status and plans. In: Association for Computing Machinery. Symposium on Information Storage and Retrieval. College Park, Maryland, 1-2 April 1971. Proceedings. University of Maryland, Conference and Institute Division, College Park, Maryland, 1971, 33-46.
(51) KEMENY, JOHN G. Large time-sharing networks. In: Greenberger, Martin; ed. Computers, communications, and the public interest. The Johns Hopkins Press, Baltimore, Maryland, 1971, 2-36.
(52) KUGEL, PETER. Dirty Boole? Journal of the American Society for Information Science, 22:4 (July/August 1971) 293-294.

(53) LANCASTER, F. WILFRID. Are we ready for on-line information retrieval? In: Association for Computing Machinery. Annual Conference. 26th, Chicago, Illinois, 1971. Proceedings. Association for Computing Machinery, New York, 1971, 565-568.

(54) LANCASTER, F. WILFRID. An evaluation of EARS (Epilepsy Abstracts Retrieval System) and factors governing its effectiveness. A report to the National Institute of Neurological Diseases and Stroke. University of Illinois, Urbana, Illinois, October 1971, 58 p.

(55) LANCASTER, F. WILFRID. Evaluation of on-line searching in MEDLARS (AIM-TWX) by biomedical practitioners. A report to the National Library of Medicine. University of Illinois, Graduate School of Library Science, Urbana, Illinois, March 1971. 31 p.

(56) LICKLIDER, J.C.R. Man-computer communication. In: Cuadra, Carlos A.; ed. Annual review of information science and technology, vol. 3. Encyclopedia Britannica, Chicago, Illinois, 1968, 201-240.

(57) LINN, WILLIAM E., JR.; REITMAN, WALTER. Referential communication in AUTONOTE, a personal information retrieval system. In: Association for Computing Machinery. Annual conference. 26th, Chicago, Illinois, 1971. Proceedings. Association for Computing Machinery, New York, 1971, 67-81.

(58) LITTLE, JOHN L.; MOOERS, CALVIN N. Standards for user procedures and data formats in automated information systems and networks. In: American Federation of Information Processing Societies. Spring Joint Computer Conference. Atlantic City, New Jersey, 1968. Proceedings, vol. 32. Thompson Book Company, Washington, D.C., 1968. 89-94.

(59) McALLISTER, CARYL. Cataloging and display of bibliographic information in an on-line catalog. In: American Society for Information Science. Annual meeting. 33d, Philadelphia, Pennsylvania, 11-15 October 1970. Proceedings, vol. 7: The information conscious society. Greenwood Publishing Corp., Westport, Connecticut, 1970, 69-72.

(60) McALLISTER, CARYL; BELL, JOHN M. Human factors in the design of an interactive library system. Journal of the American Society for Information Science, 22:2 (March/April 1971) 96-104.

(61) McCARN, DAVIS B. Getting ready. Datamation, 16:8 (1 August 1970) 22-26.

(62) MAHOOD, GERALD K. Human factors in touch-tone data systems. Bell Laboratories Record, 49:11 (December 1971) 345-348.

(63) MARCUS, RICHARD S.; BENENFELD, ALAN R.; KUGEL, PETER. The user interface for the INTREX retrieval system. In: Walker, Donald E.; ed. Interactive bibliographic search: the user/computer interface. AFIPS Press, Montvale, New Jersey, 1971, 159-202.

(64) MARTIN, THOMAS H.; PARKER, EDWIN B. Designing for user acceptance of an interactive bibliographic search facility. In: Walker, Donald E.; ed. Interactive bibliographic search: the user/computer interface. AFIPS Press, Montvale, New Jersey, 1971, 45-52.

(65) MEADOW, CHARLES T.; ed. Forum on interactive bibliographic systems. Held at National Bureau of Standards, Gaithersburg, Maryland, 4-5 October, 1971. Proceedings to be published by the U.S. Atomic Energy Commission, Technical Information Center, Oak Ridge, Tennessee, 1972.

(66) MEADOW, CHARLES T. Man-machine communication. John Wiley and Sons, New York, 1970, 422 p.

(67) MILLER, GEORGE A. Psychology and information. American Documentation, 19:3 (July 1968) 286-289.

(68) MILLER, ROBERT B. Archetypes in man-computer problem solving. IEEE Transactions on Man-Machine Systems, MMS-10:4 (December 1969) 219-241. [Reprinted from Ergonomics, 12:4 (July 1969)].

(69) MILLER, ROBERT B. Human ease of use criteria and their tradeoffs. IBM Corporation, Poughkeepsie, New York, 12 April 1971, 16 p. (Technical report TR 00.2185).
(70) MILLER, ROBERT B. Response time in man-computer conversational transactions. In: American Federation of Information Processing Societies. Fall Joint Computer Conference. San Francisco, California, 1968. Proceedings, vol. 33, pt. 1. Thompson Book Company, Washington, D.C., 1968, 267-277.
(71) MILLER, STEPHEN W. Display requirements for future man-machine systems. IEEE Transactions on Electron Devices, ED-18:9 (September 1971) 616-621.
(72) MILLS, ROGER G. Man-machine communication and problem solving. In: Cuadra, Carlos A.; ed. Annual review of information science and technology, vol. 2. Interscience, New York, 1967, 223-254.
(73) MINKER, JACK; ROSENFELD, SAMUEL. Introduction and perspectives for the 1971 ACM Information Storage and Retrieval Symposium. In: Association for Computing Machinery. Symposium on Information Storage and Retrieval. College Park, Maryland, 1-2 April 1971. Proceedings. University of Maryland, Conference and Institute Division, College Park, Maryland, 1971, 1-3.
(74) MOLL, WILHELM. AIM-TWX service at the University of Virginia: a review and evaluation. Bulletin of the Medical Library Association, 59:3 (July 1971) 458-462.
(75) MORTON, MICHAEL S. SCOTT. Management decision systems: computer-based support for decision making. Harvard University, Graduate School of Business Administration, Boston, Massachusetts, 1971, 216 p.
(76) NATIONAL ACADEMY OF SCIENCES. NATIONAL ACADEMY OF ENGINEERING. COMMITTEE ON TELECOMMUNICATIONS. Communications technology for urban improvement. National Academy of Engineering, Washington, D.C., June 1971, 218 p. (PB 200 317).
(77) NICKERSON, RAYMOND S. Man-computer interaction: a challenge for human factors research. IEEE Transactions on Man-Machine Systems, MMS-10:4 (December 1969) 164-180. [Reprinted from Ergonomics, 12:4 (July 1969)].
(78) NICKERSON, RAYMOND S.; ELKIND, JEROME I.; CARBONELL, JAIME R. Human factors and the design of time sharing computer systems. Human Factors, 10:2 (March/April 1968) 127-134.
(79) O'DEA, EDWARD P. Computer assisted instruction teaches computer system at IBM. Training in Business and Industry, 8:3 (March 1971) 33-35.
(80) OLLE, T. WILLIAM. A comparison between generalized data base management systems and interactive bibliographic systems. In: Walker, Donald E.; ed. Interactive bibliographic search: the user/computer interface. AFIPS Press, Montvale, New Jersey, 1971, 203-214.
(81) PARSONS, HENRY M. The scope of human factors in computer-based data processing systems. Human Factors, 12:2 (March/April 1970) 165-175.
(82) PORTER, ROGER J.; PENRY, J. KIFFIN; CAPONIO, JOSEPH F. Epilepsy Abstracts Retrieval System (EARS): a new concept for medical literature storage and retrieval. Bulletin of the Medical Library Association, 59:3 (July 1971) 430-432.
(83) PROKOP, J. S.; BROOKS, F. P., JR. Decision making with computer graphics in an inventory control environment. In: American Federation of Information Processing Societies. Fall Joint Computer Conference. Houston, Texas, 1970. Proceedings, vol. 37. AFIPS Press, Montvale, New Jersey, 1970, 599-607.
(84) RAE, PATRICK D. J. On-line information retrieval systems—experience of the Parkinson information center using the SUNY biomedical communication network. In: American Society for Information Science. Annual meeting. 33d, Philadelphia, Pennsylvania 11-15 October 1970. Proceedings, vol. 7: The information conscious society. Greenwood Publishing Corp., Westport, Connecticut, 1970, 173-176.

(85) SACKMAN, HAROLD. Experimental analysis of man-computer problem-solving. Human Factors, 12:2 (March/April 1970) 187-201.

(86) SACKMAN, HAROLD. Man-computer problem solving: experimental evaluation of time-sharing and batch processing. Auerbach Publishers, Inc., New York, 1970, 272 p.

(87) SACKMAN, HAROLD. Time-sharing and self-tutoring: an exploratory case history. Human Factors, 12:2 (March/April 1970) 203-214.

(88) SCHRENK, L. P. Aiding the decision maker—a decision process model. IEEE Transactions on Man-Machine Systems, MMS-10:4 (December 1969) 204-218. [Reprinted from Ergonomics, 12:4 (July 1969)].

(89) SEIDEN, HERBERT R. A comparative analysis of interactive storage and retrieval systems with implications for BCN design. System Development Corporation, Santa Monica, California, 12 January 1970, 62 p. (Technical memo TM-4421. ED 039 893).

(90) SHACKEL, B.; SHIPLEY, P. Man-computer interaction; a review of ergonomics literature and related research. Ergonomics Laboratory, E.M.I. Electronics Ltd., Hayes, Middlesex, England, February 1970, 108 p. (DMP 3472).

(91) SHERIDAN, THOMAS B. Technology for group dialogue and social choice. In: American Federation of Information Processing Societies. Fall Joint Computer Conference. Las Vegas, Nevada, 1971. Proceedings, vol. 39. AFIPS Press, Montvale, New Jersey, 1971, 327-335.

(92) SINGLETON, W. T. Display design: principles and procedures. IEEE Transactions on Man-Machine Systems, MMS-10:4 (December 1969) 181-193. [Reprinted from Ergonomics, 12:4 (July 1969)].

(93) SMITH, SIDNEY L.; GOODWIN, NANCY C. Blink coding for information display. Human Factors, 13:3 (May/June 1971) 283-290.

(94) SMITH, SIDNEY L.; GOODWIN, NANCY C. Computer-generated speech and man-computer interaction. Human Factors, 12:2 (March/April 1970) 215-223.

(95) STILLER, JOY DANCIS. Use of on-line remote access information retrieval systems. In: American Society for Information Science. Annual meeting. 33d, Philadelphia, Pennsylvania, 11-15 October 1970. Proceedings, vol. 7: The information conscious society. Greenwood Publishing Corp., Westport, Connecticut, 1970, 107-109.

(96) SUMMIT, ROGER K. DIALOG and the user: an evaluation of the user interface with a major on-line retrieval system. In: Walker, Donald E.; ed. Interactive bibliographic search: the user/computer interface. AFIPS Press, Montvale, New Jersey, 1971, 83-94.

(97) SUTHERLAND, IVAN E. Computer displays. Scientific American, 222:6 (June 1970) 56-81.

(98) TEICHNER, WARREN H. A preliminary theory of the effects of task and environmental factors on human performance. Human Factors, 13:4 (July/August 1971) 295-344.

(99) THOMPSON, DAVID A. Interface design for an interactive retrieval system: a literature survey and a research description. Journal of the American Society for Information Science, 22:6 (November/December 1971) 361-373.

(100) TIMBIE, MICHELE; COOMBS, DON H. An interactive information retrieval system; case studies on the use of DIALOG to search the ERIC document file. ERIC Clearinghouse on Educational Media and Technology, Stanford, California, December 1969, 90 p. (ED 034 431).

(101) TREU, SIEGFRIED. A conceptual framework for the searcher-system interface. In: Walker, Donald E.; ed. Interactive bibliographic search: the user/computer interface. AFIPS Press, Montvale, New Jersey, 1971, 53-66.

(102) TUROFF, MURRAY. Delphi and its potential impact on information systems. In: American Federation of Information Processing Societies. Fall Joint Computer Conference. Las Vegas, Nevada, 1971. Proceedings, vol. 39. AFIPS Press, Montvale, New Jersey, 1971, 317-326.

(103) TUROFF, MURRAY. Delphi conferencing: computer based conferencing with anonymity. Office of Emergency Preparedness. Office of the Assistant Director for Resource Analysis, Washington, D.C., March 1971, 108 p. (Technical memorandum TM-125. Also in the Journal of Technological Forcasting and Social Change, 3:2 (1972) 159-204.).
(104) UMPLEBY, STUART. Structuring information for a computer-based communications medium. In: American Federation of Information Processing Societies. Fall Joint Computer Conference. Las Vegas, Nevada, 1971. Proceedings, vol. 39. AFIPS Press, Montvale, New Jersey, 1971, 337-350.
(105) U.S. NATIONAL BUREAU OF STANDARDS; SOCIETY FOR INFORMATION DISPLAY. NBS-SID Soft Copy Conference. Gaithersburg, Maryland. 6-7 October 1970. Proceedings. Edited by Eric Swarthe and John L. Little. National Bureau of Standards, Washington, D.C., 1971. 68 p. (NBS-OIPS-71-7).
(106) VALLEE, J.; HYNEK J.; RAY, G.; WOLF, P. The organization of research data banks: experience with DIRAC-based information systems. In: American Society for Information Science. Annual meeting. 34th, Denver, Colorado, 7-11 November 1971. Proceedings, vol. 8: Communication for decision-makers. Greenwood Publishing Corp., Westport, Connecticut, 1971, 387-394.
(107) VAN DAM, ANDRIES. Data and storage structures for interactive graphics. In: Association for Computing Machinery. Special Interest Group on Programming Languages; University of Florida. Symposium on Data Structures in Programming Languages. 25-27 February 1971. Proceedings. Association for Computing Machinery, New York, SIGPLAN Notices, 6:2 (February 1971) 237-267.
(108) VAN DAM, ANDRIES; RICE, DAVID E. On-line text editing: a survey. Computing Surveys, 3:3 (September 1971) 93-114.
(109) VARTABEDIAN, ALLEN G. The design of visual displays. Bell Laboratories Record, 48:8 (September 1970) 227-231.
(110) VARTABEDIAN, ALLEN G. The effects of letter size, case and generation method on CRT display search time. Human Factors, 13:4 (July/August 1971) 363-368.
(111) VARTABEDIAN, ALLEN G. A graphic set for ASCII using a 7 x 9 dot pattern. Information Display, 8:6 (November/December 1971) 11-16.
(112) WALKER, DONALD E.; ed. Critical minutes of the workshop on the user interface for interactive search of bibliographic data bases. In: Walker, Donald E.; ed. Interactive bibliographic search: the user/computer interface. AFIPS Press, Montvale, New Jersey, 1971, 233-311.
(113) WATT, WILLIAM C. Habitability. American Documentation, 19:3 (July 1968) 338-351.
(114) WENTE, VAN A. NASA/RECON and user interface considerations. In: Walker, Donald E.; ed. Interactive bibliographic search: the user/computer interface. AFIPS Press, Montvale, New Jersey, 1971, 95-104.
(115) WIMBROW, JOSEPH H. A large-scale interactive administrative system. IBM Systems Journal, 10:4 (1971) 260-282.

6 Video Cartridges and Cassettes

RICHARD C. KLETTER

and

HEATHER HUDSON

Institute for Communication Research
Stanford University

INTRODUCTION[1]

The video cassette is a new communication tool with substantial social promise. At this point, the video cassette signals the next phase in the consumer electronics industry and most of the literature available emanates from within the industry or related services. The emphasis in the literature has thus been on the economic potential of cassettes in the marketplace rather than their social utility. The point is not that marketing cannot be socially useful but that economic concerns tend to dominate the discussion of any new technology. We are more concerned with the implications for the society of introducing another communication tool.

It is our view that no industry, no new technology can be discussed in a social vacuum. Economic factors must not dominate at the expense of human factors. Therefore, we have structured this chapter accordingly. We begin with an analysis section discussing possible effects of the video cassette on industrial training, education, libraries, and television. We attempt to mesh the hardware into existing structures, to forecast possible institutional changes, and to lead into possible new user patterns and structures. Then we examine systems representative of different technical or marketing approaches, emphasizing design options, and attempt to assess relative strengths in such areas as

[1]This report draws, in part, on a paper written in February 1971 by Richard Kletter, *Video Cassettes, a New Hardware and Its Implications* at Stanford's Institute for Communication Research funded by NSF grant GR 86.

raw stock costs, duplicating capacity, marketing approaches, as well as basic system performance.

Subsequent to this hardware discussion, the main points of the industry position are articulated, including analysis of the very different tacks taken by competing firms. Because the industry and related services dominate the literature, the bulk of the actual review is in this section. Finally, conclusions including recommendations for potential users are offered. At all times opinions expressed are the authors' own unless there is specific attribution to the references.

The purpose of this approach is to set up in effect two separate paths: one path describing the relevant social institutions and the role cassettes might play in their future, and the second path concentrating on the industry itself—its hardware and marketing strategies. Several assumptions are fundamental to this framework.

1. Although this new industry will likely target itself at industrial institutional markets first, by its own admission, success depends on acceptance for home and community use.
2. If this new industry is successful, it will have far-reaching social implications.
3. Therefore, public interest or public-sector institutions with market leverage should plan for the most socially effective use of this new technology. They should develop strategies to influence the market patterns of the industry, and develop organization patterns of cooperation to augment their influence and effectiveness.

In formulating this approach, it was necessary to strike a balance between several task options. We might have focused on those technology aspects that are in fact new or signal significant advances in existing equipment. Or, we might have settled on marketing forecasts, synthesizing the plethora of investment and sales projections available.

But the technological advances, the money, and the market merely describe the economic forces and the vested interests. It is the uses of these machines that invite the most provocative social questions. And so we opted for a framework that goes beyond the scope of most of the literature.

The seller is well represented. The manufacturer's brochures are highly convincing, the technical literature is good as far as it goes, and the newsletters provide a sort of play-by-play picture of the industry. Our hope was to aid the buyer, who must see through the rose-tinted glass of manufacturers' promises. His interests, whether as school system, library, or private consumer, seem to have been neglected. By "video cassette," or "cartridge television,"[2] we mean, generally, viewer-controlled playback systems that use television as the principal viewing device and do not depend on any outside signal for material. Cassettes are inserted in a playback machine that can be attached to the antenna leads of any standard television set.

In one sense, cassettes are just another distribution device, raising again questions of content quality and the effect of yet another tool on its users (44). Yet cassettes introduces viewer control. Choices of viewing time and place, of the number of repetitions, and of the use of features such as record and stop-action seem to suggest more than mere augmentation of current viewing habits.

But the early impact of cassettes can be expected in distribution areas with modest technical standards (e.g., training tapes). Currently, film or reel-to-reel video tape serves this function but the cost reductions offered by cassettes may change this. A likely scenario, becoming increasingly accepted, is to master the film or tape on high-quality equipment and then make copies for distribution on half-inch video tape. Cassettes offer, essentially, a further refinement in this process. With a few exceptions, the techniques are not really new but are sufficiently improved to warrant a big market push. Cassette systems will prove more reliable than reel-to-reel video systems (as will be explained later) and cheaper and easier to operate than film systems. Therefore, cassettes can be expected to make inroads in an already established area of use.

INFLUENCE OF VIDEO CASSETTES ON INFORMATION EXCHANGES

Video cassettes have been called "the most significant in its influence on mankind since Guttenberg's invention" (Littleford, 38). In fact, there are obvious parallels between the introduction of printed books and video cassettes. Both are basically advances in packaging. Medieval manuscripts were rare, expensive to duplicate by hand, and cumbersome. Erasmus said of Aquinas' *Secunda Secundae* that "No man could carry it about, much less get it into his head. . . ." Packaging makes portability of information possible and thereby introduces user control. For example, the availability of textbooks made compulsory attendance at lectures obsolete and forced the introduction of examinations. Cassette learning packages may also make education more flexible and individualized.

---

[2]The distinction between cassette and cartridge will be drawn later.

One of the major selling points of video cassettes is that a viewer can see what he wants when and where he wants—the audio-visual equivalent of the book. Of course, packaging must be combined with cost reduction if access to information via the medium is to increase. Portable manuscripts would have remained far too rare and expensive to reach most of the population. Without movable type, it is doubtful that there would ever have been much of a Renaissance or any Protestant Reformation (Eisenstein, 19). And yet, even with user control and reasonable cost, there will be no significant increase in access if the products are not readily available. Before the invention of the steam engine, it was physically difficult to transport information. Modern transportation and electronic media have overcome the problem of transmission of information through space, but we are still hampered by lack of knowledge and/or acceptance of information services. Often, residents of a community are unaware of its public libraries, crisis centers, and referral services. And awareness is only the first step toward acceptance in the process of diffusion of innovations (Rogers & Shoemaker, 54).

Access, then appears to be a function of user-control, reasonable cost, availability, and acceptance. The book eventually achieved all of these. Will the cassette achieve them? If it does, will it have as monumental an effect on our civilization as the invention of movable type? We are skeptical. Some of the major areas of potential impact are discussed below.

Industrial Training

The principal demand for a cheaper, more reliable distribution medium currently comes from large private and public institutions with broad training and sales programs (Parker & Dunn, 46). Equitable Life, for example, has already purchased cassette systems to use in sales training. Fireman's Fund, with reel-to-reel half-inch video-tape machines in field offices, seems a likely prospect for cassette hardware sales. In addition, the Department of Defense has made inquiries regarding the availability of one system, indicating that it will purchase about 1000 units if the system performance is acceptable.[3] These massive institutions can tolerate the high early prices for the systems; they are capable of arranging for their own software and distribution, and the technical staffing and maintenance expenses likely to accompany

[3]Personal communication.

the early systems can be easily assumed within their large bureaucratic frameworks.

The increased expenses of employee training, the lower cost of cassette machines as compared with current techniques, and the big sales push may persuade more organizations to adopt a video approach.

The major expenses associated with employee training programs are the cost of hiring instructors and the construction and maintenance of training centers. In addition, large expenditures are required for travel and salaries of trainees temporarily removed from their jobs, plus the cost in productivity and perhaps also in worker relations of temporarily neglecting jobs or shifting personnel. Modular cassette training packages combine portability, audio-visual presentation, and student-controlled pacing and appear to be a more economical and possibly more effective way of teaching new skills (Video Record Corporation of America, 69).

Potential applications seem almost limitless at this point. Suggested uses include state-of-the-art courses on treatment of specific diseases or injuries, which could be studied in the hospital; orientation material for new workers; upgrading of existing skills or teaching of new skills for job advancement; training of salesmen in effective sales techniques; and state-of-the-firm reports for executives.

There has been a considerable emphasis on the importance of the cassette as a sales tool for presentation of the line of equipment or services that the salesman offers. For example, Hewlett-Packard believes video cassettes can be a very effective means of presenting the range of their computer hardware and options through recorded presentations of the equipment in use, a more graphic and informative technique than the sales talk with brochures (67).

Education

The needs of the education environment are not so easy to pinpoint. Rising plant and labor costs and demands, on the one hand, for performance-based efficiency, and on the other, for more open, conceptual programs subject all levels of education to extraordinary pressures and threaten crisis solutions to complex problems. Then too, education is being defined more broadly to include lifelong learning and the capacity to reach nonmatriculating, limited-interest "students" where they live and work.

Audiovisual instruction has been touted for quite some time, yet its promise seems unrealized. New promises offer no answers to lingering questions. What is the quality of technology-intensive education and how does it vary along curricular lines? What institutional arrangements fit which social setting? What kind of access provisions will be obtained? What approaches for software development can and will be made? The final question must be what is the opportunity cost associated with the initiation of any project in a society with limited resources (or limited will)?

Many of these questions have been asked of other media but always after the fact. But this time, the big market push has not yet begun, and the questions can be addressed with some possibility of effecting action. The work of Parker, Dunn, and others at Stanford makes a strong case for technology-intensive solutions to educational problems. Parker & Dunn (46) say:

> . . .There are three education needs that might be better met in a technology-based system than in an education system depending on face-to-face instruction in school buildings. First is the need for open access so that no one in the society is denied the opportunity to learn. Second is the need for lifelong learning. Third is the need for increased variety of curriculum to meet the diversity and complexity of the physical and social environment and the interests of different subcultures. . . .

Although cassettes are included in their overall scheme, Parker and Dunn rely more on cable television (CATV) and time-shared home terminals, ruling out time-shared motion video as too expensive for perhaps 15 years. While Schramm et al. (56) address long-range plans, current cassette roles would serve present needs and practices. Audiovisual aids to accompany teachers and modular learning packages tailored to different performance levels are but a couple of possible uses employing the flexibility that cassettes offer. Cassettes will likely prove to be a great boon in the classroom for small-group individualized learning and as a convenient audio-visual supplement to basic course material. They will also be an important asset in continuing-education programs—whether they be home-study correspondence courses, night-school classes with home assignments or televised "open universities," or schools offering courses to students at home.

Among the specific educational applications of video cassettes are the following:

— description of procedural techniques for experiments, projects, etc.

— simulation and gaming experiences, requiring audiovisual cueing

— drill exercises in mathematics, languages, etc., for rote learning
— electronic blackboard displays for highly abstract topics
— preservation of behavioral specimens for imitation—e.g., drama, music, athletics, practice teaching
— curriculum enrichment through expansion of the learning environment—including documentary film, resource materials presented by specialists, more advanced extensions of the curriculum
— specific teaching elements integrated with others to make a total learning experience
— electronic learning packages to accompany correspondence courses
— total teaching, particularly through the use of linear programming designs.

Education seems ripe for cassettes but the subtle question of how the new gear will mesh with the old must be addressed. L. C. Taylor, director of a British project on the use of educational resources, cautions that prospects for large-scale implementation of cassettes in education are strictly long-term, because of lack of funds (Ryder, 55). Taylor points out that, in the United States, the total schools' purchase of learning materials is estimated at $1.5 billion annually—approximately the amount of General Motors' sales for one month. For those who immediately think of the stock-piles of unused audiovisual aids in American schools, he advises that cassette purveyors will make a more significant contribution if they focus on carefully selected areas rather than aiming at general coverage, and that cassettes will sell best if they are integrated with print materials in courses. Taylor also feels that rental of equipment and cassettes may be the only feasible way for schools to take advantage of the new medium.

A report by the National Association of Educational Broadcasters (NAEB) (43) suggests that the use of video cassettes should be managed by large-scale Public/Educational Communications Institutions (PECI). These institutions might be developed from existing educationally licensed television stations and authorities, major educational television (ETV) systems dependent on cable and Instructional Television Fixed Service (ITFS) transmission facilities, or state departments of public instruction. PECIs would use a variety of media and distribution techniques to undertake "basic and essential educational/social communications responsibilities in their communities." They would function as responsible centers for the design and production of communication techniques and materials for significant educational social tasks, resource centers providing hardware and software to institutions and groups in the community, and learning centers where instructional materials could be used for study and discussion.

The NAEB study states that cassette technology should be managed similarly to 35mm films in "studio-distribution-theatre conglomerates" that tie together "production, distribution and use." The important distinction is that the new institution could be a "publicly responsible, non-profit educationally dedicated agency operation."

The educational broadcasting industry could contribute valuable expertise to the exploitation of instructional media on the local level; it could also entrench itself as the authority over community instructional media usage, because the study suggests that each institution exercise close professional authority over the planning, production, acquisition, distribution, and measurement phases of the various communications strategies to be effected through its facilities: a rather comprehensive mandate.

The PECI is also supposed to handle relationships with cassette manufacturers, administer equipment and cassette distribution, and provide teacher-overseers for the learning centers in addition to being responsive to the needs of the community. Cooperation with institutions, such as schools, colleges, and hospitals, might be easy to arrange. However, it would be more difficult to assess the instructional needs of small groups and unorganized sectors of the community and harder for them to influence the direction of the PECI. The inherent expertise of the PECI might scare of potentially interested residents. Also, in trying to effect changes in PECI policy, the community might indeed find itself confronting another media conglomerate.

An alternative solution might be the establishment of instructional media resource centers on a state or national level staffed by experts in educational media. These centers would evaluate equipment, teaching and programming techniques, media-learning packages, and strategies for organizing and running community media centers. At the local level communities could set up their own organizations and could call upon the resource centers for advice, for example, on the most effective distribution system for cassettes or the most suitable technology to meet specified instructional needs. The resource center might also serve as a clearinghouse that would collect, compile, and analyze information relevant to users of community media. This structure would involve residents and respond to their perceived needs.

When educators were polled on the most important characteristics to be included in any video cassette or cartridge system, a significant number (82.6%) opted for a combined playback/record capacity (Tettemer & Stowers, 60). The survey also indicated the growing use especially among students and teachers, of half-inch standard reel-to-reel video-tape equipment standardized by the Electronic Industries Association of Japan (EIAJ).

The work of the Media Access Division of Portola Institute (Menlo Park, California) (Crowley & Surpin, 15) demonstrates one potential of the record capacity when linked with portable video-tape recorders and a student-centered approach to education. Media Access points out that video tape is a medium that encourages the student to learn for himself because it allows great freedom and experience in collecting and structuring information. Because the tape is cheap, erasable, and reusable, it invites experimentation, and Media Access encourages this, serving only as a resource for equipment and advice, exerting no control over the production process. They explain:

> For many [the portapak] served as an excuse to enter situations they would otherwise have been too shy to enter. And for some video was obviously a mode of communication far more natural than pen and paper. . .

Crowley and Surpin believe that the enthusiasm shown by students when they are creating with video tape could extend to other audiovisual media, as long as the format invites participation and enables them to be involved in the creative process. Record systems that allow students to shoot and edit their own material could lead to a cassette exchange newwork linking students throughout the country.

Alliances of people with video experience (e.g., Metro Media in Vancouver, Canada[4]) now teach interested community groups how to use video tape recorders (VTRs) so that they will be able to produce their own programs for cable television. This format could be extended to include cassettes or any other medium for which some form of distribution mechanism could be devised. The requirement is both to provide access to the tools and the distribution system and to offer expertise in how to exploit them.

Libraries

Public libraries may become community access or distribution centers. Libraries would simply enrich their offerings by making available

[4]Personal communication.

audio-visual materials including cassettes. They could even become a media distributor for schools, hospitals, recreation and community centers, clubs, and other organizations. This role would require a major restructuring of library services and increases in investment, storage space, personnel, and skills.

However, cable television may enable libraries to provide audio-visual materials to the community without coping with a physical distribution system. CATV subscribers could access library materials from their homes, for example, using a teleprinter or the buttons on a touch-tone telephone. A catalog of materials would be displayed on the screen, from which the home viewer could make his selection. The televised picture of a book, article, film, or cassette requested would then be transmitted to his unique cable address. The cable would have the advantage of convenience but would not preclude access to materials by nonsubscribers.

But the addition of audiovisual materials to a public library, without an electronic extension of its functions, can cause headaches in designing a system to integrate media, e.g., how to catalog—by author, title, composer, artist? Should new media be separate from books, or should there be an integrated catalog and display? The Pearl River Public Library (New York) has come up with a scheme that is popular with its patrons (Geller, 23). It plans to integrate shelving of all materials, with records of poetry reading in the poetry section, art prints near the art books, etc. Audio-visual materials have been assigned Dewey numbers and combined with books in the subject catalog. There is a separate author-title catalog with cards filed by medium. For example, recordings are entered under "audio" by composer and art prints and sculpture, under "visual" by artist. Perhaps films and cassettes would require a separate audio-visual category. There are many ways of organizing a multimedia resource system, but restructuring print-access systems to accommodate cassettes, among other things, will take some ingenuity.

In Port Washington, New York[5], a model for an expanded library, complete with portable video gear, is developing. With funds from the New York State Council on the Arts (the primary catalyst for video innovation in America), the local public library has hired a director with experience in Canada's Challenge for Change Program. He makes available portapaks, tape, and training to local citizens for their own

[5]This information comes from personal communication with people in Port Washington and others (e.g., Michael Shamberg) who have observed the project.

purposes. The tapes are on file at the library to be viewed much as reserve books are read. Most of the projects so far involve recordings of meetings and issues of community concern and the tapes provide valuable social records. There is no CATV system as yet in Port Washington, but, when one is established, the citizenry will probably be better prepared for its use than any community before it. Port Washington bears watching to determine what can be done with very limited funds in an information area vital not just to libraries but to all forms of local institutions.

Television

The video cassette's strongest suit is perhaps its capacity to break broadcasting's stranglehold on the spectrum of programs available. Coupled with an abundance of CATV channels, cassettes could fractionalize audiences so that broadcasting might become a victim of natural selection, its residual function reduced to franchising "events"—expensive operations such as a global news service, lavish entertainment packages, and "live" television, all on a scale much smaller than currently obtained.

By expanding the volume and range of programming (Guber, 30), the use of cassettes may open up access to both ends of the camera. Possible results include programming directly from people previously silent in electronic media or heard only through the filter of a network newsman.

One then wonders whether access to information and a platform for a spectrum of opinions will dramatically change the power structure of our society. It is a question approached through personal interpretation of history as much as through fact.

Given that it is possible to introduce change through greater public awareness and participation (whether the change is considered significant depends on individual ideology), what promises do video cassettes hold? The prime function in this context would appear to be as a source of diversified information that is in an easily accessible format. Users will be able to choose the optimal time and place for independent learning. The result may be a better-educated and -informed person, presumably more capable of participating in a democratic system.

But cassettes in this context are still just a one-way information source, although apparently user controlled. The medium becomes a two-way communication service if users can make their own cassette programs. Half-inch video tape has been used extensively for artistic exploration and as a catalyst in the process of social change. A recording capability would open television to the creative amateur and would provide a facility for feedback from citizen groups to decision-makers and a communication link between special-interest groups. The latter two uses imply a method of small-scale, independent duplication and a means of distribution. Community-access CATV channels could be the basis of a local information distribution system via video cassettes.

Cassette promoters tout the potential for change in the information climate, that is, the images and perspectives in public view. Changes are also possible in the kinds of people able to produce programs—cheaper production equipment and greater demand for programs mean lower production costs which mean greater numbers of people who can afford to produce.

Content diversity and home recording introduce the problem of control. Many of the proposed video cassette technologies do not have home-recording capability. Most require duplication by the manufacturer. This limitation presents several additional problems. For some systems, hundreds, or more likely thousands, of copies must be ordered to bring prices within the range of say, clubs or special-interest groups. Proponents of the Electronic Video Recording (EVR) system estimate that 2000 copies of a 25-minute program could be reproduced to sell at $18.50 each (Guber, 29). But control goes deeper than cost and duplication time. If the industry can produce and duplicate cassettes, then it becomes a gate-keeper over what programs are available to the public. The industrial counterargument will likely be that, if the public wants it, industry will make it (e.g., movies, sports, pornography), although video cassettes are claimed to offer diversity and not simply to cater to mass tastes. Minority and unpopular tastes may be once more excluded from a "legitimate" medium. (The history of certain books, e.g., *Lady Chatterley's Lover*, should prove illustrative here.)

Video tape offers the greatest possibilities for alternative production and distribution networks. Shamberg (58) suggests a video-tape cassette distribution system incorporating a Video Access Catalog. The catalog would be a taped sampler of available programs on cassettes. Subscribers could then order cassettes directly from the producer, who would keep his own master tape and control distribution and price.

Tape copies of cassette material could also be made by video recording from the television as the cassette is played through it. This approach may be adopted particularly if systems requiring duplication in the manufacturer's factory become widespread.

Centralized corporate control concerns not only subgroups but nations and cultures as well. For example, Canadian communication policy-makers must consider the possibility that a vide-cassette manufacturer will flood the market with cassettes produced exclusively in the United States. The implications may be more serious for developing countries. Gortikov (27) points out that there were no customers at the First International Cartridge TV, Videocassette & Videodisc Conference held in Cannes, but it is also true that all the firms represented were from Western Europe, the United States, and Japan. Those who can benefit most from a new inexpensive, audio-visual and portable means of communication are probably the illiterate and semiliterate people in countries poorly served with media and educational facilities. No mention of them was made at Cannes. However, if there is a market, then the cassette manufacturers are bound to go after it. The present industry structure would indicate that video cassettes will be one more promising technology dangled by the industrialized nations in front of impoverished governments searching for miracle remedies to apparently insurmountable education problems. If they bite, what hope do they have of keeping control of content and of capital generated within their own countries?

In this society, cassettes may well be one more medium accessible to the information-rich of our society (Bonnier, 8). Will the disadvantaged be able to afford a video playback (let alone record) unit or the other charges that will likely be made to view programs from cassette libraries over CATV systems? Or will they care? If cassettes become merely another home-entertainment vehicle to supplement network television, records, audio-cassettes and home movies, then accessibility becomes purely a market question and loses its social significance. One may ask whether a change in what is available will cause a change in public viewing habits. Cassettes depend on product sales—people must choose each program item. If subscribers show little interest in community access to public service and educational channels provided as part of the cable service or if subscribers must pay additional fees for "educational" programs, video cassettes that promote significant social change may suffer the fate of their print counterparts and preach primarily to the faithful.

HARDWARE

Information Sources

The different technical systems may be classified as magnetic tape, coded "miniaturized" film, laser hologram-vinyl tape, and record disc.

Other systems are the Super-8 film, various micropublishing techniques, digital-supported cathode ray tube (CRT) displays, and many, many more. Most of these systems seem peripheral to the development of the industry and are, in fact, after narrow sections of the total market. Although we are reluctant to limit chapter discussion to only the large corporate systems, they comprise the elements significant for large-scale development of the industry.

Super-8 film, in its many forms, belongs among the potentially significant technologies in this field. Yet we must exclude it from principal discussion. Super-8 involves another magnitude of hardware and standardization problems, offering only the ready availability of a wide range of prepackaged materials as its strong point. (In other words, it has some lead time in the software area.) Space limitations dictate that we make only passing references to its role in the complete cassette picture.

With several different techniques and competing, incompatible systems within many of the techniques, following the hardware progress is a confusing business. Fortunately, help is available from several sources and a brief review should reveal the kind of information each provides.

In addition to the manufacturer's brochures, several newsletters monitor the industry. *Television Digest with Consumer Electronics* (59) each week provides details on press releases, new products, changes in manufacturer or other plans, interviews with principals, coverage of conferences, and day-to-day readings of the industry barometer. The *Digest* staff cycles the subjects covered so that within perhaps each six-week period, a state-of-the-art report emerges. The *Video Cassette Sourcebook* (66) is a compilation of excerpts from the *Digest* newsletter between September 1970 and May 1971. For authoritative, up-to-the-minute, state-of-the-industry information, this is the newsletter to read.

Martin Roberts, publisher of the monthly *Video Cassette Newsletter* (65) takes a different approach. His operation is quite small and so his information turnover time is slower than the *Digest*. With one of the highest circulations in the field, Roberts offers his 1500 subscribers status reports in addition to the most significant hard-news aspects of the industry. Roberts puts things in some kind of perspective, monitoring the industry's slow, painstaking growth, and seems to be among the most reasonable of reporters. Roberts (53) has also written a book, which is a bit flashier than his newsletter. Billed as the first book on the subject (published in late 1970), it is filled with the bravado characteristic of the dawn of an industry.

A problem with early material is that, not unlike this chapter, much of it is out of date as soon as it is released, though the rate of change seems to have slowed somewhat with limited standardization, and the 1972 material should enjoy a longer life span.

A newsletter that combines the quick turnover of *Television Digest with Consumer Electronics* with the more analytical approach of Roberts is Tepfer's *The Video Play Report* (67) Published bimonthly, the *Report* includes write-ups of interviews with "manufacturers, producers, marketers and users of the video players." The interviews and reports are crisp and to the point and the quality of analysis seems to overcome the inherent public-relations nature of trade-journal interviews. As with other newsletters, each issue contains hard news and a listing of major participants in the industry, but, because each issue has one main focus, Tepfer seems able to probe deeper than his competitors.

There are other newsletters, e.g., Billboard's *VidNews* (71) all similar to one or all of those just described. Some, including Knowledge Industry's *The Video Publisher* (68), include a broader scope of information such as CATV, satellite communications, and other related fields. All the newsletters are extremely useful to anyone who wants or needs to keep close tabs on the industry. Yearly subscription costs vary from $36 for *Video Cassette Newsletter* to $75 for *The Video Publisher.*

While the newsletters deliver the details and do the time-consuming data gathering, *Video Record World* (70) provides the only full-time magazine coverage of the industry. *Video Record World* is a slick monthly published in Southern California with contributors stationed around the world. It features glib quotes from people in the entertainment business, interviews with Marshall McLuhan and Edmund Carpenter, and some decent reporting, mostly on the software. *Video World*, as it refers to itself, dwells little on the hard facts of the day-to-day industry, preferring a more theoretical orientation and not a small amount of pretention for example:

> . . .It is a magazine that will tell Darryl Zanuck what a schoolteacher in Boise is thinking and it will tell him why he ought to listen. . .It is a magazine that will allow Ethel Booth, Materials Specialist for Beverly Hills High School, to meet General David Sarnoff. . .

It is committed to the industry and its articles reflect that commitment, emphasizing organizations that share its optimism about the future. At the end of 1971, with little advertising, it had only 1000 subscribers.

Video World also makes the magazine available on audio cassette and plans to change to video when costs are substantially reduced.

Video Tape Systems[6]

A myriad of video tape systems are currently available or in the offing, but Sony, Avco, Philips and Ampex loom largest on the market.[7] Video tape is a magnetic tape that, like audio tape, can be erased and reused. Immediate viewing of recorded material is possible with no intermediate processing. The video-tape systems divide into cassette systems (Sony, Philips) and cartridge systems (Avco, Ampex).

A cassette has its own play and take-up reels in a single container. The tape is never touched outside the machine. The result is longer tape wear and greater control of the tape path. A cartridge is a single-reel unit and must be rewound before it can be removed from a player. Cartridges can be designed so that the tape need never be touched, but that would require some threading device and therefore a slight delay in start-up time. A cassette offers more reliable operation at a very slight increase in cost.

The move toward smaller, more consumer-oriented video-tape equipment, which culminated in the cassettes, began as early as 1966, when Sony introduced the first reel-to-reel battery-operated half-inch back-pack recorder (or portapak).[8] Used mainly in training and education, the portable recorder, batteries, and camera weighed under 21 pounds. Since then, inexpensive, easy-to-operate video equipment demonstrated growing popularity in the closed-circuit market. Following Sony's lead, other Japanese companies brought out portapaks but incompatibility of formats retarded overall growth. Then in April of 1970, Sony marketed its AV series of recorders and playback decks using half-inch tape. Claiming it to be the first system on the new international standard (developed by electronics companies in Japan with the Electronic Industries Association of Japan (EIAJ)). Sony offered several configurations of recorders and playback decks. Panasonic and others followed suit so that the full range of half-inch equipment includes an 18-lb. portapak capable of playback through the camera

[6]Much of the basic information from Sony, Avco, and Ampex comes from personal communication with their representatives.

[7]RCA's recently announced tape system will be a powerful contender but, as of this writing, little information is available.

[8]Broadcast video tape is 2" wide, while CATV and educational systems use 1" and 1/2" tape. The broadcast format employs a quadruplex scanning technique, which is more precise than the slant track or helical technique used in 1" and 1/2" formats. A good broadcast recorder, however, costs $50,000.

viewfinder for field monitoring (Sony), a color deck and a half-inch electronic editor (Panasonic), and, by late 1972, a color portapak.

Despite its success with half-inch reel-to-reel systems, Sony introduced a totally different and incompatible entry in the cassette field. The "newness" of a system, e.g., cassette as opposed to reel-to-reel, is often precisely what stimulates a market rather than any new work to be done by that system. Movie projectors, for example, are capable of performing some of the functions of a cassette system, albeit in a more expensive and less efficient manner, yet they have never caught on even for small groups of people. This could explain Sony's interest in a new format, per se. But the disregard for compatibility with its earlier machines indicates different expectations for cassette use and technical improvement over its predecessors.

Indeed, Sony has stressed those qualities desirable for initial cassette use, primarily reliable and high-quality playback. They play down the inherent advantages of video tape as a low-cost recording medium, with immediate feedback and thus make a definite distinction between their cassette system and their portapak.

The Sony U-Matic color video cassette system, unveiled in June of 1970 uses three-quater-inch wide video tape (Yamakawa, 75). The playback deck is about the size of an audio tape deck and includes two sound tracks for stereo or separate track performance. The player connects to the antenna terminals of any standard television set for playback in color or black and white (an RF tuner comes as part of the standard package). The system itself contains no recording function but an adapter permitting off-the-air recording may be purchased as an accessory.

In the fall of 1970, Sony claimed that when its video cassette system was released in the United States, it would sell for approximately $400. That price was considered by many as based on too optimistic an evaluation of early market demands and too low an assessment of production costs (Guber, 29). When the system was released across the United States on February 7, 1972, the list price was $995. The record/k adapter lists at $400 or about $250 above the initial estimates.

Although Sony is a large manufacturer of small vidicon television cameras (for under $500), no special camera capability for the U-Matic system is planned at this time.

The Sony cassette cost $35 and can hold up to 60 minutes of programming. Once a particular program has outlived its usefulness, the same video cassette can be used to record the next series providing additional savings. The re-recording capacity is unique to video tape at this time and constitutes a significant advantage over other technologies (Guber, 29).

The cassette would be like a milk bottle, to be filled and refilled as the contents are used up or the program becomes tiresome. The initial cost of the cassette could then be divided by the number of times it is used for re-recording programs. There is a catch. The charge for each re-recording is projected at between $3 and $5 and requires visiting a central office or mailing the cassette to a duplication facility.

In summary, Sony requires a $35 initial investment for a blank cassette in addition to the inconveniences of reprogramming. In exchange the customer is permitted an unlimited number of viewings of each program. Avco considers the Sony strategy impractical, arguing that re-recording centers will not be as available as mere distribution centers. Customers, they submit, will not want the inconveniences of locating and continually visiting such centers for reprogramming. (This is somewhat similar to the difficulty in locating video repair centers that do not require a wait of several weeks for adequate service.)

Avco and others plan to rent programs for a few dollars with the stipulation that they be returned after one viewing. The single playback requests may be enforced by counters in the cassettes that note the number of playbacks during each rental period, or by special tablocks that prevent rewind.

Restrictive rental policies should prod many a consumer into devious creativity, reminiscent of the turning back of automobile odometèrs. Avco's plan, which makes prerecorded cassettes readily available through a variety of outlets, would seem preferable at the outset.[9] It may even permit payment of a slightly higher fee for the privilege of repeated viewings over a limited period of time.

The different strategies raise an interesting question for the consumer. The Avco plan assumes that a limited number of screenings will not be a drawback and that consumers will want to keep only a few programs in a home cassette library. (Avco will sell prerecorded cartridges, but it will not re-record programs on them.) Sony's strategy is based on different assumptions, but they are a long way from implementation for the home market.

Avco's Cartrivision is a video system geared for uncharted market territory. Developed and marketed by Avco affiliate Cartridge Television Inc. (CTI). Cartrivision has begun its push for the home market. Compatible Cartrivision systems are offered under brand names sold

---

[9]Of course, as blank cassette prices drop and home recording demands increase, the Sony plan will take on added appeal.

by Admiral, Emerson, DuMont, Teledyne, Packard-Bell, Montgomery Ward, and Warwick Electronics (34). In April 1972, Warwick Electronics, which produces televisions for Sears, Roebuck & Company, began delivering to Sears the first Cartrivision units.

Described in the Cartrivision brochure as "a combination color television receiver and cartridge television recorder/player built into a single self-contained table model unit," the Avco system uses half-inch video tape (34). It is not compatible with any other system planned or currently in use. The price for Cartrivision is determined by the individual manufacturers and depends on the size of the television receiver attached. The price ranges from $850 to $1500 for the 25-inch models. Also available with the combination player is a 2-1/2 lb. instant-replay video camera, which lists at $230. The camera, with zoom lens, is attached to the combination unit so that you can either record or monitor live what the camera can pick up.

Cartridge Television Inc. is promoting the live monitor function as a home security system. The camera can be stationed near a door and monitored in another room on the television set. It is suggested as a fine way to keep tabs on a sleeping child (34).

The availability of the camera with the combination model seems of dubious advantage. Only two aperture positions, "overcast" and "bright," are offered, and mobility is limited by the length of the cable between the camera and television unit. Since the console might weigh as much as 160 lbs. (the Admiral model), it is unlikely that recording will ever occur far from the living room—and so the "bright" setting seems useless. Even an aperture setting of "overcast" (presumably wide open) with a vidicon camera, will encourage little experimentation by the indoor tape-maker.

Cartridge Television Inc. plans to market a battery-operated recorder weighing 15 lbs. in late 1973 or early 1974. This $500 unit (without the camera) promises greater programming latitude than the current model. In 1973, Cartridge Television Inc. will also introduce a separate player that connects to the antenna leads of any receiver in the same manner as the Sony system.

The Cartrivision combination model now available is considerably improved over the early demonstration models. There are now two audio tracks for stereo or separate track use (as with bilingual material), video heads can be replaced in 5 minutes in the home, a built-in cleaning process guards against dust build-up on the heads and tape path, and the picture resolution has been upgraded.

Cartrivision has a built-in timer permitting automatic off-the-air recording. You set the timer for the time to begin recording and for program length so that the system will shut off automatically when the recorded program is complete. The cartridge may then be viewed at your leisure. (The Cartrivision system uses a cartridge that has the drawbacks mentioned earlier.) Cartridges come in a variety of lengths from 15 minutes to 114 minutes. Blank tapes sell at $12.98 for 15 minutes, $18.98 for 30 minutes, $24.98 for 60 minutes, and $39.98 for 114 minutes. The price for prerecorded material will depend on the copyright arrangements. Cartrivision outlets will rent tapes from $3 to $5.

Two kinds of software services will be available from the Avco affiliate. Cartridge Television Inc. will distribute programs under its license, and it will manufacture and distribute cartridges for "video publishers" who want their material available in Cartrivision format.

In June 1971, Cartridge Television Inc. (CTI) announced that its library of Cartrivision titles had reached 850 including 207 feature films. There is an overall balance between general instructional and educational programming and entertainment. Individual cartridges include the series "The French Chef" with Julia Child; the Bolshoi Ballet; "how to" tapes on needlework, guitar, and golf; travelogues with separate English and foreign sound tracks; Russ Meyer's X-rated films; and a host of other materials. The range is broad because CTI does not know what will sell. Viewer-discretion television is an unknown luxury and nobody knows what the market will bear. Avco people expect to develop depth in those areas of their catalog that attract the greatest interest. Most software arrangements are nonexclusive. Time-Life Video, for example, will make programs available through Sony and Avco.

Avco expects marketing advantages because of its early thrust at the home market—an area, for the present, unfettered by competition. In fact, industrial and educational sales are expected because of the availability of machines in the home. If a salesman or an educator could have compatible systems in the office and at home, his use of the programs would be optimized.

Plans for the success of the combined unit seem to be predicated on the upswing in color television sales, yet it is not clear that those consumers new to color television will be interested in doubling their investment to include a built-in cartridge player. In fact, the price of the combined unit, in some cases, exceeds the cost of a high-quality color television and Avco's own separate playback deck—without the adaptability of the component system.

Experts such as Ned Feldman[10] of the RAND Corporation expect the early systems to be purchased primarily by those already watching color television and hence not interested in the combined unit. But even when cassettes become accessible to people not yet owning color television, there will be little to recommend the console approach. Both Feldman and these reviewers favor the component system. But the Avco system, even with the receiver, is still favorably priced in comparison with its competitors and in the end, that may be the telling factor.

Ampex Corporation (4), developer of the first video-tape recorders back in 1956, takes yet another approach. Threatened and impressed by the success of Sony and other half-inch tape systems, Ampex will introduce a cartridge recorder that is, at once, new, improved, *and* compatible with the Electronics Industry Association of Japan's International Type-I standard.

Manufactured by Tomaco, a joint venture with Toshiba of Japan, the Ampex Instavideo will attempt to serve educational and training needs as well as the promising home playback/recorder market. Toshiba will control distribution in Japan and Ampex (1,3), throughout the rest of the world. The 15-lb. Instavideo employs a self-threading cartridge usable on other standard reel-to-reel machines. Two audio channels permit stereo playback or two independent sound tracks for bilingual and other uses. Electronic circuitry for color recording and playback is optional.

The cost of blank Ampex cartridges was announced at about $13 for 30 minutes recording time at the Type-I standard speed or 60 minutes in an extended-play mode—a change accomplished by a simple switch. Although this tape price is far lower than other formats, it is comparable with tape costs for other Type-I standard machines. "Playing times up to two hours will be offered in subsequence configurations," claims an Ampex press release, likely referring to a full line of machines comparable to the Sony line (Ampex, 1,3).

When last announced in mid-1971, the basic monochrome player cost was projected at about $800. Record and color modules, cost an additional $100 each. A five-pound black and white camera (on paper, far superior to the Avco camera) listed for $400. However, these prices as of March 1, 1972 were being revalued upward with no firm figures established at that time (Ampex, 2). Changes in the relation of the dollar to the yen, severe financial and management problems at Ampex

---

[10]Personal communication.

(they lost upward of $80 million in 1971), and typical production problems caused the price uncertainty.

In fact, the Ampex system in general seems shrouded in uncertainty. Release was planned initially for mid-1971, but current predictions cite late 1972 as the earliest possible market time and many analysts are skeptical about that date. But Ampex officials, in a panel discussion, assured that all is well (32), emphasizing Ampex confidence in the product and its eventual market success but admitting that meeting market objectives is taking longer than expected.

The proliferation of CATV systems and the recently promulgated rule-making mandating local origination and public access to those systems created a demand for low-cost programming capabilities. While not all those demands can be met by half-inch tape machines (some require higher quality), the general trend seems clear. Television production is becoming at least slightly decentralized. Through low-cost telecommunications systems, such as the portapak, groups with common interests can share information present in a television format. Ampex (5) would like to count these groups among its clients.

Philip's Video Cassette Recorder (VCR)

Since these three video tape systems reveal confusion rather than compatibility of approach, perhaps the introduction of yet another incompatible tape system will convince readers that the state of the art is, in fact, as muddled as we claim. Philips Gloeilampenfabrieken, NV of the Netherlands, is credited with settling a similar miasma in the audio cassette field a few years ago. Philips offered competing manufacturers free use of its successful audio cassette design. The company argued that standardization would increase consumer convenience, stimulate sales, and thus enhance overall growth of the industry. The Philips audio cassette is now the standard throughout those parts of the world concerned with those virtues.

Philips (47) is currently pursuing a similar strategy with respect to its Video Cassette Recorder (VCR). VCR specifications, calling for half-inch tape, have been adopted by manufacturers throughout Europe including AEG-Telefunken, Nordmende, Grundig, Saba, Blaupunkt, and Loewe OPTA in Germany; Zanussi in Italy; Studer and Lenco in Switzerland; and Thorn in England. In addition, Matsushita (Panasonic) and Sony agreed to the Philips standard for their European distribution (Jongelie, 36).

First introduced in August 1971, VCR goes into full-scale production in 1972. Philips plans to market several models with the basic home record player selling for about $700. Virtually a television set without the picture tube, VCR includes a full tuner (Sony's U-Matic has a smaller tuner). In the near future, when receiver manufacturers provide jacks to tap directly into the receiver circuitry (for CATV as well as cassettes) by-passing the antenna, no RF tuner will be required. Playback deck costs will drop and picture quality will improve (RF units degrade the signal). In fact, Philips (47) will sell models without tuners with a price reduction of 15-20%.

The VCR cassette, with 2 reels stacked vertically (most cassettes employ 2 reels horizontally), will cost about $30 for 60 minutes of tape. Development of a thinner magnetic tape will allow longer playing time within the same paperback-book-size cassette.

The basic player contains only one audio track and has no provisions for camera or line input. These features are available on more expensive models along with an off-the-air record timer to tape programs automatically for subsequent viewing. Future machines will include editing and dubbing capabilities, stop and slow motion, and other "extras." Curiously, the more advanced future models are targeted for industry and institutional markets while the basic model now available presses for acceptance in the home.

One theory contends that institutional AV expenditures in Europe rarely approach U.S. proportions and that home consumer purchasing habits signal the more promising market. While Philips pursues the home market, it remains flexible toward developing European institutional needs.

The four video-tape designs described cover the range of approaches and represent the strongest market forces in the field. But by no means do they exhaust all the technical and marketing strategies extant. Perhaps 10 to 15 other incompatible video formats exist in some stage of development. Keeping tabs on all of the firms and systems requires constant scrutiny of the newsletters, trade journals, such as *Broadcasting*, *Variety*, and the various Billboard publications including *VidNews* and a plethora of audio-visual magazines.

The Playback Systems

Electronic video recording. Demonstrated initially in December 1968, the CBS-developed Electronic Video Recording (EVR) (9, 13) uses "miniaturized" film. The thin (8.75mm) EVR film contains two parallel rows of visuals, each with an accompanying magnetic sound track. Each row or track of visuals offers 25 minutes of programming in black and white, or 50 minutes per cartridge. Color requires two tracks, one for image and one for color, and therefore offers only 25 minutes playing time per cartridge. At the same time, color permits two audio tracks for stereo or bilingual programming. A full cartridge contains over 180,000 frames of film. Single-frame viewing, provided by an excellent stop-action capability, permits storage of a complete encyclopedia on a single cartridge.

EVR delivers the highest picture resolution of any system, thus making it eminently suitable for CATV programming. A final, yet significant advantage of EVR is its facility for high-speed, low-cost duplication. A 20-minute cartridge can be reproduced in about 30 seconds, while video tape systems have just begun to conquer real-time, i.e., a 20-minute video tape requires 20 minutes for duplication.[11] However, EVR duplication requires an expensive master film and, therefore, limits its reproduction to large runs to amortize costs. For example, the price of a 50-minute black and white cartridge, ranges from $47 each for a run of 50 to $23.10 each for a run of 2000. Color costs for 25 minutes are similarly $37.50 to $1850 (Guber, 29).

Other factors may also limit consumer appeal: the high cost of the player ($795), the expenses intrinsic to even a miniature film system, the limited lengths for color cartridges, and the lack of stereo sound in black and white. As other systems are released, these factors may reduce EVR appeal to industry as well. But EVR may already have suffered a significant economic blow because CBS has backed out of the EVR partnership (with Imperial Chemical Industries of Britain and the Chemical Industry in Basel of Switzerland). There are many possible explanations for this move, including the aforementioned limitations of the basic hardware and failure to involve Japanese firms at an early stage in product development and marketing. These and other explanations are examined in *Video Play Report* (January 17, 1972) (67) in an interview with Robert Briscoe, principal architect of the EVR policy. The rationale for CBSs decision to concern itself with software should illustrate that, despite all the attention given the magic machines, programming will ultimately be the vital force of the industry.

CBS estimates that the formalized education and training market will not develop beyond $100 million annually. The consumer market must wait until perhaps 1975 when costs are halved. The video publishing market, although promising, is not yet a reality. This latter area, including video libraries and internal corporate communications, had been CBSs central target. According to *Video Play Report*, Briscoe acknowledged that video tape might serve this market better because

[11] New developments in video tape duplication follow the hardware section.

of the limited number of cartridge copies required and the high cost of small runs in the EVR format. CBS will produce and acquire software for distribution on all cassette formats. Ironically, Motorola is a strong supporter of the software approach. In *Television Digest's Video Cassette Sourcebook* (66), a Motorola spokesman points out that, in the stereo cartridge field, players represent less than 5% gross revenues. Arguing that hardware was purely a delivery vehicle, he predicted that 75% of EVR institutional sales will be hardware/software packages.

RCAs Selecta Vision. During the early stages of color-television development, CBS and RCA introduced competing systems, each hoping to become the standard. The RCA system meshed more readily with existing hardware and thus became the standard for color systems. In addition to its technical prominence, one observer claims that RCA averaged a yearly expenditure of $30 million above sales for 10 years or $300 million to push its color system—a fact its current competitors will not forget.[12] The RCA family of video cassette products is called SelectaVision. Originally, SelectaVision referred only to the embossed hologram system—now Holotape—described below. But technological problems on the one hand and corporate flexibility on the other expanded the scope of hardware under consideration.

RCA explored virtually every cassette technique known, but current indications are that the choice has been narrowed. While continuing to develop Holotape, RCA will release a three-quarter-inch video-tape cartridge system of their own design. An RCA spokesman intimated that their video-tape system may be cheaper and less complicated than systems now available. The tape system with off-the-air and camera recording capacity would compliment playback-only Holotape as part of the SelectaVision line.

The Holotape system uses vinyl tape (Bartolini et al., 6), similar to that wrapped around meat at the supermarket—and just as cheap. The vinyl raw stock costs less than a dime for 30 minutes and once the master tape is processed, low-cost copies can be mass produced rapidly. The remarkable feature of SelectaVision is that it uses a holographic rather than a photographic process. Photography registers light-intensity variations as the patterns of an image. It is functional in virtually any light. Holography however, requires "coherent light"—light with color purity. Lasers are the only adequate source of such light, and therefore holography necessitates the use of lasers. Holotape employs low-level lasers assuring complete home safety.

---

[12]Ned Feldman of RAND, personal communication.

To play back holograms, it is necessary that a coherent light or laser beam pass through the tape. A "real image" can then be picked up by a vidicon camera housed inside the SelectaVision playback unit. RCA claims a 2,000-hour lifespan and $25 replacement fee for the home system's laser. Holograms offer an extraordinary property in that complete image information is contained throughout. Thus you can cut holograms, wet them, bend them, or whatever and even the smallest pieces will be capable of reconstructing a complete image. All that suffers is picture resolution and contrast.

In addition, the RCA embossed hologram has excellent "image immobilization" that guarantees single-frame viewing and variable forward speed. Technical advantages abound. Because an image is constantly projected toward the vidicon, no synchronization between scanner and tape speed is necessary. The complex circuitry required to stabilize a video tape picture is eliminated. Also, holograms need not be perfectly aligned to produce perfect pictures. Threading deviations is no problem and image stability is assured—as one hologram fades out, another simply fades in.

The SelectaVision player will sell for about $400 when released in late 1972, a date estimated as perhaps two years early by almost everyone except RCA. In fact, a RAND Corporation expert predicts perhaps five years before the system reaches the market.[13]

Replete with promises for the future, the technology for the moment produces only trouble. Early in 1971, the RCA prototype was without sound (no problem, but an indicator of time pressures); the picture was blurry; and the figures moved "in Chaplinesque grace." Production of SelectaVision hardware and cartridges should suffer time delays similar to EVR. Transfer to the hologram format will likely be backed up for several months after the system is released. But RCA is expected to invest more than $25 million to refine its system and promotional expenses should be even more extravagant. When completely functional, SelectaVision should attract great attention and support.

Perhaps Holotape's most promising advantage is its capacity to produce images for giant wall screens—the viewing surface of the near future. In 1969, General Telephone and Electronics Corporation developed a laser system capable of projecting color pictures from a normal television receiver onto a large wall screen.

In addition, three-dimensional hologram projection is being tested by Bell Labs and others. Experts claim that, within 15 years, it will be

---

[13]Ned Feldman, personal communication.

possible to walk around a ten-foot high, three-dimensional projection in the living room. SelectaVision's flexibility in terms of future developments signals longevity in the marketplace and warrants RCA's huge investment.

RCA is also backing up its hardware investment with software production and acquisition estimated at more than $50 million. Drawing on corporate affiliates such as NBC, RCA Records, Random House, and RCA Professional Educational Services, SelectaVision systems can claim exclusive software in addition to material commonly available from Time-Life and *The New York Times*. Finally, once the hardware is developed, Selecta Vision can call upon vast marketing resources in its attempt to capture the home market.

Teldec's videodisc. Another embossed plastic system is being manufactured by Teldec, a jointly held subsidiary of AEG-Telefunken and British Decca. First demonstrated in Berlin on June 24, 1970, the Teldec videodisc operates in much the same way as a phonograph record (Gilbert, 25 and 26). To generate a picture, however, closely packed grooves comprising about 100 times the storage capacity of an audio record are required for the system. There are approximately 120-140 grooves per millimeter and one revolution of the disc (passing through one groove) represents a complete television picture. Disc revolution speed (1800 rpm) accommodates European (50Hz) and American (60Hz) standards. The running time of a video disc is 5 minutes for a 9-inch diameter record and 12 minutes for a 12-inch diameter record. Longer black and white programs can be viewed with the aid of automatic changer equipment.

The Teldec disc, made of cheap plastic foil, can be copied at a faster rate than that of the other systems. Cheap materials and high-speed duplication contribute to projected programmed disc costs of perhaps $2.50 per hour (Berger, 7). Although we are skeptical that such a low price structure is possible, the Teldec system should still be cheaper than others including SelectaVision. The players themselves are less complicated than stereo turntables, according to Teldec officials. When Teldec is released in late 1972 or early 1973, a variety of machine configurations and prices will be available. A single-play monochrome player will cost as low as $120; a color player, about $200. When the magazine-loaded, automatic changer—with a lapse of one to two seconds between discs—is included, the price will still not exceed $350.

The automatic changer is Teldec's answer to the critics' charge that a maximum playing time of 12 minutes per disc ruled out home-market possibilities. The changer is essentially a storage magazine for discs. It requires a storage capacity only one-fifth-inch thick for two hours of playing time. The changer magazine inserts into the player in much the same manner as a blade into an injector razor system, and the video record is ready for play. A newly developed pressure pickup plays the record evenly without deterioration (more than 1000 plays are assured). The curved turntable is separated from the disc above it by a thin cushion of air preventing friction between disc and table. The air pressure prevents the disc from flattening out at high-speed rotation and requires that the disc hug the contour of the stationary turntable as it spins.

The videodisc technique signals improvement in audio records as well (Redlich, 51), reducing wear while advancing playing times and ushering in quadrophonic sound. The hiss and rumble common to phonographs will disappear. Teldec developments (e.g., information grooves one-tenth the thickness of a human hair) should have substantial impact on the industry. The discs and player will cost far less than other systems. The cueing mechanism provides swift access to any part of a program, and excellent image stability allows upside-down playback (although tape systems will still be the least cumbersome) (London Records, 40). These advantages of cost, durability, and easy handling portend success in the home market. The videodisc might also serve CATV systems in need of easy access to short messages or, perhaps, as material for inexpensive video letters or notices to employees or friends.

At the First International Cartridge TV, Videocassette & Videodisc Conference sponsored by Billboard Publications and VIDCA (April 1971, transcripts available from Billboard), Hofberg (35), a Teldec representative, outlined the disc's most dramatic potential. Because the Teldec disc is cheap, almost as thin as paper, easy to reproduce, and highly durable, it is the only format that easily fits a multimedia approach. For example, one can envision a disc with highlights of the previous day's "Big Game" included with the morning paper; or, with each physics text, one might receive a disc illustrating, say, thermodynamic principles. The videodisc blends very well with print, and so outlets such as magazines, trade periodicals, technical papers, and direct mailings would extend its marketing range beyond that of any other system. To be sure, these uses are just fantasy for the present and for perhaps five years or more, but the Teldec disc is the only system capable of fulfilling such promises.

Software production also figures prominently in future Teledec plans. Through Decca subsidiary London Records and newly created subsidiaries Argo Films and Decca Educational Services, many different production notions are being explored as Teldec regards software and hardware as two sides of the same marketing coin.

The basic systems and principal manufacturers have been described, but an industry in flux is not so simply characterized. Many firms are making commitments to separate systems in seeming competition (59). Zanussi of Italy, Philips licensee, will also distribute EVR. AEG-Telefunken, part owner of Teldec, will manufacture a tape system on the Philips standard. Toshiba, partner with Ampex in the Instavideo venture, is an EVR licensee along with Matsushita. The Matsushita tape system employs the Sony U-Matic standard along with Japan Victor and other Japanese firms and 3M in the U.S.

The interlocking license arrangements serve to further overall industry developments, or, more accurately, to safeguard the future position of each firm within the industry. Because the future is cloudy in terms of format (e.g., tape, film, plastic) and function (record or playback only) the several firms are simply hedging bets to ensure some return should a single design prevail. It is doubtful, however, that a single standard will emerge, given the incompatible techniques and the relative playback and record needs. Therefore, information in addition to that already supplied will be helpful in selecting among competing designs.

Duplication

Duplication or copying time and costs affect the prices and availability of programs on each format. If a system can churn out low-cost copies at a fraction of their playing (real) time, individual cassettes will be inexpensive and a wide variety of programs will be readily available. Different duplication techniques meet different needs. EVR requires an expensive master to generate copies, but reproduction involves only a fraction of playing time—about 30 seconds for a 20-minute cartridge. Therefore, EVR is best suited to large numbers of copies (Guber, 29).

SelectaVision also requires a master, but the raw stock, vinyl tape, is so cheap that even small runs can be processed economically. Teldec copies are produced at roughly 1/100 copy time to playing or real time. A useful discussion of current and projected costs for raw material and copies for all cassette systems can be found in Samson Reports, *The Video Cassette, Looking for a Home* (12), available from Quantum Science Corporation for $275. (Large discounts are available.)

Figures show RCA and Teldec with negligible raw stock costs both now and for the future, while magnetic tape currently costs about the same as EVR film (chromium-dioxide tapes of Sony and Philips are somewhat higher and iron-oxide tapes of Avco, slightly lower). Raw stock cost reductions for EVR await refinements in film stock (diazo film); but, according to Samson, the potential drop is only half that of magnetic tape. Developments in duplicating techniques will further enhance magnetic tape's market position. Until now, video tape could be duplicated only in real time, with a machine for each copy, creating huge operating expenses. In addition, signal degradation occurred and the copies were subject to the head wear variations of the slave or copying machine. Interchangeability problems were compounded.

Crum & Town (16) report on three alternative methods. The first method involves real-time duplication on rack-mounted printers driven by a master machine. A Sony system puts four printers on each rack (with 125 racks possible). The control printer with just five racks sells for $95,000. This system minimizes the interchange problems but does not eliminate signal degradation or inefficiency. More detailed descriptions of the complete process can be found in *Electronics* (April 12, 1971) (17) and *Video Play Report* (March 29, 1971) (67) or directly from Sony representatives.

The second method involves a form of high-speed contact duplication, and Panasonic is its principal proponent in the helical-scan format (67). (Ampex is developing a quadruplex contact system but has no plans as yet to include helical-scan capability.) The Panasonic method uses an AC bifilar method in which the master and copy tapes are wound together, coating-to-coating, onto a single reel and permeated with an AC field. Currently a one-hour tape can be reproduced in six minutes.

But as Hendershot, Dickens, Jordan, and others point out in a series of articles and symposia on various methods of duplication in the *Journal of the Society of Motion Picture and Television Engineers* (32), some fundamental problems plague this method. Both the AC bifilar method and the AC dynamic method (a similar, higher-speed version) require that a "mirror image" of the master tape be made on a special mirror recorder, in real time by electronic transfer, before mass copying can be attempted. In addition, audio tracks must be re-recorded because the AC transfer method is unable to accomplish this with acceptable quality (14).

The most promising duplication technique for video-tape cassettes involves high-speed thermal duplication made possible by the unique Curie-point properties of chromium-dioxide tape. Hendershot (31) describes in detail the technical and economic advantages of the DuPont-licensed process.

The thermal process (20) requires a chromium-dioxide mirror image duplicating master (requires no special recorder) that can be contact-copied from any type of original tape—the traditional iron oxide, the new, highly coercive and cobalt-doped oxides, or the increasingly popular chromium dioxide. The copies must all be made on chromium-dioxide tape, which requires slight adjustments in record and bias current of hardware generations now available but not for the cassette machines on the Sony or Philips standard.

Chromium dioxide and the cobalt oxides have higher storage capacities permitting slower tape speed (metallic oxides under development perform the same function at lower cost) and thus less tape per cassette, but they may demand more head maintenance or eventual changes in head design. The thermal contact method will create copies up to 32 times faster than real time for a single tape (*Electronics*, 20). The copy takes on the exact characteristics of the master so that no interchange problems and negligible signal degradation occur. Now in production, the Consolidated machines sell for $90,000 for a single helical-scan tape width and plug-in; subassemblies accommodating other helical-scan widths cost an additional $10,000 each.

INDUSTRY PROJECTION

Hardware systems abound and promoters everywhere burst with unending promises of a new culture and dramatic changes in life style. Predictions of a $1 billion-per-year market by 1980, once thought optimistic, are now part of the litany.

Hilford (33), a Columbia Pictures Cassette Vice-President, speaking in Cannes, called a projection of 40 million player homes around the world by 1980 "conservative." He pointed out that, in modern society, "the span of time between product introduction and peak production has decreased radically." For the vacuum cleaner and refrigerator, the span was 34 years, while for transistor radios, peak production was reached after only five years.

According to the Quantrum Science Corporation (12) Hilford is not too far wrong. Quantum subsidiary Samson Reports sketches a complete marketing scenario, including future sales projections, leisure time breakdowns, distribution data, and much more. The projections are based on diffusion studies of prior media, analysis of discretionary income and standard market survey techniques, but only the conclusions are presented, so critical review is somewhat difficult. The hardware descriptions can be criticized if only because they are dated. But the overall report seems well researched and, if the myriad of data tables have a corresponding basis in fact, the study may be the most readily accessible compendium.

Quantum predicts that the commercial (institutional) market will be based primarily on current uses for AV media and that the entrenched technologies such as film, overhead projection, and reel-to-reel video will retard cassette growth. By 1980, according to Quantum, the commercial market will constitute only $220 million of the total $1.8 billion market. Hardware sales to the consumer sector, which Quantum believes will explode in 1976, will reach 4% of the households in the U.S. by 1980. The report points out that, for previous systems such as black-and-white and color television, 1% market penetration was the critical mass, beyond which rapid expansion occurred and market priming was curtailed.

Consumer acceptance is contingent also upon prices. Manufacturers of the first color television sets believed costs had to be kept around $400 to attract extensive consumer support. When color sets were first listed in the U.S. Department of Commerce's report *Current Industrial Reports: Household Items* (64), the average price per set was about $360.

Success of video cassettes also hinges on availability on programming. Train stations, hotels, record and book stores, clubs, and general-purpose retail stores are all hailed as likely distribution vehicles. But with so many different formats, retailers may not be willing to take the inventory risk on a new industry.

RCA has Random House, while CBS has Columbia Records and Holt, Rinehart & Winston to facilitate distribution. The huge consumer electronics companies have their own marketing outlets (although they are not really software equipped) and brand affiliates. But the small, special-interest firms may have trouble at the outset.

If cassette programs are rented initially, retailers will be burdened with expenses for equipment and personnel to check the tapes in and out and to examine them for wear and damage. The initial returns may be lower for rent than sale. However, rental or lease may be essential to large-scale market development.

The range of issues involved in lease versus purchase of both hardware and software are examined by Grant (28) of England's Rank Audio Visual Ltd. (now providing programming for EVR). Grant cites the rental of television sets in Britain as a possible precedent and warns that the main competition for sale will likely come from budget rivalries with already existing media, particularly in education. Quantum

Science agrees that at least software rental will be more attractive during that period when consumers are deciding what to choose, now that they can choose.

The cassette industry will likely explore any and every option to bring cassettes into the daily consumer routine. Marketing techniques suggested include direct mailings, give-aways, catalogs, travel folders, and incentive selling. Hofberg (35) visualizes the siege of the home market:

> Imagine software in collaboration with advertising via the insert of premium materials sold with discounts; food advertising featuring recipes in sight and sound; home selling of golf, tennis or scuba diving lessons underwritten by equipment manufacturers and including commercials; or a play or movie with a commercial by the sponsor who subsidized the production.

Advertising is bound to bring cassettes to the public's attention and may help to reduce cost through sponsorship or subsidies. However, the price of home libraries of cassettes for once-through viewing is likely to be out of range of most potential users, at least for most of this decade. Libraries and rental agencies may become major suppliers in a return to the 19th-century method of public and especially private subscription library distribution of books.

When home phonographs first appeared, radio sales dropped slightly. Within a few years, however, radio became the advertising stage for recording artists. Aside from public appearances and print reviews, radio was the only contact that consumers had with artists and their music. Radio sales soon picked up.

Cable television (CATV) proffers similar services to cassette producers. CATV is expected to experience tremendous growth during the next decade, with subscribership growing from about 5 million homes in 1970 to perhaps 50 million homes by 1980. CATV can offer a wider variety of programs than most home consumers can afford. The monthly service charge for cable will be more reasonable and less troublesome than renting cassettes, and subsidiary cable services will be attractive.

Cable television should serve as a proving ground for prospective software producers. They may give program packages to cable systems or pay for cable advertisements to promote their software (e.g., modern film distributors). Future multichannel cable systems with two-way capability and switching mechanisms will make possible a sort of jukebox television. Cable companies could stock extensive libraries of video cassettes that the customer could order from a catalog. Two-way systems would permit direct billing for each selection.

But even pay channels on CATV can not possibly supply the same information coverage as a local library or commercial retailer. An 80-channel system can provide at most 80 programs (for the next decade or more)—or hardly enough to satisfy all of its subscribers' information needs. So CATV, as argued by Ferris (21), of Arthur D. Little, Inc. may not control the market but will spark consumer interest in cassettes. Ferris thinks the Japanese concept (Nagaoka, 41) of promoting the hardware to increase the utility of available television makes sense. Once the machine is in the home, it will be much easier to sell cassettes to the owner.

Sony and Matsushita espouse this hardware-dominated marketing approach. The assumption is that the commercial market will establish hardware reputations that will attract consumers, and the software will fall into place as the home market develops. Sony has retreated from this position somewhat since late 1970 and is now stepping up software plans.

But CBS, RCA, and Avco disagree with this strategy, perhaps because of their vantage point as entertainment conglomerates. They are pursuing different strategies in preparing software that they believe will sell the systems. Avco, for example, is offering 10% of revenue for materials ranging from "Literation 70" by New York's People's Video Theater to Highlights of the National Football League.[14] Avco expects a sellers' market, believing that hardware systems will be forced to pay for rights, perhaps even to bid competitively for software contracts because programs will sell the hardware. They feel that early procurement of nonexclusive contracts with above-average royalty payments will result in low-cost programming for a wide variety of tastes. The issue of exclusivity is an interesting yardstick with which to measure software marketing techniques. Nonexclusive contracts permit software producers to sign with any distributor with little or no money offered as an inducement. Producers are not tied to the fate of one distributor.

Such warranties are in contrast to those provided in distribution procedures for books or records where exclusivity has an advantage for the artist in that advance money and the advertising skills of the distributor are available. Some producers feel that no system will really dominate and that other hardware manufacturers will be reluctant to pick up options for programming already available in other formats.

---

[14]Personal communication.

They contend that their chances for recognition are minimized because of the restricted audience. In addition, it is argued that distributors will be reluctant to promote artists the way record companies push their private stable of talent, because other distributors are free to reap the benefits of costly promotions.[15] And there is the problem of advance money—a factor crucial to the survival of many young talents. Thus, exclusivity may be an advantage for relatively unknown programming people expecting to support themselves from cassette royalties, whereas companies such as 20th Century-Fox have their own marketing skills and require no advance funds for survival (not yet anyway).

The cassette industry promises to generate off-shoots with counterparts in the record industry. Clearinghouses with substantial capital will purchase titles and provide marketing skills. In exchange, they will pay royalties including those demanded by third parties. The programs will then be marketed under a particular "label."

The clearinghouses are not yet offering programs but Video Record Corporation of America (VCA) is producing programs now and distributing them through its video record club. The programs produced are geared for specialized institutional needs including health care, sales training, early childhood instruction. VCA (69) offers a three-year contract with any group to provide a video player (initially an EVR, but later the Norelco's reel-to-reel video machine) and a minimum of two cartridges per month to group members for $50 per person. VCA has also produced nurses' training tapes for hospitals and hopes soon to distribute its cultural enrichment programs to educational institutions.

National Talent Service (NTS) (Lollos, 39) pursues the U.S. college and university market with entertainment/informational programming of various types, including *Waiting for Godot; Salesman*, a film by the Maysles brothers; *My Lai Massacre;* and skiing films with Jean Claude Killy. The programs are distributed on reel-to-reel Sony half-inch-tape machines and shown on a multi-monitor presentation pillar. Hardware and tapes are bicycled among subscribing campuses. NTS believes that the youth market, already visually attuned, is the best place to begin large-scale diffusion of a new media system. Universities, they argue, are a likely place to introduce people to new concepts and approaches, and they plan several college programming centers to develop ideas and materials for university distribution. NTS was confronted

[15]The other side of this argument is that the less restrictive the distribution and licensing polices, the greater the overall market growth.

on the campus by students interested in doing the programming themselves. Armed with the Sony PortaPak and mindful of CATV local origination opportunities, students are exploring new notions of programming.

Perhaps the central impetus for the proliferation of "do your own television" comes from *Radical Software*, published irregularly by Raindance Corporation (51) since the summer of 1970. *Radical Software* defines three general categories of video use.

1. "Process television" or the use of video for feedback within a given context—a therapy group, a local project evaluation, a day in one's life, or simply a replay of one's own tennis serve. Production values are subordinated to content.
2. "Alternate television" or the creation and distribution of tapes about issues or opinions ignored by the mass media or filtered through the orthodoxy that characterizes network presentation. Several hundred people in the U.S. and more scattered around the world regularly exchange tapes, ideas, and experiences.
3. "Video aesthetics" attempts to use television as a light-transducing machine employing elaborate color generators and mixing devices, resulting in delicious nonrepresentational imagery. This is an art form indigenous to the electronics of television.

Radical Software also offers accurate hardware information including maintenance, design changes, and schematics to aid in promoting what the *Whole Earth Catalog* (74) used to call "more for less." If *Radical Software*, which sold over 50,000 total copies of its first five issues, spread "the word" ("do your own television"), the *Challenge for Change* newsletter created it. Published by the Challenge for Change Division of the National Film Board of Canada (11), the newsletter publicizes Canadian attempts at citizen participation in media. Intimate, forceful productions with social utility as the central concern come out of this project. The newsletter details some of the most significant experiments yet attempted in using media for social change. In addition, it provides leads on documents that analyze the various projects in greater detail.

We have attempted to describe unique approaches to the problem of video cassette software. Literally thousands of other software organizations have taken strong positions in this field, but a casual reading of the trade publications or newsletters mentioned earlier will be sufficient to keep the reader informed about a variety of software needs.

CONCLUSION

Two categories of conclusion are in order; one concerning information available in 1971, and the other concerning implications for potential users. First it seems fair to say that the conference transcripts, newsletters, and brochures that compose the bulk of the material are concerned primarily with getting the industry on its feet. Indeed, that is their reason for being—to support an emerging industry whose eventual success will reward their investment. At the same time, the Cannes transcripts, *Video Play Report*, and Samson Reports studies are useful to anyone interested in understanding likely industry directions.

According to the Samson Reports (12), initial uses of cassettes portend no major break from the past in terms of services offered and possible effects projected. Yet the experiences of earlier media, to be replaced by cassettes, receive little scrutiny in the literature. The only historical parallel drawn concerns the early standardization problems that crippled Super-8 and now threaten cassettes. Few other lessons from recent technological history are presented.

Samson Reports also predict that home use of cassettes will substitute for movie attendance and the reading of books, papers, and magazines. Home entertainment will partially substitute for outings to the cinema and sports events, and as leisure time increases so will the use of cassettes and other media. It appears to these reviewers, however, that as cassettes replace other media in information and for recreation, people will be better informed and entertained only if the quality of the communication is better than that of the modes of communication they replace.

The second set of conclusions is presented as a series of recommendations. We assume that even a cursory reading of either this chapter or segments of the literature should indicate that the industry is in flux and that last year's hardware will be more than adequate until the dust settles.

Video-tape systems are continually improving, and periods between introductions and obsolescence are shortening. The Type I-EIAJ (Electronic Industry Association of Japan) standard half-inch machines, currently enjoying rapid growth, should be equal to the distribution task until cassette duplication, maintenance, and distribution support systems stablize. At that time, perhaps in two or three years, the basic technology should be sufficiently improved to warrant replacement of reel-to-reel machines.

For playback only, requirements would seem best served by holographic or disc systems. Each of these systems looks cheaper and more dependable (once the kinks are ironed out) than film or tape. Removing the kinks should cause a delay in introduction that would merely cover the industry's incubation period.

In general, if the information requirement can be met with packaged materials, if cost is a central factor, or if stop-action or single-frame viewing is necessary, disc or holographic systems would be the wisest choice.

On the other hand, if the user intends to record his own material or exchange local information or wants to experiment with production in any way and has minimal duplication needs, then video tape has the advantage of being more flexible and universally accepted.

In any case, public institutions would be wise to work out compatible hardware arrangements and to consider separate distribution and duplication facilities to reduce costs and limit delay. If much of the hardware is in a continuous state of development, when purchases are finally made, modular or component units would seem to make the most sense. As improvements occur, only individual component changes would be necessary.

Planning either at a local or regional level or on a wider scale could avert enormous compatibility problems. The plethora of technical configurations and standards will complicate networking and simple program exchanges, require expensive duplication of equipment and, at minimum, confuse prospective buyers.

The tape-exchange patterns emerging as a result of EIAJ half-inch standardization could break down as individual groups change to incompatible cassette formats. If exchange requirements are coupled with the need for central duplication of cassettes, it would be advantageous to stay with the current reel-to-reel standard.

Since initial uses are geared for industry and training markets, consumers would do well to have corporations pay the early development costs of innovation. By the time price structure and performance approach acceptable consumer standards, some of the confusion surrounding the hardware and its capabilities may have cleared.

Walker's argument (72) that a common performance language describing common performance criteria will simplify consumer choice is only a partial answer, because the language of the training market is not the language of the home, school district, or community group. These consumers would benefit far more by waiting out the initial hardware and support system confusion. It does one little good to know the relative signal-to-noise ratios of machines for which parts and service are not available and that are unable to play the newest incompatible cassette.

If increased standardization does not result, then perhaps natural selection will narrow the field. Although there is a chance that all we have said will become obsolete during the months between manuscript preparation and release, we still believe there is ample time for the confusion to clear, and the prudent will wait until it does.

REFERENCES

(1) AMPEX CORPORATION. New product release. Ampex Corporation, Chicago, Illinois, 2 September 1970.
(2) AMPEX CORPORATION. New product release. Ampex Corporation, Chicago, Illinois, 20 January 1972.
(3) AMPEX CORPORATION. News release. Ampex Corporation, Chicago, Illinois, 24 November 1971.
(4) AMPEX CORPORATION. What is a video tape recorder? Ampex Corporation, Chicago, Illinois, September 1970.
(5) AMPEX CORPORATION. The widening world of instant replay. Ampex Corporation, Elk Grove Village, Illinois, September 1970. (Press release).
(6) BARTOLINI, R.; HANNAN, W.; KARLSONS, D.; LURIE, M. Embossed hologram motion pictures for television playback. Applied Optics, 9:10 (October 1970) 2283-2290.
(7) BERGER, ING. WOLFGANG. The video disc - a new video system. Text of lecture at AEG-Telefunken Press Conference, Berlin, Germany, 24 June 1970. London Records, New York, New York.
(8) BONNIER, LUKAS. The place of the book and magazine publishing company. In: International Cartridge TV, Videocassette & Videodisc Conference. 1st, Cannes, France, 19-23 April 1971. Billboard Publications, New York, New York, 1971, 12-15. (Booklet 5).
(9) BROWN, GEORGE. The EVR system. In: International Cartridge TV, Videocassette & Videodisc Conference. 1st, Cannes, France, 19-23 April 1971. Billboard Publications, New York, New York, 1971, 5-8. (Booklet 1).
(10) Cartridge Television News Digest. Billboard Publications, New York, New York. (Name changed in January 1972 to VidNews).
(11) Challenge for Change. National Film Board of Canada, Montreal, Canada. (Newsletter).
(12) COLTEN, ROBERT. The video cassette - looking for a home. Samson Reports (July 1971) 126 p. Quantum Science Corporation, Palo Alto, California. (Client study).
(13) COLUMBIA BROADCASTING SYSTEM. ELECTRONIC VIDEO RECORDING DIVISION. The new dimensions of television. CBS Electronic Video Recording Division, New York, New York. (Brochure).
(14) CONSOLIDATED VIDEO SYSTEMS. Video tape duplication. Consolidated Video Systems, Santa Clara, California. (Brochure).
(15) CROWLEY, PARTICK; SURPIN, SHELLEY. The high school video workshop. Big Rock Candy Mountain, 1:5 (April 1971) 20-21.
(16) CRUM, CHARLES W.; TOWN, HOWARD W. Recent progress in video tape duplication. Journal of the Society of Motion Picture and Television Engineers, 80:3 (March 1971) 179-181.
(17) Duplication spins out 500 video tape cassettes. Electronics (12 April 1971) 141. (Newsletter published by McGraw-Hill Book Co., Electronics, New York, New York).

(18) EDUCATIONAL PRODUCTS INFORMATION EXCHANGE INSTITUTE. Video cassettes - an educational products information exchange special report. Educational Products Information Exchange Institute, New York, New York, 1971, 39-44. (No. 39).

(19) EISENSTEIN, ELIZABETH L. The advent of printing and the problem of the Renaissance. Past and Present, 45 (November 1969) 19-89.

(20) Electronics (26 April 1971) 18. (Newsletter published by McGraw-Hill Book Co., Electronics, New York, New York.).

(21) FERRIS, GEORGE E. CATV: a distribution system for cartridge television. In: International Cartridge TV, Videocassette & Videodisc Conference. 1st, Cannes, France, 19-23 April 1971. Billboard Publications, New York, New York, 1971, 22-25. (Booklet 8).

(22) FORRESTER, GEORGE. Technical aspects of the Philips VCR-system. In: International Television Symposium. 7th, Montreux, Switzerland, 22 May 1971. (Transcript of speech).

(23) GELLER, EVELYN. A media troika and MARC. School Library Journal (15 January 1972) 25-29.

(24) Get yourself a lawyer. Publishers Weekly (1 March 1971) 29-32.

(25) GILBERT, J. C. G. The video disc. Wireless World (August 1970). International Business Press Association, London, England.

(26) GILBERT, JOHN. The revolutionary Teldec video disc. Gramophone (August 1970).

(27) GORTIKOV, STANLEY M. Some of the problems facing the cartridge TV industry. In: International Cartridge TV, Videocassette & Videodisc Conference. 1st, Cannes, France, 19-23 April 1971. Billboard Publications, New York, New York, 1971, 14-15. (Booklet 9).

(28) GRANT, MICHAEL. Lease versus sale. In: International Cartridge TV, Videocassette & Videodisc Conference. 1st, Cannes, France, 19-23 April 1971. Billboard Publications, New York, New York, 1971, 8-14. (Booklet 8).

(29) GUBER, PETER. The new ballgame: the cartridge revolution. Cinema, 6:1 (1970) 21-31. (Special supplement. Part of CBS/EVR, 1970 brochure).

(30) GUBER, PETER. The role of the film and TV company in entertainment programming. In: International Cartridge TV, Videocassette & Videodisc Conference. 1st, Cannes, France, 19-23 April 1971. Billboard Publications, New York, New York, 1971, 5-8. (Booklet 5).

(31) HENDERSHOT, WILLIAM B., III. Thermal contact duplication of video tape. Journal of the Society of Motion Picture and Television Engineers, 80:3 (March 1971) 175-176.

(32) High-speed video tape duplication and distribution: a panel discussion. Journal of the Society of Motion Picture and Television Engineers, 80:3 (March 1971) 182-183.

(33) HILFORD, LAWRENCE B. The home entertainment market. In: International Cartridge TV, Videocassette & Videodisc Conference. 1st, Cannes, France, 19-23 April 1971. Billboard Publications, New York, New York, 1971, 17-19. (Booklet 4).

(34) HILL AND KNOWLTON. Cartridge Television, Inc. (News releases: 28 June 1971, 25 October 1971, 8 December 1971, and 6 January 1972).

(35) HOFBERG, LEO H. How creators of videodisc and cartridge TV programmes view their function. In: International Cartridge TV, Videocassette & Videodisc Conference. 1st, Cannes, France, 19-23 April 1971. Billboard Publications, New York, New York, 1971, 10-18. (Booklet 2).

(36) JONGELIE, IR. K. TH. Magnetic recording system. In: International Television Symposium. 7th, Montreux, Switzerland, 22 May 1971. (Transcript of speech).

(37) KENNEDY, CARLOS. The Ampex Instavideo system. In: International Cartridge TV, Videocassette & Videodisc Conference. 1st, Cannes, France, 19-23

April 1971. Billboard Publications, New York, New York, 1971, 17-23. (Booklet 1).

(38) LITTLEFORD, WILLIAM D. The formation of an industry committee to examine the standardization problem. In: International Cartridge TV, Videocassette & Videodisc Conference. 1st, Cannes, France, 19-23 April 1971. Billboard Publications, New York, New York, 1971, 13-14. (Booklet 9).

(39) LOLLOS, JOHN S. Selling cartridge TV to the educational market. In: International Cartridge TV, Videocassette & Videodisc Conference. 1st, Cannes, France, 19-23 April 1971. Billboard Publications, New York, New York, 1971, 13-16. (Booklet 6).

(40) LONDON RECORDS. Video discs. London Records, New York, New York. (Brochure).

(41) NAGAOKA, TADASHI. The Matsushita system. In: International Cartridge TV, Videocassette & Videodisc Conference. 1st, Cannes, France, 19-23 April 1971. Billboard Publications, New York, New York, 1971, 14-16. (Booklet 1).

(42) NAKANO, S. The availability of cartridge TV software in Japan. In: International Cartridge TV, Videocassette & Videodisc Conference. 1st, Cannes, France, 19-23 April 1971. Billboard Publications, New York, New York, 1971, 15. (Booklet 3).

(43) NATIONAL ASSOCIATION OF EDUCATIONAL BROADCASTERS. Television cartridge and disc systems: what are they good for? National Association of Educational Broadcasters, Washington, D.C., 1971, 57 p.

(44) The old order changeth - but slowly. Royal Television Society Journal, 13:8 (March/April 1971).

(45) PARKER, EDWIN B. Technological change and the mass media. In: Schramm, Wilbur Lang; et al.; eds. Handbook of communication. Rand McNally & Co., Chicago, Illinois. (Should be available December 1972, approximately 1,000 pages).

(46) PARKER, EDWIN B.; DUNN, DONALD A. The potential of information technology. Science. (In press).

(47) PHILIPS GLOEILAMPENFABRIEKEN, NV. The Philips VCR system. Philips Gloeilampenfabrieken, NV, Eindhoven, Netherlands. (Brochure).

(48) Progress committee report for 1970. Journal of the Society of Motion Picture and Television Engineers. 80:5 (May 1971) 388-393.

(49) Proprietary rights, residual rights and copyright in cartridge TV. (Contains five speeches: Nimmer, Melville B. The legal aspect as seen from the U.S. and Canadian viewpoint. 5-13.; Tournier, Jean-Loup. The legal aspect as seen from the Western European viewpoint. 13-20.; Van Vught, Wim. Cartridge TV and the music publisher. 20-21.; Ellwyn, O. Protecting authors' rights. 22-24.; De Freitas, Dennis. Copyrighting videocassette programmes. 24-27.) In: International Cartridge TV, Videocassette & Videodisc Conference. 1st, Cannes, France, 19-23 April 1971. Billboard Publications, New York, New York, 1971, 5-27. (Booklet 7).

(50) Radical software. Raindance Corporation, New York, New York. (Newsletter).

(51) REDLICH, HORST. The video disc technique recording and reproduction. Text of lecture at AEG-Telefunken Press Conference, Berlin, Germany, 24 June 1970. London Records, New York, New York.

(52) REMLEY, FREDERICK M., JR. Activities of the helical recording subcommittee of the video tape recording committee. Journal of the Society of Motion Picture and Television Engineers, 79:12 (December 1970) 1089-1090.

(53) ROBERTS, MARTIN. Video cassettes, the systems, the market, the future. Martin Roberts and Association, Inc., Beverly Hills, California, October 1970, 153 p.

(54) ROGERS, EVERETT M.; SHOEMAKER, F. FLOYD. Communication of innovations. Free Press, New York, 1971.

(55) RYDER, LESLIE. An appraisal of the market in schools and universities. In: International Cartridge TV, Videocassette & Videodisc Conference. 1st, Cannes, France, 19-23 April 1971. Billboard Publications, New York, New York, 1971, 5-9. (Booklet 6).

(56) SCHRAMM, WILBUR LANG; POOL, ITHIEL; PARKER, EDWIN B.; MACCOBY, N.; FREY, F.; FEIN, L.; eds. Handbook of communication. Rand McNally & Co., Chicago, Illinois. (Should be available December 1972, approximately 1,000 pages).

(57) Seen and heard. Audio-Visual News, No. 1 (June 1970). W. H. Smith & Son, W. H. Smith Cassettes Ltd., London, England.

(58) SHAMBERG, MICHAEL. Guerrilla television. Holt, Rinehart & Winston, New York, New York, 1971, 150 p.

(59) Television Digest with Consumer Electronics. Television Digest, Inc., Washington, D.C. (Newsletter).

(60) TETTEMER, CLAIR R.; STOWERS, MICHAEL P. Third annual helical scan video tape recorder survey. Northern Illinois University, Division of Communication Services, Dekalb, Illinois, 21 p.

(61) TEULINGS, CHRISTIAN. The unique place of cartridge TV in entertainment and education as seen from the European viewpoint. In: International Cartridge TV, Videocassette & Videodisc Conference. 1st, Cannes, France, 19-23 April 1971, 18-21. (Booklet 9).

(62) Thermal duplicator handles all video tape formats. Electronics (26 April 1971) 26.

(63) THOMAS, HOWARD. The role of the television networks. In: International Cartridge TV, Videocassette & Videodisc Conference, 1st, Cannes, France, 19-23 April 1971, 9-13. (Booklet 6).

(64) U. S. DEPARTMENT OF COMMERCE. Current industrial reports: household items. U. S. Department of Commerce, Washington, D.C., 1962. (Series M36M-(62)-1).

(65) Video Cassette Newsletter. Edited by Martin Roberts. Martin Roberts and Association, Inc. Beverly Hills, California.

(66) Video cassette sourcebook. Television Digest, Inc., Washington, D.C., 1971, 25 p.

(67) Video Play Report. Edited by C. S. Tepfer, Ridgefield, Connecticut, 1971. (Newsletter).

(68) Video Publisher. Knowledge Industry Publications, White Plains, New York. (Newsletter).

(69) VIDEO RECORD CORPORATION OF AMERICA. Video Record. Video Record Corporation of America, Westport, Connecticut. (Brochure).

(70) Video Record World. Published by L. K. William and R. Pereira, Irvine, California.

(71) VidNews. Billboard Publications, New York, New York. (Newsletter. Name changed from Cartridge Television News Digest to VidNews in January 1972).

(72) WALKER, ROBERT H. Video tape—its impact on consumer electronics design. IEEE Transactions on Broadcast and Television Receivers, BTR-17:3 (August 1971) 160-163.

(73) WAVERIG, ELMER H. The unique place of cartridge TV in entertainment and education as seen from the U.S. viewpoint. In: International Cartridge TV, Videocassette & Videodisc Conference. 1st, Cannes, France, 19-23 April 1971. Billboard Publications, New York, New York, 1971, 8-13. (Booklet 1).

(74) Whole earth catalog. Portola Institute, Menlo Park, California, 1971.

(75) YAMAKAWA, KIOSHI. The Sony system. In: International Cartridge TV, Videocassette & Videodisc Conference. 1st, Cannes, France, 19-23 April 1971. Billboard Publications, New York, New York, 1971, 12-14. (Booklet 3).

III
Applications

The library automation literature of 1971 reflects the numerous advances made in the field during the past decade. For the first time there is an abundance of literature that concretely and realistically discusses the attempts being made at solving library problems through automation. It is more instructive than it has previously been, because it finally has become more specific as it focuses on narrower areas of library automation.

Martin's chapter describes and evaluates the recently reported work in areas such as national activities, international activities, networks and cooperative systems, systems analysis and design, applications, research, and personnel. In contrast to the past emphasis on applications, much of the current literature emphasizes cooperation, cost analyses, and education. The cooperative approach, especially, has contributed to progress in library automation. Martin feels that most of the fundamental problems of library automation have been identified, and that if more libraries would take advantage of the literature that describes and evaluates the various library automation efforts, considerable duplication of effort could be avoided.

Olson, Shank, and Olsen review the status of library and information networks, organizing their discussion around its four major aspects: social and political, administrative, economic, and technological. They point out the importance of social and political factors in the development of information networks and comment on the many different reasons for joining networks. (The social purposes of networks have recently been questioned, since few of them seem to have been developed in response to user-expressed needs.) Whatever the reasons for participation, the success of the networks depends on a high level of commitment from the supporting organizations.

Network development is still beset by administrative and economic problems. Many networks lack personnel who are qualified to plan networks and make important procedural decisions. Economic analysis of networks is weak (or lacking) and analysts fail to relate the significance of economic factors to actual network decision-making. Yet technological advances, especially those in telecommunications, may compensate for these current planning weaknesses and lead to revolutionary changes in all aspects of library service. Substantially more funds and other support are still needed to encourage the study and improvement of organizational aspects, professional leadership, technological advances, and performance evaluation of networks. Particular attention is needed on standardization and the potential problems of overlapping and competing networks. Perhaps, network organization and cooperation on a national level is needed most of all.

In Chapter 9, Gechman describes numerous activities related to machine-readable bibliographic data bases. The number of these data bases is rapidly growing, and even though he limits his review primarily to readily available data bases there is much activity to cover. Machine-readable bibliographic data bases are generated (and used) by four major groups: academic, governmental, and industrial organizations, and professional societies. The data bases created and maintained by academic groups usually focus on a specific discipline. Federally sponsored data bases—the largest in number—generally have a broader scope of coverage. Private industry is becoming increasingly involved in providing various data base services and products to customers. The data bases being produced by professional societies are few in number but tend to be of high quality.

Gechman describes the activities of ten foreign countries and of ten international organizations. He feels that international data base activity is expanding more than that in the United States. Whatever the context—national or international—there must be increased cooperation of producers, users and processors, in order to promote and support these various data base activities. If some standardization can be achieved, we should see considerable growth in library use of machine-readable data bases, in interactive retrieval, and in remote use of centralized data base management systems.

Computerized document retrieval and dissemination systems are becoming more popular as they become more efficient and practical. Brandhorst and Eckert provide a thorough review of current trends, advances, and problems of these systems. Most of the workers in this area view the 1970's positively and foresee the maturation of computerized document retrieval and a more sophisticated information community.

The year's literature, which supports this optimism, deals with important work related to on-line interactive systems, natural text approaches, human engineering, cost analyses, cooperation, standards, data base utilization, search strategies, file size, software transferability, and legal issues. Of particular interest is the development of a variety of software packages to meet a variety of user needs, economic situations, and data bases. Also of interest is the re-emergence of concern with search techniques and strategies. There is no lack of literature dealing with the evaluation of retrieval systems, but few methodical evaluations of existing systems have been done. A unique feature of the Brandhorst and Eckert chapter is a table that lists 76 institutions with computerized document retrieval systems. For each institution, information is given on the type of system(s) involved, the associated hardware and software, the developmental status, and other system characteristics.

The use of computers to aid research in the humanities has been developing slowly over the past decade. Raben and Widmann describe past and current developments and problems in the application of computers in fields such as language and literature, history, music, visual arts, archaeology and cultural anthropology. Most of the computer-aided research in the humanities has been in the language and literature field, with considerable attention being given to developing products such as indexes and concordances and to identifying unique aspects of linguistic or stylistic phenomena. The research activity in the field of history has also proved fruitful. The "New History," which emphasizes the study of mass social phenomena, requires the analysis of masses of quantitative information, and the computer provides the only feasible means of doing it.

In contrast, there has been relatively little progress made applying computers to the fields of music and art history because of the lack of agreement on a suitable encoding system. How does one express a symphony or a painting in machine-readable form? In spite of such difficulties, acceptance of the legitimacy of computer research by those involved in the liberal arts field is increasing and is gradually resulting in increased financial support, which heretofore has been severely lacking. Information scientists, as well as humanities researchers, should benefit from this research.

Blumstein examines the needs, problems, and developments in computer-based criminal justice information systems. Police information systems need improvement in real-time inquiry; court information systems need improved logistics management, as well as improved access to information on defendants and on the status of particular cases; and correctional systems need to provide information to aid in the selection of corrective treatment of individual offenders. Blumstein describes and discusses the status of specific "case-following" and "resource-management" systems. The best known prototype "case-following" system has been developed under Project SEARCH, which involves a nationwide network to maintain and exchange criminal histories among the states. Problems have arisen because of the differences among the states in criminal codes, but some compatibility has been achieved.

Studies of criminal justice information systems have been limited, so far, and evaluation of existing systems is very much needed. So too, are more comprehensive criminal justice statistics, and—particularly important—means to provide adequate privacy of information.

7 Library Automation

SUSAN K. MARTIN
Harvard University Library

INTRODUCTION

In the previous *Annual Review* chapter on the literature on library automation, Avram (2) notes that "progress is evident, but the absence of articles acknowledging the existence of some of the more fundamental problems is striking." For a variety of reasons, including technical development, the economic problems that are forcing administrators to look closely at procedures and costs, and the increasing sophistication of library staffs, this progress is gaining the momentum. The automation efforts that were funded by external sources during the past decade are now being reported in detail; these reports of five or more years of research and development do indeed address some very basic technical problems as well as the political and social questions, and provide useful information for the entire library community.

The literature reviewed in this chapter includes articles from library and information science journals, papers, proceedings of conferences, systems documentation, and books. As in previous years, the emphasis in the literature tends to lie in the area of applications. However, much of the literature deals with cooperative efforts, cost analyses, and education, lending solid support to the more technical systems descriptions.

Nine major areas have been identified for discussion: General, the "Struggle for Validity," National Activity, International Activity, Networks and Cooperative Systems, Systems Analysis, Applications, Research, and Personnel. Although a separate chapter discusses networks, this reviewer believes that cooperative developments have figured significantly in the library automation literature and in the events during the year, and this reviewer and the authors of the Networks chapter have made an attempt to minimize overlapping information.

The literature of the field has in the past been difficult to organize, as noted by several authors in previous *Annual Reviews*. Published material tended to be vague, and could be placed in any one of several of the major sections of a chapter. At this time, however, we see an increasing specificity and a reduction of the "shot-gun approach" to automation, with a large percentage of the literature focussing sharply on narrow topics. The grand-scale total systems plan, so often criticized in earlier years for being unrealistic and misleading, is now being replaced by descriptions of smaller operational systems or of the studies that must precede the implementation of a large system.

The reviews in this chapter were selected from over 400 documents of potential interest and value to the library administrator and systems analyst. The reader should note that serious research into a specific area will uncover a larger supply of material than can be included in a review chapter.

GENERAL REVIEWS AND SURVEYS

The Spring 1971 issue of *Library Resources & Technical Services* contains detailed reviews of the 1970 work in acquisitions (Fristoe & Myers, 32), cataloging and classification (Richmond, 88), and serials (Pound, 83). In the same issue, Sullivan (98) discusses developments in photoreproduction; of interest are the microform products associated with computer output, such as *Books in English*, from the Britain National Bibliography. Sullivan also describes a number of commercial services based on the computer/microform interface. These articles are good summaries of the events and literature of 1970, and similar articles in future years should provide the field with good secondary sources of documentation at a fairly comprehensive level of coverage.

The International Federation for Documentation has begun publication of a series entitled *R & D Projects in Documentation and Librarianship* (85). This series is a monthly current-awareness list of research and development projects. Retrospective search service is planned for the future; at the time of reporting, FID had data from thirty countries on 1000 projects.

Several surveys of automated library systems published during 1971 are of assistance to those who wish to locate various types of research or operational projects. *LIST 1971* (Wasserman, 103) is organized by general category or area of application. The amount of data given is, of course, dependent on the reporting institution; however, the editor's questionnaire is constructed to draw out a detailed level of information from the contributors. The main list is indexed by reporting staff member and by institution. Although the survey cannot be accepted as complete and, like any directory, becomes partially obsolete at the moment of publication, it is a helpful indication of what is happening and where. The emphasis is on research projects, but some operational systems have been included.

The LARC Association, which has produced two editions of a survey of automated library activities in the United States and Canada, has begun publication of a series entitled *A Survey of Automated Activities in the Libraries of the World*, with Volume I focussing on the libraries of the United States (LARC Association, 50). The initial section presents tables that display the survey data by application and by type of institution. Because no criteria are given for inclusion of a system, these data are only "crude measures of the actual amount of activity currently underway." Typical functions of acquisitions, cataloging, and serials systems are listed, with the equipment actually in use at selected libraries. Indexes to the survey are by application and by type of library, with an index of terms to assist in the use of the lengthy outline of application areas. The survey is arranged alphabetically by institution; each entry includes a list of projects, the type of personnel employed, equipment used, the name of the coordinator, and literature about the system. The level of information is uneven: under the "Equipment" category, one entry states that an IBM 360/65 is used, and the following entry reports that "The Library competes successfully for machine time." The twelve-volume set is intended to devote individual volumes to automation in the Far East, in China, and in Mexico, Central America and South America, as well as offering a bibliography and a handbook of library automation. No such survey has yet been attempted; this reviewer doubts, however, the value of information gathered in technologically disparate locations with less than full control over the quality of the information. Again, incomplete coverage and gradual obsolescence necessarily limit the value of the publication.

An interesting survey by McAllister (54) covers those on-line systems in the United States or Canada that handle acquisitions, cataloging, circulation, or serials; are conversational (i.e., interactive with the user); and are used for update as well as for searching. Most of these systems update files on-line; a few of the systems accumulate data online but update the major files in batch mode. McAllister suggests collecting all information about an item in a single record, with multiple indexes to serve different functions. Thus, the complete record for any document can be reached from any index, and either the index or the record may be displayed at the request of the user. This concept is diametrically opposed to the philosophy of file structure that advocates maintaining separate files for separate functions, to be linked by a pointer index.

In a newly published textbook, Heiliger & Henderson (36) offer an overview of library automation and systems analysis. Their presentation treats various applications with what may be an overly optimistic and simplified view of the potential of computers in the library. Each major section has an accompanying glossary; this reviewer found this approach novel but somewhat distracting. The discussion of technical principles is cursory, and, if the book were used as a textbook, it would need to be supplemented by additional readings. A final chapter on concepts is a philosophical treatise on library automation that is an excellent introduction for the student and provides a refreshing summary for the practitioner.

Several collections of papers were published during the year. Among the most outstanding is the collection edited by Balmforth & Cox (7). Approximately one-half of the papers included were presented at the Newcastle-upon-Tyne (England) Seminar on the Management of Computing Activity in Academic Libraries, 10-13 January 1969; the remaining contributions are presented here for the first time. Four topics are covered: the Current Situation in Library Automation, Methods and Techniques, Centralized Services, and Management Criteria. While it would be tempting to select specific chapters for review, the quality of the book is such that each paper contributes a unique viewpoint, and the level of presentation is consistently high throughout the volume. The section entitled "Current Situation in Library Automation" introduces various approaches to library automation and descriptions of the major work done in the United States, Great Britain, and Canada during the 1960's. The section on methods and techniques covers in detail the logical and physical problems of the interface between libraries and computers, without going into too much technical detail. The sections entitled "Centralized Services" and "Management Criteria" provide sound guidelines and background on these two topics. This work is essential reading for both the practitioner and the student.

Three additional collections of readings are useful as texts and reference tools. In each case, the individual papers have been treated in previous editions of the *Annual Review*. The Tauber & Feinberg (99) collection of reprinted articles on book catalogs brings together some of the best work done in this area and adds two original chapters. Kaplan (43) offers another compilation of important papers, also all previously published. Elias (26) has reprinted articles published during the 1960's; while the emphasis is on information science, several of the papers have direct application to libraries.

STRUGGLE FOR VALIDITY

In the early years of library automation, most published papers were extremely positive and unreasonably optimistic. Those who experimented with automated systems and found that their goals had to be scaled down seldom communicated this fact in the literature to the yet-uninitiated segment of the profession. In 1971 Mason (59, 60) has reported his study of systems in large research libraries by combining what this reviewer considers a modicum of truth with an emotional and little-documented attack upon the automation of libraries. Mason's worthwhile task of pointing out the flaws in our procedures has unfortunately undermined itself by including exaggerations and a poorly reasoned argument, which may cause readers to dismiss his publications as unscholarly and naive. Later issues of *College & Research Libraries* (18, 19) contain "pro" and "con" letters to the editor from the readers of the original article; especially clarifying is an exchange of correspondence between Hayes & Mason (35).

Melcher (65, 66), while stating his argument in a more balanced manner, also seems convinced that automation offers few if any benefits to libraries. He puts forth a number of sound principles of systems design, such as a cautious and well-documented approach to an automated procedure, but he presents definitions and asks questions in a way that suggests he has not had recent contact with either automated systems or libraries. J. Owen (79) uses her experience in North American to give Australian librarians an idea of the advantages and disadvantages of several widely known systems. While she is also somewhat critical of unrealistic publicity, she presents administrative guidelines for library automation.

At the time of this writing, these negative viewpoints have begun to produce reactions in the literature. Some programs have been devoted to this issue at professional meetings. It is clearly an area where facts may be selected to present a desired effect, and we hope that concerned librarians will find it possible to examine more than one side of such a controversial question. However, library systems continue as usual, and the librarians opposed to or in favor of automation retain their viewpoints. Two articles on systems, while not written in answer to these criticisms, present a highly positive picture and should be mentioned here. Warheit (102) describes types of failures of library systems and emphasizes that they are due to various human weaknesses: (1) failure to take into account lack of resources, (2) poor design, or (3) poor planning and administration. In a treatise on library systems analysis, Burns (13) discusses four phases: system survey, system analysis, system design, and implementation and evaluation of new systems. His procedure is logically and clearly explained, and his statement that "first-time processing costs, procedures, etc., are normally atypical" can be used to answer many arguments by critics of library automation.

NATIONAL ACTIVITIES

As time passes, the definition of the term "national" begins to blur. National activities have in the past been limited to the activities of the major national and Federal libraries. However, as the discussion of national programs sponsored or co-sponsored by organizations other than one of the national libraries has increased, there has arisen some confusion between the work of the national libraries and cooperative activities carried out on a national level. The National Commission on Libraries and Information Science, created late in 1971, is an agency to which the profession should be able to turn for coordination and assistance, by assuming the role that has until now been played by numerous professional groups. A central office should be more able to assign priorities and avoid duplication of effort than several organizations working independently.

Several developments have been reported by Library of Congress staff members. Avram & Maruyama (3, 4) have given progress reports on the RECON (REtrospective CONversion) Pilot Project. Test work has been carried out and sample batches of foreign language input and editing have been prepared. The typists' keying rates were not significantly lower than with English material, but editors' output compared poorly with that of English-language editing; however, the sample included less than 1200 titles. Future plans include the development of an integrated system: Multiple Use MARC System. A system of this nature may eventually permit on-line input and the correction of all types of records. Format recognition, already successful in the production of book catalogs at the Institute of Library Research, Berkeley, is being used for both MARC and RECON production work. This technique, which allows the computer to assign the tags and to format the MARC record, is achieving approximately 75% accuracy and permits the Library of Congress to discard the manual editing step that was formerly routine. Maruyama (58) describes in detail the use and impact of automatic format recognition.

From the 1970 *Clinic on Library Applications of Data Processing*, the University of Illinois (39) has compiled a number of papers devoted to discussion of MARC uses and users. A very strong technical publication, the volume contains contributions by the creators, distributors, and users of both MARC and BNB-MARC. The users' papers present in detail some of the most sophisticated techniques of handling the MARC tapes that were available at the time of writing. The network and commercial use of the MARC format is also discussed. The authors indicate not only their successes but also their problems and the attempts to resolve them.

In a specialized bibliographic essay, Stockard (97) evaluates selected official and user non-duplicative literature about MARC. Stockard's major criticism refers to the time lag between changes made at the MARC Development Office and the appearance of the documentation in the professional literature. She pays little attention to the efforts made to counteract these publication lags by means of tutorials, institutes, and the MARC users' groups of professional associations. Ayres (5) in Great Britain points out that the criticism of MARC in Britain derives mainly from suspicion and a fear of the unknown. Several positive statements are given: (1) the coverage of the system will continue to grow, (2) stripping down the MARC record for local use is cheaper than original keying, and (3) production of a tailor-made MARC tape to meet the needs of a single library may be possible in the future (this product is being offered by the Oklahoma Department of Libraries to its constituency).

Ristow & Carrington (89) describe the development of a machine-readable map description format at the Library of Congress. Their article details the means by which several libraries participated in the development of the map service and gives an enlightening description of the transition of a previously uncatalogued collection, from the initial decision to automate, through analysis, to implementation.

In an annual report of the Library of Congress Processing Department, Welsh (106) describes the work of the MARC Development Office, the Order Division, and the CARDS Project, which is intended to facilitate the production and supply of catalog cards. Hardware for Phase II of the CARDS Project was installed in 1971 to produce photocomposed card sets from machine-readable records. At a meeting of the Association of Research Libraries, Budington (11), Lazerow (51), and Johnson (41) described the pilot project of the National Serials Data Program, commenting on the difficulties of coordinating this task on the national level. The NSDP moved from the office of the Association of Research Libraries to the Library of Congress in July 1971. At the same meeting, the Ad Hoc Committee on Specifications for a Study of Automation in Research Libraries (1) cited the need for a position paper to set a national strategy for developing computer applications to deal with the functions of research libraries from 1971 through 1976. While this goal is praiseworthy, current activity in libraries usually outpaces committee efforts; a more effective way of monitoring national developments may be to delegate the responsibility to one central agency unencumbered by a plethora of committees and able to employ technical experts on a full-time basis. The National Commission on Libraries and Information Science, described above, might be an appropriate home for this type of task.

A study of the Federal library community (excluding the three national libraries) was sponsored by the Federal Library Committee, funded by the U. S. Office of Education and carried out by System Development Corporation. The goals of the study were to study and define the operations that are "susceptible" to automation and to prepare a handbook on automation for Federal librarians. Markuson et al. (55) have produced a valuable report resulting from this survey of Federal libraries. Among the findings are: (1) the majority of the more than 2000 Federal libraries are small or medium-sized and lack adequate support; (2) the libraries serve a wide range of publics in all parts of the world; (3) only fifty-nine of the libraries that reported have any kind of operational or planned automated system; (4) they lack standardization; and (5) the idea of centralized automated services is strongly supported, but immediate operational needs are given higher priority than automation. The SDC team recommended that the Federal government develop several generalized library system components to serve a number of Federal libraries, and selectively develop centralized services. A proposed program to implement the full range of recommendations should have a full-time staff. Cuadra & Pearson (24) present a summary of the survey report.

INTERNATIONAL ACTIVITIES

The author of last year's chapter remarked that 1970 was an international year for library automation. The year 1971 was not as prolific in major international developments, but attention should be paid to several works. This reviewer has observed that the vast majority of reporting on library automation comes from the United States, Canada, and Great Britain. On the other hand, the continental European countries tend to be concerned with documentation and information science and have relegated library housekeeping operations to second place in their literature. The recent acceptance of the MARC format as a standard for bibliographic interchange in machine-readable form has encouraged its use. The non-English-speaking countries of the world usually have a more centralized educational establishment, linked to the national government. The effect of this type of organization on library systems, together with an international standard and the precedents set by other countries, will be the creation of cooperative networks from the outset, as opposed to the individual trial-and-error method by which we have developed our existing knowledge and techniques of library automation.

A comparative study by Coblans (17) summarizes the trends in national planning in Great Britain, the United States, France, and Germany, and documentation on an international level. Some cost comparisons are provided and many questions about the provision of services are posed, but no solutions are suggested. This article shows both the similarity of goals and the differences of approach by different nations.

In Geneva, the International Labour Office (Schieber, 90) is designing and implementing a major information system containing modules for bibliographic information, serials control, and loan procedures. Beginning in 1964 as a card-based documentation system, the ILO-ISIS (Integrated Scientific Information System) is now a disc-based online inquiry system using a modified MARC record. Its data base contains 40,000 bibliographic records in the subject areas of social and economic development. Input and searching are done on-line, and a semi-monthly current awareness bulletin is printed. The present functions of the serials system are claiming and routing; check-in and prediction routines are not yet operational. The system produces catalogs and lists of serial records from a data base of 10,000 items. While ISIS has been an internally developed system, the International Labour Office recommends and looks forward to a study of interagency centralized processing.

A survey of British university libraries by Duchesne & Phillips (25) has determined that a great deal of effort is expended on library automation in the United Kingdom. Sixty percent of the university libraries have either operational or planned systems, all relatively independent of other institutions. Although it is not stated explicitly in the article, this trend may be due to the fact that government subsidies as a rule provide computer time in British universities.

Project LOC (Jolliffe, 42) is a cooperative effort by the British Museum and Oxford and Cambridge Universities (London-Oxford-Cambridge) to convert to machine-readable form all pre-1801 imprint bibliographic records. This is a major task, encompassing the three large libraries and all the college libraries in both universities. A pilot project attempted to match converted records automatically to ascertain the incidence of duplication, but the error rate was unacceptably high. To solve this problem, a unique method of "fingerprinting" each book was designed. In addition to the bibliographic information, six letters are copied from identical locations on three pre-determined pages of each book processed. The fingerprints are then used as keys for matching, and the record is printed out for editing if two out of three sets are identical. Swinnerton-Dyer[1] indicates that the occurrence of a false match is negligible.

Chauveinc (16) describes the use of MARC in MONOCLE (Projet de Mise en Ordinateur d'une Notice Catalographique de Livre) at the University of Grenoble. In this system some features of MARC and BNB-MARC are combined with modifications made locally for cataloging and filing. He criticizes the complexity of MARC, but MONOCLE seems to have derived an equally complex format to provide for French filing rules and cataloging practice, veering away from the international standard. Based on the work at Grenoble, a publication by Boisset & Beyssac (9) describes a project of the Fondation Nationale des Sciences Politiques. The Groupe Informatiste de Bibliothèques Universitaires et Specialisées (GIBUS) is a group of eight libraries and documentation centers that conducted a two-week demonstration of documentation and library automation attended by 2000 librarians and information scientists. The basic goal of the cooperating institutions was to observe automation in operation before actually embarking upon a program. The authors hope that GIBUS, with positive reactions from the participants, will be the point of departure for a large collaborative effort.

From Spain, Gonzalez Lopez (33) summarizes the analysis, design, and results of experience with *Resúmenes de Revistas Médicas*, a computer-produced catalog of medical journals. Some historical and technical background is given, and the necessity of cooperative work is again emphasized. The author lists and discusses computers and systems now used in Europe in relation to several well-known American systems. In November 1970, the Swedish and Danish official library departments held a conference to improve communication, discuss

[1]H. Swinnerton-Dyer, Professor of Mathematics, Cambridge University, England. Presentation sponsored by the Harvard University Library and the New England Chapter of the American Society for Information Science, 10 January 1972.

standardization and coordination, and increase awareness of the possibilities of automation in the Scandinavian countries (Hein, 38). In Norway, it is planned that the Norwegian Union Catalog of Foreign Periodicals will be developed into a retrieval system.

In Australia, Crittenden (22) reports concern about accepting Library of Congress cataloging as distributed on MARC tapes. Crittenden states that although Australian librarians feel that American cataloging may not be suitable for Australian libraries, mainly because of vocabulary differences, the use of MARC tapes would result in economic benefits despite the necessity of minor changes in vocabulary and format. Baker (6) discusses the rapid expansion of the Australian colleges of advanced education. He is concerned about the possibility that separate systems will be developed and states the obvious advantages of cooperating from the beginning, rather than discovering the need for cooperation in mid-stream. Lee (52) describes the Asian Institute of Technology in Bangkok, where processing for the 30,000-volume collection is supplemented by an off-line batch system on an IBM 1130 that produces purchase orders, information on claiming and accounting, and general statistics. Although a Kardex is maintained for check-in, the journal records have been converted to machine-readable form for listing purposes. Again, Lee stresses the need for cooperative work, showing the universality of this trend and therefore the desirability of a level of cooperation that can succeed even though the participants may be geographically removed.

Munn (71) discusses the two major problems of the developing countries: inadequate services and resources, and little or no coordination of effort. Although the problem is obvious, the efforts to solve it have in the past led to a vicious circle, creating more of the same problem. Conventional collection-building is not feasible because of the costs, but a major contribution can be made by union lists of periodicals using "canned" programs. The fifth edition of *Periodicals in East African Libraries: a Union List* in 1969 included seventy-six libraries and 465 pages, and cost less than $2000 to produce. The success of this list has given rise to the East African Literature Service, which concerns itself with current awareness service and the reproduction of materials.

NETWORKS AND COOPERATIVE SYSTEMS

Although an entire chapter of this volume is devoted to information networks, it seems appropriate to discuss library networks briefly here. For years, the call for non-duplication of effort and transferability of systems has been heard, with little response. In 1971, however, several factors combined to alter the outlook for cooperative work. First, the economic problems of the country made themselves felt on nonprofit institutions such as libraries. Second, the concept of a widely acceptable format for communication of bibliographic data became familiar, and also viable, with the second full year of distribution of MARC tapes and the initiation of the RECON pilot project. Finally, several cooperative regional groups succeeded in creating impressive automated systems serving anywhere from a few to dozens of libraries with projected overall savings of cost and immediate increase in efficiency.

A most important contribution has been made by the Information Systems Panel of the National Academy of Sciences' Computer Science and Engineering Board. An assessment of the information and technological resources of the United States showed that technological limitations are no longer a deterrent to the use of machines to handle information. The Panel (73) considered the interactions between technological and non-technological factors and made the following recommendations: (1) that a comprehensive pilot system for a national program in information usage be established; (2) that increased stress be placed on scientific design and modeling studies of information networks; and (3) that the resulting program refer specifically to data base organization and management, large-capacity storage, network distribution technologies, machine-readable catalogs, microform technology, and education. Although no sponsoring institution is suggested, the Panel clearly indicates the desirability of a national network of information, again bringing to mind the National Commission on Libraries and Information Science.

Molz (69) believes that the long-range goal of "immediacy of access to totality of information for everyone" may never be realized. Assuming that the rationale of networks is the speed of information transfer, she questions the true need for instantaneous access to information and suggests that the important factors may finally be economic limitations. Her view of a successful network includes the full participation of the public as well as internal bibliographic control. Shank et al. (91), in a study of the libraries of Western Canada, have made a series of recommendations for centralization. Developments should take place slowly by means of regional organization toward a large system, and a central coordinating agency should be established.

Fasana & Veaner (29) present selected papers from two Collaborative Library Systems Development (CLSD) conferences held in Stanford in 1968 and in New York in 1970. The three participating libraries (Columbia University, Stanford University, and the University of Chicago) ascertained early in their work that each institution should pursue the course of action originally adopted for automation, rather than attempting to design or share systems at the technical level. For this reason, the CLSD publication is not so much a description of a cooperative effort as a sharing of information and exchange of experiences during the development of three large systems projects. Presentations by librarians not directly involved with the Collaborative Library Systems Development effort complemented the reports of the collaborating libraries. Their papers also concern themselves more with systems and administrative problems than with cooperative development. The publication is a worthy addition to the literature of the subject, but it should be kept in mind that it emphasizes cooperation in the exchange of information about systems development, rather than in the exchange or transfer of the systems themselves. Fasana (28) also describes briefly the CLSD objective of developing a mechanism of cooperation among the three large research libraries, explaining further the historical background that committed each institution to its internal work first and the Collaborative Library Systems Development project second. Among the findings were (1) the realization that cooperation is not easily achieved among geographically separated institutions with existing systems programs and (2) the fact that cooperation requires a binding commitment. This reviewer believes that these simply stated facts may be the reason for the failure of many cooperative efforts.

Last year's progress included the development and successful implementation by the Ohio College Library Center of a system of providing catalog cards to over sixty member libraries for a reported cost of under ten cents per card. Representative of a subsequent trend is the proposal of the New England Library Information Network (74) to simulate the Ohio College Library Center system as it would operate in the New England region, and to place a cathode ray tube terminal in the Dartmouth College Library for direct communication with Ohio in order to compare costs and efficiency of production with the current internal cataloging procedures. Several other libraries and library cooperatives are also planning pilot projects with the OCLC system. In this experimentation, one can see not only the advantages of transferring systems, but also the disadvantages caused by equipment variances, as exemplified by the fact that OCLC is using a Sigma-5 computer. Most libraries rely on the computing facilities of a parent institution and do not have access to a Sigma series computer.

In one of several reports from the Stanford University Library, Montague (70) describes the results of a thirteen-week study of five college and university libraries to determine the costs and benefits of a network use of Stanford's automated library systems. The proposed on-line cooperative system will be implemented as a series of seven modules, each module operating at Stanford for four to nine months before it is implemented as a network module. The modules, to be developed over a period of three years, cover the areas of acquisitions and cataloging, and include a shared MARC file and a union In-process file and Catalog file. The cost studies were carried out by a team of staff members representing the technical processing departments of each institution. This team worked together to derive accurate figures with a consistently applied technique, in order to compare the actual costs of joining the network for each library.

The Five Associated University Libraries[1] (30) have published a Final Report of their feasibility study on serials control. The four tasks undertaken in this phase were: (1) literature review and bibliography; (2) analysis of non-contract libraries and other organizations; (3) study of current serials systems at the contract libraries; and (4) cost estimates of alternative system configurations. The most likely functions of the first module are: check-in, update, binding, and claiming. The cost estimates for such a system seem extremely high when the system is supported by a small number of institutions; however, the cost analysis of the manual systems presently used shows an almost equally great expenditure.

The Oklahoma Department of Libraries (75) has expanded its MARC record selection service to include selective dissemination of information. Together with the Southwestern Library Interstate Cooperative Endeavor (SLICE), it has published a description of the newly established SLICE office and the services that the office is making available to the libraries in the region (SLICE/MARC-O, 95). For the first ten months of 1972, external funding has been granted to the network, allowing the organization to operate without charging membership fees; instead, users are asked to pay only for services used. Catalog cards are printed from the MARC tapes at a cost of ten cents per request and ten cents per card printed. A variant of this service allows the user to obtain the data in machine-readable rather than printed form. Two versions of selective dissemination of information provide users with a current awareness service based on the MARC tapes; the standard service produces a weekly bibliography in any of eight specified subject areas, while the custom SDI service produces a bibliography based on an individually developed profile. SLICE systems support is also available for the planning and implementation of the SLICE/MARC-O services in member libraries.

---

[1]Cornell University, State University of New York at Binghamton, State University of New York at Buffalo, University of Rochester, University of Syracuse.

Sokoloski (96) reports on the cooperative technical processing system recently developed by the University of Massachusetts for the twenty-eight state college libraries. All monograph and serial orders are placed through the book order and selection system. IBM's FASTER software package is used to produce purchase orders, claims, and accounting records; searching is possible by main entry as well as by purchase order number, providing bibliographic as well as processing access to the file. Another centralized processing system using FASTER is described by Miller & Hodges (68). The school system of Shawnee Mission, Kansas, uses a central ordering and cataloging service, initiated and administered internally for its sixty-five school libraries. Cataloging is currently done on-line with an IBM 360/40. While overall costs have doubled, the authors cite figures that indicate that the unit-cost per item processed has dropped approximately forty percent in the transition from batch to on-line processing, with almost four times as many items handled. The bases for these figures are not given in detail, however.

A commercial use of machine-readable bibliographic data, which can be described as a transferable system, is offered by Cardset Cataloging Systems (15). From the current MARC tapes, catalog cards are photocomposed to create a microfilm reel that has six-card images per frame, to produce a six-card set complete with added entries and subject headings. Index files provide access to the microfilm cartridge by Library of Congress card number and by title; the title index includes cross references. A reader-printer equipped with card stock is able to print the full card set after the desired entry has been found.

Nance et al. (72) present the use of the TALON (for Texas, Arkansas, Louisiana, Oklahoma and New Mexico) Reporting and Information Processing System (TRIPS) for the medical library network of those five states. This straightforward and economical TWX system connects ten libraries and TALON headquarters to provide interlibrary loan service and reports statistics on loans, requests, and response time for the use of the National Library of Medicine. The estimated cost is five cents per transaction.

SYSTEMS ANALYSIS AND DESIGN

With the growth of networks, library systems analysis has undergone changes that are reflected clearly in the literature. No longer does one find an abundance of articles enumerating the steps of systems analysis in terms too broad to be immediately applicable. Instead, increasing emphasis is placed on cost analysis, evaluation of non-quantifiable variables, and other specifics that, until now, have been largely ignored by analysts and have puzzled administrators when budgets failed to balance and schedules were not met.

In a companion volume to the SDC/Federal Library Committee report, Markuson et al. (56) present valuable guidelines for automation. The report is divided into three major sections: Guidelines, describing automated library systems analysis and administrative questions; Automation Projects, listing each Federal library with one or more automated systems, describing the systems, and providing an index; and Resource Materials, giving excellent presentations of several rarely covered topics (commercial support, hardware, technical descriptions of microforms, and other technical information in descriptive and in tabular form). The clarity and level of detail of this publication make it an essential tool for library managers.

With a systems approach to design methodology, Liston & Schoene (53), after a treatment of systems design, discuss the fixed and variable parameters of a system, the options within the parameters, and the considerations to be taken in choosing from these options. They say that the sequence of decisions should begin with those features that are least controllable by the designer, and should work toward those totally within this control. This article presents an unusually concise technique with useful principles of operation.

Cuadra (23) points out some major faults in the design of current on-line systems and lists essential characteristics for successful man-machine interaction, including careful pacing of the user's activities while at the terminal, well-designed error control routines, and tutorial provisions. Cuadra feels that the potential duplication of large on-line systems on a nationwide basis is a costly and undesirable situation. He suggests that the profession attempt to be aware of, and organize for, changing technology.

A publication of Project INTREX (62) also reviews the on-line facility of bibliographic and full-text retrieval available at the Massachusetts Institute of Technology and through one unmonitored console at Harvard, and concludes that the lack of continuous assistance at the Harvard console has greatly inhibited the effective use of the system. At the Barker Engineering Library at M.I.T., by contrast, a library staff member is available for consultation during all hours of console operation. These findings should be considered seriously by those who are concerned with the use of on-line systems by the clienteles of libraries and information centers.

A discussion of a report by Payne et al. (82) appeared in last year's *Annual Review*. Since that time, a supplementary volume (Payne &

McGee, 81) has updated the documentation of an impressively growing system. The basic MARC card-production capability remains, with added displays of incoming MARC records in 3 X 5 card format. The Chicago MARC (CUMARC) file and indexes of ''wanted'' bibliographic information reflect the needs of the library for MARC records; the system reacts appropriately when the desired record becomes available. An addition to the order module is the claiming feature, which can be either automatic or initiated by a certain command. Vendors' reports resulting from claims can be recorded in the machine-readable record. In the design stage at the time of the documentation were a fund file and production of payment documents. This system is not typical because of the large amount of external funding provided over a period of several years; it is, however, an excellent example of a well-designed evolutionary system.

In a working paper based on automation at Stanford University Library, Weber (105) evaluates Stanford's experience and makes projections for the future. He states that a strictly financial outlook would dictate the discontinuance of automation. He mentions the development of cooperative efforts to ease finances and presents a reasonable approach to a large-scale automation project, if the funds are available. He predicts that by 1977 some 700,000 items would be in the data base of this system, for a projected annual cost of between $300,000 and $450,000. Of the Stanford University Library's BALLOTS system, an on-line system, he states: ''BALLOTS is not like some off-line batch systems where one can add another file or run another card deck through the machine to add bits and pieces as the system evolves.'' Weber implies that a network based on Stanford's efforts would be highly desirable—an idea that has already been accepted, as stated above in the section on networks.

Koenig et al. (47) summarize SCOPE (Systematic Control of Periodicals), a system at Pfizer, Inc., based on the card-arrival file. A cost study was made according to the net-present-value method; it was found that the break-even point for the system would be at seven years. The technique of evaluating future savings is a valid but seldom-published aspect of library systems design. This article is of interest to those concerned with cost analyses, since it gives numerical results about many variables that are difficult to quantify, such as space savings.

Ungerleider (100) reports an investigation of various microfilm readers and computer-output-microfilm indexing techniques for replacing the printed in-process list at the Yale University Library. The study compared the cost of the in-process list at present and in the future with the cost of computer output microfilm plus the readers, and compared the staff performance on three readers using two film and indexing methods. Among the conclusions are: (1) "as the cost factor of the reader increased, so did its utility," and (2) the education of staff members in the use of microfilm and readers was not a problem; the learning curve was quite steep. Computer output microfilm, with the proper indexing method and reader, is shown to be definitely competitive from the standpoints of both cost and productivity.

The Stanford University Library has consistently documented and published the results of its automation efforts. In the BALLOTS report to the Office of Education, Epstein et al. (27) gives major recommendations for the support of large on-line systems: a detailed feasibility study, sufficient outside support, professional computer management, adequate technical personnel, a specialized documentation effort, and a view toward regional planning. This reviewer fully endorses these recommendations but must question their practicality for a single institution.

Epstein's description of the operation of the prototype BALLOTS system reviews the experience during 1969 with the on-line order module. The goals of the prototype system were to overcome the geographic limitations of manual files, permit multiple access to the master file, reduce file maintenance, and lessen the effect of staff turnover. The first three goals were met. Several conclusions were drawn from the prototype experience that influenced the design of the planned production system: (1) a core resident system is too expensive for daily library production operations, primarily due to the computer pricing algorithm: the production system will use time-sharing software; (2) typewriter terminals will be abandoned in favor of cathode ray tube terminals, which have been evaluated as being more effective for bibliographic operations; and (3) file recovery procedures will be a major and critical feature of the production system.[1]

Two systems decisions in the area of circulation applications deserve mention. A study of the manual system of Queen Mary College in London is reported by Owen (78). A manual system was redesigned and then computerization was considered. After analyzing on-line and automated systems, it was found that the benefits were not worth the additional costs, and it was recommended to implement the revised manual system. At the California State College, Los Angeles (14), a policy of confidentiality of circulation records has been explicitly

[1]Private communication, Allen B. Veaner, Associate Director of University Libraries, Stanford University.

adopted. Statistics from the data processing system will be used, but details of an individual's borrowing history will not be released, and statistical analyses will be coded so that only general descriptive categories will appear. While most libraries undoubtedly follow the same course in practice, very few statements of this nature have been published.

APPLICATIONS

As in the past, a large percentage of the year's library automation literature falls into the category of documentation of specific applications. While such descriptions have been criticized in the past for being over-optimistic and unrealistic, or for describing a system under development as if it were operational, this reviewer must repeat that a trend toward more realistic reporting begins to appear in the literature. Some of the more outstanding examples are presented in this section.

Circulation

The Ohio State University Library has installed one of the most notable and unusual circulation systems operational at the time of this writing. Guthrie (34) summarizes the general goals: to provide rapid access, better control of material, query capability, production of notices, ability to reorder material, and elimination of clerical routines. A telephone switchboard is set up to handle calls from patrons who desire a specific item from the library. The switchboard operator keys on an on-line terminal the first four characters of the main entry and five characters of the first significant word of the title to retrieve the status of that record. If the book is available for circulation, a label is produced at the circulation area of that branch, and the patron may either pick up the book or have it sent to him at a university address. This telephone access, of course, is most useful for those borrowers who have a specific request (73%). A weakness of the system is the manual keying of the call number for both charging and discharging of every item, allowing for human error at several points in any transaction (IBM Corporation, 40).

A study by Simmons (94) reveals the potential by-products of a circulation system in operation at the University of British Columbia since 1965. An analysis was made of loan transactions during four one-month periods throughout the academic year. A total of 330,000 transactions were examined, and, on the basis of heavy use, 23,000 items were reported as candidates for duplicate purchase, or candidates for purchase by the undergraduate library if a large number of undergraduates borrowed the item from the research collection. As a result of this analysis, over 2000 volumes have been added to the collections. Simmons concludes his report with a system description. A data-collection system utilizing book cards was initiated in which a card was keypunched when a book was returned to the library; this process avoided the exercise of converting the entire shelflist prior to implementation of the system. After one year of operation, 50% of circulating items already contained a punched card, and at the time of this report this figure had increased to over 90% of the circulation. The system products include a daily loan list, error list, traffic analysis, and notices of overdues, recalls, fines, and faculty overdues. The cost is approximately five cents per transaction, or $80,000 annually.

Kozumplik (48) reports that the Lockheed Missiles and Space Company Library circulation system has undergone a conversion from EDP to EAM (punched card) equipment, for an annual saving of $34,000. He states that if, at any time, a computer system could provide additional cost benefit, this decision would be reconsidered. The Eastern Illinois University Library's circulation application is summarized by Rao & Szerenyi (86). The library experimented with a unit record system as early as 1965 and is now operating on an IBM 360/50, programmed in PL/I. Cathode ray tube terminals are used for on-line access to the circulation file and routines; reserves, and patron and book inquiries can be made on-line. A criculation listing is also printed out daily for back-up of the on-line system. The collection is 250,000 volumes, but no figures on average daily traffic are given. The reported annual cost of the system is $36,000. These two articles show clearly the confusion that often arises when costs are reported, since they reveal only brief information and seem to be contradictory.

At the University of Surrey, England, Cowburn (21) describes the circulation control of an 80,000-volume collection. Using Automated Library Systems (manufactured in Great Britain) peripheral devices, the system incorporates an off-line collection of data from a book card and a machine-readable borrower identification card. Contrary to the approach of the University of British Columbia, the book cards for the entire collection were punched prior to the initiation of the system and placed in the books, during a one-week period. Although the library is not charged for computer time, the system is estimated to cost £500 (approximately $1300) a month. The major disadvantages felt by the staff are the bulk of the printout and the fact that the updated list is not available for use until late morning.

Cataloging

A significant step in the automation of cataloging is the development of the Ohio College Library Center, mentioned above in the section on networks. Under the direction of Kilgour,[1] the system allows member libraries to access, search, and add to a MARC-based on-line bibliographic data base. When a search is successful, a command to produce a set of catalog cards can be given, and the cards are printed in batch mode and sent to the requesting library ready to be filed. Changes may be made in the data that are displayed as the master record; the library making those changes will receive a set of cards altered to its specifications, while the master record itself remains untouched. Original cataloging may be entered into the data base by those libraries encountering unsuccessful searches, and these records will be made available to other users of the system and tagged as being locally input. The philosophy of OCLC is to attempt, within reason, to accommodate unique library cataloging features while continuing to maintain a generalized system. The network may encounter conflicting standards when many libraries begin to input original records; the resolution of this problem will be of importance for cooperative bibliographic systems.

Kennedy (44) presents a lucid and detailed account of the cost figures that he gathered at the Georgia Institute of Technology while optimizing a MARC card production system. Findings reveal that a small library may find a large number of hits during each search of the tape, but the cost of maintaining the entire file will be prohibitive. Kennedy's conclusion is that complete MARC files will be beyond the means and abilities of most libraries, a conclusion that is borne out by the experiences of other MARC users, who usually weed the file by date or delete certain classes of materials upon accession of the tape.

Book catalogs. A worthwhile and informative study is reported by French (31), who states that the Birmingham University Library (England) is growing at a rapid rate and studies have been carried out to determine the best form for a future catalog. The card catalog has been frozen at December 1971; the specific problem described in this article is the disposition of the retrospective catalog. Characteristics and comparative costs are given for: maintaining the old card catalog, mounting and binding the cards, xerography, microfilming for mounting on an aperture card, Copyflo processing, keypunching, computer

[1]Kilgour, Frederick. Talk presented at the Annual Meeting of the American Library Association, 22 June 1971.

output microfilm, and photochromic micro-image. The reader, while left uninformed as to Birmingham's final decision, is provided with a useful summary of techniques and costs of book catalog production.

Kieffer (45) questions the book catalog form, from the point of view of a head of technical processing. She poses a series of reasonable questions that might be asked by a technical processing administrator who is confronted with the decision of whether or not to adopt book catalogs. An interesting and refreshing query is put forth: "The ALA filing rules can be programmed, but the question is, is it worth it?" Although traditional filing rules probably cannot in fact be finely programmed, much work can be devoted to forcing the computer to "file" according to this tradition. Kieffer's question is appropriate at this time, when costs are being studied and priorities examined. May we indeed allow ourselves the simpler "character-by-character" filing medium?

A giant step was taken by the New York Public Library (76) with the publication of the dictionary catalog of its research libraries. As the subtitle indicates, it is a cumulative list of authors, titles, and subjects representing books and book-like materials added to the collection since January 1971. The main catalog will continue to serve as the primary catalog, and new data are to be added to both the main catalog and the machine-readable data base in parallel until January 1972, at which time conversion to the book catalog will be complete and new data will be added only to the machine-readable file. A clearly significant decision was made at the New York Public Library; this vast and old collection, with its own cataloging rules and subject headings, will be from now on compatible with Library of Congress cataloging (an exception is the class number, which is assigned according to size). The book catalog itself is physically attractive; the information is tightly packed but the type faces vary with the data element to facilitate skimming or reading. Filing is computer-oriented, as suggested by the previously cited article, with, for example, U.S. corporate main entries interfiling with U. S. corporate subject entries and with titles beginning with U.S.

Serials

More than any other application, serials processing has shown librarians and library systems analysts that automation can be, like any serial, unpredictable. Automated applications for serials range from the simple and relatively cheap computer-produced listing to the extremely complex on-line check-in system. Serials have probably created more problems than any other automated application because the manual systems in many libraries are chaotic and appear most likely to benefit from computer control. However, rather than being the most easily automated function of the library, the serials control function has proved itself to be the most difficult to design, control and manage because of its unpredictable nature.

Although basically a review article, Bosseau's overview (10) of automation of serials control blends a description of several successfully operating serials systems with a presentation of the problems, goals, and alternatives involved in a serials application. Drawing heavily from the experience of the University of California at San Diego, Bosseau discusses the functions of serials control: production of lists and catalogs, ordering and accounting, check-in, binding and claiming. He also describes various approaches to serials control, noting the advantages and disadvantages of each alternative. The author sheds light on the slow progress of the National Serials Data Program: "The mere mention of the word 'standards' to a serials librarian usually brings a response of skepticism on the possibilities of standardizing anything about serials," but the desirability of such standardization is emphasized.

Wall (101) also reviews various techniques of serials control and proposes a system that relies on manual procedures plus a paper-tape reader and an optical character reader. His system would seem to be somewhat unwieldy and difficult to control. At the University of Kansas, a computer-printed serials list is attached to a fanfold strip that is used for marking newly arrived issues of the adjacent title (Condit, 20). Every two weeks, an optical character reader processes the detached strip and updates the master file, which contains 25,000 titles located on two campuses. Using the MARC format, the system is capable of updating, checking in, binding, and funding serial records. At the time of reporting, plans were underway to increase the flexibility of checking in, which has been limited to two issues.

Reference

Defining the scope of automation of the reference function is not easy. Information storage and retrieval are distant from the normal library automation routine, as are the indexing and manipulation of data bases. For this reason, literature concerning these areas has been omitted from this chapter. Two publications must be mentioned, however, and coincidentally they are both not only reference-oriented but also education-oriented.

In an excellent effort that produced two volumes, Mathies & Watson (63) prepared a manual for a two-day institute on computer-based reference services sponsored by the Reference Services Division of the American Library Association. Because the ERIC system was used as an example and because the thesaurus, indexes, and organizational structure were described in detail, a large portion of the manual is devoted to this service alone. The intention was to acquaint the attending librarians thoroughly with one automated reference service to give them knowledge that they could transfer to the use of other data bases. A clear and well-written chapter explains Boolean logic and how the formulation of requests can influence the results of the search by increasing or decreasing the number of terms included, or by changing the logical operators (ANDs, ORs, and NOTs). Another section describes the census tapes and their structure. The students' workbook could be either eliminated or redesigned, but the tutors' manual alone is a valuable tool.

Meredith (67) summarizes the REFSEARCH teaching language created at the Graduate School of Library Science, University of California, Berkeley. With a reference collection of some 160 items, a set of categories was developed so that any request for a reference work could be analyzed and assigned one or more "handles" from these categories. A ten-month project was required to code the collection into categories by discipline, type of approach, and other special categories. A student using the system may enter the terms that he believes fit the question being asked, and the reference works that fulfill the criteria established by the categories are typed on an interactive typewriter. This innovative approach to teaching will result in a better comprehension of the structure of a reference question. On the negative side, it might be possible for a student to leave the course without having become acquainted with basic reference works.

Selective Dissemination of Information

While a number of libraries are actively engaged in programs of selective dissemination of information (Markuson et al., 56; Heilik, 37; Mauerhoff & Smith, 64), this chapter will not detail the work but will refer the reader instead to Avram (2) and to the chapter on retrieval and dissemination systems in this volume. The relationship of an SDI function to the general library is a nebulous one; this reviewer has found that the definition of "information center" runs the gamut from an entity totally within the library organization to one that is totally unrelated to the library. The SDI operations of many special and small libraries operate with success, and managers of specialized information centers with multiple machine-readable data bases find that they must charge up to several hundred dollars per search, a consideration that is incompatible with the non-profit service mode of the library. For these reasons, the reviewer felt that in-depth review of the literature on selective dissemination of information would itself be incompatible with a chapter on library automation.

RESEARCH

The library automation field has always had the benefit not only of the work of pure researchers but also of the results of systems work and programming applications of planned or operational projects, especially in large-scale systems. The results of a systems study or the software technique developed by a library systems analyst to solve a problem are of interest and potentially great use to the rest of the library systems community. The "not invented here" syndrome (Warheit, 102) can be overcome by persistent documentation and publication of findings such as those described in this section.

The Institute of Library Research at the University of California, Berkeley (Maron & Sherman, 57), has published the reports resulting from a grant to design an information processing laboratory. This six-volume report describes the second phase of the information processing laboratory and includes users' manuals for several tex-processing programming languages developed during the progress of the research. A second report from the Institute for Library Research (Shoffner et al., 93) is the result of the File Organization Project. This seven-volume set contains a project summary, a description of the component studies, and several users' manuals. Both the descriptive and technical portions of the reports are succinct and innovative and make a valuable contribution to the field. Shoffner (92) describes the implications of automatic field recognition in the conversion of bibliographic data to machine-readable form. He relates format recognition to the principles of systems analysis and to bibliographic control procedures. Format recognition potentially reduces the total man effort expended in a conversion project, he notes; with format recognition, it is possible to group processes on the basis of classes of records rather than iterating each process for each record. The automatic field recognition used at the Institute for Library Research is the first step in a conversion process; the next step is an automatic clean-up with the assistance of an authority file. With this technique, 95% accuracy in field recognition was achieved with the initial 7000 records processed.

Further work on Project INTREX (61) summarizes the open-environment use of INTREX, in which consoles are available in the Barker Engineering Library for all who wish to make use of the system. The full-text retrieval that is a part of the design has been favorably received but is quite costly, and microfiche duplication is being promoted.[1] The closed environment experiments have entailed indicativity experiments with nine subjects over a period of several months. In these experiments, the subjects indicate the value of the citations retrieved in answer to a certain problem; the identical situation is repeated one or two weeks later to test the validity of the initial judgment. The assumption is made that in an interval of one or two weeks the subject will forget his original evaluations. This reviewer must question the small size of the experimental group as a valid measure of the success of the system.

With the increasing availability of on-line systems, more research is now being devoted to determining the best techniques for accessing large files of bibliographic records. Search codes to access main entries or titles have been discussed at length in the literature; a considerable range exists in the mode of access used by varying systems (e.g., three letters of main entry and five letters of title, or four letters of main entry and four letters of title, etc.). Newman & Buchinski (77) cite a study at the University of Saskatchewan Library to produce a compression code for the technical processing in-process file. The first algorithm used a sixteen-character title compression, twelve-character corporate entry compressions, a four-character personal entry compression, and a date code. A comparison was made with an algorithm that deleted small words and used six characters drawn from the title, six characters of main entry, and a date code. Matches made on the MARC records and the outstanding order file retrieved 78.74% and 81.1% of the items requested, respectively. After analysis, the decision was made to use four significant words from the title and four significant words from the corporate entries.

At the Ohio College Library Center, Kilgour et al. (46), in testing the utility of truncated search keys as inquiry terms in an on-line system, produced evidence that use of a three-and-three search key yields eight or fewer responses 99% of the time from a file of 16,790 title-only entries. While the results of these tests are useful, they raise the question of tolerance of multiple responses on future bibliographic files that will be far larger than 17,000 records.

[1]Private communication, Carl Overhage, Director, Project INTREX, 18 January 1972.

The implications of computerized filing have also been the subject of lengthy discussion. The earliest method of handling filing rules was to assign sequence numbers to bibliographic records to force them to file in a desired sequence. More recently, efforts have been made to use the computer's collating sequence and to persuade libraries to accept less sophisticated filing rules. Price (84) reports the work of the Library Association Working Party on Filing Rules. Although this project has certain limitations, its methodology includes the ability to supply different collating sequences by parameter and, even more important, to supply different collating sequences to different types of tags in a bibliographic record. In reviewing an experiment developed for the MARC Pilot Project, Palmer (80) describes a method of deriving filing fields from normally formatted data. The sort key inserts digits preceding each word of the main entry, makes tests for certain prefixes to close up blanks, changes Mc to Mac, and drops diacritical marks. An edit list is printed for those names of a doubtful nature; of 55,000 names, 4.1% were found to require special processing, and only 1.1% were doubtful.

PERSONNEL

Questions of personnel and staff are closely linked to the educational processes in any field. Belzer et al. (8) have published the results of a survey of information science curricula carried out by the Special Interest Group in Education for Information Science of the American Society for Information Science. The responses received from forty-five schools showed that approximately 185 courses and 242 topics had been defined. This survey was followed by a workshop to interpret the results. Using the Delphi Method, the participants in the workshop identified nine relevant factors and seven core courses in teaching information science. From Australia, where several new library schools are free to examine their goals for the future, Rayward (87) points out the dualism of attention in any profession. One must use its techniques and skills and must also engage in a constant re-examination of the underlying body or knowledge and attempt to extend it. He states that institutions involved in education must be aware of this dualism and must train sufficient numbers of librarians who are able to carry out systematic analyses and decision-making procedures.

The search for the intersection of the librarian and the data-base manager is discussed by Landau (49). The data-base manager is defined as the overall planner and administrator of the data base and its users. This definition resembles that of a librarian, with different material. At present, he says, librarians do not have the knowledge needed for management of data bases and do not feel that data base management lies within their area of responsibility. However, the librarian cannot ignore non-book information; computer specialists are beginning to design and run digital libraries. A bibliography is given in six different areas: file design, vocabulary, search strategy, software and hardware, administration, and general references.

In a paper that is based on experience with the Stanford University Library, Weber (104) advocates that design and implementation of systems require many talents in the design staff and include the participation of the users. The lack of some specified talents may force an institution to go to outside contractors for support. Although he advocates a joint computation center/library selection of staff, he points out the possible lack of commitment of computer people to the goals of the library. Library systems analysts should have the same status as staff members of other major library departments. Because a large institution is susceptible to a lack of communication, he feels that careful efforts should be made to involve the entire staff in changing procedures and policies. Burgis (12) recommends a team approach to library administration with the library systems analyst being drawn into the team function. This is an increasingly appealing concept if one accepts the likelihood that networks and centralized agencies will at some time in the future handle the more clerical aspects of a library operation, and each library will need to find its own fit within a network.

CONCLUSION

A review of the year's activities reveals that appreciable strides have now been made toward standardization of formats, transferability and sharing of systems and programs, and sharing of data bases. The published results of research in these areas should help libraries to avoid duplication of effort. The literature of 1971 was also characterized by an abundance of articles and surveys concerning interinstitutional cooperation, including automated library networks. As yet, we have identified many obstacles but discovered few solutions.

Although a few successful efforts are beginning to transfer not only the logic but complete systems from one institution to another, the method by which this cooperation is achieved is haphazard, with little coordination or overall planning. It would seem desirable for an organization with national scope, such as the newly formed National Commission on Libraries and Information Science, to be asked to assume the task of monitoring, coordinating, and planning, so that maximum use can be made of the available resources without undue constraints on the major library development efforts.

In the process of automating a library procedure, many problems are encountered and many issues are raised. Depending on the priorities of the library in question, these problems may be bypassed and left unsolved until the solution is developed at a higher level, or the library may mount a large-scale effort to supply the needed format (or data base, or subsystem). Although it frequently happens that another library has already begun similar work, very little is done to take advantage of this work or to avoid duplication of efforts. A more serious implication exists, however. As mentioned above, the pace of developments can be rapid and priorities of different libraries can vary widely. It has been the case, therefore, that one group was working on a standard format for a particular type of data, while an independent organization, adequately supported and unable to wait for the format to become official, instead developed its own new format.

The literature that focusses on patterns of staffing for an automated system still stresses the characteristics of an optimum systems staff for a library. This emphasis may be misplaced, however, since greater centralization and larger systems indicate that the individual library may no longer need a full systems staff, but may find its needs met by a systems analyst alone. The consortium or regional center, however, will need more staff members of diversified backgrounds. An administrator who is fully qualified in both librarianship and automation will be an asset to the central node; supporting him will be a highly skilled and competent technical staff.

The "clean sweep" implied by this change of staffing patterns is obviously not possible because many libraries are already involved in automation. These libraries will continue to maintain their staffs and their systems as financial and physical circumstances allow. Many of these institutions will find it possible either to join or to initiate such networks, based on their own systems. Libraries with no background in automation should now look carefully before attempting to venture alone and should consider, instead, the cooperative approach.

Librarians are becoming aware of the economic and physical problems that face them, and the attitude of this decade is not an optimistic one. They realize, for the most part, that some sort of automated procedure can assist them in processing the vast amount of information that passes through the technical services departments of the libraries of the world. Automation has not yet achieved the perfect system for any single library, but a constant awareness and continual refinement of our activities make the outlook for our use of developing technology ever more positive.

REFERENCES

(1) ASSOCIATION OF RESEARCH LIBRARIES. Ad Hoc Committee on Specifications for a Study of Automation in Research Libraries. In: Association of Research Libraries. 77th meeting, Los Angeles, California, 17 January 1971. Minutes. Association of Research Libraries, Washington, D.C., 1971, Appendix C, 79-83.
(2) AVRAM, HENRIETTE D. Library automation. In: Cuadra, Carlos A.; ed. Annual review of information science and technology, v.6. Encyclopaedia Britannica, Inc., Chicago, Illinois, 1971, 171-217.
(3) AVRAM, HENRIETTE D.; MARUYAMA, LENORE S. RECON Pilot Project: a progress report, April-September 1970. Journal of Library Automation, 4:1 (March 1971) 38-51.
(4) AVRAM, HENRIETTE D.; MARUYAMA, LENORE S. The RECON Pilot Project: a progress report, October 1970-May 1971. Journal of Library Automation, 4:3 (September 1971) 159-169.
(5) AYRES, F. H. The case against MARC: how strong is it? Library Association Record, 73:7 (July 1971) 130-131, 142.
(6) BAKER, L. R. United we stand, divided we . . . : the case for cooperation among CAE libraries. Australian Library Journal, 20:8 (September 1971) 15-22.
(7) BALMFORTH, C. K.; COX, N. S. M.; eds. Interface: library automation with special reference to computing activity. The M.I.T. Press, Cambridge, Massachusetts, 1971, 251 p.
(8) BELZER, JACK; et al. Curricula in information science: analysis and development. Journal of the American Society for Information Science, 22:3 (May/June 1971) 193-223.
(9) BOISSET, MICHEL; BEYSSAC, ROLAND. Une expérience de bibliothèque automatisée: GIBUS. Bulletin des Bibliothèques de France, 16:5 (May 1971) 259-278.
(10) BOSSEAU, DON L. The computer in serials processing and control. In: Voigt, Melvin J.; ed. Advances in librarianship, v.2, Seminar Press, New York, 1971, 103-164.
(11) BUDINGTON, WILLIAM. Research library expectations of a National Serials Data Program. In: Association of Research Libraries. 77th meeting. Los Angeles, California, 17 January 1971. Minutes. Association of Research Libraries, Washington, D.C., 1971, 21-25.
(12) BURGIS, G. C. A systems concept of organization and control for large university libraries. Canadian Library Journal, 28:1 (January/February 1971) 24-29.
(13) BURNS, ROBERT W., JR. A generalized methodology for library systems analysis. College and Research Libraries, 32:4 (June 1971) 295-303.
(14) CALIFORNIA STATE COLLEGE. LOS ANGELES. Of note - circulation records. American Libraries, 2:7 (July/August 1971) 668.
(15) CARDSET CATALOGING SYSTEMS. Users' manual. Information Design, Inc., Menlo Park, California, 1971, 22 p.
(16) CHAUVEINC, MARC. MONOCLE. Journal of Library Automation, 4:3 (September 1971) 113-128.
(17) COBLANS, HERBERT. National reports and information policy. Aslib Proceedings, 23:1 (January 1971) 24-32.
(18) College & Research Libraries, 32:5 (September 1971) 384-392. (Letters to the editor).

(19) College & Research Libraries, 32:6 (November 1971) 479-480. (Letters to the editor).

(20) CONDIT, ANNA R. Optical mark sensing of serials check-in records: a new approach to serials automation. In: American Society for Information Science. Annual meeting. 34th, Denver, Colorado, 7-11 November 1971. Proceedings, vol.8: Communication for decision-makers. Greenwood Publishing Corp., Westport, Connecticut, 1971, 287-290.

(21) COWBURN, LORNA M. University of Surrey Library automated issue system. Program, 5:2 (May 1971) 70-88.

(22) CRITTENDEN, VICTOR. The problem of perfection: Library of Congress cataloguing, MARC tapes and their use in Australian libraries. Australian Library Journal, 20:4 (May 1971) 20-22.

(23) CUADRA, CARLOS A. On-line systems: promise and pitfalls. Journal of the American Society for Information Science, 22:2 (March/April 1971) 107-114.

(24) CUADRA, CARLOS A.; PEARSON, KARL M., JR. Status and prospects of automation in the Federal library community. In: American Society for Information Science. Annual meeting. 34th, Denver, Colorado, 7-11 November 1971. Proceedings, vol.8: Communication for decision-makers. Greenwood Publishing Corp., Westport, Connecticut, 1971, 291-295.

(25) DUCHESNE, R. M.; PHILLIPS, A. B. Automation activities in British university libraries: a survey. Program, 5:3 (July 1971) 129-140.

(26) ELIAS, ARTHUR W.; ed. Key papers in information science. American Society for Information Science, Washington, D.C., 1971, 230 p.

(27) EPSTEIN, A. H.; et al. Bibliographic automation of large library operations using a time-sharing system: phase I. Final report. Stanford University Library, Stanford, California, 1971, 334 p. (ED 049 786).

(28) FASANA, PAUL J. Collaborative Library Systems Development: an experiment in the joint design of automated library systems. In: American Society for Information Science. Annual meeting. 34th, Denver, Colorado, 7-11 November 1971. Proceedings, vol.8: Communication for decision-makers. Greenwood Publishing Corp., Westport, Connecticut, 1971, 233-236.

(29) FASANA, PAUL J.; VEANER, ALLEN; eds. Collaborative Library Systems Development. The M.I.T. Press, Cambridge, Massachusetts and London, England, 1971, 241 p.

(30) FIVE ASSOCIATED UNIVERSITY LIBRARIES. Joint serials control system project for the libraries of Cornell University, University of Rochester, and the State University of New York at Buffalo. Phase I: Feasibility study. Final report. Five Associated University Libraries, Syracuse, New York, 1971, 141 p. (ED 051 827).

(31) FRENCH, THOMAS. Conversion of library card catalogues. Program, 5:2 (May 1971) 41-66.

(32) FRISTOE, ASHBY J.; MYERS, ROSE E. Acquisitions in 1970. Library Resources & Technical Services, (Spring 1971) 132-142.

(33) GONZALEZ LOPEZ, MARIA LUZ. Automatización de catálogos. Asociación Nacional de Bibliotecarios, Madrid, Spain, 1971, 143 p.

(34) GUTHRIE, GERRY D. An on-line remote access and circulation control system. In: American Society for Information Science. Annual meeting. 34th, Denver, Colorado, 7-11 November 1971. Proceedings, vol.8: Communication for decision-makers. Greenwood Publishing Corp., Westport, Connecticut, 1971, 305-309.

(35) HAYES, ROBERT M.; MASON, ELLSWORTH. Hayes and Mason on automation . . . College & Research Libraries, 32:5 (September 1971) 384-388.

(36) HEILIGER, EDWARD M.; HENDERSON, PAUL B., JR. Library automation: experience, methodology, and technology of the library as an information system. McGraw-Hill, New York, 1971, 333 p. (McGraw-Hill Series in Library Education).

(37) HEILIK, J. Information retrieval and MARC at the National Science Library. Canadian Library Journal, 28:2 (March/April 1971) 120-123.
(38) HEIN, MORTEN. Scandinavian Conference on Data Processing in Libraries. Scandinavian Public Library Quarterly, 1971:1, 47-50.
(39) ILLINOIS, UNIVERSITY OF. URBANA. GRADUATE SCHOOL OF LIBRARY SCIENCE. Clinic on Library Applications of Data Processing, Urbana, Illinois, 1970. Proceedings: MARC uses and users. Edited by Kathryn L. Henderson. University of Illinois, Graduate School of Library Science, Urbana, Illinois, 1971, 110 p.
(40) INTERNATIONAL BUSINESS MACHINES CORPORATION. DATA PROCESSING DIVISION. On-line remote catalog access and circulation control system. Pt. I. Functional specifications. Pt. II. Users' manual. Ohio State University Libraries, Columbus, Ohio, 1971, paging varies.
(41) JOHNSON, DONALD. The National Serials Pilot Project. In: Association of Research Libraries, 77th meeting, Los Angeles, California, 17 January 1971. Minutes. Association of Research Libraries, Washington, D.C., 1971, 11-16.
(42) JOLLIFFE, JOHN W. Project LOC: a talk to the Bibliographical Society, London, in April, 1971. 16 p.
(43) KAPLAN, LOUIS; ed. Reader in library services and the computer. National Cash Register Company, Washington, D.C., 1971.
(44) KENNEDY, JOHN P. File size and the cost of processing MARC records. Journal of Library Automation, 4:1 (March 1971) 1-12.
(45) KIEFFER, PAULA. Book catalog - to have or not to have. Library Resources and Technical Services, 15:3 (Summer 1971) 290-296.
(46) KILGOUR, FREDERICK; et al. Title-only entries retrieved by use of truncated search keys. Journal of Library Automation, 4:4 (December 1971) 207-210.
(47) KOENIG, MICHAEL E. D.; et al. SCOPE: a cost analysis of an automated serials record system. Journal of Library Automation, 4:3 (September 1971) 129-140.
(48) KOZUMPLIK, WILLIAM G. Circulation mechanized. Special Libraries, 62:7/8 (July/August 1971) 287-288.
(49) LANDAU, HERBERT B. Can the librarian become a computer data base manager? Special Libraries, 62:3 (March 1971) 117-124.
(50) LARC ASSOCIATION. A survey of automated activities in the libraries of the U.S. and Canada. 2d ed. Compiled and edited by Frank S. Patrinostro and indexed by Nancy P. Sanders. The LARC Association, Tempe, Arizona, 1971, 131 p. (Volume 1 of A survey of automated activities in the libraries of the world. ED 047 740).
(51) LAZEROW, SAMUEL. The national serials system: concept and commitment. In: Association of Research Libraries, 77th meeting. Los Angeles, California, 17 January 1971. Minutes. Association of Research Libraries. Washington, D.C., 1971, 17-21.
(52) LEE, HWA-WEI. Library mechanization at the Asian Institute of Technology. International Library Review, 3:3 (June 1971) 257-270.
(53) LISTON, DAVID M., JR.; SCHOENE, MARY L. A systems approach to the design of information systems. Journal of the American Society for Information Science, 22:2 (March/April 1971) 115-122.
(54) McALLISTER, CARYL. On-line library housekeeping systems: a survey. Special Libraries, 62:11 (November 1971) 457-468.
(55) MARKUSON, BARBARA; et al. Automation and the Federal library community. System Development Corporation, Falls Church, Virginia, 1971, 241 p. (ED 058 917).
(56) MARKUSON, BARBARA; et al. Handbook on Federal library automation. System Development Corporation, Falls Church, Virginia, 1971, paging varies.
(57) MARON, M.E.; SHERMAN, DON. An information processing laboratory for

education and research in library science: phase 2. University of California, Berkeley, Institute of Library Research, September 1971, 122 p. (Volume 1 of a 6-volume report).
(58) MARUYAMA, LENORE S. Format recognition: a report of a project at the Library of Congress. Journal of the American Society for Information Science, 22:4 (July/August 1971) 283-287.
(59) MASON, ELLSWORTH. Along the academic way. Library Journal, 96:10 (15 May 1971) 1671-1676.
(60) MASON, ELLSWORTH. The great gas bubble prick't or, computers revealed by a gentleman of quality. College & Research Libraries, 32:3 (May 1971) 183-196.
(61) MASSACHUSETTS INSTITUTE OF TECHNOLOGY. Project INTREX. Semi-annual activity report, 15 March - 15 September 1971. Massachusetts Institute of Technology, Cambridge, Massachusetts, 1971, 122 p. (ED 053 772).
(62) MASSACHUSETTS INSTITUTE OF TECHNOLOGY. Project INTREX. Semi-annual activity report, 15 September 1970 - 15 March 1971. Massachusetts Institute of Technology, Cambridge, Massachusetts, 1971, 85 p. (ED 047 739).
(63) MATHIES, M. LORRAINE; WATSON, PETER G. Computer-based reference service: a pre-conference institute of the Reference Services Division, American Library Association, Dallas, Texas, 18-19 June 1971. Tutors' manual. American Library Association, Chicago, Illinois, 1971, 199 p.
(64) MAUERHOFF, GEORG R.; SMITH, RICHARD G. A MARC-II-based program for retrieval and dissemination. Journal of Library Automation, 4:3 (September 1971) 141-158.
(65) MELCHER, DANIEL. Cataloging, processing, and automation. American Libraries, 2:7 (July/August 1971) 701-713.
(66) MELCHER, DANIEL. Melcher on acquisition. American Library Association, Chicago, Illinois, 1971, 169 p.
(67) MEREDITH, J. C. Machine-assisted approach to general reference materials. Journal of the American Society for Information Science, 22:3 (May/June 1971) 176-186.
(68) MILLER, ELLEN WASBY; HODGES, B. J. Shawnee Mission's on-line cataloging system. Journal of Library Automation, 4:1 (March 1971) 13-26.
(69) MOLZ, KATHLEEN. Gradus ad Parnassum. Illinois Libraries, 53:3 (March 1971) 185-191.
(70) MONTAGUE, ELEANOR. Summary of a feasibility study on the participation of four colleges and universities in a Stanford University Library automation network. Stanford University, SPIRES/BALLOTS Project, Stanford, California, 1971, 72 p.
(71) MUNN, R. F. Use of modern technology in the improvement of information resources and services in developing countries. International Library Review, 3:1 (January 1971) 9-13.
(72) NANCE, RICHARD E.; WICKHAM, W. KENNETH: DUGGAN, MARYANN A computer system for effective management of a medical library network: an overview. Southern Methodist University, Dallas Texas, 1971, 13 p. + appendix. (Technical report CP-71005).
(73) NATIONAL ACADEMY OF SCIENCES. COMPUTER SCIENCE AND ENGINEERING BOARD. INFORMATION SYSTEMS PANEL. Libraries and information technology - a national systems challenge. A report to the Council on Library Resources, Inc. National Academy of Sciences, Washington, D.C., 1972, 95 p.
(74) NEW ENGLAND BOARD OF HIGHER EDUCATION. A proposal to test the transferability of the Ohio College Library Center computer system to the New England Library Information Network. (Submitted to the Council on Library Resources). New England Board of Higher Education, Wellesley, Massachusetts, 1971, paging varies.

(75) New service available. Oklahoma Department of Libraries Automation Newsletter, 3:2-3 (October/December 1971) 17-20.
(76) NEW YORK PUBLIC LIBRARY. Dictionary catalog of the research libraries; a cumulative list of authors, titles and subjects representing books and book-like materials added to the collections since January 1971. October 1971, A-Z. New York Public Library, New York, 1971, 553 p.
(77) NEWMAN, WILLIAM L.; BUCHINSKI, EDWIN J. Entry/title compression code access to machine readable bibliographic files. Journal of Library Automation, 4:2 (June 1971) 72-85.
(78) OWEN, D. G. A computer circulation system feasibility study. Program, 5:1 (January 1971) 16-18.
(79) OWEN, JEANNE C. Marriage à la mode: libraries and computers in the U.S. Australian Library Journal, 20:5 (June 1971) 16-20.
(80) PALMER, FOSTER M. Automatic processing of personal names for filing. Journal of Library Automation, 4:4 (December 1971) 185-197.
(81) PAYNE, CHARLES T.; McGEE, ROBERT S. The University of Chicago Library bibliographic data processing system: documentation and report supplement. University of Chicago Library, Chicago, Illinois, 1971, 159 p.
(82) PAYNE, CHARLES T.; McGEE, ROBERT S.; FISHER, ELLEN R. The University of Chicago Library bibliographic data processing system; documentation and report as of October 31, 1969. University of Chicago Library, Chicago, Illinois, October 1970, 287 p.
(83) POUND, MARY. Serials: a review of 1970. Library Resources and Technical Services, 15:2 (Spring 1971) 143-149.
(84) PRICE, A. The implementation of filing rules by computer. fProgram, 5:3 (July 1971) 161-164.
(85) R & D projects in documentation and librarianship. Federation Internationale de Documentation, The Hague, Netherlands, 1971 + .
(86) RAO, PALADUGU V.; SZERENYI, B. JOSEPH. Booth Library on-line circulation system (BLOC). Journal of Library Automation, 4:2 (June 1971) 86-102.
(87) RAYWARD, W. BOYD. The new technology and education for librarianship. Australian Library Journal, 20:5 (June 1971) 12-15.
(88) RICHMOND, PHYLLIS A. The year's work in cataloging and classification. Library Resources and Technical Services, 15:2 (Spring 1971) 151-157.
(89) RISTOW, WALTER W.; CARRINGTON, DAVID K. Machine-readable map cataloging in the Library of Congress. Special Libraries, 62:9 (September 1971) 343-352.
(90) SCHIEBER, WILLIAM D. ISIS (Integrated Scientific Information System): a general description of an approach to computerised bibliographical control. International Labour Office, Geneva, Switzerland, 1971, 115 p. (ED 054 801. Available from International Labour Office, Washington Branch, 666 Eleventh Street, Washington, D.C.).
(91) SHANK, RUSSELL; et al. A library network for Western Canada: automation for rationalization in college and university libraries in Alberta, Saskatchewan, and Manitoba. Kent State University, Center for Library Studies, Kent, Ohio, 1971, 78 p. (ED 053 773).
(92) SHOFFNER, RALPH M. Some implications of automatic recognition of bibliographic elements. Journal of the American Society for Information Science, 22:4 (July/August 1971) 275-282.
(93) SHOFFNER, RALPH M.; CUNNINGHAM, JAY L.; HUMPHREY, ALLAN J. The organization and search of bibliographic records in on-line computer systems: project summary. University of California, Berkeley, Institute of Library Research, 1971. (In press. Volume 1 of a 7-volume series).
(94) SIMMONS, PETER. Collection development and the computer: a case study in the analysis of machine readable loan records and their application to book selec-

tion. University of British Columbia, School of Librarianship, Vancouver, British Columbia, Canada, 1971, 63 p. (ED 054 817).

(95) SLICE/MARC-O: a project of the Southwestern Library Association. Description of services. Prepared cooperatively by Oklahoma Department of Libraries and SLICE Office Director, December 1971, 16 p.

(96) SOKOLOSKI, JAMES S. Data processing at the University of Massachusetts Library. American Library Association, 20 June 1971, 19 p. (Unpublished paper presented at the meeting of the Information Science and Automation Division COLA Discussion Group).

(97) STOCKARD, JOAN. Selective survey of MARC literature. Library Resources and Technical Services, 15:3 (Summer 1971) 279-289.

(98) SULLIVAN, ROBERT C. Developments in photoreproduction of library materials, 1970. Library Resources and Technical Services, 15:2 (Spring 1971) 158-190.

(99) TAUBER, MAURICE F.; FEINBERG, HILDA. Book catalogs. Scarecrow Press, Metuchen, New Jersey, 1971, 572 p.

(100) UNGERLEIDER, S. LESTER. Study of useability of computer output microfilm in the technical processing area of the Yale University Library. Yale University Library, New Haven, Connecticut, 1971, paging varies. (Unpublished report).

(101) WALL, R. A. A proposed experiment in automated serials accessioning. Program, 5:3 (July 1971) 141-151.

(102) WARHEIT, I. ALBERT. When some systems fail - is it the system or the librarian? Wilson Library Bulletin, 46:1 (September 1971) 52-58.

(103) WASSERMAN, PAUL; ed. LIST 1971: library and information science today. Science Associates, New York, 1971, 397 p.

(104) WEBER, DAVID C. Personnel aspects of library automation. Journal of Library Automation, 4:1 (March 1971) 27-37.

(105) WEBER, DAVID C. Working paper on the future of library automation at Stanford. Stanford University Library, Stanford, California, 1971, 65 p. (Unpublished internal document).

(106) WELSH, WILLIAM J. The Processing Department of the Library of Congress in 1970. Library Resources and Technical Services, 15:2 (Spring 1971) 191-214.

8 Library and Information Networks

EDWIN E. OLSON
University of Maryland
and
RUSSELL SHANK
Smithsonian Institution
and
HAROLD A. OLSEN
University of Maryland

INTRODUCTION

Overview

We have focused upon analytical writing about networks and networking, going as far as possible into the literature of all types of networks—library, computer, information centers, and multimedia centers. We have tried to avoid simple description of current activity in networking in favor of literature that analyzes the interrelation of component parts of a network or discusses the critical areas where the network impinges on its social, political, economic, and technical environment.

We have organized our discussion of the literature around four topics which we believe are crucial for explaining the distinctive character of the network phenomenon—the dynamic social and political environment of networking, the administrative processes, economic aspects, and technological developments. In the final section and conclusion we attempt to tie together our analysis of these network components and suggest implications for building networks of the future.

We have compiled a short and somewhat normative list of what we see as the essential characteristics of a library and information network:

(1) A network's function is to marshal resources from its environment to accomplish results beyond the ability of any one of its members.

(2) A network has developed an organizational design and structure that allows it to establish an identifiable domain and exercise appropriate influence over the members.

(3) It has a base in communications technology.

A number of authors present definitions that overlap with definitions of a library or information center or cooperative activity in providing information services (Clapp, 28; Budington, 22; Adams 1). Swank's list of properties of an information network (144) also contains some that are not unique to networks, but his paper does provide a useful review of network activity, organized around these six properties:

(1) They have information resources.
(2) Readers or users are usually remote from the main source of information.
(3) Schemes are used for the intellectual organization of documents or data, such as directories for use by readers or users.
(4) Resources are delivered to readers or users.
(5) There is a formal organization of cooperating or contracting information agencies for presenting different data bases and/or groups of users.
(6) There are bidirectional communications, preferably using high-speed long-distance electrical signal transmission with switching capabilities and computer hook-ups.

Most studies in the literature are descriptive and narrow, focusing on a single aspect of network performance or a single network function (such as facsimile transmission or interlibrary loan). The quality of analysis is often spotty, with deficient documentation of the assumptions and procedures of analysis. The significance of such studies is only to the specific context in which they were performed, since they provide no sound basis for aggregating, generalizing, or comparing the results. Still, some of these studies can provide important clues about what might be revealed by systematic analysis, and a few studies do provide examples of good analysis that others may find useful to follow.

Readers who wish to keep up with developments in networking are referred to the following bibliographies and directories. Stenstrom (138) has developed an annotated bibliography of cooperative efforts of libraries covering 1940 to 1968, and Babcock (9) has updated it through 1971. Kruzas & Schnitzer (80) have developed an encyclopedia of information systems and services that include over 150 networks and cooperative programs. DeLanoy & Cuadra (38) developed a directory containing 125 entries, each describing a functioning academic library consortium.

Scope of Chapter

This chapter covers materials and documents published in 1969, 1970, and 1971, with emphasis on 1971. The last chapter on information networks in the *Annual Review* covered 1968 literature (Overhage, 111). Samuelson's chapter (124) last year covered literature for 1969 and 1970, but emphasized international information transfer. Accordingly, we have not emphasized international aspects, nor have we stressed the automation aspects of networking, which are covered in the automation chapter in this and previous volumes of the *Annual Review*. Since this is the first *Annual Review* chapter that explicitly focuses upon *library* networks, we have given them special emphasis.

Two surveys of networks are included in this review (Olson, 108, Patrick, 114). Although Olson was primarily concerned with identifying the dimensions of networks related to manpower considerations and Patrick surveyed only academic library consortia, both cover many aspects of the network phenomenon. We have scattered references to these surveys and to several other works throughout the chapter in the appropriate categories.

DYNAMIC ENVIRONMENT

Rationale and Impetus for Networks

The resort to networking by many library and information institutions may be symptomatic of the difficulties they face in dealing with their rapidly changing environment, particularly in two areas:

(1) Most libraries and information centers are subunits of some larger organization, which limits the number of options open to them as the larger organization modifies its goals or structure; and

(2) Many libraries and information centers are located in the public sector, and are limited in adjusting to changes in their environment (new demands, new technology, etc.) because of the bureaucratic inertia that is frequently associated with large scale public sector organizations.

These two characteristics seem to be of less concern in the private sector, where reorganization can be achieved through other means, particularly corporate merger or outright purchase of information activities. Public sector information activities do not have recourse to merger and consolidation. Instead, they must go the bureaucratic reorganization route, a procedure fraught with social and political negotiations and delays. Thus, the plea "Let's set up a 'network'" may just be the public bureaucrat's way of saying "We ought to merge," but because he lacks the authority or means of merging, he resorts to networking.

External pressure from political funding sources has forced cooperation in many areas (Kaser, 72; Patrick, 114). Olson (108) found that over one-half of all networks in his survey attribute their formation to the availability of government funds or the development of government programs. Heaps & Cooke (62) discuss the growth of scientific and technical information networks in Canada. They believe that networks spring from an awareness of the social responsibilities of scientists for information transfer; a feeling on the part of governments that information transfer is important for economic and/or military reasons; and a sense of frustration among those who need information about innovations in science, who are hampered by the lack of knowledge and understanding of the most recent developments in science.

Document overlap among member libraries may be a good or bad thing, depending on whether a network is envisioned as a device to reduce acquisition costs in individual libraries or as a device to enlarge each library's access to materials. In the state of Washington, where Reynolds et al. (120) found that 90 percent of the books published in the U.S. during 1968 were in one or more of 10 libraries in the state, network development is seen as a means of avoiding needless duplication of materials. Altman (2), who was interested in the feasibility of establishing interlibrary loan networks among public secondary school libraries, found that collections in schools are not alike. She says that schools could offer enough different titles to students engaged in independent study that it would be worthwhile to pool their collections through interlibrary loan. Sloan (133) suggests it would be useful to view networks as exchange systems into which libraries enter because they expect to receive benefits in exchange for the resources they contribute.

Perhaps the most commonly cited impetus for network development is the inability of a single library to provide adequate library service if programs are based only on local initiative and local resources (Pings, 117). Casey (24) agrees that no library can be self-sufficient, regardless of the size of its resources or user population. Chapin (26) disagrees. He says that most types of libraries for most types of user groups are self-sufficient, citing the availability of materials in microform and the users' needs for mostly recent material. According to Chapin, most users already have access to most of the documents they need; the development of expensive networks will do little more than make available 3 or 4 percent of additional material which is of minor importance to the user. We would disagree with Chapin about the self-sufficiency of libraries, but we agree that a network must demonstrate a favorable cost-benefit ratio to justify its worth.

The question of the legitimacy of networks is also raised by Heaps & Cooke (62), who argue that an information network should grow out of informed public policy. The social purpose of a network is called into question; networks do not seem to have been developed in response to a need expressed by the citizenry. Heaps & Cooke wonder whether the public is willing to pay for scientific information, given their more pressing concerns about such issues as consumer protection.

The working group summary on network services of the Airlie Conference (174) stated that the major goal of a library network should be to facilitate learning. They identified bibliographic access, mediation of user requests, delivery to users, and education as principal components of a network of library and information centers. Heinich (63) states that it is possible that formal instruction (with accreditation) and informal instruction may become the most important use of networks in the future. Although learning may be the network goal of the future, present network activity, at least in academic library consortia, is geared toward activities that require the least amount of investment and compromise and have the most tangible results (Patrick, 114). The most common activities are in the areas of interlibrary loan, reciprocal borrowing, delivery, and photocopying. Unless external funding is available, academic library consortia do not undertake such activities as large-scale automated catalog-card production, which require a great initial financial investment, considerable time before benefits are realized, and agreement on cataloging practices and standards.

Political and Legal Bases

The political environment—a network's power resources and the limitations upon its authority and influence—varies widely from one network to another. In the networks surveyed by Olson (108) many of the member libraries are virtually autonomous. The members are often located in different political jurisdictions and have strong bonds to parent institutions. Often the financial base is not under the network's control.

The legal bases of networking, for example, are tenuous at best. Duggan (43) says the current ambiguous laws and vague contracts require that network participants act as if they had a clear legal basis for their actions. She believes that formal written agreements of some type are essential in operating a successful network because contracts imply commitment and networks cannot operate without full commitment from participants.

About one-half of the library networks and consortia surveyed have some kind of written agreement such as a contract, a constitution, articles of incorporation, or a charter, according to Patrick (114) and Olson (108). Yet in only rare cases do networks penalize any member who wishes to withdraw—an indication of the great autonomy of members and the meager stakes members have in network membership.

A crucial factor that can either constrain or aid network development is the existing arrangements between the parent organizations, particularly the goal-setting carried on at the institutional level with implications for library and information service and the extent of commitment to network development at the highest levels. To promote such a commitment, one network—the Five Associated University Libraries (51)—brought together a symposium of librarians and university presidents to alert the latter to some of the conditions that prevented more daring and perhaps more fruitful cooperative ventures.

Conant (30) is concerned that the development of metropolitan library networks should receive the highest priority. He believes that, although there are no specific requirements for metropolitan library networks in the present federal legislation or administrative policy, it is a mistake to postpone action. He points to the complexities of life in metropolitan communities and the inadequacies of local governments, which are forcing state and federal governments to take major responsibility for planning the physical and social development of cities. Multipurpose regional planning agencies form the skeletal structure for future *de facto* metropolitan governments.

In New England, according to Hope (65), all six states now have an interstate library compact law. The compact administrators (the six heads of the state library agencies) form the governing board for the district. The board has power to administer cooperative programs, but so far no regional program has been initiated.

Leadership in the States

Healey (61) examines the organizational arrangements for public-academic library cooperation in Rhode Island and discusses the importance of a government structure as a base for networks. He believes that states are the obvious basis for a general-purpose network because:

(1) The use of state boundaries eliminates innumerable boundaries of local political jurisdictions;

(2) Most states are large enough to serve as a base for most network purposes;
(3) States are sources of fiscal support with revenues not available to local government; and
(4) State library agencies can provide leadership to all types of libraries.

Nelson & Nelson (102) also list a number of ways in which state librarians can assist in the integration of library service within their geographic area. In the master plan for a California library network, it is pointed out that the orderly operation of a statewide network involving both geographical and specialized systems requires a network center for the entire state. The California State Library will perform this function because of its experience with interlibrary loan and reference services, the existing communications and shipping facilities, its function as the administrator of library funds from state and federal sources, and its potential as a statewide processing center.

Rhode Island library law was changed in 1967 to authorize the Department of State Library Services to administer all library programs, deleting the limiting word "public" (Hope, 65). Therefore, interrelated library systems are legally spelled out as systems having resource centers to coordinate school, public, academic, and special libraries within the system. In Connecticut, responsibility for the administration of the statewide library service and statewide library development was transferred from the Department of Education to the Connecticut State Library. The trend in New England seems to be greater centralization of statewide responsibility and planning of library service of all types.

Hacker (58) provides a useful jurisdictional, legal, and political review of the development of library networks in the state of New York, including the difference between the legislation and the appropriations route in financing network plans. The reasons he gives for some of New York's legislative success in developing networks include: (1) there are effective working partnerships among influential people in the state; (2) state studies have given an opportunity for leadership to emerge; (3) network developers have had sound knowledge of how decisions on major legislation were reached and by whom; (4) there has been effective low-key and informed lobbying by leadership personalities in the state; (5) developers have had patience, persistence, and a willingness to compromise, to accept "half a loaf" in the interest of progress; (6) the state has had good timing and good luck; and (7) the way was paved by developers of a few county library systems that were visible successes. Weber & Lynden (169) and Patrick (114) also identify the importance of key individuals with sufficient time, energy, and vision to see a network through its formative period. St. Angelo et al. (123), in their study of state library legislation, conclude that effective leadership within state library agencies is a more important variable than the resources of the state in the development of quality library programs.

ADMINISTRATIVE PROCESSES

One of the few papers specifically tackling organizational aspects of network development is that of Kraemer (79), who reviews the Urban Information Systems Interagency Committee (called "USAC"). Organized in Washington, D.C., USAC began in 1968-69 as a consortium of nine federal agencies concerned with information support to urban programs, with the Department of Housing and Urban Development as the lead agency. This group was initially set up on an ad hoc basis to facilitate intergovernmental cooperation in urban information systems research and development. USAC became more formalized with extensive contractual relations with several municipalities interested in developing information systems for their operations; these municipalities also entered into the series of contractual relations with other organizations (private systems, software firms, universities, research centers) to put together the capability required for such development. Kraemer believes that USAC may, in its further evolution, provide a model of flexible administrative organization within a complex interorganizational environment, thus serving as a framework for creative federalism.

Planning

Slamecka (130) reminds us that networks can be developed in one of two ways—by beginning with existing systems and services and improving their efficiency or by formulating new objectives and functions for a to-be-designed system. Usually, however, networks are built upon something. For example, the Agricultural Sciences Information Network (ASIN) will be built upon a network of libraries because they exist and are already functionally responsible for information dissemination. It is to be hoped that the network will provide the organizational structure and resources for the systematic growth of cooperative efforts. The Needs and Development group of the Airlie House Conference (173) also felt that networks should evolve out of existing systems to preserve freedom of choice and local autonomy for individual libraries and information services.

The study of academic library consortia by DeLanoy & Cuadra (38) has developed a list of 24 steps in four phases (exploratory, planning, development, and operation and evaluation) that should be useful for planning. A number of respondents in this study said they might have saved four or five years of effort if they had known in the beginning what they know now.

A unique approach to planning a network that allowed prospective members to study the costs and benefits involved was described by Epstein et al. (45). For Stanford's SPIRES-BALLOTS project, they conducted a study of the feasibility of a regional library automation network. Prospective members of the network were brought together one day a week for 13 weeks. The goals were to acquaint them with the BALLOTS project, to develop and test a standardized methodology to permit comparisons between libraries of the costs and times required to perform a specified activity, to determine ways in which the project could be made of greater use to other libraries, and to prepare reports to the directors of the libraries that would allow them to assess the costs and benefits of participation in the BALLOTS Regional Network. This project appears to be unique in developing an assessment methodology and in giving librarians a short course to help them decide whether or not to join the network.

Preplanning and planning efforts to launch a network are described by a Booz, Allen & Hamilton, Inc. (16) study that prepares an agenda for research and demonstration for network development in the Washington metropolitan area, based on 50 in-depth interviews with people knowledgeable in the field.

Pings (116) presents an unusually detailed and candid statement of the formation of a regional medical library program that portrays the problems involved in determining objectives and setting up policies and procedures for a decentralized network. In another paper, Pings (117) describes the first-year experience of a network—its accomplishments, problems, and potential. Hacker (58) describes the development of three generations of networks in New York. The orderly development of the biomedical communications network is described by Davis (35); the network is also useful as a prototype of a network that, according to her, has adjusted to user needs and to social and technological changes.

Several reports of NLM-sponsored activities provide cost analyses or management discussions concerning regional library planning and development; most of them are reported in the *Bulletin of the Medical Library Association* (19, 21, 96, 109, and 135).

Decision-Making

To resolve conflicts at all stages of network development, decision-making mechanisms are necessary. Conflict can be particularly acute in establishing priorities for network activity. Miller's response (91) to the often-asked question, "Why don't we pick just one thing and do that?" is "Which one thing?" Because the autonomy and priorities of each library participant virtually always exceed the extent of the commitment to the network, decision-making about network priorities must be a search for elements that either transcend the prerogatives of the separate units or are no threat to the continued functioning of the separate units (Pings, 115). The process of conflict resolution requires negotiation and compromise. In a decentralized network, according to Pings, if one participating library finds it cannot accept responsibility for certain services, either the network finds a suitable procedure acceptable to all libraries or the services must be shifted from one participating library to another. This requires a constant evaluation of objectives, and it may produce inequalities in responsibilities among participating libraries.

The conflict inherent in network decision-making was also illustrated by the *Library Journal* account of the Ramapo-Catskill Library System (40). In the early years, the system functioned primarily to serve and strengthen local libraries by giving cash grants. But as the system developed, headquarters began to claim more and more of the income for its own operation and eventually cut out the cash grants. The services offered at the system level were perceived to be in direct competition with the needs of local members for materials and some of the basics of library service that the grants had made possible.

The problem of setting up a decision-making procedure to represent local interests is also addressed by Bridegam & Meyerhoff (21) in discussing the Regional Medical Library Program in New York. Olson (108) found, however, that in many cases networks are overly democratic. When asked what percentage of the members have to agree to important cooperative decisions before they can become policy and be implemented, about one-fourth of the cooperatives that he surveyed indicated that 70 percent or more, in many cases 100 percent of the membership, had to agree. In only about one-third of the cooperatives was less than majority agreement required.

Several authors stress that it is important not to be afraid of developing policies and procedures that may require changes in the attitudes and behavior of users and librarians in the participating libraries (Pings, 115; Sypert, 146). Equally important is the courage to adopt policies and procedures that set limits on what the network will or will not do. One of the reasons given for the success of the Minnesota Interlibrary Teletype Experiment (MINITEX) is its refusal to be all things to all people (Stanford, 136). The project supplies documents from the University of Minnesota's collection but it defines and limits the conditions of access and the scope of their service.

Manpower

The Network Services Group of the Airlie House Conference (174) stated that the ultimate success of library communication and information networks will rest on the capacity of qualified personnel to propose, develop, implement, and interpret the services required. Kaser (72) believes that cooperative work requires people with appropriate insight, temperament, and allegiance to cooperation, which may have to be developed by a program of involvement and education.

The directors of a cooperative should be persons who can use the power of suggestion and persuasion to get things done, according to Patrick (114). To be more effective in their jobs, many directors express the wish that their training had included more emphasis on administration and management and on fiscal, legal, and political aspects of information service (Olson, 108). Many also wanted additional training in public relations, psychology, systems analysis, and data processing. Conant (30) believes these skills are necessary for building institutions that cross political boundaries. New directions in library school education, including more extensive field experiences in the networks being developed, may provide a start toward meeting these needs. Martin (89) believes that problem-oriented seminars that include both professionals and lay people are important for the development of metropolitan library networks. This kind of manpower training should be useful in breaking down the isolation of one type of library from another and the barriers between the suburbs and the city.

This review of network organization suggests that many networks have a minimum capability to plan, provide leadership, resolve conflicts, and make important decisions about their priorities and procedures. In the face of severe conflict, many networks may not be able to mobilize sufficient resources to hold the members together.

ECONOMIC ASPECTS

In this section on the economic aspects of information networks, our focus remains analytic. But due to the paucity of such analytic studies we also include some items that describe but do not analyze network economic data. Several other studies are included that review information activities that are not truly networks but can serve as components of networks: centralized processing facilities, interlibrary loan operations, common carriers, and so on. The analytic techniques used in these studies represent the best practice and knowledge available now and can probably be generalized to more comprehensive economic analyses of networks.

In assessing the literature, one difficulty becomes evident: the tendency of information professionals to reduce economic analysis to simple reports of costs, thereby confusing *economics* with *economy*. Simple budget or expenditure data do not constitute economic analysis, though such figures can be raw material for analysis. And what appears to be "hard data" in print often turns out to be ambiguous and impossible to interpret, due to inadequate detail on how the figures were derived. This problem plagues economic analysis of all information activities, a judgment shared by Wilson in Chapter 2. Furthermore, most discussions of network economics appear to be symbolic exercises that recognize the significance of economic factors in network planning and management but fail to link the various economic aspects to overall network decision-making. Therefore, the studies reviewed here were selected because they document analytic assumptions, measurement procedures, and data limitations.

The framework used in organizing this section is developed more fully in the recent review of the literature on the economics of information by Olsen (107). Current studies on network economics rarely encompass more than one of the three framework factors—supply, demand, and adjustment mechanism. Very few studies address all three. This limitation is unfortunate because the major power of economic analysis stems from examining the interaction of these factors.

Supply-Factor Studies

Most materials on the economics of networks fall into the supply-factor category, but they are limited to descriptions of supply-factor characteristics—costs, production function analysis (organizing the resources and technology used in operations) and, occasionally, capital budgeting. These economic aspects are often included as part of a larger report, usually a chapter on the estimated costs of a network configuration. Typically, studies treat only one aspect of network activity such as TWX, interlibrary loan, or central processing of materials. The result is a very fragmented, often fuzzy picture of network supply factors.

These criticisms of the general contribution made by current studies may seem harsh, but good cost analyses of network production functions are essential for making sound economic judgments of network activity and are fundamental aids in administering networks.

Despite the shortcomings, some supply-factor studies do provide useful guidance for others interested in network activity. A good example is the study done by Montague (93) as part of the SPIRES-BALLOTS project at Stanford University. During a 13-week cooperative workshop, staff members from five colleges and universities near Stanford explored the feasibility of joining together in a network. examined the impact such a network would have on participants, and estimated the network operating costs using the SPIRES-BALLOTS capability. The report can serve as a how-to guide to simple cost analysis supporting network planning and illustrates the type of cost analysis needed by information managers before they decide whether to participate in an operational network.

In a similar vein is a study by Miller (92) of the Five Associated University Libraries (FAUL), centered in Western New York; it analyzes the technical service operations in the libraries of one of its members. Miller restricts his analysis primarily to descriptions of operational procedures and resources that can serve as the basis for a later cost analysis. At the time of his study, the FAUL group planned to extend this analysis to each of the five library systems in a sequential manner, rather than following the all-at-one-time strategy used by the Stanford group. The FAUL group also studied the supply problems of other possible network functions—document delivery (i.e., interlibrary loan) and book storage (113, 39). Two studies (52, 137) describe their development of a master file of document citations in machine-readable format compatible with MARC output.

A cost analysis of a much different network was that done for the Lister Hill Center for Biomedical Communications of the National Library of Medicine by Dei Rossi et al. (36). They estimate networking costs for TV broadcast of biomedical information, using as a basis common-carrier facilities and their current tariff rates. Because common carriers currently maintain a highly discriminatory pricing structure for one-time broadcasts vs. continuous broadcasts, the per-hour use charge decreases as continuous broadcast time increases, a fact reflected in the study cost estimates. This study methodology should prove helpful to others considering the use of common carrier facilities in networks.

The measurement of labor costs presents great difficulty in complex information activity. Spencer (135) reports on a general method for determining labor costs of interlibrary lending and photocopying, along with the unit costs derived at the Mid-Eastern Regional Library in Philadelphia. She found that the costs of providing a photocopy did not exceed the cost of lending the original document under comparable circumstances.

In a related study of interlibrary loan activity at the University of Colorado medical library, Braude & Holt (19) developed an analytic model that should have more general applicability. They compared the cost-performance trade-off between TWX and mail modes of supplying interlibrary loans, pointing out that a critical factor in providing such service efficiently is the time requirements of the user for the material demanded. (Their point illustrates that good administrative practice requires knowledge of both supply and demand factors.) They do a fine job of relating both results and methodology to prior pertinent work.

Dougherty & Maier (41) provide excellent documentation on the experimental operation of a cooperative centralized processing system serving Colorado academic libraries. Operations in the acquisitions-cataloging cycle were monitored, to provide measures of performance and costs of most internal and external aspects of this system. The relationships formed between the central agency and participating libraries were also studied in terms of their human-factor aspects. Among the performance features analyzed were lag-time in executing orders, customer acceptance of prespecified system outputs, vendor discount negotiations and delivery times, processing lag-time, catalog copy sources, and the impact of differences in participating library systems. To help others learn from the experience of this project, the authors discuss key questions that others should address before launching similar projects. The report considers most of the fundamental economic issues all library and information networks must resolve in their development: finances, fiscal relations, product diversity, standardization of specifications, interface procedures, production load variance, errors and quality control, use of specialists, training of staffs, etc.

Other reports on centralized processing include those by Hargrove & Stirling (60), for the California State Library, and Hopkins (66), for the Ohio College Library Center, and a report for the Southwestern Library Interstate Cooperative Endeavor (SLICE) (131). However, these three reports describe operating data, pricing policy, or cost estimates without the interpretation or problem analysis given in the Dougherty & Maier (41) study.

The RICE (Regional Information and Communication Exchange) project aims to improve scientific efforts in the Gulf Coast region using an information network approach; results of the first 17 months of the project are summarized by Ruecking (122). He lists problems similar to those discussed by Dougherty & Maier in evaluating network activity including the increased complexity of cost analysis in cooperative endeavors. Of interest to groups considering networks that link information analysis centers is a brief preliminary cost study by Marron (85). He notes the difficulties of using budget data for cost analysis.

Finally, Sypert (146) reports on still another network supply function in a description of the statewide reference network in Colorado. On the economic aspects of the network activity, she concludes that "no valid or reliable cost analysis can be made due to lacking information of actual operational costs, units of reference service, and expected and actualized benefits, all of which are necessary for cost benefit measurement." This statement is true of many recent studies concerning network activity economics, but few of them have been so forthright in stating their difficulty. Clearly, data required for economic analysis of networks should be generated as a routine part of ongoing operations; developing the means to measure performance takes planning.

Demand-Factor Studies

Studies in the demand-factor category range from simple demand projections used in network planning to more complex models linking demand estimates to various determinants of demand. These analyses are often used to estimate supply factors needed for various network levels of output. Demand-factor studies warrant attention by information managers because they lay the groundwork for establishing the benefits to be derived from various information outputs and eventually should be useful in making estimates of the value of information activities. Despite their utility, there are relatively few demand-factor studies of networks.

To estimate demand loads on a full-scale national system of one particular type, Dei Rossi et al. (37) extrapolated data on the experience of an existing telephone access information center that provided recorded topical messages for physicians in Wisconsin; these data were drawn from an earlier study (172). Probably the most interesting finding is the significance of promotion (advertising) as a determinant of level-of-service use. The study suggests that well-planned promotions can raise usage levels in a fairly predictable fashion. But a key question is left open: do one-time users stimulated by promotion eventually become confirmed users? If not, then usefulness of promotion is doubtful.

A second, very useful study in the demand-factor category addresses one of the more traditional forms of information networking: interlibrary loan. This study, by Palmour et al. (112) gives detailed costs of interlibrary loan functions, as performed by a sample of 12 major research libraries, the primary focus being the calculation of per-transaction costs. In addition, a simple cost model is presented that could be used by other libraries to estimate the costs of their own interlibrary loan activity. The report also presents an extensive analysis of interlibrary loan patterns of use based on a sample of 71 academic libraries. A major finding reconfirms the heavy lending load borne by major academic libraries in today's interlibrary loan network.

Blackburn (13) has written an entertaining yet provocative discussion concerning interlibrary loan demands. While he draws largely on Canadian experience, his mathematical formulation appears to fit U.S. experience. He too found a heavy lending burden imposed on major library collections by the current interlibrary loan network.

In a broad-brush study for NASA, Sedlacek et al. (127) focus on satellite-type services warranting government encouragement for implementation and eventual use in communications networks. Following a requirements analysis approach, they develop an information-transfer-demand taxonomy and project trends for each demand category, using expert opinion plus correlations with economic and demographic variables.

One conclusion is that the lack of "highly specialized" terminals, capable of meeting detailed user requirements, is a major bottleneck in current network development. The study illustrates how a fairly "macro" approach can partially overcome severe data limitations concerning specific individual demands for information. The methodology developed for this study provides a promising approach to tackling some key issues in estimating demands for network outputs in a number of other contexts.

Finally, a brief but tantalizing discussion of economic analysis, using a supply and demand modeling approach, is presented by the staff of Project INTREX (90). While not addressed specifically to networks, the discussion has significant implications concerning networking, particularly in terms of linkages between libraries using advanced computer-based technology and major publishers generating machine-readable files (with special attention to file overlaps).

Other Pertinent Studies

Following the framework used in organizing this part of the review chapter, this section focusses on studies of adjustment mechanisms (such as markets) which link information supply and demand factors, since such analysis provides the basis for evaluating the overall economic performance of information activity and for assessing public policy concerning these activities. Unfortunately only three studies were found that specifically extend their analysis to an examination of the adjustment mechanism in a network context, and all three studies are limited to the private sector communications industry.

A report by Irwin (68) provides an up-to-date analysis of the trends toward vertical integration in the telecommunications industry (mergers linking producers) and points out the impact this trend has on industry performance, particularly in terms of future networking possibilities.

A somewhat similar study by Borchardt (17) also examines the electronic communications industry, but more from a legal than an economic perspective. This study is directed at evaluating and managing the structural problems of this industry resulting from the interaction of public regulation and rapidly changing technology.

Cowan & Waverman (31) examine whether data processing services and common-carrier linkages in a computer network should be integrated. They discuss the technical factors influencing design and implementation of computer systems that offer both communication and data-processing services and conclude that present technology yields only minor economies through integrating these two functions.

The studies cited above examine information activities by enterprises generally classed as public utilities, subject to government regulation. But since much of their activity is modulated by some form of market mechanism, they are usually treated as if located in the private sector. Unfortunately no comparable studies were found that provide a comprehensive economic analysis of information networks in the public sector. Nor do any studies analyze the interaction between public and private sector groups with respect to networking. Yet a few studies are worth citing here because they point the way toward analysis of public sector information networks.

Perhaps the closest approximation to such analysis is a report by Hirsch & Sonenblum (64). They propose the design of information systems that would generate regional accounts, similar to our national income accounts—which measure the Gross National Product—but indicating the quality of urban regional environments and associated public programs in the given area. These data accounts would be used to improve decision-making by public officials. This study is complemented by the report of the President's Commission on Federal Statistics (164), which assesses the status of statistical effort in government, including problems in linking agency statistical programs, using a supply-demand perspective in their discussion.

Berg (11) provides a searching examination of the role of scientific societies and the rationale for cooperative relations among them. He summarizes briefly but well the economic characteristics of information activity that tend to encourage cooperation and network development. Although the focus is on journals in economics, pertinent experience of other disciplines as well as other types of information activities are discussed. His points are reinforced by two recent reports. One (97) growing out of the Committee on Scientific and Technical Communication (SATCOM), set up by the National Academy of Sciences and the National Academy of Engineering effort, suggests that the publishing programs of many small societies would be improved by federation. The other (98), prepared by the National Academy of Sciences, for the Council on Library Resources, discusses both technical and socioeconomic factors in the design of information systems; it states: "to develop information systems consistent with geographic dispersion of information resources and information users, increased stress must be placed on scientific design and modeling studies of broadly based information networks."

A few of the major information system development programs in the scientific and technical area are also beginning to indicate that their plans have network implications. Reference to such thinking can be found in the recent programs planned for the American Chemical Society (3) and the American Institute of Physics (4). In general, however, little explicit attention has been given to actual network configuration or the potential of networking between major information systems or between these systems and the original generators of information and their ultimate consumers or their agents. A couple of recent conference reports do touch on these aspects. One held by the National Federation of Science Abstracting and Indexing Services (101) explores interfaces between primary and secondary services plus various aspects of cooperative activity among secondary services. The Association of Scientific Information Dissemination Centers (7), recently organized to foster communication among information centers, also has sponsored some meetings to explore network potential among its members; one report (7) highlights economic issues concerning the interaction between data-base suppliers and processing centers and describes exploratory network effort among some members. Perhaps the most interesting and provocative such exploration grew out of a workshop sponsored by NASA at Auburn University (155), which developed the concept of User Network for Information Storage, Transfer, Acquisition, and Retrieval (UNISTAR). The report documents the results of a training exercise in systems engineering that approached the general problem by developing a management system for scientific and technological information under the executive branch of the U.S. Government. While the word "network" is not explicitly mentioned, the prospects for further vertical integration and horizontal consolidation activities are explored by means of a network approach.

Little attention has been given in the literature to macroeconomic analysis concerning networks. However, Baumol (10) provides an initial analytic framework for developing a macroperspective that might be used for macroeconomic analysis of information networks. Also, a provocative series of works describes recent major efforts sponsored by the Canadian Government (125) to study their information activities using a macro viewpoint. In terms of comprehensiveness and use of systematic analysis, this series of reports comprises perhaps the best studies available on information networks from a national viewpoint. The section on economics probably pushes to the limit the existing knowledge base concerning information networks and their economc analysis (126).

TECHNOLOGICAL DEVELOPMENTS

Networks among libraries serve cooperation by providing for the sharing and exchange of bibliographic and reference services, and text. Telecommunications technology increasingly offers capabilities that can be applied to these data information and text transfer tasks.

With the growth of machine-readable data bases in libraries, the increase in the amount of library work carried out on teletype circuits, and the beginnings of on-line computerized cataloging and reference services, the special communications needs of libraries are forcing an upgrading in kind and quality of technical effort in communications. The result, according to a lengthy special report in *Business Week* (119), is a revolution in the phone business.

According to these reviewers, this revolution, along with a number of independent developments and new technologies, may also revolutionize the kind, quality, and pattern of service in libraries. Bystrom (23) presents a comprehensive overview and analysis of these many activities in telecommunications, both public and private, that may contribute to a growing base for progress in the development of networks for libraries and information systems. From among these activities, Norwood (104) adds a depth of understanding of the potential applications of technical developments in satellite and cable communications to library network functions. Both of these papers, together with the Simms & Fuchs (129) review of communication technology published in the 1970 *Annual Review*, provide an excellent tutorial base for understanding the complex technology of networking and the legal, social, and financial aspects of telecommunications.

The probability that a new kind or level of network service can be conceptualized in the library world has been raised by two decisions of the Federal Communications Commission (FCC). The first, known as the Carterfone decision (154), allows users to attach any manufacturer's terminals to their telephones, in contrast to the former restriction that they use only equipment supplied by the telephone companies. This decision opened the flood-gates of invention for new terminals for attaching computers, typewriter keyboards, facsimile machines, and other signal-generating devices to telephone lines. The library network planner thus has more latitude in setting system specifications, and equipment inventories such as are published regularly in various trade journals (147, 148, 149, 150, and 153) are essential reference sources. Kessler & Wilhelm (76) provide a tutorial explanation of narrow-band communication terminals with suggestions for their use in interlibrary communication. Another FCC decision (154) has authorized the establishment of special-purpose communications carriers in competition with the telephone companies.

Glaser (56) describes the plans for a large-scale nationwide carrier network designed principally for computer-to-computer linkages by Data Transmission Corporation (DATRAN). Two key characteristics of the DATRAN system (34) of importance for library networks are: (a) it is an all-digital system obviating the need for special devices to convert computer signals into the kinds of signals that are used in telephone work; and (b) the price of communications will be independent of distance, reducing the cost of long-distance links among libraries. Frank (53) describes both the proposed DATRAN and the Microwave Communications, Incorporated (MCI) point-to-point network. It is impossible to tell at this time which of these special carriers will better serve library networking. The DATRAN concept appears to be more universal, while the MCI concept may provide more tailored capabilities.

Computer Networks

The data-transmission function among libraries will also benefit from the developmental work in computer networks, most of which now use telephone facilities. Late in 1971, the National Library of Medicine (NLM) was preparing to introduce a new service, MEDLINE (162), through TYMSHARE, a commercial computer network service using telephone lines. This service provides access to the NLM computer via phone in a number of cities throughout the nation. MEDLINE provides an on-line bibliographic searching capability for medical schools, medical libraries, hospitals, and research institutions throughout the country. The data base contains 400,000 literature citations and is still growing. MEDLINE operates on NLM's IBM 370/155 computer and can support up to 45 simultaneous users. The system can be accessed by teletype, from IBM 2741 and other terminals operating at 148 or 300 words per minute. The development of MEDLINE is an extension of AIM-TWX (Abridged Index Medicus via the Teletypewriter Exchange Network), an experimental service introduced in June 1970.

The reports (163) of the experiences of eleven NSF-funded regional cooperative computer networks indicate general success with the cooperative concept; technological problems arose chiefly in the matter of terminal selection and ineptness of several of the telephone companies that were new to the business of computers on their lines.

The ARPA computer network cited by Samuelson (124) in last year's *Annual Review* remains the most visible and perhaps the best conceived computer network. It links several computers into a network, in contrast to the computer networks noted above, most of which link users to a central computer. LeGates (81) provides a nontechnical description of the ARPA network, its design, topology, equipment and protocols.

These reviewers believe that regional sharing of computing facilities appears to be the viable way to extend computing capabilities and the concomitant specialized manpower to small campuses for educational and interlibrary information services. In the library setting, the success of the concept is evidenced by the inauguration of on-line cataloging services by the Ohio College Library Center (OCLC) on August 26, 1971. By September 10, twenty libraries were cataloging by remotely accessing the OCLC computer, and OCLC was producing 2000 cards a day off-line. The *Ohio College Library Center Newsletter* (105) is useful reading, not so much for the specific solutions to problems that arise in on-line cataloging, but as evidence of the bugs that even the best-designed network will face in operation.

Technology of image transmission by telecommunications has not yet advanced to a point where it is practical for wide-scale library applications. Jackson's report (69) of experiences with facsimile experiments in the Pennsylvania State University system indicates that the speed of transmission of facsimile is still relatively slow and the cost relatively high, particularly when compared to a user's need. A tabulation of facsimile equipment published in *Communication News* in February 1972 (29) lists several dozen facsimile terminals of different operating speeds. The user must still trade off quality of reproduction or size of page transmitted to gain speed. As yet this tradeoff reduces the readability of transmitted pages of library text below the acceptable level when the signal is carried on telephone lines. Project INTREX (90) reports acceptable experience in transmitting images of microfiche text by cable to a video screen in the MIT Engineering Library. The storage device has limited capacity at present but its expansion should pose no insurmountable technical difficulty.

Cable Television

The resumption of growth of cable television (CATV) following the issuance in early 1972 of FCC regulations covering cable operations (156) may presage a new era of improvement in image-transfer services for libraries. By 1971 there were approximately 2750 CATV systems, serving about 6,000,000 subscribers in the United States.

The Sloan Commission on Cable Communications (132) estimates that between 40 and 60 percent of all homes in the nation will be reached by cable by the end of the decade. Smith (134) describes the many individual locations into which the resulting broadband communication pipeline extends as the "wired nation" and views the phenomenon as one of the potentially major change agents in society.

The Sloan Commission's report contains an exceptionally clear discussion of the technology of broadband communications by Ward (167). He covers switching and two-way communication, which will add new dimensions to information-service networks among libraries, information centers, and users. The two-way communication capability that will be required of all franchises, allowing at least voice or telephone signals to be transmitted from homes to CATV studios with full audio and visual communication back to the homes, is discussed in detail by Jurgen (71) with brief technical descriptions of a number of proposed systems.

The existence of an expanded capacity for telecommunications, both in number of channels and bandwidths for all purposes, will create a challenge to information agencies and libraries to offer innovative services beyond those presently known. Creative programming for information services for the public on CATV channels is described by Crichton (32); Price (118) and Roud (121) in special background studies for the Sloan Commission; the National Academy of Engineering (99); and Graetz (57). The National Academy of Engineering proposes among other things that community information centers and interactive information retrieval systems in an educational setting be established as part of a total urban telecommunications system. New York

City announced a proposal (83) to turn the neighborhood branches of its public library system into just such centers. The Mitre Corporation (165) issued a special report describing the proposed wiring of Washington, D.C. Feldman's examination (50) of the potential for cable communications to serve the function of the Lister Hill National Center for Biomedical Communication for applying existing and advanced technology to the improvement of biomedical communications of all kinds is appropriate to other disciplines and environments. He covers the relation of cable communications to terrestrial television broadcasting and the possible systems developments, including systems competitive with CATV.

There have been a few small starts in the use of CATV for special communication processes. Stetten (139) and Volk (166) describe a two-way information retrieval and dissemination system with home access to a computer via telephone and CATV devised by the Mitre Corporation, now being demonstrated in Reston, Virginia. The Natrona County Public Library in Wyoming began cablecasting special programs and visual reference services in 1971 (Dowlin, 42). Kenney & Norwood (75) have produced an introductory statement on CATV for librarians, with views on programming potential and suggestions for action by librarians in order to gain access to channels. The potential of CATV for schools, with special importance to libraries and information centers for sharing resources as "schools without walls," is set forth in a simple but comprehensive pamphlet issued by the National Education Association (100).

All of these documents are meant to be provocative; none propose outlandish uses and services. They show that the cable link, while established at first to provide standard television fare to subscribers, actually can become a broad-purpose information service carrier, with enough capacity to make communication back to the transmitting source (e.g., classroom, computer, studio) practicable. In surveying the array of technological innovations, Morris (94) suggests that instructional and media centers must soon become electronic centers so that many forms of information retrieval and distribution can be interconnected for service.

The new FCC regulations on cable television give libraries and other educational and information agencies five years to prove that they can make use of the channels reserved for them. This challenge must be met lest we find that what these reviewers conceive of as a real potential for service through telecommunications networking becomes just another mad chase after technology.

Communications Satellites

Communications satellites extend the range and number of high-quality communications channels for all purposes. Because a satellite can "see" a vast portion of the earth, oceans and mountains are eliminated as difficult hurdles for communications links, and the cost of communication is independent of the distance between sender and receiver. These are major advantages of a satellite-based communication system. It is still too early to predict the specific role of satellite facilities in information networks, but Chayes (27) foresees the development of station-to-station communication without the need for national centers, and the linking of the many thousands of CATV systems, as likely areas of special impact.

A number of applications for domestic satellite systems are pending consideration by the FCC. For the present, however, satellites are available only for international commercial uses, for governmental services, and for certain experimental applications. Several of these experiments involve libraries. In one test sponsored by the National Academy of Sciences, the John Crerar Library will be linked with a library in Argentina, in a study of possible use of the satellite to replace commercial teletype for international network communications (128). Requests for information will arrive at the John Crerar Library by the satellite link; information will be air-mailed to Argentina. Experiments are proposed or underway for other applications such as the National Library of Medicine's service to the medical community in Alaska and the University of Hawaii's reference and facsimile service in the Pacific Basin region (23). Such tests are now conducted on the National Aeronautics and Space Administration (NASA) Applications Technology Satellites (ATS), which the agency will continue to launch (47). The library community, it is hoped, will have especially designed experiments and equipment on future satellites to test a wide range of interlibrary communications. Fortunately, the 1971 World Administrative Radio Conference on Space Telecommunications reserved the 2500 to 2690 megaHertz band for these and other educational services (67).

BUILDING MULTIORGANIZATION COMPLEXES

The task of building multiorganization complexes to deal with the social problems of a technological society is the central challenge for those engaged in administrative processes, according to Thompson (152). He says, however, that there is no one best way to build these complexes, that only the humans involved in the administrative process can judge which adaptations are appropriate. The Needs and Development group of the Airlie House Conference (173) recommended that a receptive environment and organizational framework be provided for network development, that pluralistic financial support be provided, that professional expertise and technical skills be developed, that research be undertaken to understand network needs and assess performance, and that network demonstrations be set up.

Theory and Model Building

Important groundwork in the development of theoretical models of networks has been undertaken by Duggan (43); by Kochen (78); and by a group at Southern Methodist University, under Nance et al. (95), who provide a mathematical look at an information network, including measures of network structure, in particular the accessibility and flexibility in message transfer.

Nance et al. (95) believes that general mathematical models are useful in removing ambiguity and in clarifying the logical nature of networks. He points out that a person may disagree with the definitions, assumptions and axioms about networks that are stated in a model, but if the mathematics are correct, one cannot disagree with the validity of the conclusions developed. Moreover, a model can be manipulated to reveal how it responds to various input configurations. The analyst also can attempt to enrich the model to make any improper assumptions seem more in line with reality.

Nance's model suggests how a network can provide the greatest possible benefit for the total group by providing for the optimal flow of messages from node to node in a communication transfer. His work on the design of library information networks has also used concepts developed by graph theorists (Bhat et al., 12).

Models of specific network functions and their interrelation are also useful. For example, Reynolds et al. (120) developed quantitative models (linear equations) for functions of interlibrary loan, technical services, and collection management for each of three systems configurations: the present system in the state of Washington, regional networks, and a statewide network. Bhat et al. (12) developed a Markovian model for total network costs associated with each of three decisions about whether to satisfy a request, reject it, or refer the message to the succeeding node in the network hierarchy.

Basic and applied studies, as described above, are essential for building any systematic theory or models about networks. As illustrative of these needs, we cite Blasingame & DeProspo (14), who complain that there has been a general lack of alternative theoretical models and objective tests of performance to guide the development of public library networks. Patrick's report (114) of the System Development Corporation study offers a useful beginning with guidelines for planning academic library consortia. To be of maximum use, additional research is needed to develop decision criteria to help consortia members and funders choose between alternative structures, processes, and services. Network participants need quantitative models or decision tables to help them assess their constraints and opportunities, determine their priorities, and then choose appropriate network configurations. Dunn (44) introduces some of the problem areas in networking and proposes a decision analysis methodology for the selection of alternatives in designing networks.

Methods of Evaluation

Evaluation is an increasingly important topic. A number of studies have pointed to factors that would indicate the benefits or success of a network's overall performance or its performance in selected areas. Some have also advanced our understanding of how quantitative methodology can be used to make evaluation convincing to funders and users.

Although most networks have some means of monitoring their operations, few have developed the kind of computer system discussed by Nance et al. (96). Their library Network Management and Information System (NEMIS) was developed to aid in the general analysis of a regional medical library network in Texas. The system generates output statistics on disposition of requests, elapsed time for completing filled requests, time to clear unfilled requests, arrival time, distribution of requests by day and month, and various other measures of activity and performance.

The Reynolds et al. study (120) also describes the type of data collection and analysis techniques required to evaluate library operations. The study team applied some of these techniques in the state of Washington to determine the relative cost and benefits of alternative configurations of (1) the present system, (2) regional networks in the state, and (3) a statewide network. Although projected costs alone are insufficient for selecting one of the three systems, they conclude that a statewide network offers most benefit in terms of access to resources and the opportunity to draw on technology and specialized personnel.

Most evaluative studies of networking have focused on interlibrary loan (ILL) programs. Warner (168) develops an analytical approach to determine ILL network effectiveness; he believes his approach should be useful and applicable to networks with a similar organizational hierarchy. His major point is that, in a system where different units play a role in completing ILL requests, meaningful assessment of the effectiveness of the total network must comprehend individual library unit contributions to the system in terms of both the input to each unit and the input to the system. In the Maryland ILL network he studied, network effectiveness is shown to be greater than either the mean effectiveness of component units or the effectiveness of any one of the component units.

Two studies related to ILL—specifically TWX communications among libraries—illustrate this type of network activity, one by Stanford (136) and one by the Texas State Library (151).

Kenney (74) concludes that turnaround time is probably the largest single factor contributing to the failure or success of any ILL network. It is determined by the availability of bibliographic tools, trained staff, photocopy facilities, and, most important, the establishment of clear procedures and policy statements by all participants. She believes that system performance can be measured by four factors: volume, percentage of filled requests, elapsed time, and decrease in costs. Faibisoff (46) appraises the effectiveness of the coordinated delivery system for the South Central Research Library Council, Ithaca, New York, and concludes that a combined use of the public library systems' delivery services and United Parcel Service is the most satisfactory. This combination of delivery services reduced costs, allowed for personal interchange between the libraries, and fostered shared resources of both public and academic libraries of the region. Patrick (114) found that, of 125 academic consortia, 66 percent used informal feedback from library personnel as an evaluative technique, whereas about one-half queried ultimate users of services. Twenty-nine percent used analysis of costs and usage statistics, 21 percent used formal surveys of operations of participating libraries, 13 percent used operations research analysis such as workload and cost-effectiveness trade offs, and 10 percent did formal studies of the ultimate users of consortia services.

While not focusing on network activity per se, the study by George (55) on DDC's provision for automatic selective documentation services documents experience pertinent to networks considering this activity. The paper by Wente (170) on NASA/RECON, an on-line retrieval system, also documents experience that may serve as a guide in the establishment of on-line access networks featuring user interaction.

Standardization and Compatibility

In a rapidly developing technical area where a large number of individuals and institutions promote their equipment and procedures as standards with which others should be compatible, controversy and confusion are the norm. Stevens (142) provides a most comprehensive exposé of the ramifications of these issues, the requirements for compatibility, the types of interface that are most tractable with regard to compatibility, and the problem areas wherein network interfacing difficulties are most likely to occur. She notes that although there is voluminous literature about compatibility requirements in networks, very little of this literature is directly addressed to compatibility problems in network interfacing. The notable exceptions are the standards themselves, and the publication in 1971 of the *American National Standard Format for Bibliographic Information Interchange on Magnetic Tapes* (6) is a landmark event.

Bonn (15) notes that the development of standards for multiaccess computer networks is touching on too few issues and argues that progress must be speeded up lest the investment in equipment and systems becomes so great that shifting to a standard will be too costly. He proposes that the standards concept that is inherent in COBOL and other programming languages be extended to file formats and network control procedures. Specifically, he encourages the efforts now getting underway in ANSI Committee X.3 on the development of data descriptive languages.

The pervasive need for standards is documented in a report by Stevens (141) for the Lister Hill Center. The areas of concern for standards work include the communications system, the physical media, programming language and data formats, descriptive and subject cataloging, output and display, buffering, and protection requirements. The ramifications of the drive for standardization can be seen via the *Federal Information Processing Standards Index* (161). Because the Federal Government is the largest single user of computers, and the major generator of information and data bases, it would be well for all who work in networking in information systems to become acquainted with this effort.

Miller (91) discusses the problems of working towards a compatible machine system within a network, including the human factors problems and the inability of the more highly mechanized members to change their systems.

Overlapping and Competing Networks

At present we have only crude analytical techniques to use in assessing whether joining networks is indeed an optimal course of action for libraries and information centers. We are in this quandary because we cannot say what network to join—a local, partial network, or a national one such as the Center for Research Libraries, or both. If it were an either/or decision, perhaps that question could be handled, but as Miller (91) and Patrick (114) point out for academic libraries, a single library could be embedded in as many as 15 networks. How many large organizational units can a library be involved in without being tripped up by conflicting loyalties and demands for its resources? Is it true that library goals and functions are so divisible that membership in a pluralism of networks will be worth the cost?

Many authors believe that the successful network will be found on a local or state level. Aines (158) believes that success will come in spearhead projects rather than across-the-board advances. If networks demonstrate a string of successes, he says, society will provide the recognition and resources needed to advance further. Fasana & Veaner (49) would agree that the most promising approach to developing transferable library systems seems to be local efforts by participating libraries that are financially and administratively committed to the cooperative effort.

Most authors who discuss a national role in networking believe, according to Davis (35), that it must be developed from "vigorous, lively, and progressive systems at a local or regional level." The kind of success demonstrated in the Ohio College Library Center, Kilgour (77) believes, should be replicated by two or more participants before a national library authority is established to manage the network and facilitate the switching of messages.

One reason for doubt about effective action on the national level is the lack of centralized control over information services in the U.S. Unlike Sylvestre (145), who describes the possibility of national networking in Canada, U.S. authors Wigington & Wood (171) are pessimistic about the development of any kind of total national uniformity in the representation and handling of information, since they see eight major centers of influence at the national levels:

(1) national libraries;
(2) abstracting and indexing services;
(3) major scientific and technical societies and their publications and conferences;
(4) large mission-oriented activities of the U.S. Government;
(5) organizations that develop and sell communication, computer, and information technology on which a modern national network depend;
(6) consumers of information, a large heterogeneous group of persons and organizations with diverse and sometimes conflicting needs;

(7) commercial publishing and information-handling enterprises; and
(8) generators of information in a multitude of forms.

They conclude that there is no single entity with sufficient skills, prestige, resources, and authority to assume the role of monolithic manager. Evolution of a national information network will come if the networks grow together, forced by common need and by the recognition of all parties that cooperation and perseverance alone will lead to the desired result.

In the meantime, there are a number of specific problems that are calling for national solutions. Jeffs (70) and the Association of Research Libraries are concerned about the possibility of a National Lending Library for Periodicals. The Center for Research Libraries (25) is planning to make a significant expansion in its acquisition of currently published journals. Cuadra (33) believes we need national guidance to answer questions such as how many MARC, ERIC, Chemical Abstracts, or NASA data bases there must be in the country. Adams (1) raises questions about responsibility for national leadership in regard to developing something like the *Union List of Serials*. He recommends that development of union lists first be approached on a national basis, with remnants of the task left for regional organizations. Otherwise, he says, we shall be burdened for years to come with fragmentary and partially compatible bits and pieces of an uneconomical network. Avram & Pulsifer (8) recommend a national bibliographic service that could build on present Library of Congress services as a bibliographic record for all documents published in the United States.

The Airlie House Conference (5) stresses the need for a nationally coordinated development to avoid duplicate expenditures and the entrenchment of local systems developed without benefit of common standards and protocols. The Conference passed a formal resolution that the new National Commission on Libraries and Information Science be made a focal point for devising a national network of libraries and information centers. The resolution stated that, as a matter of priority, the Commission "devise a comprehensive plan to facilitate the coordinated development of the nation's libraries, information centers, and other knowledge resources." More specifically, the Commission was asked:

(1) to describe the advances made in network development;
(2) to pinpoint the strengths and weaknesses of information access among different constituencies, geographic regions, and groups;

(3) to coordinate its programs closely with the Office of Telecommunications Policy and the Federal Communications Commission;
(4) to designate or recommend establishment of a national center to coordinate the establishment of standard bibliographic data records for all forms of material;
(5) to support the establishment of interdisciplinary educational and training programs to equip librarians and information scientists with the technical knowledge required of them in library and information networks at all levels; and
(6) to coordinate development of the national plans for a library and information network with those of other countries.

In a review of the Conference, Aines (158) expresses doubts that the National Commission will have the authority needed to make recommendations. Rather than the development of a national network, he expects networking to occur in smaller-scale efforts, primarily in areas where there are intense problems requiring rapid and efficient handling of data and information, e.g., to overcome pollution, reduce crime, or improve health services.

Licklider (84) believes that networks planned now will probably be significant more because of their influence in laying out and building the road to the future than because of their improvement of library and information services. By the 80s or 90s, he believes, most serious intellectual work will be done "on line" with an electronic information network.

CONCLUSION

We must conclude this chapter on a somewhat uncertain note concerning the future of network development. Although the general feeling about networks remains optimistic as in previous years, there is a difference. Funders are more wary and anxious for manifestations of benefits, researchers are more aware of the complexities of network development and implementation, and planners are focusing upon careful social and technical engineering of the basic steps required to put a network on firm footing. The political and economic environment is unstable, and many networks are uncertain about how to face the future. Yet networks are appearing in increasing numbers and with greater variety in structures, functions, and services.

Two important questions dominate today's network activity:

(1) Why should a library or information facility join a network?

(2) What configuration of networks is most effective in exploiting modern technology and in meeting the changing needs of users?

The answer to the first question depends on a satisfactory answer to the second one. It would be comforting to report that the information community already can answer these questions. We cannot do so. Some partial knowledge is evolving and further experience will provide more raw material for answers. But no recognized focal point for professional leadership and planning—for developing the general knowledge needed to design, manage, and assess networks—has emerged. We must devise better ways to learn from experience what works best and to establish from research what is generally significant.

A related question that began to appear this past year may recur with greater frequency and intensity. The question is: Whom should the network serve and whom does the network represent? With some evidence that even small multicounty networks can become unresponsive to the needs perceived by individual libraries, it is appropriate to question the responsiveness of networks. The question may be particularly acute for networks capable of spanning various sectors, disciplines, or missions, because they require collective decision-making. These networks need to devise an effective means to achieve efficient and responsive performance in serving a range of participants. Those network structures that have a central direction have a special problem: they must develop effective feedback from their participants or incur the risk of members dropping out because the network does not meet their needs. Establishing funding procedures linked to quality performance seems one promising approach in meeting this challenge.

Some of the planning studies we reviewed suggest that networks may function as a means for perfecting markets for various information outputs, especially products derived from advanced information technology. For example, networks can increase market density (i.e., broaden the scale of user access) and make information products economically justifiable by bringing together buyers or users with similar needs. Networks can improve the efficiency of specialized facilities and professional expertise by an improved division of labor among various elements of the network. Networks planned with these two aspects in mind can become effective mechanisms for improving the responsiveness of information suppliers to the various needs of users.

In fostering network development, the greatest need is establishing a solid organizational base capable of providing the leadership and solving the funding issues posed by networks. Some federal agency with a mission of incorporating information network development appears the most probable base. But the great risk is that networks funded solely by the Federal government will develop insulated from the discipline and guidance provided by user information demands. A cross sector (government and nongovernment) configuration in network development, although more painful to develop, may prove to be most effective in the long run. This approach could resolve key issues at minimum risk. What solution eventually develops should be a major topic in the next *Annual Review* chapter on library and information networks.

REFERENCES

(1) ADAMS, SCOTT. Progress toward a national serials data system. Library Trends, 18:4 (April 1970) 520-536.

(2) ALTMAN, ELLEN. The resources capacity of public secondary school libraries to support interlibrary loan: a systems approach to title diversity and collection overlap. Rutgers University, Graduate School of Library Service, New Brunswick, New Jersey, October 1970, 230 p.

(3) AMERICAN CHEMICAL SOCIETY. A five-year plan for implementing programs 1971-1975. Information systems plan. American Chemical Society, Washington, D.C., September 1970, 127 p. (ED 046 477).

(4) AMERICAN INSTITUTE OF PHYSICS. The AIP program for physics information: a national information system for physics and astronomy 1972-1976. American Institute of Physics, New York, June 1971, 74 p. (Report no. ID71P. ED 051 849).

(5) AMERICAN LIBRARY ASSOCIATION; U.S. OFFICE OF EDUCATION. Conference on Interlibrary Communications and Information Networks. Airlie House, Warrenton, Virginia, 28 September - 2 October 1970. Proceedings. Edited by Joseph Becker. American Library Association, Chicago, Illinois, 1972, 354 p.

(6) AMERICAN NATIONAL STANDARDS INSTITUTE. COMMITTEE Z-39. American national standard format for bibliographic information interchange on magnetic tapes. American National Standards Institute, New York, 1971. (Z39.2-1971).

(7) ASSOCIATION OF SCIENTIFIC INFORMATION DISSEMINATION CENTERS. Summary of proceedings of ASIDIC meeting. September 26-28, 1971, Arlington Park Towers Hotel, Arlington Heights, Illinois.

(8) AVRAM, HENRIETTE D.; PULSIFER, JOSEPHINE S. Bibliographic services for a national network. In: Conference on Interlibrary Communications and Information Networks, Airlie House, Warrenton, Virginia, 28 September - 2 October 1970. Proceedings. Edited by Joseph Becker. American Library Association, Chicago, Illinois, 1972, 92-100. (ED 057 853).

(9) BABCOCK, JULIE. Cooperation between types of libraries 1968-July 1971. An annotated bibliography. Drexel University, Graduate School of Library Science, Philadelphia, Pennsylvania, September 1971, 27 p.

(10) BAUMOL, WILLIAM. A cost benefit approach to evaluation of alternative information provision procedures. Mathematica, Princeton, New Jersey, January 1971, 204 p.

(11) BERG, SANFORD V. Increasing the efficiency of the economics journal market. Journal of Economic Literature, 9:3 (September 1971) 798-813.

(12) BHAT, U. NARAYAN; NANCE, RICHARD E.; KORFHAGE, ROBERT R. Information networks: a probabilistic model for hierarchical message transfer. Southern Methodist University, Institute of Technology, Computer Science/Operations Research Center, Dallas, Texas, November 1971, 17 p.

(13) BLACKBURN, ROBERT. Of mice and lions and battleships and interlibrary things. Institute for Professional Librarians of Ontario Quarterly, 13:2 (October 1971) 68-79.

(14) BLASINGAME, RALPH; DePROSPO, ERNEST R., JR. Effectiveness in cooperation and consolidation in public libraries. In: Voigt, Melvin J.; ed. Advances in librarianship. Academic Press, New York, 1970, 189-206.

(15) BONN, THEODORE H. Standards for computer networks. Computer, 4:3 (May/June 1971) 10-14.

(16) BOOZ, ALLEN & HAMILTON, INC. A research design for library cooperative planning and action in the Washington, D.C. metropolitan area. District of Columbia Public Library, Washington, D.C., August 1970, 77 p. (ED 040 306).

(17) BORCHARDT, KURT. Structure and performance of the U.S. communications industry: government regulation and company planning. Harvard University, Graduate School of Business Administration, Division of Research, Boston, Massachusetts, 1970, 180 p.

(18) BRACKEN, MARILYN C. An analysis of the evolution of the National Library of Medicine: implications for the development of scientific and technical information networks. American University, Washington, D.C., 1971.

(19) BRAUDE, ROBERT M.; HOLT, NANCY. Cost-performance analysis of TWX-mediated interlibrary loans in a medium-sized medical center library. Bulletin of the Medical Library Association, 59:1 (January 1971) 65-70.

(20) BRETZ, RUDY. A taxonomy of communication media. Educational Technology Publications, Inc., Englewood Cliffs, New Jersey, 1971, 192 p. (ED 048 723).

(21) BRIDEGAM, WILLIS E., JR.; MEYERHOFF, ERICH. Library participation in a biomedical communication and information network. Bulletin of the Medical Library Association, 58:2 (April 1970) 103-111.

(22) BUDINGTON, WILLIAM S. Network alternatives and solutions for storage. Library Trends, 19:3 (January 1971) 329-340.

(23) BYSTROM, JOHN. Telecommunication networks for libraries and information systems approaches to development. In: Conference on Interlibrary Communications and Information Networks, Airlie House, Warrenton, Virginia, 28 September - 2 October 1970. Proceedings. Edited by Joseph Becker. American Library Association, Chicago, Illinois, 1972, 27-43.

(24) CASEY, GENEVIEVE. Emerging state and regional library networks. In: Conference on Interlibrary Communications and Information Networks, Airlie House, Warrenton, Virginia, 28 September - 2 October 1970. Proceedings. Edited by Joseph Becker. American Library Association, Chicago, Illinois, 1972, 288-293. (ED 057 849).

(25) Center for Research Libraries (CRL) proposes U.S. national lending library for journals. Information, 3:6 (November/December 1971) 285-287.

(26) CHAPIN, RICHARD E. Limits of local self-sufficiency. In: Conference on Interlibrary Communications and Information Networks, Airlie House, Warrenton, Virginia, 28 September - 2 October 1970. Proceedings. Edited by Joseph Becker. American Library Association, Chicago, Illinois, 1972, 54-58. (ED 057 850).

(27) CHAYES, ABRAM. The impact of satellites on cable communications. A paper prepared for the Sloan Commission on Cable Communications. (No publisher or place given). May 1971, 30 p.

(28) CLAPP, VERNER W. Public libraries and the network idea. Library Journal, 94:2 (15 January 1970) 121-124.

(29) Communications News facsimile buyer's guide. Communications News, 9:2 (February 1972) 30-31.
(30) CONANT, RALPH W. The sociological environment. In: Eastlick, John T.; ed. The changing environment of libraries. American Library Association, Chicago, Illinois, 1971, 4-19.
(31) COWAN, DONALD D.; WAVERMAN, LEONARD. The interdependence of communications and data processing: issues in economics of integration and public policy. Bell Journal of Economics and Management Science, 2:2 (Autumn 1971) 657-677.
(32) CRICHTON, JUDY. Toward an immodest experiment in cable television modestly produced. A paper prepared for the Sloan Commission on Cable Communications. (No publisher or place given), March 1971, 27 p.
(33) CUADRA, CARLOS A. Keynote: Library automation and networks. In: Matzek, Richard A.; ed. Network concepts: four points of view. Catholic Library Association, Haverford, Pennsylvania, 1971, 4-18.
(34) The DATRAN network—an exclusive special report on details of proposed all-digital network for computer communications. Telephony, 180:10 (8 March 1971).
(35) DAVIS, RUTH M. The national biomedical communications network as a developing structure. Bulletin of the Medical Library Association, 59:1 (January 1971) 1-20.
(36) DEI ROSSI, J. A.; HEISER, R. S.; KING, N. S. A cost analysis of minimum distance TV networking for broadcasting medical information. RAND Corporation, Santa Monica, California, February 1970, 84 p. (RM-6204-NLM, ED 038 988).
(37) DEI ROSSI, J. A.; LINDHOLM, C. R.; MILLS, G. F.; SUMNER, G. C. A telephone access biomedical information center. RAND Corporation, Santa Monica, California, April 1970, 56 p. (RM-6205-NLM).
(38) DeLANOY, DIANA D.; CUADRA, CARLOS A. Directory of academic library consortia. System Development Corporation, Santa Monica, California, September 1971. (TM-4597/003/00).
(39) DINKA, TESFAYE; OKUTCU, DAVUT. An analysis of book storage and transportation requirements of the Five Associated University Libraries. Five Associated University Libraries, Syracuse, New York, August 1970, 38 p. (ED 049 767).
(40) Divorce: N.Y. style. Library Journal, 96:13 (July 1971) 2257-2262.
(41) DOUGHERTY, RICHARD M.; MAIER, JOAN M. Centralized processing for academic libraries. The final report (Phase III, January 1 - June 30, 1969) of the Colorado Academic Libraries Book Processing Center: the first six months of operation. Scarecrow Press, Metuchen, New Jersey, 1971, 254 p.
(42) DOWLIN, KEN. Natrona County Public Library initiates telecasting. Outrider, 4:1 (January 1972) 1-2.
(43) DUGGAN, MARYANN. Library network analysis and planning (LIB-NAT). Journal of Library Automation, 2:3 (September 1969) 157-175.
(44) DUNN, D. A. Principles of telecommunications planning. In: Conference on Interlibrary Communications and Information Networks, Airlie House, Warrenton, Virginia, 28 September - 2 October 1970. Proceedings. Edited by Joseph Becker. American Library Association, Chicago, Illinois, 1972, 163-169 (ED 057 862).
(45) EPSTEIN, A. H.; FERGUSON, DOUGLAS; MONTAGUE, ELEANOR. An on-line network—cooperative planning with several libraries. In: American Society for Information Science. Annual meeting. 34th, Denver, Colorado, 7-11 November 1971. Proceedings, vol. 8: Communication for decision-makers. Greenwood Publishing Corp. Westport, Connecticut, 1971, 227-231.
(46) FAIBISOFF, SYLVIA G. Appraisal of the effectiveness of CODE: the coordinated delivery system for the South Central Research Library Council, January to December 1970. South Central Research Library Council, Ithaca, New York, 19 April 1971, 27 p. (ED 049 777).

(47) FAIRCHILD INDUSTRIES. Communications satellites. Fairchild Industries, Germantown, Maryland, 1971. (Unpaged).
(48) FASANA, PAUL J. Collaborative library systems development: an experiment in the joint design of automated library systems. In: American Society for Information Science. Annual meeting. 34th, Denver, Colorado, 7-11 November 1971. Proceedings, vol. 8: Communication for decision-makers. Greenwood Publishing Corp., Westport, Connecticut, 1971, 233-236.
(49) FASANA, PAUL J.; VEANER, ALLEN; eds. Collaborative library systems development. M.I.T. Press, Cambridge, Massachusetts, 1971, 224 p.
(50) FELDMAN, N. E. The potential role of cable television in wideband distribution systems: a working note prepared for the National Library of Medicine. RAND Corporation, Santa Monica, California, October 1970, 137 p. (WN-7088-NLM).
(51) FIVE ASSOCIATED UNIVERSITY LIBRARIES. Rationalizing research libraries in the '70s. Proceedings of a symposium sponsored by the Five Associated University Libraries, November 12, 1970. Five Associated University Libraries, Syracuse, New York, [1971], 41 p. (ED 049 769).
(52) FIVE ASSOCIATED UNIVERSITY LIBRARIES. SYSTEMS COMMITTEE AND MASFILE INPUT GROUP. MASFILE-I pilot project. Final report. Five Associated University Libraries, Syracuse, New York, 11 April 1969, 30 p. (ED 028 801).
(53) FRANK, RONALD A. Fact or promise? New carriers affect all users. Special report: communications, part I. Computerworld, 6:2 (12 January 1972) 10-11.
(54) GARTLAND, HENRY J. New trends in medical libraries in hospitals. Paper given at the Medical Library Association Conference, New Orleans, Louisiana, May 1970, 15 p. (Unpublished).
(55) GEORGE, RAY L. Automatic selective documentation services. Defense Documentation Center, Alexandria, Virginia, March 1971, 105 p. (AD 722 425).
(56) GLASER, MICHAEL L. Application for data transmission network: system description. Exhibit 1 for presentation by DATRAN to FCC. Docket No. 18920. Data Transmission Company, Falls Church, Virginia, 29 p. (n. d.).
(57) GRAETZ, ROBERT E. State of the city reporting: a new form of social intelligence. In: American Society for Information Science. Annual meeting. 34th, Denver, Colorado, 7-11 November 1971. Proceedings, vol. 8: Communication for decision-makers. Greenwood Publishing Corporation, Westport, Connecticut, 1971, 323-326.
(58) HACKER, HAROLD S. Implementing network plans: jurisdictional considerations in the design of library networks. In: Conference on Interlibrary Communications and Information Networks, Airlie House, Warrenton, Virginia, 28 September - 2 October 1970. Proceedings. Edited by Joseph Becker. American Library Association, Chicago, Illinois, 1972, 223-247. (ED 057 869).
(59) HAMBLEN, JOHN W. Central computer center organization and computer systems: Options for institutions of higher education. AEDS Journal, 4:4 (June 1971) 109-122.
(60) HARGROVE, THOMAS L.; STIRLING, KEITH H. California State Library: processing center design and specifications, vol. V: Cost analysis. Supplemental volume. University of California, Institute of Library Research, Berkeley, California, 1970, 94 p. (ED 043 356).
(61) HEALEY, JAMES S. Public-academic library cooperation. College and Research Libraries, 32:2 (March 1971) 121-126.
(62) HEAPS, DOREEN M.; COOKE, G. A. National policies, national networks, and national information studies in Canada. In: American Society for Information Science. Annual meeting. 33d, Philadelphia, Pennsylvania, 11-15 October 1970. Greenwood Publishing Corp., Westport, Connecticut, 1970, 199-203.
(63) HEINICH, ROBERT. Some social considerations of networking. In: Conference on Interlibrary Communications and Information Networks, Airlie House, War-

renton, Virginia, 28 September - 2 October 1970. Proceedings. Edited by Joseph Becker. American Library Association, Chicago, Illinois, 1972, 257-265. (ED 057 871).

(64) HIRSCH, WERNER Z.; SONENBLUM, S. Selecting regional information for government planning and decision-making. Praeger Publishers, New York, 1970, 198 p.

(65) HOPE, ARLENE. When I was five: half a decade of LSCA in New England. Library Journal, 94:18 (15 October 1969) 3622-3625.

(66) HOPKINS, JUDITH. Manual for OCLC catalog card production. Revised and enlarged. Ohio College Library Center, Columbus, Ohio, February 1971, 69 p. (ED 046 471).

(67) International accord on satellites—JCET position adopted world-wide. JCET News, 3:7 (July 1971) 1-5.

(68) IRWIN, MANLEY R. The telecommunications industry: integration vs. competition. Praeger Publishers, New York, 1971, 223 p.

(69) JACKSON, W. CARL. Telefacsimile at Penn State University: a report on operations during 1968-1969. Library Resources and Technical Services, 15:2 (Spring 1971) 223-228.

(70) JEFFS, JOSEPH. The periodical resources center: a lovely unicorn. In: Association of Research Libraries Minutes, 78th Meeting, Colorado Springs, Colorado, 14-15 May 1971. Association of Research Libraries, Washington, D.C., 64-69.

(71) JURGEN, RONALD K. Two-way applications for cable television systems in the 70s. IEEE Spectrum, 8:11 (November 1971) 39-54.

(72) Kaser on consortia: a "spiritual" problem. Library Journal, 95:17 (1 October 1970) 3234.

(73) KATTER, ROBERT V.; McCARN, DAVIS B. AIM-TWX: an experimental on-line bibliographic retrieval system. In: Walker, Donald E.; ed. Interactive bibliographic search: the user/computer interface. Proceedings of a Workshop on "The User Interface for Interactive Search of Bibliographic Data Bases" held in Palo Alto, California, on 14-15 January 1971. AFIPS Press, Montvale, New Jersey, 1971, 121-141.

(74) KENNEY, BRIGITTE L. Network services for interlibrary loan. In: Conference on Interlibrary Communications and Information Networks, Airlie House, Warrenton, Virginia, 28 September - 2 October 1970. Proceedings. Edited by Joseph Becker. American Library Association, Chicago, Illinois, 1972, 121-131. (ED 057 857).

(75) KENNEY, BRIGITTE L.; NORWOOD, FRANK W. CATV: visual library service. American Libraries, 2:7 (July/August 1971) 723-726.

(76) KESSLER, WILLIAM J.; WILHELM, MICHAEL J. Narrow bandwidth telecommunications. In: Conference on Interlibrary Communications and Information Networks, Airlie House, Wārrenton, Virginia, 28 September - 2 October 1970. Proceedings. Edited by Joseph Becker. American Library Association, Chicago, Illinois, 1972, 170-182.

(77) KILGOUR, FREDERICK G. A regional network—Ohio College Library Center. Datamation, 16:2 (February 1970) 87-89.

(78) KOCHEN, MANFRED. Directory design for networks of information and referral centers. In: Annual Conference of the Graduate Library School, University of Chicago. 35th. Chicago, Illinois, 2-4 August 1971. Proceedings. Operations research: implications for libraries. Edited by Don R. Swanson and Abraham Bookstein. University of Chicago, Graduate Library School, Chicago, Illinois, 1971, 31 p.

(79) KRAEMER, KENNETH L. USAC: an evolving intergovernmental mechanism for urban information systems development. Public Administration Review, 31:5 (September/October 1971) 543-551.

(80) KRUZAS, ANTHONY T.; SCHNITZER, ANNA ERCOLI; eds. Encyclopedia of information systems and services. Edwards Brothers, Ann Arbor, Michigan, 1 June 1971, 1200 p.

(81) LeGATES, JOHN C. The ARPA network technical aspects in nontechnical language. Interuniversity-Communications Council (EDUCOM), Princeton, New Jersey, 11 July 1971, 27 p.

(82) Library network/MEDLARS technical bulletin. National Library of Medicine, No. 21-32, January/December 1971.

(83) Library urban info network scheme explained to NYLA. Library Journal, 96:20 (15 November 1971) 3707-3708. (LJ News).

(84) LICKLIDER, JOSEPH C. R. A hypothetical plan for a library-information network. In: Conference on Interlibrary Communications and Information Networks, Airlie House, Warrenton, Virginia, 28 September - 2 October 1970. Proceedings. Edited by Joseph Becker. American Library Association, Chicago, Illinois, 1972, 310-316. (ED 057 876).

(85) MARRON, HARVEY. Information network development—cost data for the operation of a decentralized information network: Educational Resources Information Center. Information Storage and Retrieval, 6:2 (June 1970) 221-227.

(86) MARSCHAK, JACOB. Economics of information systems. Journal of the American Statistical Association, 66:333 (March 1971) 192-219.

(87) MARSCHAK, JACOB. Economics of inquiring, communicating, deciding. University of California, Western Science Management Institute, Los Angeles, California, January 1968. (AD 668 496. Based on the Richard T. Ely Lecture delivered at the American Economic Association session of 28 December 1967.).

(88) MARSCHAK, JACOB. Optimal symbol-processing: a problem in individual social economics. Behavioral Science, 16:3 (May 1971) 202-217.

(89) MARTIN, LOWELL A. The suburban system in metropolitan library networks. Illinois Libraries, 53:3 (March 1971) 197-213.

(90) MASSACHUSETTS INSTITUTE OF TECHNOLOGY. Project Intrex, semiannual activity report, 15 March 1971 - 15 September 1971. Massachusetts Institute of Technology, Cambridge, Massachusetts, 15 September 1971, 122 p. (PR-12. ED 053 772).

(91) MILLER, RONALD F. Network organization, a case study of the Five Associated University Libraries (FAUL). In: Conference on Interlibrary Communications and Information Networks, Airlie House, Warrenton, Virginia, 28 September - 2 October 1970. Proceedings. Edited by Joseph Becker. American Library Association, Chicago, Illinois, 1972, 266-276. (ED 057 872).

(92) MILLER, RONALD F. A study of technical services operations in the libraries of the State University of New York at Buffalo. Five Associated University Libraries, Syracuse, New York, June 1970, 35 p. (TRTS 70-1. ED 049 790).

(93) MONTAGUE, ELEANOR. Summary of a feasibility study on the participation of four colleges and universities in a Stanford University library automation network. Stanford University, SPIRES/BALLOTS Project, Stanford, California, November 1971, 72 p.

(94) MORRIS, LLOYD P. Teleducation: networks for knowledge. Library Trends, 19:4 (April 1971) 482-492.

(95) NANCE, RICHARD E.; KORFHAGE, ROBERT R.; BHAT, U. NARAYAN. Information networks: definitions and message transfer models. Southern Methodist University, Computer Science/Operations Research Center, Dallas, Texas, July 1971, 26 p. (CP-710011).

(96) NANCE, RICHARD E.; WICKHAM, W. KENNETH; DUGGAN, MARYANN. A computer system for effective management of a medical library network. Journal of Library Automation, 4:4 (December 1971) 213-220.

(97) NATIONAL ACADEMY OF SCIENCES. COMMITTEE ON SCIENTIFIC AND TECHNICAL COMMUNICATION. Report of the task group on the economics of primary publication. National Academy of Sciences, Committee on Scientific and Technical Communication, Washington, D.C., 1970, 255 p. (PB 194 400).

(98) NATIONAL ACADEMY OF SCIENCES. COMPUTER SCIENCE AND ENGINEERING BOARD. INFORMATION SYSTEMS PANEL. Libraries and information technology—a national system challenge: a report to the Council on Library Resources, Inc., National Academy of Sciences, Printing and Publishing Office, Washington, D.C., 1972, 95 p.

(99) NATIONAL ACADEMY OF SCIENCES. NATIONAL ACADEMY OF ENGINEERING. COMMITTEE ON TELECOMMUNICATIONS. Communications technology for urban improvement: report to the Department of Housing and Urban Development. National Academy of Sciences, National Academy of Engineering, Washington, D.C., June 1971, 218 p. (PB 200 317).

(100) NATIONAL EDUCATION ASSOCIATION. DIVISION OF EDUCATIONAL TECHNOLOGY. Schools and cable television. National Education Association, Washington, D.C., 1971, 66 p.

(101) NATIONAL FEDERATION OF SCIENCE ABSTRACTING AND INDEXING SERVICES. 1971 annual meeting digest. Washington, D.C., 22-24 February 1971. National Federation of Science Abstracting and Indexing Services, Philadelphia, Pennsylvania, 1971, 62 p.

(102) NELSON, CHARLES A.; NELSON, ANNE H. Systems and networks: the state library role. American Libraries, 2:8 (September 1971) 863-887.

(103) NIELSON, NORMAN K. The merit of regional computing networks. Communications of the ACM, 4:5 (May 1971) 319-326.

(104) NORWOOD, FRANK P. Telecommunications programs affecting library network development. In: Conference on Interlibrary Communications and Information Networks, Airlie House, Warrenton, Virginia, 28 September - 2 October 1970. Proceedings. Edited by Joseph Becker. American Library Association, Chicago, Illinois, 1972, 59-68.

(105) Ohio College Library Center Newsletter. Ohio College, Library Center, Columbus, Ohio.

(106) OLIVER, PAUL. Cooperative university computer centers—a provincial outlook. In: American Society for Information Science. Annual meeting. 34th, Denver, Colorado, 7-11 November 1971. Proceedings, vol. 8: Communication for decision-makers. Greenwood Publishing Corp., Westport, Connecticut, 1971, 205-208.

(107) OLSEN, HAROLD ANKER. The economics of information: bibliography and commentary on the literature. ERIC Clearinghouse on Library and Information Sciences, Washington, D.C., January 1971, 30 p. (ED 044 545).

(108) OLSON, EDWIN E. Interlibrary cooperation. Final report. Maryland University. School of Library and Information Services, College Park, Maryland, 1970, 151 p. (ED 046 421).

(109) OPPENHEIMER, GERALD. The Pacific Northwest Regional Health Sciences Library: a centralized operation. Bulletin of the Medical Library Association, 59:2 (April 1971) 237-241.

(110) Organization profile: Association of Scientific Information Dissemination Centers. Information, 3:2 (March/April 1971) 110-112.

(111) OVERHAGE, CARL F. J. Information networks. In: Cuadra, Carlos A.; ed. Annual review of information science and technology, vol. 4. Encyclopedia Britannica, Chicago, Illinois, 1969, 339-378.

(112) PALMOUR, VERNON E.; BRYANT, EDWARD C.; CALDWELL, NANCY W.; GRAY, LUCY M. A study of the characteristics, costs, and magnitude of interlibrary loans in academic libraries. Westat Research, Inc., Rockville, Maryland, September 1971, 134 p. (To be published by Association of Research Libraries, Washington, D.C., 1972).

(113) PAN, ELIZABETH; MILLER, RON; EVANS, GLYN T. Materials transfer: a report of a pilot document delivery service, November 1969-June 1970. Five Associated University Libraries, Syracuse, New York, September 1971, 48 p. (FTM 70-4).

(114) PATRICK, RUTH J. Guidelines for the development of academic library consortia. System Development Corporation, Santa Monica, California, 15 November 1971, 200 p. (TM-4597/005/00).
(115) PINGS, VERN M. Interlibrary cooperation, a second year review of the Kentucky, Ohio, Michigan Regional Medical Library program. Kentucky, Ohio, Michigan Regional Medical Library, Detroit, Michigan, April 1971, 54 p. (Papers and reports no. 9. ED 048 889).
(116) PINGS, VERN M. Kentucky, Ohio, Michigan Regional Medical Library program: a discussion of its formation. Kentucky, Ohio, Michigan Regional Medical Library, Detroit, Michigan, April 1969, 30 p. (Papers and reports no. 3. ED 035 424).
(117) PINGS, VERN M. KOMRML, the first year's experience. Kentucky, Ohio, Michigan Regional Medical Library, Detroit, Michigan, March 1970, 52 p. (Papers and reports no. 5. ED 044 148).
(118) PRICE, MONROE E. Content on cable: the nascent experience. A paper prepared for the Sloan Commission on Cable Communications. (No publisher or place given), September 1970, 48 p.
(119) The revolution in the phone business. Business Week, 2202 (6 November 1971) 66-69, 72-74.
(120) REYNOLDS, MARYAN E.; TAYLOR, DAVID W.; MEIER, ROBERT C.; MILLER, ROGER L.; STANFIELD, JONATHAN; SCHOLZ, WILLIAM H. A study of library network alternatives for the state of Washington. Final report. Washington State Library, Olympia, Washington, January 1971, 317 p. (ED 045 862).
(121) ROUD, RICHARD. Cable television and the arts. A paper prepared for the Sloan Commission on Cable Communications. (No publisher or place given), March 1971, 37 p.
(122) RUECKING, FREDERICK, JR. A science improvement program for the Gulf Coast region. Rice University, Fondren Library, Houston, Texas, 25 May 1970, 104 p. (PB 197 249).
(123) ST. ANGELO, DOUGLAS; HARTSFIELD, ANNIE MARY; GOLDSTEIN, HAROLD. State library policy: its legislative and environmental contexts. American Library Association, Chicago, Illinois, 1971, 128 p.
(124) SAMUELSON, KJELL. International information transfer and network communication. In: Cuadra, Carlos A.; ed. Annual review of information science and technology, vol 6. Encyclopedia Britannica, Chicago, Illinois, 1971, 277-324.
(125) SCIENCE COUNCIL OF CANADA. Scientific and technical information in Canada, part I. Queen's Printer for Canada, Ottawa, Ontario, Canada, 1969, 62 p. (Special study no. 8).
(126) SCIENCE COUNCIL OF CANADA. Scientific and technical information in Canada, part II, chapter 7: economics. Queen's Printer for Canada, Ottawa, Ontario, Canada, 1969, 63 p. (Special study no. 8).
(127) SEDLACEK, W. C.; LEONARD, R. E.; BURTT, J. E. Information transfer systems requirement study. Final report. Lockheed Missiles and Space Co., Sunnyvale, California, March 1970, 126 p. (N70-22171).
(128) Service via satellite: Crerar to Argentina. Library Journal, 96:12 (15 June 1971) 2034.
(129) SIMMS, ROBERT L., JR.; FUCHS, EDWARD. Communication technology. In: Cuadra, Carlos A.; ed. Annual review of information science and technology, vol. 5. Encyclopedia Britannica, Chicago, Illinois, 1970, 113-139.
(130) SLAMECKA, VLADIMIR. Methods and research for design of information networks. Library Trends, 18:4 (April 1970) 551-568.
(131) SLICE/MARC-O description of services. Oklahoma Department of Libraries, Oklahoma City, SLICE Office, Dallas, Texas, December 1971, 16 p.
(132) SLOAN COMMISSION ON CABLE COMMUNICATIONS. On the cable: the television of abundance. McGraw-Hill, New York, 1971, 256 p.

(133) SLOAN, ELAINE F. Toward an understanding of library cooperatives as organizations. February 1970, 29 p. (ED 047 752).
(134) SMITH, RALPH LEE. The wired nation. The Nation, 210:19 (18 May 1970) 582-606.
(135) SPENCER, CAROL C. Unit costs of interlibrary loans and photocopies at a regional medical library. Bulletin of the Medical Library Association, 58:2 (April 1970) 189-190.
(136) STANFORD, EDWARD B. MINITEX 1969-1970: a report on a pilot demonstration project. University of Minnesota, University Libraries, Minneapolis, Minnesota, September 1970, 16 p+ .
(137) STATE UNIVERSITY OF NEW YORK AT BUFFALO. TECHNICAL INFORMATION DISSEMINATION BUREAU. MASFILE-II pilot project. Final report. Five Associated University Libraries, Syracuse, New York, June 1970, 47 p. (MF 15.6. ED 051 826).
(138) STENSTROM, RALPH H. Cooperation between types of libraries 1940-1968: an annotated bibliography. American Library Association, Chicago, Illinois, 1970, 168 p.
(139) STETTEN, KENNETH J. Interactive television software for cable television applications. The Mitre Corporation, Washington, D.C., June 1971, 10 p. (MTP-354).
(140) STEVENS, MARY ELIZABETH. Interlocking directories—problems and prospects of network referral resources. U.S. Department of Commerce, National Bureau of Standards, Washington, D.C., May 1971, 146 p. (Report 10 473).
(141) STEVENS, MARY ELIZABETH. Problems of network accounting, monitoring and performance measurement. U.S. Department of Commerce, National Bureau of Standards, Washington, D.C., September 1970, 136 p. (PB 198 048).
(142) STEVENS, MARY ELIZABETH. Standardization, compatibility and/or convertibility requirements in network planning. U.S. Department of Commerce, National Bureau of Standards, Washington, D.C., May 1970, 369 p. (PB 194 179).
(143) STEVENS, NORMAN D. MEDLARS: A summary review and evaluation of three reports. Library Resources and Technical Services, 14:1 (Winter 1970) 109-121.
(144) SWANK, RAYNARD C. Interlibrary cooperation, interlibrary communications and information networks—explanation and definition. In: Conference on Interlibrary Communications and Information Networks, Airlie House, Warrenton, Virginia, 28 September - 2 October 1970. Proceedings. Edited by Joseph Becker. American Library Association, Chicago, Illinois, 1972, 18-26. (ED 057 847).
(145) SYLVESTRE, GUY. The prime mover: the role of the national library. In: Canadian Library Association. Annual conference. 25th, Hamilton, Ontario, Canada, 20-25 June 1970. Proceedings. Into the seventies—challenge of change. Canadian Library Association, Ottawa, Ontario, Canada, 1970, 12-21.
(146) SYPERT, MARY. An evaluation of the Colorado Statewide Reference Network. University of Denver, Graduate School of Librarianship, Center for Communication and Information Research, Denver, Colorado, April 1971.
(147) Telecommunications acoustic coupler survey. Telecommunications, 4:10 (October 1970) 18-20.
(148) Telecommunications hard-copy survey. Telecommunications, 4:12 (December 1970) 16-20.
(149) Telecommunications modem survey. Telecommunications, 4:2 (February 1970) 12-20.
(150) Telecommunications on-line minicomputer survey. Telecommunications, 5:11 (November 1971) 23-26.
(151) TEXAS STATE LIBRARY. AUSTIN. FIELD SERVICE DIVISION. Evaluation number two, Texas State Library communication network, 1969. Texas State Library, Austin, Texas, 1970, 68 p. (ED 046 406).

(152) THOMPSON, JAMES D. Organizations in action. McGraw-Hill, New York, 1967, 192 p.
(153) TOOMBS, ROBERT. Considering telecommunications? Select the right modem. Computer Decisions, 3:7 (July 1971) 16-19.
(154) Unanimous FCC vote ok's carriers' entry. Computerworld, 5:22 (2 June 1971) 1, 3.
(155) UNISTAR: User Network for Information Storage, Transfer, Acquisition, and Retrieval. Final report. Auburn University, School of Engineering, Auburn, Alabama, October 1970, 305 p. (CR-61333. ED 047 693. Available from National Technical Information Service, Springfield, Virginia. NASA-71-10806).
(156) U.S. FEDERAL COMMUNICATIONS COMMISSION. Cable television service: cable television relay service. Federal Register, 37 (12 February 1972) 3252-3341.
(157) U.S. FEDERAL COMMUNICATIONS COMMISSION. Docket 16942. In the matter of use of the Carterfone device in message toll telephone service. U.S. Federal Communications Commission, Washington, D.C., 27 June 1968.
(158) U.S. FEDERAL LIBRARY COMMITTEE. Proceedings of the Federal Library Committee meetings, December 16, 1970 and April 28, 1971 on implications to the federal library community of the Airlie Conference on Interlibrary Communications and Information Networks, 28 September - 2 October 1970. U.S. Federal Library Committee, Washington, D.C., June 1971, 24 p. (ED 054 781).
(159) U.S. GENERAL ACCOUNTING OFFICE. Information gathering and disseminating activities of the National Library of Medicine. Government Printing Office, Washington, D.C., 1970, 41 p.
(160) U.S. NATIONAL AERONAUTICS AND SPACE ADMINISTRATION. What NASA/RECON can do for you. National Aeronautics and Space Administration, Office of Technology Utilization, Scientific and Technical Information Division, Washington, D.C., November 1970, 12 p.
(161) U.S. NATIONAL BUREAU OF STANDARDS. Federal information processing standards index. Government Printing Office, Washington, D.C., 1 January 1971, 134 p. (FIPS publication no. 12).
(162) U.S. NATIONAL LIBRARY OF MEDICINE. MEDLINE Communications network, 1971. National Library of Medicine, Bethesda, Maryland, 1971, 3 p. (Processed).
(163) U.S. NATIONAL SCIENCE FOUNDATION. A first report on an exploratory program of regional cooperative computing activities: a program conducted by the National Science Foundation in cooperation with selected institutions of higher learning. Oregon State University Computer Center, Corvalis, Oregon, 1970, 148 p. (CCR 70-12).
(164) U.S. PRESIDENT'S COMMISSION ON FEDERAL STATISTICS. Federal statistics: report of the President's Commission. 2 vols. Government Printing Office, Washington, D.C., 1971.
(165) Urban cable systems. The Mitre Corporation, Washington, D.C., 1971, 305 p. (Report M 71-64).
(166) VOLK, JOHN. The Reston, Virginia, text of the Mitre Corporation's interactive television system. The Mitre Corporation, Washington, D.C., May 1971, 18 p. (MTP-352).
(167) WARD, JOHN A. Present and probable CATV/broadband-communication technology. In: Sloan Commission on Cable Communications. On the cable: the television of abundance. McGraw-Hill, New York, 1971, 179-212.
(168) WARNER, EDWARD S. A tentative analytical approach to the determination of interlibrary loan network effectiveness. College and Research Libraries, 32:3 (May 1971) 217-221.
(169) WEBER, DAVID C.; LYNDEN, FREDERICK C. Survey of interlibrary cooperation. In: Conference on Interlibrary Communication and Information Net-

works, Airlie House, Warrenton, Virginia, 28 September - 2 October 1970. Proceedings. Edited by Joseph Becker. American Library Association, Chicago, Illinois, 1972, 69-84. (ED 057 852).

(170) WENTE, VAN A. NASA/RECON and user interface considerations. National Aeronautics and Space Administration, Washington, D.C., January 1971, 5 p.

(171) WIGINGTON, RONALD L.; WOOD, JAMES L. Standardization requirements of a national program for information transfer. Library Trends, 18:4 (April 1970) 432-447.

(172) WISCONSIN, UNIVERSITY OF, MADISON. DEPARTMENT OF POSTGRADUATE MEDICAL EDUCATION. A study on the feasibility of establishing a national medical dial access information retrieval system. University of Wisconsin, Department of Postgraduate Medical Education, Madison, Wisconsin, 1970, 131 p.

(173) Working group summary on network needs and development. In: Conference on Interlibrary Communication and Information Networks, Airlie House, Warrenton, Virginia, 28 September - 2 October 1970. Proceedings. Edited by Joseph Becker. American Library Association, Chicago, Illinois, 1972, 13-17.

(174) Working group summary on network services. In: Conference on Interlibrary Communication and Information Networks, Airlie House, Warrenton, Virginia, 28 September - 2 October 1970. Proceedings. Edited by Joseph Becker. American Library Association, Chicago, Illinois, 1972, 85-91.

9 Machine-Readable Bibliographic Data Bases

MARVIN C. GECHMAN
Information General, Inc.

INTRODUCTION

The advent of machine-readable data bases is one of the most significant forward steps in information retrieval. Currently, the creation and application of these data bases are in a period of very rapid growth. This reviewer sees a great need for a review of "what is going on" because there is so much going on. It is the goal of this chapter to fulfill that need even though it is difficult to hold this dynamic field static for a good meaningful look.

Scope of Coverage

Literature input to this review was taken from *any* available literature describing data base activities in 1971. Because this is a first-time chapter solely devoted to machine-readable bibliographic data bases, reference is made to important contributions as far back as 1969. The field is changing so rapidly that contributions made prior to 1969 are of limited value.[1]

The phrase "machine-readable data base" covers a tremendous number of applications. To keep this chapter within reasonable proportions, a stringent selection criteria was employed restricting input to

---

[1]The author is grateful to many contributors, too numerous to acknowledge individually, whose personal correspondence served as a valuable input to this chapter.

data bases containing machine-readable *bibliographic records* including document surrogates and indexes to the literature and data (but not the raw data itself). A distinction is made between data bases and data banks. This criterion excludes data banks involving atmospheric phenomena, satellite experiments, labor statistics, criminal records, IRS data, etc. The only exceptions are census, patents, and legal data tapes.

There are no restrictions as to subject or discipline but the applications lean heavily toward scientific and technical information because that is where most of the activity is. Record-keeping activities have been excluded (e.g., circulation, serials control, and medical records). Data bases used for publication purposes only, and automated photocomposition or typesetting are included only if they are subsequently used to provide literature-searching services. Also excluded are data bases used with proprietary systems or services restricted to a specific user group (e.g., employees of an organization). In other words, the data base must be "available." Exceptions to *all* of the above exclusion rules apply where noteworthy literature was produced.

Apologies are made at the outset for the brief treatment of each data base or search service. The length of the review chapter precluded detailed descriptions. Indeed, the 1971 study of data bases by Information General, Inc. (109) required up to 50 pages to describe some data bases adequately. Furthermore, a complete discussion of data bases would cover cost data, software packages, retrieval languages, and remote access; all of these subjects had to be omitted, for brevity.

Historical Perspective

Although this chapter has no direct counterpart in previous volumes, data bases have been discussed in previous chapters written by Landau (131) in 1969, Wente & Young (255) in 1970, and Magnino (143) in 1971. An interesting growth pattern can be observed from the following excerpts of the conclusions reached by these reviewers:

> . . .1968 was truly a year of evolution . . . .Many concepts, techniques and trends reached an advanced state of development. . . .(131).
>
> . . .(in 1969) applications, particularly increased uses of bibliographic data tapes, were numerous; true innovations were few. . . .(255).
>
> . . .literature of 1970 reports much more specialization and operational applications. . . we have come of age. . .magnetic tape information services are being

applied to operational environments. . .the number of data bases being offered is encouraging. . . (143).

In 1969, the Organisation for Economic Co-operation and Development (OECD) prepared "An Inventory of Some English Language Secondary Information Services in Science and Technology" compiled by Lee (137). Indicative of the state of the art in 1968, it listed 47 organizations offering 90 publications; about 50 were prepared using magnetic tape to some degree. It appears that about 25 of these bibliographic data bases were available under purchase or lease agreements.

In 1971, in a joint survey with the United Nations Economic Commission for Europe, OECD (174) issued an updated version of the inventory seven times larger than the original inventory. It covers 100 organizations worldwide providing 141 information systems or services. Of these, 108 produce machine-readable data bases used in conjunction with their publications. A little more than half (only 56) of the tapes are available for purchase or lease. Most of the others use their tapes for literature-searching services. On the basis of the OECD inventories, it can be concluded that the number of available data bases doubled in the past two to three years (assuming both inventories were equally comprehensive at the time of their preparation).

Other surveys (primarily restricted to scientific and technical disciplines) help to show the growth of machine-readable data bases between late 1969 and mid-1970. The American Library Association (ALA, 15) prepared a reference guide in 1969 to 18 sources of data bases; only 10 were noted as available. In 1970, the American Institute of Physics, working under an NSF grant, prepared a survey of scientific-technical tape services. The survey, published in conjunction with the American Society for Information Science (ASIS), was compiled and edited by Carroll (48). Of the 50 data bases described, originating from 26 sources, about 40 were bibliographic and currently available. The ASIS Special Interest Group on SDI conducted a survey in 1969, compiled by Housman (104), that identified 45 users of 12 data bases. An annotated bibliography of 40 available data bases was presented in 1970 by Gechman (86). The handbook by Hayes & Becker (93) contains a useful inventory of data bases plus an excellent discussion (Chapter 19) of mechanized information services emphasizing machine-readable data bases.

Two derivations from the Carroll survey appeared in 1971; a profile of scientific tape services was prepared by Gehl & Slamecka (88), and by Weinstock (252), who briefly described 20 data bases that he interestingly classified into three research and development groups: ongoing R&D, current R&D reports, and past R&D results. *LIST-1971*, edited by Wasserman et al. (251), covers over 800 research efforts as of late 1970, including many involving data bases. The *Encyclopedia of Information Systems and Services*, edited by Kruzas et al. (129), first published in 1971, is a monumental effort that should serve as an extremely valuable reference tool to the profession as a whole. Over 140 organizations who produce or use machine-readable data bases are described. Although the 12 indexes are good, the massive volume would be easier to use if the descriptions were organized into subject categories, such as manual systems, automated systems, software and services, etc.

Chapter Organization

This chapter review differs from existing data base surveys in one major respect: everything has been screened out except machine-readable bibliographic data bases and processing services that are available to external users. It cannot be claimed that all applications were identified; however, due to the homogeneity of the screened input, it is believed to be an accurate representation of machine-readable bibliographic data base activities underway worldwide as of late 1971.

These activities have been organized into five separate groups: (a) academic, (b) government, (c) industry, (d) professional societies and nonprofit groups, and (e) foreign countries and international organizations. Within each group, related data base activities are sub-grouped; organizational paragraph headings are used throughout. This approach was, in the author's opinion, necessary in order to describe the multitude of ongoing activities clearly and systematically.

DATA BASE ACTIVITIES IN ACADEMIC GROUPS

The creation and maintenance of machine-readable bibliographic data bases requires rather extensive resources. As a result, the academic groups are primarily users rather than creators of data bases. There are, however, a number of data bases produced by the academic sector. Many academic users offer their services (in a commercial fashion) in order to offset development costs.

Regional Dissemination Centers

A network of Regional Dissemination Centers (RDCs) is maintained by NASA at six universities. The RDC network has access not only to the NASA data base, but also to other government and commercial data bases. Each RDC provides current awareness and retrospective search services to local and fee-paying industrial clients. The six RDCs are listed below.

University of Connecticut. One of the largest users of machine-readable data bases is the New England Research Applications Center

(NERAC). In 1971, NERAC had access to 28 data bases covering a wide area of technology (NERAC, 166).

Indiana University. The Aerospace Research Applications Center (ARAC) was founded in 1962 as one of NASA's original RDCs (ARAC, 2). A guide to preparing a profile search strategy at ARAC for CA Condensates was prepared by Hartwell (92).

University of New Mexico. The Technology Applications Center services the southwest (230; Kruzas et al., 129).

North Carolina Science and Technology Research Center. STRC is closely tied to the three Triangle Universities—Duke University, the University of North Carolina, and North Carolina State University. Its last Annual Report (NCSTRC, 168) indicated they were actively serving 107 clients and 19 universities (in 10 southeastern states) with 11 data bases. The computer center also offers searches of the Textile Information Retrieval Project (TIRP) data base developed at MIT. Work & Phillips (266) conclude that future developments of this data base should come from the joint efforts of universities and the textile and fibers industries.

University of Pittsburgh. The Knowledge Availability Systems Center (KASC) has been offering information services on a fee basis since 1964. KASC data bases access over a million document references, and the Center is growing at a rate of 43,000 items per month (185).

University of Southern California. The Western Research Applications Center (WESRAC), NASA's RDC for the western states, offers a customized Technology Intelligence Program to business, local government, and research organizations. It includes search options of batch processing or on-line access (WESRAC, 256).

Office of Science Information Services

The Office of Science Information Services at NSF supports research and development efforts directed toward the use of machine-readable data bases. Some of the projects supported were conducted at the Universities of Georgia and Pittsburgh; Lehigh University; UCLA; and Ohio State and Stanford Universities.

University of Georgia. The Computer Center at UGA is one of the most active users of multiple machine-readable data bases. Search services were provided from 17 data bases in 1971. All data bases are converted to a Standard File Format (SFF) for search with the UGA Text Search System. Over 2.8 million document records were available in SFF and being searched routinely by the center in 1971 for 900 users, which is triple the number from the preceding year; only 6 percent of the users were external to the University System. Services from data bases produced by commercial firms are noticeably absent, primarily because of the higher cost over those developed elsewhere. Park & Gibson (178) give an interesting account of UGA operational experiences. They found it necessary to edit the data base files for consistency, and to some extent for accuracy, because the data bases are "by-products of the publishing business, and as such are not the optimal form for use in search services." (What "optimal form" is, or should be, was not defined.) They found that about 10 percent of the current awareness update tapes were unusable and had to be returned for replacement.

The annual report to NSF (UGA, 45) gives an excellent account of 1971 activities. Of special interest is a communication link with the University of Pittsburgh, implemented as part of an information service exchange experiment. Park (177) describes the development of the on-line computer system for management of search profiles. Carmon & Park (46) present a detailed discussion of the cost factors involved in the operation of an information dissemination center.

Lehigh University. The Center For Information Sciences is developing an on-line conversational scientific information retrieval system called Project Leadermart (NSF, 243). Various retrieval service alternatives were being studied in 1971. During 1972, a communication link with UGA was planned.

University of California, Los Angeles. The Campus Computing Network at UCLA is developing a Center For Information Services that will include the acquisition of selected machine-readable data bases (NSF, 245).

Ohio State University. The Mechanized Information Center (MIC) is developing an automated, multidisciplinary university-centered information system (NSF, 244). In 1971, the MIC provided current awareness services derived from four multidiscipline data bases. Unduplicated entries were merged into one data base and searched biweekly for over 300 patrons.

Stanford University. In their annual report to NSF (Parker, 179), Stanford's Institute for Communication Research reported on progress in development of a user-oriented, interactive, on-line retrieval system. A prototype system, SPIRES-I (Stanford Physics Information Retrieval System), was implemented in 1969. Its primary data base is a High Energy Physics Preprints file. This data base, keyboarded at Stanford, has been made available on magnetic tape for experimental use at other facilities. For SPIRES-II, the acronym is the same except "physics" has been changed to "public" to account for its expanded coverage, which will include behavioral sciences and African studies when fully operational.

Stanford also utilizes the DESY High Energy Physics Index originating in Germany. When complete, the DESY file will contain approximately 50,000 items. Stanford is exploring the possibility of making these tapes available to other users. The preprint and DESY data bases are expected to provide on-line access to virtually all high-energy-physics literature, published and unpublished, since 1968.

Experimental Programs

Noteworthy experimental programs using machine-readable data bases, were conducted in 1971 at Cornell University, Massachusetts Institute of Technology, and Syracuse University.

Cornell University. Since 1964, the Department of Computer Science has been experimenting with automated information processing techniques with a project called the SMART System. Salton (195) summarized 27 theoretical and experimental studies. The SMART System utilizes a number of machine-readable data base subsets.

Massachusetts Institute of Technology (MIT). Project INTREX is a series of experiments in information transfer designed to have application to university library services in the 1970s. The latest semiannual activity report (MIT, 151) contains a useful analysis of machine-readable data bases from the viewpoints of overlap and cost per item included on the tape. Nine data bases were involved in the overlap study and 33 data bases were involved in the cost analysis. The INTREX experimental data base adds about 3000 documents per year; over 18,000 document records were in the file in 1971. Details related to the encoding and generation of the data base are given by Benenfeld (33).

Syracuse University. The Syracuse School of Library Science constructed, operated, and evaluated an experimental on-line reference retrieval system using free-text indexing. The Psychological Abstracts tape was used to develop a data base of over 35,000 entries. The project, known as the Syracuse University Psychological Abstracts Retrieval Service (SUPARS), is described in a six-section final report by Cook et al. (59). Frierson & Atherton (80) described the results of a survey of attitudes toward SUPARS. They found a definitely positive reaction toward SUPARS and computerized information retrieval systems in general.

Other Academic Users

Illinois Institute of Technology (IIT). Another active academic user of machine-readable data bases is the Computer Search Center at the

IIT Research Institute (IITRI). Four data bases were searched on a production basis in 1971 and an operational capability existed for three more. A set of preprocessor programs has been prepared to handle virtually any incoming data base for editing and conversion to the standard IITRI format. The experiences of IITRI in handling and searching a variety of data bases are described in two papers by M. Williams (259, 260). Schipma et al. (201) analyzed the content and format of seven data bases and found great discrepancies in the presentation of essentially similar bibliographic data; they suggested use of standards.

Schipma (200) describes a research program at IITRI to investigate the feasibility of merging multiple data bases and methods of inverting and compressing large data bases to permit economical searches. A dictionary arrangement technique for natural-language text searching, called the "Least Common Bigram: A Dictionary Arrangement Technique for Computerized Natural-Language Text Searching" is described by Onderisin (172). The method, based upon certain statistical characteristics of a data base, yielded a 400 percent improvement over the traditional dictionary look-up. M. Williams (261) discusses the use of a "personal" disc or tape file that can be inexpensively stored and retrieved when needed. Such a personal disc library could be used in lieu of a personal hard-copy file containing references the user might wish to access at a later date. It is, essentially, a prescreened tailor-made data base.

University of Florida. The State University System of Florida (SUNIFLO) Information Network, provides census data and related products. The University of Florida, Florida State University, and the University of South Florida all participate in the Census Access Program (CAP) administered directly through the library rather than the computing center (108). The University of Florida also provides searches on two additional data bases: (a) MARC II, and (b) CAIN (cataloging and indexing) tapes from NAL.

Other Data Base Generators

Most of the data bases generated in the academic sector concentrate on a specific discipline and are an outgrowth of work being carried on at the respective college or university. Some of the significant data bases are described.

Bowling Green State University. The Philosophy Documentation Center maintains a tape data base used as input to the Philosopher's Information Retrieval System (PIRS). PIRS provides SDI services, including abstracts, covering articles and books on topics in philosophy from 1967, and plans to include bibliographic data back to 1945 (BGSU, 39).

University of California, Berkeley. The Institute of Library Research (ILR) at Berkeley has been preparing a union catalog for the nine campuses of the university covering 1963-1967 (ILR, 112). It will be produced in printed form (about 90 volumes), in microform, and on tape for general distribution. The project status report by Shoffner et al. (211), indicates that the file is estimated to contain 800,000 unique titles and will cost $8000 for the first tape set. The status report claims that ILR is producing the largest file of MARC II-structured records in the world. It should be noted, however, that the ILR format deviates somewhat from the full MARC II format.

According to Shoffner (209, 210), the approach developed to convert and organize the file of over one million catalog cards represents an important breakthrough. Essentially, the procedure involves getting the records into machine form at the least cost and then using computer algorithms (rather than extensive human editing) to clean up the file. In addition, ILR is planning a second supplement in magnetic tape form covering 1968-1972. Both of the above projects are intended to be supplementary to MARC II. Special attention was given in planning the strategy for the second supplement to minimize the likelihood of overlap with the RECON Project at LC (Shoffner, 211).

City University of New York. After four years of activity as an Urban Renewal Demonstration Project, Project URBANDOC issued a three-volume final report in 1971 (Sessions & Sloan, 206, 207, 208). The three volumes are concerned with the applicability of computerized documentation techniques to the literature of urban planning and renewal. The Project evolved from a need for improving bibliographic services in urban affairs—specifically, urban renewal. URBANDOC was one of the first computerized information systems to deal specifically with the social sciences; it disproved the myth that social sciences were not amenable to modern techniques of documentation. Publication of the final reports mark the end of the URBANDOC Project. Although its mission (to test the applicability of computerized documentation techniques to the social sciences) was accomplished, it was concluded that an operational documentation center for urban affairs could not financially support itself without some subsidy.

University of Tulsa. The Information Services Department has been abstracting current worldwide technical literature and patents covering petroleum exploration, development, and production since 1961. The data base is prepared from over 650 sources. The abstracts are published in a weekly bulletin and cumulative indexes, on magnetic tape, are available to subscribers at four-month intervals (UT, 229). A technical description of the information system is given by Martinez (147) including an elaborate indexing system based on controlled-vocabulary and concept indexing. A good description of the computer process for generating printed indexes to "Petroleum Abstracts" is discussed by Martinez et al. (148).

Other Academic Data Base Activities. The following universities provide computer literature searches from the data base subject areas indicated. In some cases, access to other processing services supplements in-house capabilities:

(a) University of California, Berkeley—Lawrence Radiation Laboratory;

(b) University of Dayton—Aerospace Materials Information Center (Scheffler & March, 198);

(c) University of Georgia—Center For Management Systems Development and Analysis (management information systems);

(d) Georgia Institute of Technology—The Technical Information Service (GATTIS);

(e) University of Iowa—Iowa Drug Information Service (drugs and drug therapy);

(f) Johns Hopkins University—Laboratory in Behavioral Physiology;

(g) University of Louisville Library—The Louisville Information Referral Center;

(h) University of Michigan—Information System for Asian Studies (social sciences and humanities in Asia);

(i) University of Minnesota—Family Study Center (marriage and family);

(j) Notre Dame—Radiation Chemistry Data Center;

(k) Rice University—the Regional Information and Communication Exchange (RICE);

(l) University of Southern California—the National Information Center for Education Media (NICEM) covering audio-visual (non-book media) materials distributed in the U.S. (Rufsvold & Guss, 194);

(m) University of Washington—Primate Information Center.

Most of these activities are described by Kruzas (129).

DATA BASE ACTIVITIES IN GOVERNMENT AGENCIES

A year-long study completed in July 1971 by System Development Corporation (SDC), under contract to USOE, resulted in one of the most intensive investigations of the Federal library community ever undertaken (Markuson et al., 144, 145). It provided considerable data relative to the use of machine-readable data bases by this group. Respondents reported that local resources are inadequate to support automation; they favor standardization and centralized automation support and services. The study found that the cost of independent automation of the Federal library community would be prohibitive.

The use of bibliographic data bases is not restricted to the library community; therefore, this reviewer believes the actual use of machine-readable data bases in the Federal Government is much higher than that reported by the Federal library community responding to this survey. Many government computer organizations provide services from external data bases. For example, in mid-1971 the Division of Computer Research and Technology (DCRT) established a computer-based chemical information system for the NIH scientific community. The initial input data base chosen for this current awareness service was CBAC (from CAS). The description below identifies 17 government organizations who produce 24 data bases; only eight of these organizations were mentioned by survey respondents. In addition, at least 15 more data bases were identified that are purposely excluded because their use is restricted to local users. It appears that the library community is unaware of the many government data bases produced and used on a local level.

Both this reviewer and the SDC survey reached the conclusion that Federal libraries (and users) have accepted the concept of services offered from machine-readable data bases and believe that the potential of either mail or on-line access is a feasible augmentation of local library capabilities. However, to exploit this potential fully, government libraries must somehow tie into data base services offered by non-library groups.

U.S. Government agencies produce more data bases than do any other group referred to in this review. Most of them appear to be designed for specific internal uses and serve a relatively small audience. However, most of the largest machine-readable data bases are also produced by the government. The following descriptions cover only the major data bases produced.

National Libraries

Each of the three national libraries, Library of Congress, National Agricultural Library, and the National Library of Medicine produces a machine-readable data base of major significance.

Library of Congress. Without a doubt, the most significant development in the last three years, relative to machine-readable data bases, is that of the MARC (Machine-Readable Catalog) tapes prepared by LC. MARC development has had a worldwide impact on automated bibliographic activities. These activities have been described by Avram (21) in last year's *Annual Review* and in the chapter by Martin in this volume. The significance of the MARC II tapes justifies a brief review of 1971 activities here.

Late in 1971, the MARC file approached 250,000 records. There were over 60 subscribers to the weekly tape service containing about 75,000 records per year. LC also provided searches at cost. The MARC Development Office prepared a succinct and well written general background of MARC-related topics (US/LC, 237) and a manual describing specifications for magnetic tapes containing catalog records for motion pictures, film strips, and other pictorial media (US/LC, 236). The use of a computer to assign content designators and field codes to unedited bibliographic data in order to create MARC records (which is known as format recognition) is described by Maruyama (149). Avram (20) describes the evolving MARC system and how it pertains to the concept of a data utility. Ristow & Carrington (191) and Carrington & Mangan (47) describe how the MARC system provides the medium through which map cataloging records are converted to machine-readable form. Changes to the MARC Serials Format are described in an addendum manual prepared by LC (US/LC, 238). A review of the latest progress report for the RECON Pilot Project was prepared by Avram & Maruyama (24).

Use of the MARC II data base is widespread; considerable literature has been produced related to these experiences (Stockard, 218; Henderson, 97). An excellent review of the program for utilizing the MARC II data base in a cooperative SDI system in Canada is described by Mauerhoff & Smith (152), and an operating SDI service that uses weekly MARC II tapes at the Oklahoma Department of Libraries is described by Bierman & Blue (37). File size and the cost of processing MARC records are described by Kennedy (121), who concludes that the ratio of titles selected to titles read from the cumulative file is the most significant determinant of cost. He suggests that, to have an economical system, an effective formula for limiting the growth of the file must be developed. Another discussion involving criticisms of MARC was prepared by Ayres (25), who suggests ways of using MARC at the local level.

There have been many commercial uses of the MARC II data base including services offered by AUTOCOMP and Inforonics (Kruzas et al., 129). On-line applications include: the Stanford Ballots System (Parker, 179); SDC's ALPS system; and the Ohio College Library Center (OCLC), which was being tested and evaluated during late 1971 (Hopkins, 103). One of the most exciting uses of the MARC II data base is generation of the CARDSET Cataloging System produced by Information Design, Inc. (IDI, 107). The MARC II tapes are processed through a COM (computer output microfilm) system at IDI that puts the complete MARC II data base on 16mm microfilm cartridges. A motorized cartridge drive rapidly locates the desired frame. The system produces fully-headed card sets on pre-scored card stock at a cost of ten cents per set.

National Agricultural Library. NAL is responsible for the worldwide collection and dissemination of agricultural information. The Cataloging and Indexing System (CAIN) has been used since 1970 to build the data base. Lebowitz & Johnson (136) describe aspects of the automation effort and call the CAIN tapes the "heart" of the system. A later document by Van Dyke & Ayer (249) describes an interactive system using CRT terminals for input, update, and access to the CAIN data base. NAL serial records are being converted to machine-readable form for transmission (in MARC II communication format) to the National Serials Data Bank being created by the three national libraries (NFSAIS, 160). Input of machine-readable bibliographic data bases from outside sources into an NAL master data bank was studied by Auerbach Corporation (Landau, 130, 133).

National Library of Medicine. The extensive biomedical data base, MEDLARS (Medical Literature Analysis and Retrieval System), prepared by NLM, contains over 1.5 million citations to articles published since 1963. Approximately 200,000 citations are added annually from 2300 biomedical periodicals; about one half of these articles are in languages other than English. Two NLM manuals describe the principles of MEDLARS (NLM, 242) and MEDLAR services (NLM, 240), which make automated bibliographic search services available through 11 regional centers in the U.S. and eight centers in other countries.

MEDLINE (MEDLARS on-line), initiated in 1971, was spurred by the success of AIM-TWX (Abridged Index Medicus via Teletypewriter Exchange Network), an experimental service inaugurated by NLM in 1970. The AIM-TWX system is a modification of SDC's ORBIT (On-Line Retrieval of Bibliographic Information Time-Shared) system. The MEDLINE data base is composed of about 400,000 citations to articles from more than 1000 journals indexed for MEDLARS since January 1969. McCarn (141) published a full description of the AIM-TWX experimental system. The nature of information communication networks including advantages, configurations, costs, and plans for a national on-line medical bibliographic system is discussed by McCarn

(142). In related papers, Davis (63) describes the evolving structure of a national biomedical communications network; the Toxicology Information Program (TIP) of the NLM is discussed by Kissman (126). TIQRC (Toxicology Information Query Response Center), located at Oak Ridge provides on-line access to the TIP data base and others.

Other NIH Data Bases

Several other data bases are produced within the NIH complex in addition to the NLM data bases. Three significant ones are described below:

Food and Drug Administration. FDA produces a machine-readable version of its National Drug Code (NDC) directory. The NDC magnetic tape extract contains drug product information voluntarily supplied to FDA by cooperating drug firms. A nine-character identification code has been assigned to 23,000 drug products. The data base is available from the National Technical Information Service; it is updated three to four times per year. Slavin (234) describes the development and application of the NDC.

National Clearinghousefor Mental Health Information. NCMHI is a national center for the world's mental health literature. The system contains citations and abstracts to over 150,000 documents. Requests for individual computer searches are currently available without charge (NCMHI, 155).

National Institute of Neurological Diseases and Stroke. NINDS supports the operation of the Neurological Information Network comprising three interrelated information centers: (a) The Brain Information Service operated at UCLA; (b) The Information Center for Hearing, Speech, and Disorders of Human Communication at the Johns Hopkins Medical Institutions; and (c) The Epilepsy Abstracts Retrieval System (EARS) an on-line system providing access to the Epilepsy Abstracts data base operated for NINDS by Mead Data Central, Inc. Porter (186) describes the EARS concept as applicable to any scientific literature storage and retrieval system. The tape data base, produced at The Parkinson Disease Information Center (now defunct), is available from NINDS (U.S./NIH, 239).

Data Bases Within DOD

Many machine-readable data bases are being used within the Department of Defense (DOD). Two that are available to external users are produced by DDC and the USAF:

Defense Documentation Center. DDC provides four types of magnetic tape products from the DDC collection dating back to 1958. The Automatic Magnetic Tape Dissemination Service provides a semimonthly update of all DDC-accessioned report data on non-returnable "mini-reels." DDC offers a magnetic tape version of "Defense R & D" (the 1960's compendium) as well as the current series for this decade. Retrospective bibliographies on magnetic tape contain the same information as the printed bibliographies. DDC is also developing an SDI package for use with its magnetic tape products (NFSAIS, 159). Development of the DDC remote on-line retrieval system was described in detail by Bennertz (34). This document should be of value to other installations embarking on an on-line development effort.

Department of the Air Force. The USAF's LITE (Legal Information Through Electronics) System is a full-text search and retrieval program designed primarily to process statutory and regulatory material. The system utilizes direct access and tape storage devices. Search services are free to all users of DOD and available to others for a fee (DAF, 233).

R&D Data Bases

Most of the data bases described contain references to research and development activities. There are seven data bases, however, that are primarily concerned with R&D in the areas of nuclear science, education, transportation, aerospace, research in progress, plus the related subject of patents.

Atomic Energy Commission. AEC produces magnetic tapes containing descriptor terms, descriptive cataloging, and abstract numbers for each issue of *Nuclear Science Abstracts* (NSA). Over a dozen users subscribed to the tape service during 1971 on an experimental basis; one of these offered an SDI service on a commercial basis. Plans are being made to sell these tapes (NFSAIS, 158). The report by Pflueger (183) discusses controls, the sources and types of data input, and the management information extracted. A progress report on ORCHIS (Oak Ridge Computerized Hierarchical Information System) at the Oak Ridge National Laboratory is described by Brooks (42). Of the 30 data bases involved, 18 contain bibliographic data holding over 145,000 entries. SDI services were supplied from three of them. A variation of the Lockheed DIALOG and NASA/RECON on-line computerized retrieval systems is in operation at ORNL and is accessed by CRT terminals at six remote sites. Plans include the expansion of the communication system to as many as 100 terminals and to five years of *NSA* plus the inclusion of other large bibliographic data bases.

U.S. Office of Education. USOE sponsors the Educational Resources Information Center (ERIC), a nationwide system that acquires, stores, and makes available educational research information. A network of specialized clearinghouses provides the input. Report literature is covered from 1966 on and journal literature from January 1969 on. Under a special authorization by USOE, Leasco Systems and Research Corporation produces and sells the ERIC tapes (Leasco, 135). An opinion paper by Paisley (175) provides "constructive criticism" of the ERIC system and suggests methods to bring the ERIC data base to the attention of practitioners.

Highway Research Board. The data base generated by the Highway Research Information Service (HRIS) contains 45,000 references to literature on transportation research. About 10,000 new items are added annually from over 3700 worldwide sources. File searches and SDI services are available (HRB, 99).

National Technical Information Service. NTIS has offered magnetic tape access to its collection since 1970. Approximately 2000 citations to unclassified literature are added monthly and the tapes are issued twice monthly. NTIS receives input from several government agencies including NASA, AEC, DDC, and other DOD. No software programs are provided and limited search services are available (Carroll, 48).

National Aeronautics and Space Administration. NASA prepares a machine-readable data base on its aerospace literature file composed of over half a million documents and growing at the rate of about 60,000 new reports per year. Subjects are categorized under 34 headings. The NASA file is especially strong in instrumentation and scientific methodology. Plans have been underway to make the data base commercially available; however, access to this data base has been possible for several years through a network of Regional Dissemination Centers (RDCs; see academic section). Use of the NASA RDC network and the accessibility of NASA's technology transfer program are described in (230). Most of the recent literature related to the NASA data base involved the on-line system, NASA/RECON, implemented in 1969 to access the data base from 22 remote locations. An evaluation of the NASA/RECON system is presented by Coles (57) and user interface consideration was described by Wente (254).

Smithsonian Institution. The Smithsonian Science Information Exchange, Inc. (SSIE) annually collects up to 100,000 single-page records of research projects (public and private) in progress. The machine-readable record contains a technical summary of the project, plus the name of the supporting agency, the names of persons working on it, and where the research is performed. The tape data base is available in general or specific fields to meet the requestors requirement (SSIE, 247).

Patent Office. A full-text communications format for patents, now being used at the U.S. Patent Office, is described by Nugent (169). Three output tapes are involved in the system including a bibliographic tape used for publication of the "Official Gazette." The data base will initially be used internally; ultimately, public access and use are planned. Nugent believes that the development of new techniques for full-text natural-language processing constitutes the major challenge and opportunity for the information industry in the early 1970's; this advance is the next needed breakthrough in information science and has applications far beyond patent processing.

Data Bases Related to Environmental Subjects

In 1971, two data bases concerning environmental matters were produced by EPA and NOAA. More attention is now being directed to subjects related to the environment and an increase in the number of data bases in this area can be expected.

Environmental Protection Agency. The Air Pollution Technical Information Center (APTIC) collects and disseminates domestic and foreign literature pertaining to air pollution. Computer searching of the data base, containing over 25,000 technical documents, is provided by APTIC to official personnel; the New England Research Applications Center provides literature searches of the APTIC data base for other users (NERAC, 166).

National Oceanic and Atmospheric Administration. NOAA operates the Environmental Science Information Center (ESIC). A progress report is presented by Freeman (79), who describes two concepts to which ESIC is turning its attention: ENDEX (Environmental Data Index) and OASIS (Oceanic and Atmospheric Scientific Information System). ENDEX is to be developed as a one-stop system providing comprehensive reference to information on the environment. OASIS is an experiment providing SDI services to NOAA scientists. Ten commercially available data bases are involved. When OASIS becomes fully operational, ESIC hopes to be able to offer SDI services to the environmental science community.

DATA BASE ACTIVITIES IN INDUSTRY

Although still in its infancy, the "information industry" does exist. Despite the ever-present competition with the government and nonprofit sectors, it is generally acknowledged that the information enterprise will someday be a growth industry. At its third annual meeting in 1971, the Information Industry Association (IIA) discussed many aspects of the information industry including machine-readable data bases (91). The majority of commercial and industrial organizations that use machine-readable data bases provide services that are restricted to in-house personnel. These applications are excluded from this review. The following organizations provide external services for a fee:

Dow Chemical Company. A current awareness service is available from two CAS data bases; retrospective searches are not run, but current awareness citations are printed within a week of receipt of the tapes. A "Profile Preparation Manual" is provided to all subscribers. Brown (43) discusses costs and derivation of charges at the Dow Information Center, which uses five data bases.

Information Interscience, Inc. 3i offers SDI and retrospective services from seven data bases covering biomedicine and drugs, chemistry, engineering, physics, electrical and electronics engineering (III, 110). 3i is under license to provide services in the USA from several data bases generated in Europe: INSPEC (Barlow, 31), and the drug literature and biomedical data bases prepared by the Excerpta Medica Foundation.

Hughes Aircraft Co. The Electronic Properties Information Center (EPIC) provides information services on the electronic, optical and magnetic properties of materials. Five data bases are used involving about 35,000 document references (Kruzas, 129).

System Development Corporation. An educational information search service, derived from the ERIC data base, is provided by the SDC/ERIC search service; it is an on-line system accessed by the user through a remote terminal. The ERIC data base is available for searching nationwide via an ordinary telephone or TWX system (SDC, 220). An excellent review of the advantages and problem areas involved in using on-line systems was given by Cuadra (61).

Westat Research, Inc. This firm has made extensive use of the 1970 U.S. census summary tapes including the CENSTAT (Census Statistics) program used for processing census tapes through any of the 37 public data centers of Control Data Corporation's CYBERNET System. Census data applications are described by Dietz (65, 66).

Xerox Corp. The Xerox Education Group plans to offer SDI services to paying customers covering the engineering, chemistry, pharmaceutical and other scientific disciplines. This activity began with acquisition of Share Research Corporation and its proprietary software in August 1971. Additional data bases are to be added to the file during 1972 (Xerox, 268; NFSAIS, 160). A subsidiary, University Microfilms, produces DATRIX (Direct Access To Reference Information; a Xerox Service), a retrospective bibliographic service providing access to over

150,000 doctoral dissertations published since 1938 (Xerox, 267). Scott & Asleson (205) argue the merits of the international retrospective index. Xerox is also considering the availability of two additional data bases derived from the Bowker file: *Books in Print* and *Advanced Book Information* both of which are already computerized (NFSAIS, 160).

The RINGDOC Distribution System (RDS) is a cooperative venture of several pharmaceutical firms. System design and programing was performed by Pfizer Pharmaceuticals, Inc. in 1969-1970. In 1971 there were seven subscribers (Pfizer, Lederley, Lilly, Merrell, Squibb, Upjohn, and Wyeth) and the service included the RINGDOC, VETDOC, and PESTDOC data bases provided by Derwent Publications, Ltd. (Buckley, 44). Punched cards are sent weekly from Derwent to the Pfizer facilities in England; there, the complete tape is prepared and sent by air mail to New York, where extract tapes are prepared containing the appropriate data, and in the proper format, for each subscriber.

Pfizer-Searle. Literature search services of the three RDS data bases were provided by a software system developed at Pfizer and known as ARCS (Automated Ring Code Search). An in-house study compared use of the Derwent data bases against the CBAC (Chemical-Biological Activities) data base (Devon, 64). At the automated level, the two services performed equally well; however, a significant improvement in the Derwent service was possible with programming changes to ARCS. Early in 1972, ARCS was being superseded by a new search package developed through a joint venture by Pfizer and Searle. The system, to be known as SPRING (Searle-Pfizer RINGDOC), has an on-line query-edit program and specimen file against which the user can edit and hone his queries; the query is then added to a queue for overnight batch processing. Literature search services are available to all Derwent subscribers and the software package can be purchased.

Corporate Literature-Retrieval Systems

Several large corporate-wide literature retrieval systems exist including those at IBM and GT&E:

IBM Technical Information Retrieval Center. A well-organized user's guide to the computerized literature search services at ITIRC was prepared by Hines (101). The ITIRC system and the user's guide are excellent models for designers of SDI and current awareness systems. Input comes from internal sources plus five external data bases. ITIRC is attempting to eliminate duplication in three external data bases. The high-quality abstracts and excellent coverage are reported to be well received by the ITIRC subscribers. However, the delays between document publication and availability of the abstract on tape are a major cause for complaints. This disadvantage, it is believed, is far outweighed by ITIRC's ability to cover a broad spectrum of information at a relatively low cost.

General Telephone and Electronics Laboratories. The conceptual design of a corporate-wide technical reports processing system at GTEL is described by Gechman & Kieswetter (87). This system, especially suited to the technical communication needs of large and decentralized firms, linked external data bases with internal report collections and literally "managed" these collections. Automatic ordering of external reports and a unique distribution system highlight the design. In 1971, services were being provided by GTEL from three bibliographic data bases to corporate subscribers; external services were available under specific limitations (Kruzas et al., 129).

SDI Services

The following two organizations are examples of internal SDI services in industry:

Marathon Oil Company Research Center. The use of commercially available bibliographic data bases is described by Sturdivant (219). Marathon used four petroleum-related data bases in 1971 and plans to add more. The paper discusses various degrees of success experienced with outside search services, what the data bases are being used for, and how to "get your feet wet" in computer searching.

Squibb Institute of Medical Research. Over 100 users are served by an in-house information storage and retrieval system that uses internal and external data bases. Bennett & Frycki (35) describe the selection and processing of external data bases. The RINGDOC data base (Derwent), the principal external data base, is converted to a form acceptable to the direct access computer software package INQUIRE (developed by Infodata Systems, Inc., 106). Squibb also operates a group-SDI service based on weekly ASCA tapes from ISI (Frycki, 81).

Multidisciplinary Data Bases

Two major industry generators of multidisciplinary data bases are CCMIC and ISI:

CCM Information Corporation. CCMIC generates seven magnetic tape data bases. Four involve scientific and technical subject areas: (a)

PANDEX—covering 2400 journals cover-to-cover and including 250,-000 articles per year; (b) *Current Index to Conference Papers*—a monthly tape covering 110,000 papers delivered at worldwide conferences; (c) TRANSDEX—a monthly tape covering medical and technical subject areas translated from more than 145 countries; (d) *Bibliography of Agriculture*—derived from the monthly CAIN tapes (from NAL) covering 5000 journals and 120,000 articles per year. The other three data bases generated by CCMIC cover the social sciences: (a) *Current Index to Journals in Education*—a monthly tape generated from hard copy provided by USOE covering 20,000 articles per year; (b) *Research in Education*—a monthly service derived from the ERIC tapes (produced by Leasco) covering 10,000 research documents with full abstracts; and (c) TRANSDEX—a monthly tape covering 30,000 articles in the social sciences.

In addition, two data bases, generated by others are available through CCMIC: (a) *Government Reports Announcements* (formally USGRDR) provided by NTIS—a bi-weekly tape covering 50,000 government technical reports with abstracts; and (b) MARC II tapes. CCMIC extracts two weekly tapes from MARC II covering scientific and non-scientific areas. All three are converted to PANDEX format for common searching via fully supported software.

Institute for Scientific Information. The development and use of "citation indexes" by ISI is described by Garfield (84) and Weinstock (253). ISI prepares three tapes from 2500 journals in the fields of applied science, engineering and technology, medicine, psychology and psychiatry, and the behavioral sciences. The weekly Source Tapes contain over 6000 references to journal article titles. The weekly combined Source and Citation Data Tape contains the title of the original papers plus references cited in those papers. In 1971, the data base added 400,000 current articles and four million citations. The cumulative data base includes over 1.5 million source items and 20 million references.

The index Chemicus Registry System (ICRS) is a monthly computerized chemical compound data retrieval system prepared by ISI. The system uses the "Wiswesser Line Notation" and contains about 4000 new compounds per month. ISI also provides software packages as well as a weekly SDI service called ASCA-IV (Automatic Subject Citation Alert). Fenichel (6) describes an effective computer-assisted system for editing input to the subject index of ISI's science and technology data base. Garfield & Malin (85) describe how a national system and network can be economically developed in a foreign country by a link into available systems such as that offered by ISI.

Law and Patent Data Bases

Two firms—Aspen Systems Corporation and IFI/Plenum Corporation—produce and maintain very large data bases concerning laws and patents from which they provide search services.

Aspen Systems Corporation. The laws of all fifty states are stored on random-access magnetic disc packs, and ASC claims it is the nation's largest data bank. The data base contains over 200 million words of statute law in full-text form. Searches can be ordered of the statutes of one or all states or special combinations. A custom automatic scanning service called Statutes in Point, for recently enacted legislation, is available. Other computerized services range from full-text printout to KWIC indexes of every meaningful word in the abstracts (ASC, 221).

IFI/Plenum Data Corporation. The Uniterm Magnetic Tape Index to all U.S. chemical and related patents since 1950 contains more than six million references recorded from approximately 260,000 patents. The bi-monthly tapes may be leased or IFI/Plenum will conduct searches. Flexible search programs have been developed for customized screening and searching. In 1971 IFI purchased the DuPont patent data base and began merging the two files into a single data base searchable by fragments, compounds and general terms (IFI, 105).

Other Centers and Services in Industry

The American Bibliographical Center-Clio Press, Inc. maintains a data base covering history and political science from which search services are planned (ABC-CLIO, 1); Compendium Publishers International Corp. offers Search-Data, produced monthly in 19 subject sections from 1000 trade journals, covering chemical industry data related to marketing, production and commercial intelligence (Carroll, 48); Predicasts, Inc. offers three tapes containing bibliographic references to 300-500 sources of data on events and financial and market statistics on corporations and industries (Carroll, 48); Preston Technical Abstracts Company offers the tape or search services covering gas chromatography literature from 1952 (over 20,000 abstracts) and a Nuclear Magnetic Resonance Literature Retrieval System (Preston, 187, 188).

The following services, derived from magnetic tape data bases, are described by Kruzas (129): (a) Paul DeHaen, Inc. offers DeHaen Drugs in Prospect Index in a magnetic tape version; (b) The Environment Information Center, operated by Ecology Forum, Inc., offers computer searches on environmental-related matters; and (c) Interdok Corp. stores data on conference proceedings, and search services are available.

DATA BASE ACTIVITIES IN PROFESSIONAL SOCIETIES AND NON-PROFIT GROUPS

Professional societies (including non-profit associations and foundations) who produce bibliographic data bases are relatively few in number but their data bases rank high in quality and usefulness. They have not been major users of data bases other than their own. However, there now seems to be a shift toward more use of external tapes by these groups. The rapidly growing disciplines of chemistry and biology are covered by a series of data bases produced by CAS and BIOSIS:

American Chemical Society (ACS). The Chemical Abstracts Service (CAS), a division of ACS, is the world's largest secondary information service in chemistry and chemical engineering. It processes over 1100 abstracts and 15,000 index entries each working day. About 350,000 abstracts were entered in 1971, and 600,000 a year are expected to be entered by 1980 (Baker, 28). It took 50 years for CAS to publish two million abstracts; the third million took eight years; the fourth million, under five years, the fifth million took 40 months. At this rate, the ten-million mark will be passed by 1982 (NFSAIS, 160).

To cope with this growth, CAS has, with support from NSF, moved toward computerization of its total information handling and publishing operations. Early in 1972, 20 percent of the abstracts appearing in *Chemical Abstracts* (CA) were processed and prepared for printing by computer; the remainder of CA will be converted to computer-based production over the next several years. All of the CA indexes were produced by computer by mid-1971 (NFSAIS, 159). The CAS information system is an evolving and dynamic system, and is described in an excellent overview of the total system (CAS, 53). A number of important changes to the CAS tape services took place in 1971 and early 1972. CAS leases eight magnetic tape data bases; most have corresponding but inequivalent printed versions, and a tape subscription includes a copy of the printed issue.

Chemical Titles is a biweekly alerting service containing about 5000 titles from 700 primary journals, selected to be abstracted in CA. Four current-awareness tape services are offered: (a) Basic Journal Abstracts (BJA) is issued biweekly and contains abstracts from 49 basic chemical journals; (b) CA Condensates is a weekly service corresponding to CA issues providing a rapid scan of references to the 12,000 journals and patents (issued by 26 countries) covered in CA; (c) Chemical-Biological Activities (CBAC) is a biweekly tape covering biological activities of chemical compounds with full abstracts; (d) Polymer Science and Technology (POST) is a biweekly tape covering macromolecular chemistry containing full abstracts. In January 1972 the printed editions of CBAC, POST-J (journals) and POST-P (patents) were discontinued. CBAC became only a computer-readable service covering the first five Biochemistry sections of CA (NFSAIS, 159; CAS, 54).

Two retrospective services are offered by CAS: (a) CA Integrated Subject File (ISF) is a semiannual tape index to CA designed for searching; (b) Patent Concordance refers all duplicate patents (by number and issuing country) to the abstract of the first equivalent patent published previously in CA; it is issued semiannually. Patents constitute about 25 percent of the total CA coverage (Baker et al., 29). Also available is a reference tape called CAS Source Index (CASSI), updated quarterly and containing holdings of 325 libraries in the U.S. and 72 libraries in 27 other countries (CAS, 54). The Eighth Collective Index to CA (1967-1971) will have an estimated 80,000 pages in about 45 volumes. It will be the first collective searchable by computer (via the ISF tapes). However, the ISF for the eighth collective period will fill more than 90 reels of tape (NSFAIS, 160).

By mid-1972, all CAS computer-readable services were converted to a Standard Distribution Format (SDF). An *SDF Technical Specifications Manual* (ACS, 11) describes the format and characteristics of SDF. In addition, a *Data Element Specifications Manual* is available for each tape included (ACS, 3, 4, 5, 6, 7, 8, 9, 10).

The handling of names for chemical substances within the overall CAS index production system, including the CAS Chemical Registry System, which controls this indexing vocabulary, is described by Rowlett & Tate (192). The registry number is a unique number assigned by computer to each chemical substance when it first enters the CAS data base; over two million different substances have been identified. Baker et al. (28, 29) examine the changing patterns and trends in international communication of chemical technology. Computerization has helped to offset the roughly 15 percent increase in operating costs and the CA annual growth of 8.2 percent each year for the last 20 years. Formal agreements with organizations in the United Kingdom and West Germany who are participating with CAS in an international chemical informaton system help to reduce costs by sharing the burden of input.

Biosciences Information Service. BIOSIS offers BA Previews, a tape service containing over 18,000 index entries to references published in *Biological Abstracts* and *Bioresearch Index* occurring about one month in advance of the printed versions. BA Previews references more than 7500 serials from 94 countries covering published data in the bioscientific field (BA, 26). Also, three current awareness services are available including: CLASS (Current Literature Alerting Search Service), a custom group-profile service and standard profile searches (NFSAIS, 158). In 1971, BIOSIS initiated an experimental tape service called "Toxitapes" to identify information requirements of industrial toxicologists and measure the effectiveness of various indexing techniques applied to this literature. Schultz (202) discusses the requirements for exchange of toxicology information. Rubinstein & Qazi (193) describe alternatives to searching a chemical toxicants file. In collaboration with the Toxicology Information Program at NLM, BIOSIS inaugurated a monthly abstract journal called "Health Effects of Environmental Pollutants" (HEEP). The ancillary magnetic tape service is derived from *Biological Abstracts* and MEDLARS. It consists of complete bibliographic citations and search terms but no abstracts (NFSAIS, 159).

Data Bases in Other Disciplines

Literature relating to the disciplines of physics, mathematics and engineering are covered by the data bases produced by the American Institute of Physics, American Mathematical Society, and Engineering Index.

American Institute of Physics. In January 1972, AIP began a new concept in science communication called Current Physics Information (CPI). The CPI program provides eight products in multiple formats. The monthly magnetic tape, SPIN (Searchable Physics Information Notices), is the heart of the information system. Each tape issue contains over 2000 references (with abstracts) selected from over 60 physics journals. AIP (14) gives SPIN technical specifications; the AIP program for physics information (AIP, 13) describes CPI plans up until the year 1976. Herschman (98) prepared an excellent review of AIP's information programs. CPI products are intended for current awareness services; retrospective services are provided through an arrangement with IEE using their INSPEC tapes. SPIN is available in AIP or IBM TEXT-PAC formats (AIP, 14) and in Remote File Management System format for CDC users (Parsons, 181). SPIN contains the reel and frame number of the full-text microform backup for each article cited.

American Mathematical Society. AMS prepared a manual in 1971 describing five data bases available on magnetic tape (Walker, 250). One tape contains 15,000 entries from 200 mathematical journals published worldwide; about 1000 new entries are added monthly. A second tape contains references from the first 23 volumes of *Mathematics of Computation*. The third tape contains all bibliographic entries from *Mathematical Reviews* from 1964-1967 (80,000 records when completed). The last two tapes are special files on number theory and group theory references published in *Mathematical Reviews* since 1940.

Engineering Index, Inc. Since 1969, EI has produced COMPENDEX, a tape version of *EI Monthly*, containing about 7000 abstracts per month obtained from over 3500 sources of literature spanning all engineering disciplines (EI, 71). Tape subscribers receive, without charge, two useful search tools: (a) SHE (Subject Headings for Engineering), an authority list containing over 12,000 terms used as a controlled vocabulary; and (b) PIE (Publications Indexed for Engineering), a listing of journals currently abstracted and indexed (EI, 72).

COMPENDEX contains many data access points, including full abstracts, providing the option of full-text or discreet searching of the data base. EI does not provide software or search services; however, searching is available worldwide through a number of information centers (EI, 72). 3i announced availability of a computer program package for searching COMPENDEX which is available in TEXT-PAC input format and, in 1971, was also offered in the ANSI Z39.2 format. Hisinger (102) documented experiences and costs incurred in using COMPENDEX in an operational SDI service. Woods (265) described the development of a Transdisciplinary Engineering Information Program (TEIP) involving the conversion of the EI production system to computerized publishing. TEIP will ultimately allow for high-speed current awareness services and direct input of machine-readable data from outside sources.

Bibliographic references to the related areas of geology and petroleum are covered by two data bases generated by American Geological Institute and American Petroleum Institute.

American Geological Institute. Since 1969, AGI has maintained the Geological Reference File (GEO-REF) covering over 2000 serials in 21 related fields such as geochemistry, petroleum exploration, and paleontology. About 50,000 citations are added annually. The data base can be purchased or searched via remote terminal. Lloyd (138) discusses the overall design concepts of an information system for the geosciences.

American Petroleum Institute. Indexes to the *Abstracts of Refining Literature and Patents* are available on tape to API subscribers. With the API indexes, subscribers have access to over 15,000 abstracts per year covering refining and petrochemicals plus patents issued in ten countries. The cooperative and complimentary abstracting and indexing services for the petroleum industry, operated by API and the University of Tulsa, are described by Brenner & Helander (41). API also offers a weekly SDI service for readers of *Chemical Abstracts* by matching subscribers profiles against the CA Condensates tape (Brenner, 40).

The subject of psychology and related areas is covered by a data base and various access services provided by APA; data bases covering paper chemistry and textiles are prepared by the Institute of Paper Chemistry and the Institute of Textile Technology.

Institute of Paper Chemistry. IPC leases three tape by-products of the *Abstract Bulletin of the Institute of Paper Chemistry* (ABIPC: (a) Complete Text of the citation and abstract; (b) the ABIPC Citation Tape including author, title, and journal or patent reference; and (c) the Keyword Supplement to the ABIPC consisting of an inverted file of keywords and associated abstract numbers. The tapes are available in cumulative form back to 1969 (IPC, 113). To facilitate retrieval, IPC provides two search programs designed for IBM 360 computers: (a) LIRES-M (Literature Retrieval System—Multiple Search) permits many profiles to be searched at one pass of a keyword tape; and (b) LIRES-MC (Literature Retrieval System—Multiple Searching, Complete Text), permits direct-language searching of the complete text tape. Truncating and weighting techniques can be employed in using LIRES-MC. A third innovation is a merged tape combining keywords with complete text; the use of LIRES-MC with the merged tape provides multiple search options (IPC, 115). IPC also provides a monthly SDI service against its own data base as well as a current awareness service based on CA Condensates (IPC, 114).

Institute of Textile Technology. ITT provides literature search services from its data base of 70,000 abstracts that have appeared in *Textile Technology Digest* since 1966. The abstracts are assigned "key terms" from the printed thesaurus used to facilitate retrieval. Monthly computer input of the key term index (the 1971 *Digest* contained over 30,000 abstracts) is available in the form of punched cards or magnetic tape (ITT, 116).

American Psychological Association. Since 1968, with support from NSF, APA has been developing a National Information System for Psychology. In 1971, APA offered three ways of accessing *Psychological Abstracts* (*PA*) using magnetic tape (APA, 17). The primary tape service PATELL (*PA* Tape Edition—Leased or Licensing) is distributed quarterly. About 23,000 items with abstracts are cited per tape issue. The second service is PADAT (*Psychological Abstracts*—Direct Access Terminal), an on-line service. The third service is PASAR (*PA* Search and Retireval), a retrospective search service. An excellent report on the cost-effectiveness of retrospective search systems was performed for APA by King & Caldwell (125). The report by Booz, Allen & Hamilton, Inc. (38) evaluated the potential market for *PA* computer tapes and estimated the general market for psychological information.

NELINET and DUALabs are two non-profit organizations who are making extensive use of the MEDLARS and Census tapes respectively:

National Data Use and Access Laboratories, Inc. This non-profit corporation was established specifically to assist census data users in obtaining access to census data on magnetic tape and to computer programs. DUALabs services the START (Summary Tape Assistance, Research, and Training) community as well as the general public. This is a group that pooled their funds and commissioned DUALabs to develop computer programs for using the 1970 census summary tapes; Beresford et al. (36) describe these programs.

New England Library Information Network. In 1971, NELINET provided over 36,000 custom catalog card sets derived from MARC II tapes to 30 New England universities and colleges and three affiliates. Operated for NELINET by Inforonics, Inc., the master file contained over 160,000 MARC records by year's end. With a grant from the Council on Library Resources, NELINET conducted an audit of its system and tested the transferability of the Ohio College Library Center (OCLC) computer system to a NELINET counterpart. A user evaluation and demonstration of the OCLC on-line system was performed at the Dartmouth College library. Dartmouth was connected on-line to the OCLC computer in January 1972 (163, 190).

Other Centers and Services. Four organizations maintain six data bases involving metals and materials: (a) the Aluminum Association has made available tape access to *World Aluminum Abstracts* (NERAC, 166); (b) the American Society for Metals produces METADEX (Metals Abstracts Index) on tape containing over 2300 citations to literature of metallurgy and related aspects of physics and chemistry dating back to 1966—search services are available (154); (c) the Battelle Memorial Institute offers literature searches from three data bases prepared by the Composites Information Center (fiber technology), Copper Data Center, and the Defense Metals Information Center; and (d) the Copper Development Association maintains a machine-searchable data base for its members (Markuson et al., 145).

The American Society of Hospital Pharmacists has, since January 1970, put into machine-readable form the entire contents of its *International Pharmaceutical Abstracts* (IPA). A description of the automation system was described by Tousignaut (228). All or any specific part of *IPA* can be made available on tape; special searches are also conducted. The Pharmaceutical Manufacturers Association offers search services derived from the MEDLARS tape; in 1971, PMA initiated a new service based on the "research in progress" tapes from the Smithsonian Institute (PMA, 184).

INTERNATIONAL DATA BASE ACTIVITIES

Data base activities, current and planned, by international organizations and in countries outside the United States are growing at an exceptionally high rate. An update of this chapter in a few years could, conceivably, require a separate chapter to handle international data base activities. The following descriptions include only major activities identified during the review and are not intended to be fully comprehensive. Activities in international organizations are discussed after the descriptions pertaining to individual countries.[2]

Activities In Foreign Countries

Canada. A large proportion of the papers presented at the 1970 and 1971 annual meetings of the Western Canada Chapter of ASIS dealt with some aspect of machine-readable bibliographic data bases (Dolan & Koole, 67; Dolan & Perzel, 68). CAN/SDI has been operated by the National Science Library (NSL) since 1969 for Canadian scientific and technical subscribers. By early 1972, CAN/SDI was searching nine data bases and processing about 4500 profiles per month. The nine tapes are preprocessed into a common format for standardized searching. Additional data bases in the humanities and social sciences are planned.

Gaffney (83) described the current status, problems, and future plans of CAN/SDI. Wolters & Brown (263) reported on user reaction to CAN/SDI, and Heilik (96) discussed the MARC II format adopted by the CAN/SDI software system. The paper by Mauerhoff & Smith (152) is an excellent review of the MARC II program and its application to Canadian SDI systems. The Pollution Information Project is creating a data base on pollution and environmental quality control; on-line searching is available through use of search programs developed at Queen's University.

The Quic/Law system, under development at Queen's University since 1969, is an on-line retrieval system initially intended for the legal profession and now being applied to other disciplines. In 1971, Queen's

---

[2]The author is grateful to many international contributors too numerous to acknowledge individually. Special acknowledgement is due Miss Judith A. Werdel, Office of the Foreign Secretary, National Academy of Science, who contributed initial references to potential international users and producers of machine-readable data bases.

University offered on-line searching of two legal data bases (Supreme Court Reports back to 1923 and the Statutes of Canada in French and English) and was preparing three others. Research work on data bases at the University of Alberta included: (a) a program to provide rapid retrospective searching of large document data bases through automatic compression of data, minimization of input-output operations, and minimum internal memory requirements (Thiel & Heaps, 225); (b) techniques to optimize and measure the effectiveness of data base retrieval systems (Heaps, 94); and (c) coding, storage, and search techniques of a large data base (Heaps, 95). Experience at the University of Calgary has yielded a set of COMPENDEX profiling guides (Standera, 214, 215) and a Text-PAC input brochure (Standera, 217). Standera (216) also provides an evaluation of retrospective searching of COMPENDEX using TEXT-PAC.

Czechoslovakia. The State Information Policy Program of Czechoslovakia includes plans to construct a unified, integrated system of scientific, technological and economic information in the period of 1971-1975. The principles of the computer system ASTI (Automated System for Sorting Information), which will be used as a basis for the development of a unified computer system, is described by Fendrych & Fogl (76). According to OECD (174), the following search services are available: (a) the Research Institute of Radiohygienics maintains an index to literature in radio-biology and radio-hygienics; (b) a Bibliographic Review in Geology called GEO-INDEX is sponsored by the Czech office for geology; (c) the Automated System of Information (ASI), covering coal mining and related fields, is sponsored by the Ministry of Industry; (d) the Automated Information and Documentation System (AIDS) covers computing techniques and automation and is sponsored by the Czech Office for Technical Development; (e) the State Technical Library maintains a data base called New Books Abroad, covering politics, history, sociology, and psychology. Chemopetrol in Prague is licensed to search CAS tapes (CAS, 54).

Denmark. The National Technological Library of Denmark (NTLD) experimented with six data bases and currently operates a multidisciplinary SDI service derived from three data bases. Hisinger (102) describes this service and documents total costs in connection with the COMPENDEX tape. The library has prepared instructions for the use of COMPENDEX, Chemical Titles, and CA Condensates (161, 162). ELDOK (Elektro Dokumentation) is a Danish retrieval system covering literature and patents on electronics (OECD, 174).

France. Mechanization of *Bulletin Signaletique* began in 1971 and all sections will be available on tape in 1972; it covers scientific and technical fields. Centre National de la Recherche Scientifique provides SDI services and leases the tapes (NFSAIS, 159, 160). According to OECD (174), the following search services are available: (a) Institut Textile de France provides search services from their TITUS data base covering physics and chemistry applied to textiles; (b) the French Institute, IFAC, provides a tape (DARIUS) covering the agriculture and technology of tropical and sub-tropical fruits; (c) searching of scientific, technical and economic disciplines of interest to national defense is derived from CEDOCAR (Centre de Documentation de L'Armement); (d) OECD Development Centre maintains AUTODOC (Automatic Documentation Section) covering socio-economic, labor, and agriculture.

Germany. In 1970, the world's oldest comprehensive scientific abstracting and indexing service, *Chemisches Zentralblatt*, was replaced by a two-part computer-based system: ChemInform-Organic and ChemInform-Inorganic. The magnetic tape service for the data on inorganic chemistry is prepared by a division of the West German Chemical Society, Chemie-Information-und-Dokumentation Berlin (CIDB); it covers journal literature only (CIDB, 55). Patents dealing with inorganic chemistry may be added in 1972. The organic chemistry portion of ChemInform is fed into the data base produced by Internationale Dokumentationsgesellschaft für Chemie (IDC). This tape contains encoded structures of organic compounds, and reaction schemes, bibliographic data, and data on concepts in chemistry. Input to the IDC data base comes from both CIDB and the Derwent Central Patent Index (EUSIDIC; 75). CIDB also offers SDI services, and CIDB and IDC are cooperating with CAS in an international chemical information system (NFSAIS, 159). The Arbeitsgemeinschaft Chemie Dokumentation (AGCD) chemical data base appears within three weeks of original journal publication. AGCD also searches CAS data bases for German users (EUSIDIC, 75). DESY (Deutsches Erektronen-Synchrotron) produces a data base on high-energy physics that is available in the U.S. via Stanford University. According to OECD (174), the following German data bases are available: (a) NMB (Informationsdienst für Nuklearmedizin) covers nuclear medicine and biology; (b) Deutsches Rechenzentrum Darmstadt covers the disciplines of forest science, wood technology, and related fields; (c)Bibliographie Pedagogik covers education, psychology and sociology; (d) Dokumentationaring Betriebswirtschaft covers various management science subject areas.

India. The Bhabha Atomic Research Centre in Bombay is developing an SDI service using the monthly INIS Atomindex magnetic tapes; they also provide Indian input to INIS. Kamath & Malwad (120) describe the expanding uses of computerized information storage and retrieval systems in India. Plans for 1972 include the acquisition of further bibliographic data bases and development of software to increase the Centre's capability to provide SDI and current awareness services.

Israel. Most of the data base systems in Israel became operational since 1969. The country is gaining SDI experience, and the feasibility of creating various subject-oriented data bases is being studied. According to Elgad (70), the following is an incomplete list of data base systems operating in 1971: Responsa is a full-text retrieval system for a large data base of Hebrew legal material. The Vulcani Institute of Agricultural Research has developed a real-time system for locating agricultural literature. A similar but less complex system in the area of fish production and utilization is being developed at the Sea Fisheries Research Station. The Ministry of Defense generates and operates an SDI system in the field of electronics and related subjects. The Center of Scientific and Technological Information (COSTI) operates a current-awareness system using two external data bases and more are planned; 18,000 notifications per month are produced; COSTI also provides a computer-generated index to current scientific research in Israel (Keren et al., 124); the third edition of the Index will cover about 6000 research projects. The Ministry of Defense maintains an accessions file from over 30 participating libraries from which several information services are available. COSTI has also developed a unique system for working with machine-readable files and the system, known as SWAP/FILE, is intended to serve as a "data bank of data banks" in Israel (Wollmann & Cohen, 262).

The Netherlands. The Netherlands Organization for Chemical Information (NOCI), a division of the Royal Netherlands Chemical Society, provides current-awareness and retrospective searching services derived from CAS tapes (NOCI, 164). In 1971, the Central Organization for Applied Scientific Research in The Netherlands (TNO) began processing Inspec tapes (from UK) for Dutch and Danish customers (EUSIDIC, 75). The Excerpta Medica Foundation generates a comprehensive medical data base and offers a weekly SDI service called Drugdoc. The entire data base, or any subset, is available on tape; 3i is the U.S. distributor of these tapes and services. Two evaluation studies comparing computerized drug information services were conducted by pharmaceutical firms in The Netherlands and they provided favorable remarks about Excerpta Medica (Smith et al., 213; Scott et al., 204).

Sweden. The libraries at the Royal Institute of Technology (RIT), Stockholm, and the Swedish Atomic Energy Establishment (AB Atomenergi) offer a comprehensive SDI service involving 14 data bases. Two of these data bases are generated by RIT: (a) MECHEN—covers literature in mechanical engineering and metallurgy involving about 40,000 references annually; and (b) WOOD—in collaboration with the

Swedish Forest Products Research Laboratory, RIT adds about 15,000 references annually in the field of wood technology. Two data bases are accessed on-line. The remainder are run in-house and are reformatted for searching with a retrieval package called ABACUS into a format identical to the proposed ISO tape format. Tell (222) describes retrieval efficiency from titles of three data bases using ABACUS. Three papers describe the SDI system at RIT, its applications, and the preparation of standard profiles: Gluchowicz (90), Tell (223), and Tell & Froderstrom (224). Part of the medical, biological and chemical program at the Bio-medical Documentation Centre (BMDC) of the Karolinska Institutet involves search services from CAS tapes (EUSIDIC, 75; CAS, 54).

United Kingdom. The Office for Scientific and Technical Information (OSTI) financially supports a major proportion of British work related to bibliographic data bases. A list of 1971 grants (OSTI, 170) includes 60 projects; about 25 were related (directly or indirectly) to machine-readable data bases. Nearly half of these were funded in 1971 and were described in OSTI quarterly newsletters (OSTI, 171). Most of the projects are being carried out in about 25 universities or colleges. For example, the Imperial College of London, maintains a data base on rock mechanics dating back to 1870. A significant portion of a book edited by two British specialists in library automation (Balmforth & Cox, 30) is directed to detailed descriptions of the MARC/BNB (British National Bibliography) records. It describes many aspects of library automation including costs.

The United Kingdom Chemical Information Service (UKCIS) provides a range of computer-based information services in chemistry and related fields from four CAS data bases (UKCIS, 231); the MEDLARS data base is expected to be added in 1972 (EUSIDIC, 75). Kent (122) describes a new UKCIS inverted-file-search system, INFIRS, intended to be applicable to data bases ranging in form from free-text to controlled language. Kent also discusses the performance and cost of free-text search systems (123).

Derwent Publications Ltd. has been operating the Central Patents Index (CPI) since early 1970. CPI is chemically oriented and has 12 subject sections; these are further broken down into 135 classes for SDI and searching purposes (Derwent, 51). There are 12 CPI tapes; five are used for searches resulting in accession number "hits"; the others are "print" tapes containing abstracts and bibliographic data. New records are issued on weekly mini-tapes; all other tapes are issued quarterly. Computer programs are available to accomplish the search and printout; additional programs are planned for 1972 (Derwent, 52).

Two subscriber meetings were held in Washington, D.C. and Frankfurt, Germany in December 1971 (Derwent, 58). Derwent proposes to set up in London a separate computer-based World Patent Documentation Center that is planned to be operational by 1973 and to cover 14 countries. In addition to patents, Derwent produces three tapes containing literature references: (a) RINGDOC—pharmaceutical literature references from 300 journals; (b) VETDOC—veterinary literature references taken from over 125 journals; (c) PESTDOC—pesticidal literature references from nearly 200 journals. Search services and tape derivatives from these data bases are provided in the U.S. by Pfizer, Inc. as discussed above.

The Institution of Electrical Engineers (IEE) operates INSPEC (International Information Service in Physics, Electrotechnology, Computers, and Control) adding nearly 149,000 abstracts in 1971. Tapes are available covering all or part of the data base with or without abstracts and are being used by centers in Sweden, Canada, the U.K. and the U.S. to provide local SDI and/or retrospective services. INSPEC Topics, a set of standard profiles, was started in mid-1970, and a progress report was produced in 1971 (117). Barlow (31) discusses the application of INSPEC services to electronics and Clague (56) describes the SDI services offered. IEE is actively pursuing a program leading to extension of data base coverage and technical improvements in input and output techniques.

The Mass Spectrometry Data Centre (MSDC) is an international center for the collection and distribution of mass spectral data. Six computer-based search services and over 250 journals are scanned monthly; relevant article references are available on tape (MSDC, 150). In 1969, the Shirley Institute began a five-year project to develop the system and services (computer-based where appropriate) necessary to establish a textile information center. Cumberbirch & Ellis (62) describe project development work and the complete system outline. A tape data base was supplied routinely during the second half of 1971 by the Specialized Textile Information Service. The tape covers about 7000 items per year from the World Textile Abstracts (Shirley, 212).

Activities In International Organizations

Commission of the European Communities. CEC involves ECSC (European Coal and Steel Community), the Common Market and EURATOM (European Atomic Energy Community). The possibility of incorporating a number of data bases into the European information network that the Community expects to set up is being examined.

Plans are underway to make the ENDS (European Nuclear Documentation System) data base available in 1972 (OECD, 173).

European Space Research Organization. ESRO (Paris) provides bibliographic input of European aerospace publications from 10 countries to NASA and, in return, has access to the NASA data base via the on-line NASA/RECON network. Several terminals are operational in Europe and the network is being expanded (OECD, 173).

Food and Agricultural Organization. Since 1969, FAO (Rome) has been examining the need and feasibility of a "world agriculture information system." Dubois (69) outlines the evolution of such a system. At the FAO Conference in 1971 a resolution, a program, and a budget were approved for the generation of AGRIS (the International Information System for the Agricultural Sciences and Technology). Magnetic tapes are among the recommended output services (FAO, 78). The system is expected to be fully operational by the end of 1973. Existing FAO technical assistance projects have contributed to a network of agricultural documentation centers in developing countries. For example, the Centre National de Documentation of Morocco has placed over 10,000 Moroccan agricultural documents into machine-readable form and is preparing computer-generated indexes. Other projects are being developed for about 20 countries including three regional groups in the Senegal River Basin (Africa), Central America, and South-East Asia (NFSAIS, 160).

In addition, FAO is collaborating with an international group (from the public and private sectors) to produce *Aquatic Sciences and Fisheries Abstracts* (19), which first appeared in 1971. All journal data are available for retrospective searching. Zentralstelle für Maschinelle Dokumentation in Frankfurt, Germany, is developing the computer retrieval system, expected to be operational in 1973. Over 3000 journals will be covered; abstracts are being prepared by Information Retrieval Limited in London.

International Federation for Documentation. FID (The Netherlands), a nongovernmental organization, has over 30 committees including a committee on Operational Machine Techniques and Systems (FID/OM) engaged in research on machine-readable data bases (OECD, 173).

International Food Information Service. IFIS, a collaboration of institutes from four countries, produces the abstract journal *Food Science and Technology Abstracts* (FSTA), which is also available on tape from the German manager of IFIS (Schutzsack, 203). FSTA covers about 14,000 references per year in food science and related chemistry (IFIS, 118).

International Labour Office. The Central Library and Documentation Branch of ILO (an agency of the United Nations in Geneva) has developed and implemented an Integrated Scientific Information System (ISIS). In 1971, the Bibliographic Control subsystem contained over 46,000 abstracts in the fields of labor economics and sociology. The data base allows batch or remote terminal inquiry. A slightly modified MARC II structure is used. ISIS is described in a manual issued by ILO (119). An earlier discussion of ISIS objectives was given by Thompson & Schieber (227). Thompson (226) also gave cost estimates for searching a large-scale bibliographic social science data base. An interesting byproduct of the ISIS work is an algorithm for compaction of alphanumeric data described by Schieber & Thomas (199). Using the technique of replacing two alphabetic characters frequently used in combination with one unused special character code, they achieved a compression ratio of 43.5 percent.

International Nuclear Information System. INIS, a section of the International Atomic Energy Agency (Vienna), has a data base covering nuclear science literature since 1970. Over 100 member states provide worldwide input in this cooperative effort. Bibliographic records and subject descriptions are provided on monthly tapes (in MARC II format), which can be used as a basis for a national nuclear information service. The tapes are available to any international organization. Pelzer (182) describes the INIS formation and operation and outlines services planned for the future. Over a dozen reports are available describing various aspects of the system, one of which gives specifications and record formats of the magnetic tapes (INIS, 111).

Organisation for Economic Co-operation and Development. OECD (Paris) has an Information Policy Group actively promoting international cooperation and compatibility of machine-readable information systems among its more than 20 member countries. In line with this objective, two important documents were issued in 1971: a compendium on information activities of international organizations (OECD, 173), and a worldwide inventory of major information services (OECD, 174). Machine-readable data base services are described in both publications.

United Nations Educational, Scientific and Cultural Organization and the International Council of Scientific Unions. UNESCO/ICSU created a central committee in 1967 to conduct a feasibility study on the establishment of a world science information system (UNISIST). A feasibility study report was issued in 1971 (UNESCO/ICSU, 232). A fundamental concept of UNISIST is the transfer and exchange of bibliographic data in machine-readable form.

United Nations Industrial Development Organization. UNIDO (Vienna) is implementing INDIS (Industrial Information Processing System), a computerized international clearinghouse for industrial information. In 1971, INDIS was abstracting at the rate of 5000 documents a year (OECD, 173).

STANDARDIZATION AND COOPERATIVE EFFORTS IMPORTANT TO MACHINE-READABLE DATA BASES

In their 14th Annual Report, the Council on Library Resources (60) declared that the level of investment required to reap the benefits of the emerging national complex of machine-readable data bases is far beyond the individual budgeting capacity of any but the very largest libraries. They believe that small and medium-sized libraries should band together in local, state, or regional consortia and thus pool their assets and efforts. This trend is, and has been, growing worldwide.

The Association of Scientific Information Dissemination Centers (ASIDIC) is an active group composed of organizations who process two or more machine-readable data bases produced by outside suppliers. ASIDIC has formed a Cooperative Data Management Committee and its chairman (Williams, 258) gave a preliminary report that suggested a "cooperative network of centers" to help reduce the financial burden and ensure the availability of data bases having limited appeal. A European counterpart to ASIDIC was formed in 1970 and is known as the European Scientific Information Dissemination Centers (EUSIDIC): it grew out of an informal group known as CHEOPS. EUSIDIC publishes an informative newsletter called NEWSIDIC (75).

Numerous cooperative operations are discussed above in the descriptions of ongoing data base activities—especially international activities. Implicit and essential to such cooperation is the establishment of standards. Work in this area was at least as active in 1971 as the progress reported by Parkins & Kennedy (180) in 1970. Important documents on bibliographic tape standards appearing in 1971 included the American National Standards Institute's standard for bibliographic information interchange on magnetic tape (ANSI, 16); a description of the work carried out by the International Organization For Standards/Technical Committee 46 (ISO/TC46) by Lochard (139); Data Element Definitions For Secondary Services produced by the Common Practices and Standards Committee of the National Federation of Science Abstracting and Indexing Services (NFSAIS, 157); an important session at the Annual Meeting of NFSAIS (156) on standard data elements and formats for bibliographic tapes, as well as reports on cooperative studies, which included initial findings of the BIOSIS/CAS/Ei study of journal overlap (Wood et al., 264); new developments in an information interchange of bibliographic data elements in machine-readable format (Avram & Curran, 22); and a progress report on the UNISIST/ICSU-AB working group on bibliographic descriptions (Martin, 105) in which a reference manual on machine-readable bibliographic descriptions was described (it is expected to be finished by the group in early 1973).

The MARC II format, for transfer of bibliographic data on magnetic tape, was first published in 1968 (Avram et al., 23) and is in wide use today. Many of the tape generators use different formats and even some of the standards developed since 1968 differ somewhat from MARC II; however, the MARC II format is the most widely used, and many systems have been developed with at least a MARC-like format, making them essentially compatible. LC is continually updating and improving the standard and applying it to other media such as maps, films, serials, and books (47, 191, 235, 236, 238).

The lack of standards is probably the greatest deterrent to the accelerated use of machine-readable bibliographic data bases. It is not possible (in the author's opinion) to realize the full potential of this powerful tool without establishment and adoption of uniform data elements, tape formats, coding conventions, etc. The dilemma exists because most suppliers market magnetic tape data bases as a byproduct of their publication activities. The suppliers' production problems are numerous and they have varied motivations. There are a host of problems associated with standardization that can only be overcome through cooperation of producers, users and processors. The critical need for cooperation was aptly stated by Adkinson in his address to NFSAIS and ASIDIC (NFSAIS, 156):

> The scientific and technical information activities in the United States will never gain the stature nor develop the necessary services so long as the participants view this area as an arena of competition instead of a platform for hard headed realistic cooperation and coordination. . .individual biases in technical presentation and organization cannot be tolerated. . . .

FUTURE TRENDS

There were few reports in 1971 specifically concerning the future of bibliographic data bases except for the interesting presentation by

Klempner (127) and, to some extent the paper by Becker (32). The following trends have been observed during preparation of this review:

New Medium for Library Resources. If the current trend continues, libraries will cease to relinquish to computer centers the responsibility of providing information services from machine-readable data bases (including both bibliographic and digital data tapes). These services should become and are becoming, natural extensions of the other graphic and hardcopy services most libraries now provide. Some libraries have resented large bibliographic data bases because of their potential for by-passing the library; however, progressive librarians are now making machine-readable data bases a vital part of the library's program.

Interactive Retrieval. The rapid movement toward on-line terminal searching, which is well underway, can only add to the growth potential of machine-readable data bases. A two-year pilot program (Carville et al., 49) concluded that on-line reference retrieval will largely replace present tape-driven systems in a few years. It does appear that the economics of spinning tapes (especially for retrospective retrieval) will eventually give way to the more attractive approach of on-line searching coupled with novel storage media and search techniques. This development will involve data compression techniques, mass storage devices with high packing densities, full-text natural language processing techniques, storage media such as videotape and computer output on microform (COM), and direct searching of microfilmed files by computer (CIM) such as the "programmable film reader" described by Menkus (153).

Networks. The lack of adequate computer resources, and the high costs associated with the set-up of a computerized information center, have resulted in an increasing trend toward networks that use centralized computer facilities. The above discussions of international activities and cooperative efforts make this trend quite clear. Work in this area is already underway as can be seen in Samuelson's (196, 197) papers on the coordination of diversified data bases and information networks through the use of referral directories and relay switches.

Growth. The rapid growth of machine-readable data bases is obvious to anyone attempting to keep abreast of developments. In the above discussions of activities in the USA, 97 data bases produced by 62 organizations were identified. Only five of these were in a planning stage; 56 can be leased or purchased and 68 are available for searching. At least 150 data bases, in the U.S. alone, should be available by 1975. The *rate* of growth internationally appears to be greater than in the

U.S. It has been recognized that the slow rate of economic and technological growth in the "developing" countries of the world has been, in part, a result of insufficient use of existing information essential to this development. About 45 data bases generated in ten countries have been identified above plus 10 more under development by international organizations. About one-third can be leased or purchased; the rest are available for searching only. In the next few years, the number of international data bases should increase dramatically.

Data Base Management. There is a strong need for, and trend toward, the development of systems and procedures to provide effective data base *use*. As Landau (132) correctly states, ". . .machine-readable data bases are multiplying faster than they can be metabolized by the information community." The current availability of data bases and processing services offers the modern library an unprecedented wealth of information to help serve its patrons. For this resource to be fully exploited, operational tools and techniques must be developed and librarians and information scientists must be trained to use them. Standardization will facilitate data base management. Without standardization, use of many data bases may become impractical. If each data base developer goes his own way, without attempting to cooperate with others in some way, progress toward standardization will, indeed, be slow. But if standardization and other problems are solved, the door will be wide open to extensive and effective use of machine-readable bibliographic data bases.

REFERENCES

(1) ABC-CLIO. System ABC. American Bibliographical Center-Clio Press, Inc., Santa Barbara, California, 1970.

(2) AEROSPACE RESEARCH APPLICATIONS CENTER. ARAC services catalog and guide to standard interest profiles. Indiana University Foundation, Aerospace Research Applications Center, Bloomington, Indiana, April 1970, 77 p.

(3) AMERICAN CHEMICAL SOCIETY. Data content specifications for basic journal abstracts in standard distribution format. American Chemical Society, Chemical Abstracts Service, Columbus, Ohio, 1971, 66 p.

(4) AMERICAN CHEMICAL SOCIETY. Data content specifications for CA condensates in standard distribution format, revised. American Chemical Society, Chemical Abstracts Service, Columbus, Ohio, 1971, 109 p.

(5) AMERICAN CHEMICAL SOCIETY. Data content specifications for chemical-biological activities in standard distribution format, revised. American Chemical Society, Chemical Abstracts Service, Columbus, Ohio, 1971, 114 p.

(6) AMERICAN CHEMICAL SOCIETY. Data content specifications for chemical titles in standard distribution format. American Chemical Society, Chemical Abstracts Service, Columbus, Ohio, 1972, 32 p.

(7) AMERICAN CHEMICAL SOCIETY. Data content specifications for patent concordance in computer-readable form in standard distribution format. American Chemical Society, Chemical Abstracts Service, Columbus, Ohio, 1972, 23 p.

(8) AMERICAN CHEMICAL SOCIETY. Data content specifications for polymer science and technology in standard distribution format, revised. American Chemical Society, Chemical Abstracts Service, Columbus, Ohio, 1972, 122 p.

(9) AMERICAN CHEMICAL SOCIETY. Data content specifications for the CA integrated subject file in standard distribution format. American Chemical Society, Chemical Abstracts Service, Columbus, Ohio, 1971, 62 p.

(10) AMERICAN CHEMICAL SOCIETY. Data content specifications for the "Chemical Abstracts Service Source Index" in standard distribution format. American Chemical Society, Chemical Abstracts Service, Columbus, Ohio, 1972, 153 p.

(11) AMERICAN CHEMICAL SOCIETY. Standard distribution format technical specifications, revised. American Chemical Society, Chemical Abstracts Service, Columbus, Ohio, 1971, 60 p.

(12) AMERICAN INSTITUTE OF PHYSICS. A program for a national information system for physics, 1970-1972. American Institute of Physics, New York, New York, 57 p.

(13) AMERICAN INSTITUTE OF PHYSICS. INFORMATION DIVISION. The AIP program for physics information: a national information system for physics and astronomy 1972-1976. American Institute of Physics, New York, New York, June 1971, 74 p.

(14) AMERICAN INSTITUTE OF PHYSICS. INFORMATION DIVISION. Searchable physics information notices (SPIN). Technical specifications. American Institute of Physics, New York, New York, January 1971, 20 p.

(15) AMERICAN LIBRARY ASSOCIATION. REFERENCE SERVICES DIVISION. A guide to the selection of computer-based science and technology reference services in the U.S.A. American Library Association, Chicago, Illinois, 1969, 29 p.

(16) AMERICAN NATIONAL STANDARDS INSTITUTE. American national standard for bibliographic information interchange on magnetic tape. American National Standards Institute, Inc., New York, New York, 1971, 34 p. (ANSI-Z39.2-1971).

(17) AMERICAN PSYCHOLOGICAL ASSOCIATION. Tape services: PASAR—PADAT—PATELL. American Psychological Association, Washington, D.C., 1971. (Information packet).

(18) ANZELMO, FRANK D. A data-storage format for information system files. IEEE Transactions on Computers, C-20:L (January 1971) 39-43.

(19) Aquatic Sciences and Fisheries Abstracts. Aslib Proceedings, 23:6 (June 1971) 272.

(20) AVRAM, HENRIETTE D. The evolving MARC system: the concept of a data utility. In: Proceedings of the 1970 clinic on library applications of data processing: MARC uses and users. Edited by Kathryn Luther Henderson. University of Illinois, Graduate School of Library Science, Urbana, Illinois, 1971, 1-26.

(21) AVRAM, HENRIETTE D. Library automation. In: Cuadra, Carlos A.; ed. Annual review of information science and technology, vol. 6. Encyclopaedia Britannica, Chicago, Illinois, 1971, 171-217.

(22) AVRAM, HENRIETTE D.; CURRAN, ANN T. New developments in an information interchange of data elements in machine-readable format for bibliographic data. In: Bowker annual of library and booktrade information, 1971. R. R. Bowker, New York and London, England, 1971, 104-106.

(23) AVRAM, HENRIETTE D.; KNAPP, JOHN F.; RATHER, LUCIA J. The MARC II format, a communications format for bibliographic data. U.S. Library of Congress, Information Systems Office, Washington, D.C., January 1968, 167 p.

(24) AVRAM, HENRIETTE D.; MARUYAMA, LENORE S. The RECON pilot project: a progress report, October 1970-May 1971. Journal of Library Automation, 4:3 (September 1971) 159-169.

(25) AYRES, F. H. The case against MARC: how strong is it? Library Association Record, 73:7 (July 1971) 130-131, 142.

(26) BA previews—advance information on magnetic tape. Biosciences Information Service, Philadelphia, Pennsylvania. (Advertising brochure).

(27) BACKER, STANLEY; VALKO, EMERY I.; eds. Thesaurus of textile terms covering fibrous material and processes. M.I.T. Press, Cambridge, Massachusetts, 1969.

(28) BAKER, DALE B. World's chemical literature continues to expand. Chemical & Engineering News, 49:13 (July 1971) 37-40.

(29) BAKER, DALE B.; TATE, FRED A.; ROWLETT, RUSSELL J., JR. Changing patterns in the international communication of chemical research and technology. Presented before the Division of Chemical Literature, ACS/CIC Joint Conference, Toronto, Ontario, Canada, 26 May 1970, 90-98.

(30) BALMFORTH, C. K.; COX, N. S. M. Interface: library automation with special reference to computing activity. The M.I.T. Press, Cambridge, Massachusetts, 1971, 1-251.

(31) BARLOW, D. H. Information services for the world's electronics engineers. INSPEC: The Institution of Electrical Engineers, London, England, November/December 1971, 136-140.

(32) BECKER, JOSEPH. Trends in library technology. Special Libraries, 62:10 (October 1971) 429-434.

(33) BENENFELD, ALAN R. Generation and encoding of the Project INTREX augmented catalog data base. Massachusetts Institute of Technology, Electronic Systems Laboratory, Cambridge, Massachusetts, August 1968, 54 p.

(34) BENNERTZ, RICHARD K. Development of the Defense Documentation Center remote on-line retrieval system—past, present, and future. U.S. Defense Documentation Center, Alexandria, Virginia, March 1971, 48 p. (AD 720 900).

(35) BENNETT, RALPH E.; FRYCKI, STEPHEN J. Internal processing of external reference services. The Squibb Institute for Medical Research, New Brunswick, New Jersey. Journal of Chemical Documentation, 11:2, (1971), 76-83.

(36) BERESFORD, JOHN; BROWN, LAWRENCE, III; HILL, GARY; CITRO, CONSTANCE; BRADY, JOYCE. Computer programs used by the 1970 Census START Community. Presented at the Population Association of America Annual Meeting, 1971, 16 p.

(37) BIERMAN, KENNETH JOHN; BLUE, BETTY JEAN. A MARC-based SDI service. Journal of Library Automation, 3:4 (December 1970) 304-319.

(38) BOOZ, ALLEN AND HAMILTON, INC. Economic analysis related to the future market for psychological information. American Psychological Association, Washington, D.C., May 1970, 25 p.

(39) BOWLING GREEN STATE UNIVERSITY. PHILOSOPHY DOCUMENTATION CENTER. The philosopher's information retrieval system (PIRS)—general information. Bowling Green State University, Bowling Green, Ohio, 1971, 1 p. (Data sheet).

(40) BRENNER, EVERETT H. API begins new SDI service with CA condensates. Newsletter of the American Society for Information Science, 9:5 (September/October 1970) 7.

(41) BRENNER, EVERETT H.; HELANDER, DONALD P. Petroleum literature and patent retrieval; centralized information processing. Special Libraries, 10:3 (March 1969) 146-152.

(42) BROOKS, A. A. Orchis progress report. Oak Ridge National Laboratory operated by Union Carbide Corp. for the U.S. Atomic Energy Commission, 7 February 1972, 22 p.

(43) BROWN, MARILYN T. Dow current awareness service. Presented at the 1970 Spring ASIDIC Meeting, Session on Historical and Projected Center Costs, Atlanta, Georgia, 19 March 1970, 13 p.

(44) BUCKLEY, JAY S., JR. RINGDOC distribution system (RDS). Presented at PMA-Science Information Subsection Meeting, Philadelphia, Pennsylvania, 12-14 March 1972.

(45) CARMON, JAMES L. Annual report to the National Science Foundation on grant GN-851 to expand the University of Georgia Information Center, Computer Center. University of Georgia, Athens, Georgia, 1 October 1970-30 September 1971.

(46) CARMON, JAMES L.; PARK, MARGARET K. Cost factors in the operation of an information dissemination center, University of Georgia. Presented at the March 18-19, 1970, meeting of the Association of Scientific Information Dissemination Centers, Atlanta, Georgia, 10 p.

(47) CARRINGTON, DAVID K.; MANGAN, ELIZABETH U. Data preparation manual for the conversion of map cataloging records to machine-readable form. U.S. Library of Congress, Washington, D.C., 1971, 317 p.

(48) CARROLL, KENNETH D. Survey of scientific-technical tape services. American Institute of Physics, New York, New York, September 1970, 64 p.

(49) CARVILLE, M.; HIGGINS, L.D.; SMITH, FRANCIS J. Interactive reference retrieval in large files. Information Storage and Retrieval, 7:5 (December 1971) 205-210.

(50) CCM INFORMATION CORPORATION. Science-technology-education-guidance-social science; 1971-1972 programs and services. CCM Information Corporation, New York, New York, 16 p. (Advertising brochure).

(51) Central Patents Index: general instruction manual—1972: 2d edition. Derwent Publications Ltd., London, England, 1972, 48 p.

(52) Central Patents Index: tapes and programs. Derwent Publications Ltd., London, England, (Instruction Manual No. 5 (a)). 1972, 17 p.

(53) CHEMICAL ABSTRACTS SERVICE. Chemical Abstracts Service Information System. American Chemical Society, Chemical Abstracts Service, Columbus, Ohio, 8 p. (Pamphlet).

(54) CHEMICAL ABSTRACTS SERVICE. Information Services - 1972. American Chemical Society, Chemical Abstracts Service, Columbus, Ohio, December 1971, 51 p. (Catalog).

(55) CIDB. (Chemie-Information-und-Dokumentation Berlin). The Chem Inform Data Base. Western German Chemical Society, Chemie-Information-und-Dokumentation, Berlin, Germany, 2 August 1971, 13 p. (In German).

(56) CLAGUE, P. INSPEC and selective dissemination of information. Presented to the Yorkshire Branch of the Library Association at York University, 11 November 1970, INSPEC, London, England, 1971, 4 p.

(57) COLES, VICTOR L. Evaluation of a remote console information retrieval system (NASA/RECON). Paper presented at the Forum on Interactive Bibliographic Systems, U.S. National Bureau of Standards, Washington, D.C., October 1971, 29 p.

(58) Computer meeting: Frankfurt/Washington, December 1971. Derwent Publications Ltd., London, England, 1971.

(59) COOK, KENNETH H.; TRUMP, LYNN H.; ATHERTON, PAULINE; KATZER, JEFFREY. SUPARS: Syracuse University psychological abstracts retrieval service. Large scale information processing systems. Final report to the Rome Air Development Center. Syracuse University, School of Library Science, Syracuse, New York, July 1971. (Six sections).

(60) COUNCIL ON LIBRARY RESOURCES. Council on Library Resources 14th annual report, for the period ending June 30, 1970. Council on Library Resources, Washington, D.C., 1970, 54 p. (ED 049 798).

(61) CUADRA, CARLOS A. On-line systems: promise and pitfalls. Journal of the American Society for Information Science, 22:2 (March/April 1971) 107-114.

(62) CUMBERBIRCH, R. J. E.; ELLIS, K. C. Computer-based textile information services. Textile Institute and Industry, March 1971, 69-73.

(63) DAVIS, RUTH M. The National Biomedical Communications Network as a developing structure. Bulletin of Medical Library Association, 59:1 (January 1971) 1-20.
(64) DEVON, T. K. A comparative study of the CBAC and Pfizer ARCS services—in-house study Pfizer Inc., Groton, Connecticut, 1971, 5 p.
(65) DIETZ, STEPHEN K. Census data applications. Presented at the Urban and Regional Information Systems Association Annual Meeting, 9 September 1971, 7 p.
(66) DIETZ, STEPHEN K. Social indicators developed from 1970 census data. Prepared for the National Meeting of the American Institute of Planners, 26 October 1971, San Francisco, California, 11 p.
(67) DOLAN, F. T.; KOOLE, K. E.; eds. Proceedings: Second Annual Meeting, Western Canada Chapter, American Society for Information Science, 14-15 September 1970, Vancouver Public Library. University of Calgary, Calgary, Alberta, Canada, December 1970, 191 p. (ED 050 791).
(68) DOLAN, F. T.; PERZEL, L. P.; eds. Proceedings: Third Annual Meeting, Western Canada Chapter, American Society for Information Science, 3-5 October 1971, Banff School of Fine Arts. October 1971, 152 p. (Available from the University of Calgary, Calgary, Alberta, Canada.).
(69) DUBOIS, G. International cooperation in information storage and retrieval in the field of agriculture. Sixteenth Conference of International Organisations for the Joint Study of Programmes and Activities in the Field of Agriculture in Europe, Paris, France, February 1971, 23-26.
(70) ELGAD, REUBEN. Computerization of information activities in Israel. Bulletin—Israel Society of Special Libraries and Information Centres-Conference Issue, 3:1 (August 1971) 27-32.
(71) ENGINEERING INDEX. COMPENDEX: computerized engineering indexes. Engineering Index, Inc., New York, New York, 1971, 12 p. (Brochure).
(72) ENGINEERING INDEX. Engineering Index—1972 catalog. Engineering Index, Inc., Marketing and Business Services Division, New York, New York, 16 p.
(73) EPSTEIN, A. H.; et al. Bibliographic automation of large library operations using a time-sharing system: phase I. Final report. Stanford University Libraries, Palo Alto, California, April 1971, 334 p. (ED 049 786).
(74) EPSTEIN, A. H.; FERGUSON, DOUGLAS; MONTAGUE, ELEANOR. An on-line network—cooperative planning with several libraries. In: American Society for Information Science. Annual meeting. 34th, Denver, Colorado, 7-11 November 1971. Proceedings, vol. 8: Communication for decision makers. Greenwood Publishing Corporation, Westport, Connecticut, 1971, 227-231.
(75) EUROPEAN ASSOCIATION OF SCIENTIFIC INFORMATION DISSEMINATION CENTRES. NEWSIDIC-Information Bulletin of EUSIDIC, No. 2 (May 1971).
(76) FENDRYCH, M.; FOGL, I. J. The Czechoslovak computer information system ASTI. Information Storage and Retrieval, 7:12 (December 1971) 245-248.
(77) FENICHEL, CAROL. Editing the Permuterm Subject Index. In: American Society for Information Science. Annual meeting. 34th, Denver, Colorado, 7-11 November 1971. Proceedings, vol. 8: Communication for decision makers. Greenwood Publishing Corporation, Westport, Connecticut, 1971, 349-353.
(78) FOOD AND AGRICULTURE ORGANIZATION OF THE UNITED NATIONS. Note on the proposed international information system for the agricultural sciences and technology (C71/INF/13) and program of work and budget 1972-73 (C71/LIM/59). FAO Conference, Rome, Italy, 6-25 November 1971.
(79) FREEMAN, ROBERT R. Environmental information: new developments in NOAA. In: American Society for Information Science. Annual meeting. 34th, Denver, Colorado, 7-11 November 1971. Proceedings, vol. 8: Communication for decision makers. Greenwood Publishing Corporation, Westport, Connecticut, 1971, 115-119.

(80) FRIERSON, ELEANOR; ATHERTON, PAULINE. Survey of attitudes towards SUPARS. In: American Society for Information Science. Annual meeting. 34th, Denver, Colorado, 7-11 November 1971. Proceedings, vol. 8: Communication for decision makers. Greenwood Publishing Corporation, Westport, Connecticut, 1971, 65-67.

(81) FRYCKI, STEPHEN J. Information transfer from source to user utilizing a pharmaceutical data base. In: Annual National Information Retrieval Colloquium, 8th, Philadelphia, Pennsylvania, 6-7 May 1971. Proceedings, 306-333.

(82) FURGOTSON, JAMES M., JR. Design, construction and applications of well and production data systems. In: American Society for Information Science. Annual meeting. 34th, Denver, Colorado, 7-11 November 1971. Proceedings, vol. 8: Communication for decision-makers. Greenwood Publishing Corporation, Westport, Connecticut, 1971, 99-105.

(83) GAFFNEY, INEZ M. CAN/SDI: current status and future. Presented at: Cacul Workshop on Library Automation, Vancouver, British Columbia, Canada, 19-20 June 1971, 1-6.

(84) GARFIELD, EUGENE. Citation indexing for studying science. In: Nature-International Journal of Science, vol. 227 (15 August 1970) 669-671.

(85) GARFIELD, EUGENE; MALIN, MORTON V. The International Network of ISI-Linked National Information Centers. Presented at the International Conference on Information Science, Tel Aviv, Israel, 29 August-3 September 1971, 7 p.

(86) GECHMAN, MARVIN C. Analysis of technical data bases and processing services. In: American Society for Information Science. Annual meeting. 33d, Philadelphia, Pennsylvania, 11-15 October 1970. Proceedings, vol. 7: The information conscious society. Greenwood Publishing Corporation, Westport, Connecticut, 1970, 97-99.

(87) GECHMAN, MARVIN C.; KIESEWETTER, GEORGE H. Development of a corporate-wide technical reports processing system. In: American Society for Information Science. Annual meeting. 32d, San Francisco, California, 1-4 October 1969. Proceedings, vol. 6: Cooperating information societies. Greenwood Publishing Corporation, Westport, Connecticut, 1969, 361-367.

(88) GEHL, JOHN M.; SLAMECKA, VLADIMIR, A. Profile of scientific-technical tape information services. Georgia Institute of Technology, School of Information and Computer Science, Atlanta, Georgia, 1971.

(89) GERMAN FOUNDATION FOR DEVELOPING COUNTRIES. Symposium on Documentation Planning in Developing Countries at Bad Godesberg, 28-30 November 1967. German Foundation for Developing Countries, Bonn, Germany, 1970, 122 p. (ED 049 791).

(90) GLUCHOWICZ, Z. Selective dissemination of information— a transdisciplinary information retrieval system at The Royal Institute of Technology, Stockholm, Sweden, IAG Journal, 4:2 (1971) 131-148.

(91) Government easing attitude toward private enterprise in use of Federal information. Publishers Weekly, 12 April 1971. (Reprint).

(92) HARTWELL, IEVA O. Search manual—a guide to preparing profile search strategies. Indiana University Foundation, Aerospace Research Applications Center, Bloomington, Indiana, February, 1971.

(93) HAYES, ROBERT M.; BECKER, JOSEPH. Handbook of data processing for libraries. Becker and Hayes, Inc., Bethesda, Maryland, 1970, 885 p.

(94) HEAPS, H. S. Criteria for optimum effectiveness of information retrieval systems. Information and Control, 18:2 (March 1971) 156-167.

(95) HEAPS, H. S. Efficient coding, storage, and search methods for information retrieval. Canadian Symposium on Communication, Montreal, Quebec, Canada, November 1970, 33-34.

(96) HEILIK, J. Information retrieval and MARC at the National Science Library. Canadian Library Journal, 28:2 (March/April 1971) 120-123.

(97) HENDERSON, KATHRYN L.; ed. MARC uses and users. Proceedings of the 1970 Clinic on Library Applications of Data Processing. University of Illinois, Graduate School of Library Science, Urbana, Illinois, 1971, 113 p.
(98) HERSCHMAN, ARTHUR. Keeping up with what's going on in physics. Physics Today, 24:11 (November 1971) 22-29.
(99) HIGHWAY RESEARCH BOARD. Highway research information service. Highway Research Board, Washington, D.C., January 1972 (Brochure).
(100) HILLIKER, BRIGITTA. Selective dissemination of information using the chemical titles tape service. Journal of the American Society for Information Science, 22:5 (September/October 1971) 356. (Letters to the editor).
(101) HINES, DAVID L. User's guide to the computerized literature search services of the IBM Technical Information Retrieval Center (ITIRC). IBM Technical Information Retrieval Center, Rochester, Minnesota, 17 September 1971, 27 p. (Technical report 07.450).
(102) HISINGER, B. A multidisciplinary and computerized SDI service for industry and research—practical experience and costs. Information Storage and Retrieval, 7:4 (November 1971) 175-187.
(103) HOPKINS, JUDITH. Manual for OCLC catalog card production. Revised and enlarged. Ohio College Library Center, Columbus, Ohio. (ED 046 471).
(104) HOUSMAN, EDWARD M. Survey of current systems for selective dissemination of information (SDI). In: American Society for Information Science. Annual meeting. 32d, San Francisco, California, 1-4 October 1969. Proceedings, vol. 6: Cooperating information societies. Greenwood Publishing Corporation, Westport, Connecticut, 1969, 57-61.
(105) IFI/PLENUM DATA CORP. IFI expanded patent information retrieval system. IFI/Plenum Data Corp., Arlington, Virginia, January 1972, 3 p. (Advertising literature).
(106) INFODATA SYSTEMS. Inquire—technical summary. Infodata Systems, Inc., Arlington, Virginia, July 1969, 25 p.
(107) INFORMATION DESIGN. CARDSET cataloging systems—a library microfilm system. Menlo Park, California, 1971, 4 p. (Advertising brochure).
(108) Information for campus, community, and commerce. University of Florida Libraries, 1:3 (November 1971) 2 p. (Gainesville, Florida).
(109) INFORMATION GENERAL INC. Magnetic tape data base study; vol. 1: summary report. Information General, Inc., Needham, Massachusetts, June 1971, 30 p.
(110) INFORMATION INTERSCIENCE INC. Bio-medical data base. Chemical data base files. Drugdoc biomedical data base. Engineering data base. 3i total information program. Information Interscience, Inc., Philadelphia, Pennsylvania, 1970. (Advertising brochures).
(111) INIS: magnetic tape specifications and record format. International Atomic Energy Agency, Vienna, Austria, February 1971, 26 p. (IAEA-INIS-9. Rev.1).
(112) INSTITUTE OF LIBRARY RESEARCH. Union catalog supplement project, a brief summary. University of California, Institute of Library Research, Berkeley, California, 11 November 1970, 4 p.
(113) INSTITUTE OF PAPER CHEMISTRY. The Division of Information Science, list of magnetic tapes and microforms for lease. Institute of Paper Chemistry, Appleton, Wisconsin, July 1971. (Data sheet).
(114) INSTITUTE OF PAPER CHEMISTRY. Supplement to the abstract bulletin: current awareness (SDI) service from chemical abstracts condensates. Institute of Paper Chemistry, Division of Information Services, Appleton, Wisconsin, 1 January 1972. (Data sheet).
(115) INSTITUTE OF PAPER CHEMISTRY. Supplement to the abstract bulletin: new services for computerized information retrieval. Institute of Paper Chemistry, Division of Information Services, Appleton, Wisconsin, 1 January 1972. (Data sheet).

(116) INSTITUTE OF TEXTILE TECHNOLOGY. Textile Information Center Services. Institute of Textile Technology, Charlottsville, Virginia, January 1972, 4 p. (Catalog).

(117) INSTITUTION OF ELECTRICAL ENGINEERS. INSPEC: research and development—a progress report. Institution of Electrical Engineers, London, England, March 1971, 27 p.

(118) INTERNATIONAL FOOD INFORMATION SERVICE. Magnetic tapes from FSTA-Food Science and Technology Abstracts. Institut für Dokumentationswesen, Frankfurt, Germany, n.d., 5 p.

(119) INTERNATIONAL LABOUR OFFICE. ISIS-Integrated Scientific Information System-A. General description of an approach to computerized bibliographical control. International Labour Office, Geneva, Switzerland, 1971, 115 p.

(120) KAMATH, V. A.; MALWAD, N. M. Computerized information storage and retrieval systems in India with special reference to the activities of the Bhabha Atomic Research Centre. Presented at the International Conference on Information Science, Tel Aviv, Israel, 29 August-3 September 1971, 13 p.

(121) KENNEDY, JOHN P. File size and the cost of processing MARC records. Journal of Library Automation, 4:1 (March 1971) 1-12.

(122) KENT, A. K. INFIRS—The UKCIS inverted file information retrieval system. United Kingdom Chemical Information Service, Nottingham, England, July 1970, 13 p. (Internal working document).

(123) KENT, A. K. Performance and cost of free-text search systems. Information Storage and Retrieval, 6 (1970) 73-77.

(124) KEREN, C.; ARBEL, B.; PARNES, H.; FICHMAN, N. A computer-produced index to current scientific research in Israel. Contributions to Information Science No. 2. Israel Society of Special Libraries and Information Centres, Tel Aviv, Israel, 1969, 51 p.

(125) KING, DONALD W.; CALDWELL, NANCY W. Cost-effectiveness of retrospective search systems. American Psychological Association, Washington, D.C., March 1971, 27 p.

(126) KISSMAN, HENRY M. Toxicology information program of the National Library of Medicine. Presented at 162d ACS Meeting, Washington, D.C., 12-17 September 1971.

(127) KLEMPNER, IRVING M. Librarianship and bibliographic data bases in the 70's. Presentation at the Colloquium on Machine-Readable Bibliographic Data Bases; Their Creation and Use. State University of New York at Albany, School of Library and Information Science, Albany, New York, 20-21 April 1971, 12 p.

(128) KOENIG, MICHAEL E. D.; BUCKLEY, JAY S., JR.; DETMER, JAMES M. SPRING (Searle-Pfizer RINGDOC) system. Part I-introduction, system requirements, overview of SPRING; Part II-user/patron convenience; Part III-system design. Presented at Special Meeting—Derwent Subscribers Meeting for Computer Applications, Washington, D.C., 3 December 1971, 7 p.

(129) KRUZAS, ANTHONY T.; SCHNITZER, ANNA ERCOLI; VAREKAMP, LINDA E.; eds. Encyclopedia of information systems and services. Edwards Brothers, Ann Arbor, Michigan, 1971, 1109 p.

(130) LANDAU, HERBERT B. Design criteria for a multi-input data base for the National Agricultural Library. In: American Society for Information Science. Annual meeting. 32d, San Francisco, California, 1-4 October 1969. Proceedings, vol. 6: Cooperating information societies. Greenwood Publishing Corporation, Westport, Connecticut, 1969, 101-104.

(131) LANDAU, HERBERT B. Document dissemination. In: Cuadra, Carlos A.; ed. Annual review of information science and technology, vol. 4. Encyclopaedia Britannica, Chicago, Illinois, 1969, 229-270.

(132) LANDAU, HERBERT B. The proliferation of machine-readable data bases: current problems. Presented at the Annual National Information Retrieval Colloquium, 8th, Philadelphia, Pennsylvania, 6-7 May 1971. Drexel Library Quarterly, 8:1 (January 1972) 63-69.

(133) LANDAU, HERBERT B. Research study into the utilization of machine-readable bibliographic data bases—final report. Auerbach Corporation, Philadelphia, Pennsylvania, 30 June 1969, 60 p. (Technical report 1582-100-TR8. PB 184 616).

(134) LAWFORD, HUGH; LATTA, KEITH; VON BRIESEN, RICHARD. The QUIC/LAW system of editing and retrieving legal documents. Queen's University, Kingston, Ontario, Canada, 1970, 8 p.

(135) LEASCO SYSTEMS & RESEARCH CORP. ERIC PROCESSING AND REFERENCE FACILITY. ERIC master files. Leasco Systems & Research Corp., Bethesda, Maryland, May 1971, 10 p.

(136) LEBOWITZ, ABRAHAM I.; JOHNSON, CAROL A. Automation at the National Agricultural Library. U.S. National Agricultural Library, Beltsville, Maryland, April 1970, 17 p.

(137) LEE, CALVIN MARK. An inventory of some English language secondary information services in science and technology. Organisation for Economic Co-Operation and Development, Paris, France, June 1969, 48 p.

(138) LLOYD, JOEL J. Design and building of an information system for the geosciences. In: American Society for Information Science. Annual meeting. 34th, Denver, Colorado, 7-11 November 1971. Proceedings, vol. 8: Communication for decision makers. Greenwood Publishing Corporation, Westport, Connecticut, 1971, 121-123.

(139) LOCHARD, JEAN. Automatic processing of documentation and standards. Unesco Bulletin for Libraries, 25:3 (May/June 1971) 143-150.

(140) LOCKHEED MISSILES & SPACE COMPANY. An introduction to the ISI/DIALOG on-line retrieval system. Demonstrated at the American Society for Information Science Annual Meeting, Philadelphia, Pennsylvania, October 1970, 1-7.

(141) McCARN, DAVIS B. AIM-TWX: an experimental on-line bibliographic retrieval system. Presented at The User Interface for Interactive Search of Bibliographic Data Bases Workshop, Sponsored by the AFIPS Information Systems Committee, San Jose, California, 14-15 January 1971, 19 p.

(142) McCARN, DAVIS B. Networks with emphasis on planning an on-line bibliographic access system. Information Storage and Retrieval, 7:6 (December 1971) 271-275.

(143) MAGNINO, JOSEPH J., JR. Document retrieval and dissemination. In: Cuadra, Carlos A.; ed. Annual review of information science and technology, vol. 6. Encyclopaedia Britannica, Chicago, Illinois, 1971, 219-245.

(144) MARKUSON, BARBARA EVANS; WANGER, JUDITH; SCHATZ, SHARON; BLACK, DONALD V. Automation and the Federal library community. System Development Corporation, Falls Church, Virginia, July 1971. (SDC report TM-WD-5402).

(145) MARKUSON, BARBARA EVANS; WANGER, JUDITH; SCHATZ, SHARON; BLACK, DONALD V. Handbook on Federal library automation. System Development Corporation, Falls Church, Virginia, July 1971. (SDC report TM-WD-5400).

(146) MARTIN, M. D.; WOOD, J. L. A progress report. The UNISIST/ICSU-AB Working Group on Bibliographic Descriptions. In: International Council of Scientific Unions Abstracting Board, Full Board Meeting, Columbus, Ohio, July 1970. Proceedings. 49-62.

(147) MARTINEZ, SAMUEL J. An information system for petroleum engineering technology. IEEE Transactions on Engineering Writing and Speech, EWS-13:2 (September 1970).

(148) MARTINEZ, SAMUEL J.; ANIS, MOHAMMED; BUTHOD, PAUL; HELANDER, DONALD P. Machine generation of information retrieval indexes. The University of Tulsa, Proceedings of the 6th Annual National Colloquium on Information Retrieval, 8-9 May 1969, 51-65.

(149) MARUYAMA, LENORE S. Format recognition: a report of a project at the Library of Congress. Journal of the American Society for Information Science, 22:4 (July/August 1971) 283-287.

(150) MASS SPECTROMETRY DATA CENTRE. Mass Spectrometry Bulletin. Data Sheets. Data on Tape. Mass Spectrometry Data Centre, AWRE, Aldermaston, Berkshire, England, 1971, 5 p.

(151) MASSACHUSETTS INSTITUTE OF TECHNOLOGY. Project INTREX. Semi-annual activity report, 15 March 1971-15 September 1971. Massachusetts Institute of Technology, Cambridge, Massachusetts, 15 September 1971, 124 p. (ED 053 772).

(152) MAUERHOFF, GEORG R.; SMITH, RICHARD G. A MARC II-based program for retrieval and dissemination. Journal of Library Automation, 4:3 (September 1971) 141-158.

(153) MENKUS, BELDEN. Retention of data for the long term. Datamation, (15 September 1971) 30-32.

(154) METADEX, metals abstracts index on magnetic tape. ASM Metals Information, American Society for Metals, Metals Park, Ohio, 1971.

(155) NATIONAL CLEARINGHOUSE FOR MENTAL HEALTH INFORMATION. Scientific Information Notes, 2:6 (1970) 287-289. (Information center profile).

(156) NATIONAL FEDERATION OF SCIENCE ABSTRACTING AND INDEXING SERVICES. Annual meeting 1971 digest, Washington, D.C., February 22-24, 1971. National Federation of Science Abstracting and Indexing Services, Philadelphia, Pennsylvania, 1971, 52 p.

(157) NATIONAL FEDERATION OF SCIENCE ABSTRACTING AND INDEXING SERVICES. Data element definitions for secondary services. National Federation of Science Abstracting and Indexing Services, Philadelphia, Pennsylvania, June 1971, 10 p. (Report no. 3).

(158) NATIONAL FEDERATION OF SCIENCE ABSTRACTING AND INDEXING SERVICES. News from Science Abstracting and Indexing Services, 13:2 (April 1971).

(159) NATIONAL FEDERATION OF SCIENCE ABSTRACTING AND INDEXING SERVICES. News from Science Abstracting and Indexing Services, 13:4 (August 1971).

(160) NATIONAL FEDERATION OF SCIENCE ABSTRACTING AND INDEXING SERVICES. News from Science Abstracting and Indexing Services, 13:6 (December 1971).

(161) NATIONAL TECHNOLOGICAL LIBRARY OF DENMARK. DOCUMENTATION DEPARTMENT. Guide to computerized information retrieval, COMPENDEX, computerized engineering index. National Technological Library of Denmark, November 1970, 14 p.

(162) NATIONAL TECHNOLOGICAL LIBRARY OF DENMARK. DOCUMENTATION DEPARTMENT. Instructions in the use of the chemical data bases: chemical titles and chemical abstracts condensates. National Technological Library of Denmark, 1971, 17 p.

(163) NELINET grants from CLR. CHANNEL—The Newsletter of the New England Library Information Network, 1:5 (November 1971) 1-2.

(164) NETHERLANDS ORGANIZATION FOR CHEMICAL INFORMATION. We perform in seconds what would cost you hours. The Royal Netherlands Chemical Society, Netherlands Organization for Chemical Information, The Hague, The Netherlands, n.d., 4 p. (Pamphlet).

(165) New England Board of Higher Education. Machine-Readable Data Bases. CHANNEL—The Newsletter of the New England Library Information Network, 1:3 (September 1971) 1.
(166) NEW ENGLAND RESEARCH APPLICATION CENTER. What is NERAC? University of Connecticut, Storrs, Connecticut, 1971, 35 p.
(167) NORTH AMERICAN ROCKWELL CORPORATION. Technical information processing system. North American Rockwell Corporation, Anaheim, California, 1970, 47 p.
(168) NORTH CAROLINA SCIENCE AND TECHNOLOGY RESEARCH CENTER. Annual report on a regional technology transfer program. North Carolina Science and Technology Research Center, Research Triangle Park, North Carolina, 1 September 1969-31 October 1970, 76 p.
(169) NUGENT, WILLIAM R. The U.S. Patent Office data base: a full text communications format for computer-aided classification, retrieval, and examination of patents. In: American Society for Information Science. Annual meeting. 34th, Denver, Colorado, 7-11 November 1971. Proceedings, vol. 8: Communication for decision-makers. Greenwood Publishing Corporation, Westport, Connecticut, 1971, 179-184.
(170) OFFICE FOR SCIENTIFIC AND TECHNICAL INFORMATION. Current Grants. Office for Scientific and Technological Information, London, England, September 1971, 5 p.
(171) OFFICE FOR SCIENTIFIC AND TECHNICAL INFORMATION. OSTI Newsletters: 1971-1 (March); 1971-2 (June); 1971-3 (September); 1971-4 (December). Office for Scientific and Technical Information, London, England, 1971.
(172) ONDERISIN, ELAINE M. The least common bigram: a dictionary arrangement technique for computerized natural-language text searching. IIT Research Institute, Chicago, Illinois, March 1971, 18 p.
(173) ORGANISATION FOR ECONOMIC CO-OPERATION AND DEVELOPMENT. Information activities of major international organisations. Organisation for Economic Co-operation and Development, Directorate for Scientific Affairs, Paris, France, 1971, 175 p. (Addendum-I, October 1971, 7 p.).
(174) ORGANISATION FOR ECONOMIC CO-OPERATION AND DEVELOPMENT. Inventory of major information systems and services in science and technology. Organisation for Economic Co-operation and Development, Paris, France, 1971, 350 p. (ED 051 839).
(175) PAISLEY, WILLIAM J. Improving a field-based "ERIC-like" information system. Journal of the American Society for Information Science, 22:6 (November/December 1971) 399-408.
(176) PALMER, DAVID C. Planning for a nationwide system of library statistics. American Library Association, Chicago, Illinois, May 1970, 110 p. (Available from the Superintendent of Documents, U.S. Government Printing Office, Washington, D.C., GPO HE 5.215:15070).
(177) PARK, MARGARET K. Development of an on-line computer system for management of search profiles. Presented at the Association of Scientific Information Dissemination Centers meeting, Rochester, New York, 23 September 1970.
(178) PARK, MARGARET K.; GIBSON, JOHN A. Operational experience of an information dissemination center for computer-based bibliographic text services. Presented at American Society for Engineering Education, Annual Meeting, U.S. Naval Academy, Annapolis, Maryland, 21-24 June 1971, 19 p.
(179) PARKER, EDWIN B. Stanford Public Information Retrieval System: 1970-71 annual report to the National Science Foundation. Stanford University, Institute for Communication Research, Palo Alto, California, December 1971, 14 p. plus appendices.
(180) PARKINS, PHYLLIS V.; KENNEDY, H. E. Secondary information services. In: Cuadra, Carlos A.; ed. Annual review of information science and technology, vol. 6. Encyclopaedia Britannica, Chicago, Illinois, 1971, 247-275.

(181) PARSONS, RONALD G. An adaptation of the AIP "Searchable Physics Information Notices" for use on CDC 6000 series computers. University of Texas, Center for Particle Theory, Austin, Texas, September 1971, 17 p. (CPT-118).

(182) PELZER, CHARLES W. The International Nuclear Information System. Presented at the 45th Annual Conference of Aslib, Darmstadt, Federal Republic of Germany, October 1971. International Atomic Energy Agency, Vienna, Austria, 1971, 20 p.

(183) PFLUEGER, MARGARET L. Management information obtained from bibliographic data. In: American Society for Information Science. Annual meeting. 34th, Denver, Colorado, 7-11 November 1971. Proceedings, vol. 8: Communication for decision-makers. Greenwood Publishing Corporation, Westport, Connecticut, 1971, 355-361.

(184) PHARMACEUTICAL MANUFACTURERS ASSOCIATION. Second computer based information service now available from PMA. Pharmaceutical Manufacturers Association, Washington, D.C., 1971, 4 p.

(185) PITTSBURGH, UNIVERSITY OF. Knowledge availability systems center: information services of the KAS Center—A NASA regional dissemination center. University of Pittsburgh, Pittsburgh, Pennsylvania, n.d. (Brochure).

(186) PORTER, ROGER J.; PENRY, J. KIFFIN; CAPONIO, JOSEPH R. Epilepsy abstracts retrieval system (EARS); a new concept for medical literature storage and retrieval. Bulletin of the Medical Library Association, 59:3 (July 1971) 430-432.

(187) PRESTON TECHNICAL ABSTRACTS COMPANY. Computer-based NMR literature retrieval system. Preston Technical Abstracts Company, October 1970, 6 p. (Pamphlet).

(188) PRESTON TECHNICAL ABSTRACTS COMPANY. Computerized information retrieval system of the gas chromatography literature. Bulletin 15A. Preston Technical Abstracts Company, 1971.

(189) PRINCETON MICROFILM CORPORATION. Technical document retrieval system. Princeton Microfilm Corporation, Princeton, New Jersey, November 1971, 29 p.

(190) Research information program. CHANNEL—The Newsletter of the New England Library Information Network, 2:1 (January 1972) 3.

(191) RISTOW, WALTER W.; CARRINGTON, DAVID K. Machine-readable map cataloging in the Library of Congress. Special Libraries, 62:9 (September 1971) 343-352.

(192) ROWLETT, RUSSEL J., JR.; TATE, FRED A. A computer-based system for handling chemical nomenclature and structural representations. Presented to the XXIII Conference of the International Union of Pure and Applied Chemistry in Boston, Massachusetts, July 1971, 10 p.

(193) RUBINSTEIN, RICHARD I.; QAZI, ARLENE. Alternatives to searching semantic surrogates of chemical structures. Presented at the Middle Atlantic Regional Meeting, ACS, Baltimore, Maryland, 5 February 1971. Journal of Chemical Documentation, 11:2 (1971) 110-115.

(194) RUFSVOLD, MARGARET I.; GUSS, CAROLYN. Software: bibliographic control and the NICEM Indexes. School Libraries, 20:2 (Winter 1971) 11-20.

(195) SALTON, GERARD. The SMART retrieval system experiments in automatic document processing. Prentice-Hall, Inc., Englewood Cliffs, New Jersey, 1971, 547 p.

(196) SAMUELSON, KJELL. Coordination of diversified data-bases and information networks through multiclassificatory concept notation in relay-switches and referral-directories. In: International Federation for Documentation (FID), Central Classification Committee (CCC), Classification Research (CR), Operational Machine Techniques and Systems (OM), Theory of Machine Techniques and Systems (TM), Seminar, 2d, Frankfurt, Germany, 1-5 June 1970. Proceedings. 11 p.

(197) SAMUELSON, KJELL. Relay-switches and referral directories for international data-bases and information networks. Presented at the FID/CCC-CR-TM Conference in Hercegnovi, Yugoslavia, 27 June-1 July 1971, 11 p.
(198) SCHEFFLER, FREDERIC L.; MARCH, JACQUELINE F. Evaluation of the selective dissemination of information (SDI) program for the Aerospace Materials Information Center. University of Dayton, Research Institute, Dayton, Ohio, March 1971, 88 p. (AFML-TR-71-11. ED 050 775).
(199) SCHIEBER, WILLIAM D.; THOMAS, GEORGE W. An algorithm for compaction of alphanumeric data. Journal of Library Automation, 4:4 (December 1971) 198-206.
(200) SCHIPMA, PETER B. Term fragment analysis for inversion of large files. IIT Research Institute, Chicago, Illinois, 4 June 1971, 16 p.
(201) SCHIPMA, PETER B.; WILLIAMS, MARTHA E.; SHAFTON, ALLAN L. Comparison of document data bases. Journal of the American Society for Information Science, 22:5 (September/October 1971) 326-332.
(202) SCHULTZ, LOUISE. Measuring the requirements for exchange of toxicology information. Presented at the Division of Chemical Literature, American Chemical Society Meeting, Los Angeles, California, 30 March 1971, 18 p.
(203) SCHUTZSACK, UDO. Trends of mechanized documentation in food science and nutrition in the Federal Republic of Germany. In: International Congress of Food Science and Technology. 3d, Washington, D.C., 9-14 August 1970. Proceedings. Institute of Food Technologists, Chicago, Illinois, 1970, 111-116.
(204) SCOTT, E. J.; TOWNLEY, H. M.; STERN, B. T. A technique for the evaluation of a commercial information service and some preliminary results from the DRUGDOC Service of the Excerpta Medica Foundation. Information Storage and Retrieval, 7:4 (November 1971) 149-165.
(205) SCOTT, RALPH L.; ASLESON, ROBERT F. Critique and rejoiner. Wilson Library Bulletin, 46:1 (September 1971) 73-77.
(206) SESSIONS, VIVIAN S.; SLOAN, LYNDA W. Urbandoc/a bibliographic information system. Vol. 1: demonstration report. The City University of New York, New York, 1971, 166 p. (URBANDOC-71-1. ED 051 821).
(207) SESSIONS, VIVIAN S.; SLOAN, LYNDA W. Urbandoc/a bibliographic information system. Vol. 2: technical supplement 1/general manual. The City University of New York, New York, 1971, 208 p. (URBANDOC-71-2. ED 051 822).
(208) SESSIONS, VIVIAN S.; SLOAN, LYNDA W. Urbandoc/a bibliographic information system. Vol. 3: technical supplement 2/operations manual. The City University of New York, New York, 1971, 243 p. (URBANDOC-71-3. ED 051 823).
(209) SHOFFNER, RALPH M. Catalog supplement project report to the Library Council. University of California, Berkeley, California, 11 November 1971, 36 p.
(210) SHOFFNER, RALPH M. Some implications of automatic recognition of bibliographic elements. Journal of the American Society for Information Science, 22:4 (July/August 1971) 275-282.
(211) SHOFFNER, RALPH M.; CUNNINGHAM, JAY L.; HUMPHREY, ALLAN J. Catalog supplement project report to the Library Council. University of California, Berkeley, California, 23 April 1971, 45 p.
(212) SHIRLEY INSTITUTE. Specialized textile information service; format for data base. Shirley Institute, Manchester, England, April 1971, 7 p. (Provisional outline).
(213) SMITH, D. R.; BEAUCHAMP, R. O., JR.; GARBER, J. L.; DOUGHERTY, M. A. Computerized drug information services. Paper presented at a meeting of the Pharmaceutical Manufacturers Association, Washington, D.C., March 1971.
(214) STANDERA, OLDRICH R. COMPENDEX profile adjustment manual. Information Retrieval Research Council of Alberta, Edmonton, Alberta, Canada, November 1970, 24 p.

(215) STANDERA, OLDRICH R. COMPENDEX profiling guide. The University of Calgary, Information Systems and Services Division, Calgary, Alberta, Canada, June 1971, 33 p.

(216) STANDERA, OLDRICH R. COMPENDEX/Text-Pac retrospective search. The University of Calgary, Information Systems and Services Division, Data Centre, Calgary, Alberta, Canada, May 1971, 62 p. (Report no. 9).

(217) STANDERA, OLDRICH R. Text-Pac input, bulletin and indexes. The University of Calgary, Information Systems and Services Division, Calgary, Alberta, Canada, January 1971, 22 p.

(218) STOCKARD, JOAN. Selective survey of MARC literature. Library Resources & Technical Services, 15:3 (Summer 1971) 279-289.

(219) STURDIVANT, CLARENCE A. Use of commercially available machine-readable bibliographic files in petroleum research. In: American Society for Information Science. Annual meeting. 34th, Denver, Colorado, 7-11 November 1971. Proceedings, vol. 8: Communication for decision-makers. Greenwood Publishing Corporation, Westport, Connecticut, 1971, 125-127.

(220) SYSTEM DEVELOPMENT CORPORATION. SDC/ERIC. An educational information search service. 1971. (Advertising brochure).

(221) System 50 for state statutes—the nation's largest full-text data bank. Aspen Systems Magazine, 1:2 (1970). 7 p. (Aspen Systems Corp., Pittsburgh, Pennsylvania).

(222) TELL, BJORN V. Retrieval efficiency from titles and the cost of indexing. Information Storage and Retrieval, 7:5 (December 1971) 241-243.

(223) TELL, BJORN V. SDI—selective dissemination of information. Libri, 21:1-3 (1971) 193-199.

(224) TELL, BJORN V.; FRODERSTROM, STIG. Computerized information system for design engineering: experiences with SDI and standard profiles in Sweden. In: Information Systems for Designers, University of Southampton, Southampton, England, 1971, 11 p. (Paper 10).

(225) THIEL, L. H.; HEAPS, H. S. Program design for retrospective searches on large data bases. Presented at Third Cranfield International Conference on Mechanized Information Storage and Retrieval Systems, July 1971, 38 p.

(226) THOMPSON, G. K. Some cost estimates for bibliographical searching in a large-scale social sciences information system. Presented at the Second International Conference on Mechanized Information Storage and Retrieval Systems, Cranfield, England, 2-5 September 1969. Information Storage and Retrieval, 6 (1970) 179-186.

(227) THOMPSON, G. K.; SCHIEBER, W. D. Computerized information systems and development assistance. In: Industrial Research and Development News, 3., 1970, 1-5 (ID/SER.B/13).

(228) TOUSIGNAUT, DWIGHT R. A new era for IPA. International Pharmaceutical Abstracts, 7:1 (15 January 1970) 3. (Editorial).

(229) TULSA, UNIVERSITY OF. INFORMATION SERVICES DEPARTMENT. Petroleum information storage & retrieval services, indexes and search tapes to petroleum abstracts. University of Tulsa, Information Services Department, Tulsa, Oklahoma, January 1972, 12 p.

(230) Tune in to NASA's technology transfer program and profit. Plastics World, (December 1970).

(231) UNITED KINGDOM CHEMICAL INFORMATION SERVICE. Computer-based services: general descriptions. United Kingdom Chemical Information Service, The University, Nottingham, England, March 1971, 17 p.

(232) UNITED NATIONS EDUCATIONAL, SCIENTIFIC AND CULTURAL ORGANIZATION; INTERNATIONAL COUNCIL OF SCIENTIFIC UNIONS. UNISIST: synopsis of the feasibility study on a world science information system. United Nations Educational, Scientific and Cultural Organization; International Council of Scientific Unions, Paris, France, 1971, 90 p.

(233) U.S. DEPARTMENT OF THE AIR FORCE. OFFICE OF THE JUDGE ADVOCATE GENERAL. The LITE (Legal Information Thru Electronics) system. U.S. Department of the Air Force, Denver, Colorado, 1 March 1971, 19 p.

(234) U.S. FOOD AND DRUG ADMINISTRATION. The origin, development and application of the National Drug Code. Presented at the Annual Meeting of the American Pharmaceutical Association, Montreal, Quebec, Canada, 19 May 1969, 5 p.

(235) U.S. LIBRARY OF CONGRESS. MARC DEVELOPMENT OFFICE. Books: a MARC format, specifications for magnetic tapes containing monographic catalog records in the MARC-II format, 5th ed. U.S. Library of Congress, Washington, D.C., 106 p. (In press).

(236) U.S. LIBRARY OF CONGRESS. MARC DEVELOPMENT OFFICE. Films: a MARC format. Specifications for magnetic tapes containing catalog records for motion pictures, filmstrips, and other pictorial media intended for projection. U.S. Library of Congress, Washington, D.C., 1970, 66 p. (Available from the U.S. Government Printing Office, Washington, D.C.).

(237) U.S. LIBRARY OF CONGRESS. MARC DEVELOPMENT OFFICE. Information on the MARC system, 2d ed. U.S. Library of Congress, Washington, D.C., 1972, 31 p.

(238) U.S. LIBRARY OF CONGRESS. MARC DEVELOPMENT OFFICE. Serials: a MARC format. Addendum number 1. U.S. Library of Congress, Washington, D.C., 1971, 31 p. (Available from the U.S. Government Printing Office, Washington, D.C.).

(239) U.S. NATIONAL INSTITUTES OF HEALTH. NATIONAL INSTITUTE OF NEUROLOGICAL DISEASES AND STROKE. Parkinson Information Center final progress report: 1 January 1970 - 30 September 1970. U.S. National Institutes of Health, National Institute of Neurological Diseases and Stroke, Bethesda, Maryland, 1970, 35 p.

(240) U.S. NATIONAL INSTITUTES OF HEALTH. NATIONAL LIBRARY OF MEDICINE. Guide to MEDLARS services: a brief description of the system with emphasis on the automated bibliographic search service. U.S. National Institutes of Health, National Library of Medicine, Bethesda, Maryland, 1971, 22 p. (DHEW publication no. (NIH) 72-225. Revised August 1971).

(241) U.S. NATIONAL INSTITUTES OF HEALTH. NATIONAL LIBRARY OF MEDICINE. Medline: National Library of Medicine fact sheet. U.S. National Institutes of Health, National Library of Medicine, Bethesda, Maryland, January 1972.

(242) U.S. NATIONAL INSTITUTES OF HEALTH. NATIONAL LIBRARY OF MEDICINE. The principles of MEDLARS. U.S. National Institutes of Health, National Library of Medicine, Bethesda, Maryland, 1970, 77 p. (Available from the U.S. Government Printing Office, Washington, D.C.).

(243) U.S. NATIONAL SCIENCE FOUNDATION. OFFICE OF SCIENCE INFORMATION SERVICES. Research and university information systems program: Lehigh University. U.S. National Science Foundation, Office of Science Information Services, Washington, D.C., August 1971, 2 p.

(244) U.S. NATIONAL SCIENCE FOUNDATION. OFFICE OF SCIENCE INFORMATION SERVICES. Research and university information systems program: Ohio State University. U.S. National Science Foundation, Office of Science Information Services, Washington, D.C., November 1970, 2 p.

(245) U.S. NATIONAL SCIENCE FOUNDATION. OFFICE OF SCIENCE INFORMATION SERVICES. Research and university information systems program: University of California at Los Angeles. U.S. National Science Foundation, Office of Science Information Services, Washington, D.C., January 1971, 2 p.

(246) U.S. NATIONAL SCIENCE FOUNDATION. OFFICE OF SCIENCE INFORMATION SERVICES. Research and university information systems program: University of Pittsburgh. U.S. National Science Foundation, Office of Science Information Services, Washington, D.C., December 1970, 2 p.

(247) U.S. SMITHSONIAN INSTITUTION. SCIENCE INFORMATION EXCHANGE. A national collection of current research information. U.S. Smithsonian Institution, Science Information Exchange, Washington, D.C., February 1971, 13 p.

(248) VALLEE, J. F.; HYNEK, J. A.; RAY, G. R.; WOLF, P. The organization of research data banks. In: American Society for Information Science. Annual meeting. 34th, Denver, Colorado, 7-11 November 1971. Proceedings, vol. 8: Communication for decision-makers. Greenwood Publishing Corporation, Westport, Connecticut, 1971, 387-394.

(249) VAN DYKE, VERN J.; AYER, NANCY L. Interactive systems approach to sophisticated batch processing: multipurpose cataloging and indexing system (CAIN). U.S. Department of Agriculture, National Agricultural Library, Beltsville, Maryland, 1971, 16 p.

(250) WALKER, GORDON L. Bibliographic data tapes. American Mathematical Society, Providence, Rhode Island, September 1971.

(251) WASSERMAN, PAUL; DANIEL, EVELYN; LOGAN, KAY; eds. Library and information science today. Science Associates/International, Inc., New York, New York, 1971, 397 p.

(252) WEINSTOCK, MELVIN. Availability, sources terms and conditions of lease, and copyright aspects of major machine readable bibliographic data files. Paper presented at the Colloquium on Machine-Readable Bibliographic Data Bases: their Creation and Use. State University of New York, School of Library Science, Albany, New York, 20-21 April 1971, 19 p.

(253) WEINSTOCK, MELVIN. Citation indexes. In: Encyclopedia of library and information science, vol. 5. Marcel Dekker, New York, 1971, 16-40.

(254) WENTE, VAN A. NASA/RECON and user interface considerations. Presented at the AFIPS Information Systems Committee Workshop on the User Interface for Interactive Search of Bibliographic Data Bases, San Jose, California, 14-15 January 1971, 15 p.

(255) WENTE, VAN A.; YOUNG, GIFFORD A. Current awareness and dissemination. In: Cuadra, Carlos A.; ed. Annual review of information science and technology, vol. 5. Encyclopaedia Britannica, Chicago, Illinois, 1970, 259-295.

(256) WESTERN RESEARCH APPLICATIONS CENTER. Technology intelligence for business, industry and government. University of Southern California, Los Angeles, California, 1971, 4 p. (Brochure).

(257) WILLIAMS, JOHN H., JR. An iterative browsing technique. Annual progress report (March 1, 1970—February 28, 1971). International Business Machines Corp., Federal Systems Div., Gaithersburg, Maryland, April 1971, 30 p. (AD 722 672).

(258) WILLIAMS, MARTHA E. Cooperative data management for information centers. Presented at joint meeting, Association of Scientific Information Processing Centers, National Federation of Science Abstracting and Indexing Services, Washington, D.C., 24 February 1971.

(259) WILLIAMS, MARTHA E. Experiences of IIT Research Institute in operating a computerized retrieval system for searching a variety of data bases. Presented at the Third Cranfield International Conference on Mechanized Information Storage and Retrieval Systems, Cranfield, England, 21 July 1971.

(260) WILLIAMS, MARTHA E. Handling of varied data bases in an information center environment. Presented at the Conference on Computers in Chemical Education and Research, Northern Illinois University, DeKalb, Illinois, 23 July 1971, 22 p.

(261) WILLIAMS, MARTHA E. Use of machine-readable data bases by scientists and engineers. American Society for Engineering Education. Annual meeting, 21-24 June 1971, U.S. Naval Academy, Annapolis, Maryland, 1971.

(262) WOLLMANN, P.; COHEN, Y. An information system with automated data processing files. Presented at the International Conference on Information Science, Tel Aviv, Israel, 29 August—3 September 1971, 5 p.

(263) WOLTERS, PETER H.; BROWN, JACK E. CAN/SDI system: user reaction to a computerized information retrieval system for Canadian scientists and technologists. Canadian Library Journal, 28:1 (January/February 1971) 20-23.

(264) WOOD, JAMES L.; FLANAGAN, CAROLYN; KENNEDY, H. E. The Biosis/CAS/Ei overlap in monitored journals. In: American Society for Information Science. Annual meeting, 34th, Denver, Colorado, 7-11 November 1971. Proceedings, vol. 8: Communication for decision-makers. Greenwood Publishing Corporation, Westport, Connecticut, 1971, 237.

(265) WOODS, BILL M. Design and development of a transdisciplinary engineering information program. Presented at the Third Cranfield International Conference on Mechanised Information Storage and Retrieval Systems, Cranfield, England, 20 July 1971, 25 p.

(266) WORK, ROBERT W.; PHILLIPS, DENNIS M. A study of textile information systems. Final report. North Carolina State University, Raleigh, North Carolina, June 1970, 40 p. (ED 049 794).

(267) XEROX. DATRIX, direct access to reference information. University Microfilms, Ann Arbor, Michigan. (Advertising brochure).

(268) XEROX EDUCATION GROUP. Selective dissemination of information—Xerox (SDI-X). Xerox Education Group, Stamford, Connecticut, 8 p. (Advertising brochure).

10 Document Retrieval and Dissemination Systems

WESLEY T. BRANDHORST
ERIC Processing and Reference Facility (LEASCO)
and
PHILIP F. ECKERT
NASA Scientific and Technical Information Facility (INFORMATICS TISCO)

Owen Glendower: "I can call spirits from the vasty deep."
Hotspur: "Why, so can I, or so can any man;
But will they come when you do call for them?"

Henry IV, Part I; Act III: Sc. 1

INTRODUCTION

Definitions/Terminology

The following definitions will be used:

Document Retrieval—the searching of a collection of documents (or document surrogates) in response to a question, and the detection of relevant documents (or references to documents) that either answer the question in themselves or that can be further scanned to determine the answer. Synonymous with "Reference Retrieval." To be distinguished from systems designed to retrieve directly useful data, i.e., data retrieval, fact retrieval, question-answering systems, and from systems for the actual physical storage, compaction, shelving, fetching, copying, or transmitting of entire documents.

Document Dissemination—the delivery of documents (or document surrogates such as references) to the information consumer. This may be in response to a specific inquiry/question/profile or it may be in response to general user interest in a given area (as in the form of an abstract journal). The physical form employed by the dissemination technique may vary considerably.

There is little that is new in these definitions. They follow closely in the footsteps of predecessor ARIST chapters. The concepts of document retrieval and document dissemination are obviously closely related. Retrieval is usually performed in order to disseminate. It is possible to discuss retrieval in the abstract quite apart from what may come after; however, in the real world of operational information systems, retrieval is not performed for its own sake but always in response to a need or as a prelude to some form of dissemination of the "answer." Whereas dissemination invariably follows retrieval, it can also take place independently. Document data may be captured, stored, manipulated, and promulgated *en masse* in the form of a secondary publication covering a period of time, without any retrieval operations *per se* being employed. The usual situation, however, and the one focused on in this chapter, is to find retrieval and dissemination closely intertwined in an information system.

Scope and Coverage

Predecessor chapters have generally emphasized techniques at the expense of applications in specific situations. Insofar as this chapter appears under the major heading "Applications," however, material dealing with the application of document retrieval to a particular field or environment has not been excluded simply because it does not include a new technique. On the other hand, papers on retrieval theory or strategies in the abstract have not been neglected. Likewise, current issues and trends in retrieval or dissemination, as exemplified in the community as a whole, are covered, even though some are not embodied in the literature of specific systems. This chapter emphasizes computerized techniques for searching for documents with certain attributes. Noncomputer retrieval techniques (i.e., Uniterm cards, edge-notched cards, optical coincidence techniques, microform search and display methods) have never been accorded more than cursory treatment in the past and are not covered here. The reader interested in manual systems is referred to a new text by Jahoda (80) intended for the researcher in any subject field "who desires to improve the index to his document collection or start an index. . .but does not quite know how to go about it." It is the major publication of the year dealing with manual document retrieval systems.

Dissemination as a separate endeavor was not well covered in the literature this year and this is reflected in the chapter. The best (and nearly the only) report concentrating on this topic is Weil's (232) state-of-the-art review ofdocument access and delivery. He is undoubtedly correct in asserting that alerting and retrieval systems generally ignore this more mundane problem. Lastly, it is emphasized that this chapter is very much a review of the literature that appeared during the year and makes no attempt to cover existing document retrieval systems comprehensively.

Relation to Other Chapters

As is usually the case, several other chapters in this year's volume deal with topics closely related to the subject of this chapter. The principal interconnections are with the chapters on "Document Description and Representation," "File Organization, Maintenance, and Search," "User Interface in Interactive Systems," and "Conversion and Use of Machine-Readable Data Bases." Similarly, there are five ARIST chapters in previous volumes that can be identified as direct predecessors of the "Document Retrieval and Dissemination" topic. For the convenience of the reader, these are listed by the year covered, as follows: 1967—Brown & Jones (21); 1968—Berul (17), Landau (107); 1969—Wente & Young (236); 1970—Magnino (122).

Organization

This chapter is organized into four sections. The introduction defines the terms used in the chapter title, outlines the scope and coverage of the chapter, and identifies the relation to other chapters in this same volume and to equivalent chapters in earlier volumes. The second section deals with the major trends and directions identified by authors or discernible in the literature. The third section is divided into two main parts: a treatment of the literature by some major topics, e.g., reference works, data bases, software packages, search strategies, and evaluation; and a tabular treatment of specific operational and experimental systems, subdivided in what has almost become a traditional way: Government, Industry, Academic/Professional/Nonprofit. There is a brief Conclusion section. The attempt throughout has been to let the natural organization of the literature organize the chapter.

CURRENT ISSUES AND TRENDS

Historical Analyses and Forecasts

Several authors made significant attempts during 1971 either to identify the trends now influencing us or to look into the future. Cuadra (38), commenting on the future of on-line systems, makes the point, clearly verifiable in the literature, that the desirable features of on-line retrieval interfaces are only now being defined and tested in a systematic way; i.e., we are only just getting down to serious and scientific efforts to human engineer for user acceptance of these systems. He identifies the major national challenge of the next few years in this area to be the avoidance or limitation of wasteful and expensive duplication in providing nationwide search access to the hundreds of public and private data bases that will become available.

Ebersole (42) covers a broad range of subjects including general time-sharing technology and micropublishing. He spends some time, however, on the "ideal" search system and provides a good example of the greater acceptance amongst professionals of both natural-language-based approaches and automatic, algorithmic, and heuristic processes. Ebersole believes that the increasing success of these approaches may presage a decline in the importance of thesauri and manual indexing. At the same time, he makes a key point that can be found in the work of several authors this year: a thesaurus may be as essential for natural-language-based systems as it is for manually indexed systems and maybe even more so. Such a thesaurus would be internal to the computer, rather than external, and would be used for synonym control and the automatic mapping of terms; it would improve recall, now one of the weakest features of natural language systems, and would reduce inverted file size, a major problem with really large natural-language data bases.

Harmon (62) has prepared a fascinating think-piece on the evolution of information science. He pinpoints the year 1957 as the midpoint of a shift of attention from manual to computer-based retrieval systems. He sees information/document retrieval as an "important tributary" which, with other streams, gave birth to modern information science. He believes that a period of unified but confused growth is drawing to a close, suggesting an end to the era of the generalist in information science. He estimates that in the early 1970's information science will achieve completeness as a disciplinary system. He predicts state of relative maturity for the discipline, with pronounced specialization in its ranks, in approximately 20 years (1990).

Rolling (162) identifies present trends in several areas and, by extrapolation, establishes a model of an optimal information system for 1975. In software he sees a mushrooming development of specialized software by organizations independent of the computer manufacturers. Software packages will be prepared for groups of users representing similar interests. Rolling also subscribes to the idea that the amount of terminology control must increase with the degree of automation; i.e., automatic indexing makes it imperative to identify large array of word forms, including prefixes, suffixes, and truncations. Thesauri will continue to develop but after a few years a limited number of authoritative and compatible thesauri will emerge. He does not think automatic indexing will replace manual indexing unless abstracts are already available in machine-readable form as a by-product of publication. Retrieval strategies will benefit from a variety of new techniques: relevance feedback, wherein a query is automatically reformulated and rerun after a complete or partial relevance assessment by the user of the items retrieved on a first run; clustering of documents into "super-documents" on the basis of the presence of associated terms or term combinations, thereby reducing computer search time and cost, and improving relevance; application of the so-called "bit-screen" technique, where every term is identified by a single bit in a given position of the store, allowing strong compression of the file.

Salton (164) goes so far as to say "The current retrieval systems exhibit so many shortcomings that present operations are not likely to be maintained for long." He foresees the following as necessary future standard features: (1) exhaustive automatic indexing; (2) ranked search output; (3) truly fast response times (hinging on clustered files); (4) interactive retrieval operations (of the relevance feedback type); and (5) dynamic file organization, accommodating changes in document indexing and classification over time.

Sharp (190) finds the question of whether we shall in the future be using controlled or free languages in retrieval systems to be one of the most fundamental issues facing us today. In a year that showed a slight resurgence of interest in classification for retrieval purposes, Sharp was one of the few suggesting that we should abandon attempts at sophisticated classifications. He finds that on-line systems, designed for limited fields, and to be handled directly by the seachers themselves, are clearly the way of the future.

Subjects Emphasized in the Year's Literature

The literature of 1971, unavailable for the most part to the authors referred to above at the time they wrote, supports many of their claims but goes beyond them in the number and variety of detectable trends. After each of the paragraphs that follow are listed the most important works supporting and exemplifying the observation.

Information science as an emergent discipline. There is a definite feeling circulating that the field is beginning to coalesce, to acquire an identity. There is an active search for clear definition of this identity to combat the loss of effectiveness that goes with a hazy self-image. Though research directions appear to be cloudy, we nevertheless are seeing better and better scientific work and more of the quantification that necessarily goes with such work (Elias, 44; Harmon, 62; Saracevic, 171).

On-line interactive systems. Batch systems appear to have reached a plateau of effectiveness. Potential for dramatic improvement seems to lie in the direction of closed-loop systems providing immediate iterations based on user reactions to computer activity and feedback to the programs. New search strategies are possible in such an environment (Cuadra, 38; Ebersole, 42; McAllister & Bell, 116; Salton, 166, 168; Williams, 237, 238; Wolfe, 244).

Natural text approaches. If the 60's saw the peak of thesaurus activity, the 70's are likely to see the peak of natural-text processing by computer, even though as yet the techniques are far from perfected and the results far from satisfactory. Data bases built up primarily for publication purposes form ready-made reservoirs of natural text to be addressed from the retrieval point of view (Barker et al., 12; Choueka et al., 25; Corbett, 31; IBM, 77; Klingbiel 93, 94; Negus, 140; Nugent, 142; Parker, 148; Salton, 168; Tell et al., 205; Townley, 209; Woods, 247).

Automatic processes (let-the-computer-do-it). There appears to be an ever-increasing tendency to let George (the computer) do it. As the activities are better understood and better reduced to formalisms, the frailties of human manipulation are exposed. People are simply more *willing* to let the computer do it. This holds both for input (automatic indexing) and for output ("more-of-the-same" techniques, generally known as relevance feedback) (Barker et al., 13; Borbash, 18; Counts, 33; Klingbiel, 94; Salton, 163, 166, 167, 168; Schiminovich, 176; Shapiro & Stermole 189; Vernimb, 223; Williams, 237, 238).

Human engineering. In the design of the initial on-line systems, the focus was on the system itself and its capabilities. The user was secondary. The instruction pattern tended to resemble the language used by programmers. We are finally seeing attention devoted to the user and his human and educational limitations. As on-line systems become more widespread, they must necessarily be designed for a broader spectrum of user (Cuadra, 38; Fried, 49; Katter et al., 86; McAllister & Bell, 116; Shapiro & Stermole, 189; Walker, 228; Wente, 235; Wolfe, 244).

Cost analyses. A sign of the times. With money scarce, staffing levels lean, and subsidization hard to come by, a new cost consciousness has arisen. There was already a move in this direction due to the frustration caused by lack of comparable cost data from system to system; the movement has been accelerated by the cooler economy. Budget cutbacks and cost benefit analyses both require development and examination of statements of priorities (Counts, 34; King & Bryant, 90; King & Caldwell, 91; Lancaster, 105; Lutz, 114; Olsen, 143; Price, 155). Also see Chapter 2 in this volume.

Information as a resource. There is a new realization that information is a resource, to be handled like any other, to be paid for like any other. The place of information in the society is being defined slowly but surely. The exact relationships that should obtain among libraries, information centers, information analysis centers, referral centers, national libraries, government data banks, and information industry companies are being worked out. Many public policies relating to information are being pushed actively toward resolution, e.g., copyright law revision, "fair use" copying, cable television, user charges, software patentability, government procurement practices (hardware, software, publishing of government data, etc.). The National Commission on Libraries and Information Science was established during the year (P L 91-345, July 20, 1971) with a broad mandate to identify and develop solutions for national informational needs and to advise the Government on the handling of information resources (Counts, 34; Ebersole, 42; Geise, 52; Rees, 159; UNESCO, 213, 212; Weil, 232).

Cooperation. The recognition that it is impossible to go it alone is widespread. Network operations are on the increase and plans for cooperation permeate the field. The ICSU/UNESCO feasibility study for a "World Science Information System," known as UNISIST, defines its subject "as a flexible network evolving from an extension of voluntary cooperation of existing and future services" (UNESCO, 212, 213). Examples of some cooperative ventures are: the International Nuclear Information System (INIS), (El-Hadidy, 43; IAEA, 75; Pelzer et al., 150; Woolston et al., 248); CAN/SDI, the national selective dissemination service offered by the Canadian National Science Library (Brown, 20; Mauerhoff, 126; Wolters & Brown, 245); the efforts of Stanford's BALLOTS (Bibliographic Automation of Large Library Operations using a Time-Shared System) to expand cooperatively in the San Francisco Bay area (Epstein et al., 45); and the French-German cancer research documentation collaboration, known as SABIR (Systeme Automatique de Bibliographie, d'Information et de Recherche) (Kohler & Wagner, 97; Sandor, 169).

Standards. A necessary concomitant of people working together is standards. This year we have seen final publication of the *American National Standard for Bibliographic Information Interchange on Magnetic Tape* (ANSI, 4); the draft *American National Standard Guidelines for Thesaurus Structure, Construction, and Use* (ANSI, 5); the UNESCO guidelines for monolingual thesauri (UNESCO, 211); the Aslib draft of standards for printed computer output (8); the NFSAIS suggestions for standard definitions of data elements and standard usage of these elements by secondary services in building citations for different types of literature (NFSAIS, 139); Nugent's (142) proposal for an international full-text communications format for patents; and the various Federal Information Processing Standards (FIPS) efforts (NBS, 218). The widespread recognition of the importance of standards is evident in the field in innumerable small ways.

Data base utilization. New data bases are being made available with regularity. Organizations planning publishing activities automatically plan for a by-product data base. For further discussion see the section of this chapter dealing with data bases in machine-readable form and see Chapter 9 in this volume. (ACS, 2; AIP, 3; APA, 6; Dollar, 40; Menkus, 129; NFSAIS, 139; Schipma et al., 179; Schultz, 183; Weinstock, 233).

File size. With increased activity in on-line systems, and with maturing data bases, a new urgency has come to file size problems (bearing on response times), file partitioning, file compression, and clustering of docments. Villers & Ruth, (226) provide an annotated bibliography of data compression and compaction literature. Thiel & Heaps (206) describe an experimental system involving ingenious coding techniques for automatic compression of both sequential files of accessions and inverted index files. All data are coded and compressed on entry and decoded and expanded upon output. Salton (166, 168), among many others, discusses the concept of a "clustered file" wherein items with similar content identifications are placed in the same groups or clusters. Then in a search, only a few groups of documents need to be examined. He also develops the concept of "document space modification," wherein document records on the file are actually altered on the basis of user activities, rendering them more similar to the queries that found them relevant and less similar to the queries that found them irrelevant, thereby improving clustering. (Johnson & Briggs, 82; Katcher, 85; Knott, 95; Mulford & Ridall, 137; Resnikoff & Dolby, 160; Rolling, 162; Salton, 164; Schieber & Thomas, 175; Thiel & Heaps, 206; Welch, 234).

Software transferability. Everybody used to build his own. Now everybody is interested in finding somebody else's package that can be made to work (deBoer, 39; Seiden, 186). One of many specific examples is the project of the New England Library Information Network (NELINET) to test the transferability of the Ohio College Library Center's (OCLC) computer-based bibliographic system to NELINET and to other groups of libraries (CLR News Release #320, January 7, 1972).

Classification. An interest in classification always seems to be there, not far below the surface, as a steady current. This year the same is true, although it may appear a little strange that an interest in classification should go along with such a strong interest in natural text. UNISIST (UNESCO, 212, 213) refers repeatedly to the Universal Decimal Classification (UDC) and a significant number of reports during 1971 dealt with UDC (Caless et al., 23; McCash & Carmichael, 121; Schneider, 181; Stueart, 202). Schneider (180) also provides an annotated bibliography of 26 papers related to the use of classifications in automated systems; Weeks et al. (231) provide a selected bibliography of 384 items dealing with UDC. The renewed interest in classification may be related to the "waning" of the thesaurus period and to the push toward international cooperation; classification moves easily across language barriers.

Search system growth and convergence. Search systems are getting more numerous, but they are also getting to be more alike. At the top level, the systems that are competing for the major on-line CRT efforts involving bibliographic data are boiling down to a handful. These few keep improving, adding features, and getting more alike in the process. Across the entire range of applications the number of search systems is increasing, but at the world-class level the real heavyweights are few in number and not increasing much. Attention is focusing on the few that can really deliver. Surveys are provided by Fong (47) and Seiden (186).

Library science. There are at least three separate trends of interest in this area: (1) Library automation activities, and certain concepts that have heretofore been identified more with information science than library science, are beginning to get together. An example is the use on library-generated files of a compressed "search code" for the unique identification of bibliographic entities (Long & Kilgour, 111; Long et al., 112; Newman & Buchinski, 141); (2) Librarians are increasingly worried about the response of their profession to the challenges of automation. Landau (106) accuses librarians of having "a love affair with the paper storage medium," and advises them for their own survival to become experts in "the organization, storage, retrieval, and use of information regardless of what storage medium and level of mechanization are applied to it"; (3) Library schools published extensively during the year and the evidence is that there is little danger that the new crop of graduates from these schools will fail to make use of the computer. The major examples of document retrieval work reported are the Syracuse University Psychological Abstracts Retrieval Service (SUPARS), an on-line free-text reference retrieval system (Cook et al., 28), and the University of California at Berkeley's REF-SEARCH, an on-line system for retrieving those reference works in which the user will have the greatest chance of finding the answer to his question (Meredith, 130). Other work is reported by Artandi & Struminger (7) from Rutgers and by Jahoda & Foos (81) from Florida State.

Legal issues. General copyright law revision (S.644, before Congress in late 1971), recognized by all to be needed, has been postponed this year again, as it has been for several years past. Copyrights due to expire at the end of 1970 were extended through 1971 by the Copyright Extension Bill (PL-91-555). Copyrights due to expire at the end of 1971 were extended by S. J. Res. 132, signed November 24, 1971. The Judiciary Committee Report on the resolution (H.Rept.92-605) states that revision has been delayed because of the cable television controversy. The now-famous *William & Wilkins* case, involving the publishing house versus the National Library of Medicine resulted in a Commissioner's report to the U.S. Court of Claims recommending that "the Court conclude as a matter of law that plaintiff is entitled to recover reasonable and entire compensation for infringement of copyright." This case is considered by many to be a crucial test of the judicial doctrine of "fair use" and the famous gentleman's agreement between the American Council of Learned Societies and the National Association of Book Publishers that came to be known as the "single copy doctrine." Should the judges follow the commissioner's report, it seems likely now that the case will go on appeal to the Supreme Court. The patentability of software is another question that is likely to be settled in the near future by the Supreme Court. Until 1969, the Patent Office followed a policy of rejecting applications for patents on computer programs. In 1970, in response to Court of Customs and Patent Appeals decisions, the Patent Office began issuing patents on computer programs. A key case, *Gottschalk vs. Benson and Tabbot* was the subject of a petition for *certiorari* filed by the U.S. Solicitor General on behalf of the Patent Commissioner. This is the only case of this kind to date in which accompanying hardware or machinery reflecting the "invention" was not included. The Information Industry Association has filed an *amicus* brief in the case urging the Court to make a decision. The IIA brief states, "A definite answer to the question of patentability of computer programs is needed to provide the business community more certainty in its transactions which involve and depend on the proprietary status of computer programs."

Search strategies. The single most discussed search strategy during the year was a technique known variously as "relevance feedback" or "pattern recognition." For further discussion of this technique and others, see the section of this chapter on Search Strategies. (Borbash, 18; Salton, 165; Stanfel, 199; Vernimb, 223; Wagoner, 227; Williams, 237, 238).

COMPUTERIZED DOCUMENT/REFERENCE RETRIEVAL AND DISSEMINATION SYSTEMS

Reference and General Works

In 1971 there is evidence that the formal publishing efflorescence associated with our emerging discipline is continuing. Kruzas & Schnitzer (101) produced the first edition (a second is being planned) of a directory (somewhat misnamed "encyclopedia") of information systems and services in the U. S. and Canada. "This publication. . .has selected. . .those organizations and services which are principally concerned with storage, retrieval, and dissemination of information, and in addition, are innovative, experimental, or non-conventional. A major emphasis is on computerization. . ." This is an excellent reference work. A total of 833 systems are presented alphabetically and described thoroughly, without stinting on space. The "SDI Systems" index entry lists 144 systems, 17% of the total systems described. Kent & Lancour (89) continue with their ambitious project to publish an 18-volume complete and authoritative conventional encyclopedia covering both theory and practice in the fields of library science and information science. Each volume contains about 100 subjects with 80-90 comprehensive articles containing extensive bibliographies. Volume 4, Canada-Clumps, was published in 1971 and contains articles on several topics relating to document retrieval, e.g., "Citation Indexes," by Melvin Weinstock.

Wasserman (229), with the help of the staff and students of the University of Maryland School of Library and Information Services, has produced a directory entitled LIST (*Library and Information Science*

Today). This work, subtitled "an international registry of research and innovation," is a direct descendant of the National Science Foundation's (NSF) now defunct *Current Research and Development in Scientific Documentation* (CRDSD). According to the Introduction, the focus is on ongoing research and "the most exciting, interesting, and prototypical work underway in the field." It lists a total of 820 different research efforts; 31 projects appear under the heading "Retrieval of Documents and Citations"; 35 projects appear under the heading "Dissemination of Information." This is a useful and well-indexed reference work in an area that has not seen a steady provider since NSF abandoned *CRDSD*. Current plans are to continue it on an annual basis.

In late 1970, a large book of original source readings in the field of information science, compiled and edited by Saracevic (171) at the Case Western Reserve School of Library Science, made its appearance. This work contains 65 basic readings that have appeared since 1950 in a variety of journals. Emphasis is on theory and experimentation rather than technology and practical applications. All the papers contain aspects of scientific generalization and the search for laws. No specific systems are described. The intent of the compiler was to provide an indication of the overall framework, structure, connections, and directions of the field of information science, as well as to provide an educational text for learning and teaching. The chapters entitled "Structure of Information Retrieval Systems"; "Question, Handling, and Search Procedures"; and "Dissemination" contain one important group's concepts of the major theoretical papers that support practical work in document retrieval and dissemination systems. Highlighting the strength of the search for historical perspectives, a second book of 19 original source readings was produced by ASIS in 1971, under the editorship of Elias (44). Selection was made by the ASIS Education Committee during 1968-1970. The original objective was to create "an introductory book of readings in information science" for the use of instructors. Additional criteria were that it be "relatively easy to read for beginning students" and "likely to be useful for a number of years." Unfortunately, the title "Key Papers," and the introduction which speaks of "classics of our field," establishes a second set of objectives in conflict with the desire to provide easy-reading introductions for students. The result is a mixed bag featuring some truly key papers such as Luhn's on automatic abstracting and Maron's on automatic indexing, and other, not-so-key, basic or definitional papers or reviews of prime topics.

A number of textbooks were published during the year. Jahoda (80) deals mainly with manual document retrieval systems for use by individual researchers. He treats this as primarily an indexing problem. A variety of indexes are discussed, including coordinate indexes, edge-notched cards, optical coincidence systems, citation indexes, etc. Kent (88) has reissued a textbook originally published in 1962 and again in 1966. Unfortunately the author does not advise the reader concerning what is new, old, unchanged, or rewritten since the previous editions. Kent maintains that "consideration of the computer has led to neglect of fundamentals." This reviewer would disagree with this contention. The explicitness required by the design of computer systems has forced us to look at our procedures and traditions critically and with the scales off our eyes for the first time in many cases. The computer has led to a reexamination of our fundamentals, not to a neglect. King & Bryant (90) offer an excellent distillation of the experience of Westat Research Inc. in the area of evaluation of information services. The book gives guidance in what to measure, how to measure, and how to interpret results. Meetham (128) presents a "popularized" text suitable for the nonspecialist interested in a quick introduction to information retrieval. It is kept simple and nontechnical, and color graphics abound. Price (155) provides a very meaty tutorial syllabus on the subject of collecting and reporting information system costs. There are a variety of real-life examples that will prove helpful for those faced with designing cost control and reporting systems. Salton (168) has edited a text containing 27 of the most important contributions from the SMART project since its inception through 1969. The text should be of greatest value as a reference volume for the professional practitioner working in the area of the design and operation of automatic information systems. Vickery (225) has prepared a text on the techniques of information retrieval that draws heavily on his own past work (four chapters have previously appeared in print) and expertise (bibliographic description and subject analysis, as opposed to computers). This is a book about practice rather than theory and it is heavily laced with sample and illustrative material, bespeaking its use in teaching.

The remaining reference material is of a less formally published nature. The Organisation for Economic Co-Operation and Development (145) has prepared an inventory of 126 "major" mechanized information systems in science and technology. Coverage is international and the social sciences are included. Fong (47) has produced a useful comparative feature analysis of eight major document processing systems: CIRCOL (IBM's DPS); DDC (prototype on-line system); ITIRC

(IBM's TEXT-PAC); Mead DATA CENTRAL; MEDLARS II; the New York Times Information Bank; ORBIT II; RECON/STIMS. The Association Française des Documentalistes et des Bibliothécaires Spécialises (10) has devoted an entire issue of the journal *Documentaliste* to a review of computerized documentation systems in France and French-speaking countries. Some of the systems covered are: SYDONI (Systeme de Documentation Notariale Informatique); DOCILIS (Documents et Interrogations Libres); MONOCLE (Mise en Ordinateur d'une Notice Catalographique de Libre). An excellent 236-item bibliography is included. The journal *Information* published, during the course of the year, a number of retrieval-related "Organization Profiles" and "Information Center Profiles." Examples are the Association for Computing Machinery's Special Interest Group on Information Retrieval (SIGIR) (Nance, 138); the National Federation of Science Abstracting and Indexing Services (NFSAIS) (Keenan, 87); the Electronic Properties Information Center (EPIC) (Veazie, 222); Battelle's Copper Data Center (Covington, 36). IBM (76), in one of its periodic forays into the field, has issued, as an IBM Manual, a basic primer or introduction to information retrieval. It is concise and well done at this level and virtually all basic terms in the field are mentioned and distinguished from one another. Its treatment of classification schemes and subject headings is rather biased, however, and the document clearly constitutes a brief for natural-text approaches.

The National Archives has issued two handbooks in its Records Management Handbook series. The first deals with information retrieval systems (216) and is aimed at informing and assisting the Government manager. The entries are brief and nontechnical notices of the existence of systems, and do not evaluate or cross-compare them. Forty-nine systems are described, 22 of which are termed "Document Reference Systems." The word document in this handbook refers to virtually any kind of piece of paper, e.g., engineering drawings, patents, etc. The microform retrieval handbook (217) is very thorough, with a concluding section covering various special-purpose storage and retrieval devices and nonconventional systems requiring computer capability: Microform Data Systems' MINDEX, Kodak's MIRACODE, Image Systems' CARD, AIL Information Systems' FILESEARCH IV, Sanders-Diebold's SD-500, Mosler's 20/20 System.

Standards work has the capacity to affect document retrieval and dissemination systems in a variety of ways: information interchange, retrieval vocabularies, data representations and codes, etc. In the thesaurus area, the American National Standards Institute, Z39 Committee (5) circulated in draft form a full set of guidelines for thesaurus structure, construction, and use. UNESCO (211), in related work, distributed guidelines for the establishment and development of monolingual scientific and technical thesauri for information retrieval. Probably the single most comprehensive standards reference work that appeared in 1971 was the National Bureau of Standards' (218) index to Federal Information Processing Standards (FIPS). This publication aims at making available in a single document, information on standards activities at the federal, national, and international level in the field of information processing. A directory of standards committees at these levels, and their members, is provided. There is a unique cross-reference index between International (ISO), National (ANSI), and Federal (FIPS) standards. Descending from the international and national planes, we find a useful work by the NFSAIS Working Group on Data Elements (139) for the benefit of secondary dissemination services. They have selected and described a set of common data elements which they recommend as either essential or supplementary to the identification or description of several types of items (e.g., journal articles, journal issues, books, dissertations, patents, maps, technical reports, meeting proceedings, etc.) contained in current bibliographic records of the primary abstracting and indexing services. The Aslib Computer Applications Group, Working Party on Information Retrieval (8) provides an interesting first try at a set of criteria for printed computer output from retrieval efforts (e.g., page size, headings, layout, format, columns, element identification, line lengths, punctuation, running over, justification, print quality, character set, paper stock, etc.).

A work that because of its breadth of vision defies easy classification but that represents information science at its best, was produced by Resnikoff & Dolby (160). The principal objective of their study was to develop a general model for "information access systems." The paper is statistically and mathematically oriented and contains a wealth of tables and graphs depicting the growth, properties, and interrelation of various information-bearing entities, such as words, sentences, titles, indexes, books, and libraries. In this sense it is a useful reference for statistical analyses of the English language, the entity involved in most of our retrieval efforts. Several stimulating hypotheses are propounded. For example, "access systems," as they define them, are plotted according to mean size in characters. Emerging from this is the suggestion that levels of access proceed, in terms of their size in characters, according to exponential powers of 30, e.g., book title = 30^1 characters, table of contents = 30^2, book index = 30^3, book = 30^4, etc. What makes this one of the more interesting works produced during 1971, however, is the steadfast insistence on examining what the properties of things really are rather than a reliance on what people think they are or ought to be.

Data Bases in Machine-Readable Form

In 1970 we had the American Institute of Physics' compilation by Ken Carroll entitled a *Survey of Scientific-Technical Tape Services*. In 1971 we had Kruzas & Schnitzer's *Encyclopedia of Information Systems and Services* (101). It is safe to say that new and up-to-date surveys of data bases (commercially available and otherwise) are under way right now for publication in 1972. It is a fast-growing field and, if events proceed as they have in the past, we can expect to see the continued proliferation of published information and hence of data bases. The American Institute of Physics' program of services, known as Current Physics Information (CPI) is a good example of the current trend toward a wide variety of output formats (for different users and different needs) existing as a kind of constellation around a central data base (Koch, 96). There are hundreds of data bases and yet most are specialized and small. Carroll identifies 56 of the larger and commercially available variety. There are probably only about 20 that could really be called "popular." The University of Georgia Information Center processes fourteen data bases (Carmon, 24; Park et al., 147). The IIT Research Institute's Computer Search Center concentrates on chemical data bases and currently has a stable of seven (Schipma et al., 179). The Association of Scientific Information Dissemination Centers (ASIDIC) conducted a survey of its members and found that 26 respondents were using a total of 31 data bases (Williams, 240).

Prices for data bases vary considerably. Weinstock (233) provides a highly readable survey of the prices, availability, terms and conditions of lease, and copyright aspects of the major data bases. According to Weinstock, base lease costs cluster around $4,000 - $8,000 per year, not including various royalty arrangements on the number of users serviced or the number of "hits" generated during the lease period. An unusually inexpensive data base is that of the Educational Resources Information Center (ERIC) which, as a by-product of a Government abstract journal publishing activity, sells for as little as $50 a tape ($150 a complete set) (Burchinal, 22; Marron & Sullivan, 123).

Dollar (40) examines, from the historian's viewpoint, the documentation surrounding data bases. This unusual "long view" poses the interesting question, "Will machine-readable records become as inscrutable as the Egyptian hieroglyphics?" (Inspire your programmer with the thought that his documentation can be the Rosetta Stone of tomorrow!) Menkus (129) discusses the physical considerations pertaining to magnetic tape as a long-term data-storage medium. Rather (158) reviews the major obstacles and problems to be met with in interchanging machine-readable bibliographic records on the international level. Mauerhoff & Smith (127) review and provide a bibliography of existing retrieval systems designed to operate on the potentially largest data base of all, the Library of Congress's MARC II files. The birth of a new data base, an experimental tape service known as TOXITAPES, is described by Schultz (183). Explanatory manuals to accompany data bases, and interpret them to the recipients, have seen many improvements of late (APA, 6; AIP,3), with that of the Chemical Abstracts Service (ACS, 2) providing a model that all could well follow.

Data bases are usually created for purposes and in formats unique to each supplier. Service centers providing search services (most prominently SDI) against these data bases have likewise tended to develop their own unique software, each incorporating those search capabilities which they feel best fit with their user community, their economic situation, and their particular selection of data bases. As the number of service centers making use of the data bases increases, the amount of duplicative reformatting (preprocessing to their own local format) of data bases increases. Schipma et al. (179) review the physical and conceptual organization of several important data bases, in effect, doing the kind of comparative analysis of data bases that each user of multiple data bases must now perform on his own. There will likely be a heavy increase in work performed in this area in the future. Schneider (181) recommends that the tape-producing systems redesign their distribution formats to facilitate searching rather than their own publication efforts. This is unlikely to happen, but there is clearly a great need for a generally accepted distribution standard. One may eventually emerge in the form of the new ANSI Standard for Bibliographic Information Interchange on Magnetic Tape (4). Williams (239) reports on the work of the ASIDIC Standards Committee in the area of "cooperative data management." This term encompasses ventures strictly beween searching centers (e.g., ensuring the availability of data bases that have limited appeal) and also those ventures that involve interaction between the suppliers (wholesalers) and the centers (retailers). It is apparent that many of the directions searching centers might consider, e.g., sharing of resources through a network, an intermediate preprocessing center between supplier and centers, repackaging, redistribution of data on new media such as computer output on microform (COM), creation of merged data bases, creation of retrospective files, and creation of personal files, could have a serious impact on the suppliers (i.e., the geese that lay the golden eggs).

Most of the present major users of machine-readable data bases for searching purposes are members of either the Association of Scientific Information Dissemination Centers (ASIDIC) or the European Association of Scientific Information Dissemination Centers (EUSIDIC). Both organizations publish newsletters which are valuable sources of information concerning data base development. For additional information concerning data bases, see Chapter 9 in this volume.

Software Packages

ACM's Symposium on Information Storage and Retrieval (9) divides information retrieval systems into three categories: (1) document-retrieval systems, (2) generalized data-management systems, and (3) question-answering systems. Software used in the field can be similarly divided. Of the three groups, question-answering systems are at the most experimental stage and are of least concern in this chapter. Specialized document-retrieval systems and generalized data base management systems (DBMS) are closely related, in that in past years there have been many attempts to avoid the expense of designing and implementing the former by using existing packages of the latter variety (alternatively called data-management systems, generalized information-retrieval systems, information-management systems, file-management systems, etc.).

Software specifically designed for document retrieval operations almost always specifies its own fixed file structure. The installer of such a package must adjust his data base to the internal structure of the software package, i.e., he must either build his data base to the required specifications or he must convert an existing data base to the new format. (This is in contrast to the usual DBMS practice of permitting wide varieties of files and data to be accepted as long as what comes in is "defined" for the system. The DBMS then handles the data in its own internal way, usually unknown to the user, and takes over the entire range of file building, maintenance, and update activities.)

The differences between the two types of systems have never been well understood by the noncomputer-oriented professional, and considerable survey and review effort over the past few years has gone into sorting out the many options, summarizing, and imposing some order on a chaos of systems. Berul (17), in reviewing the 1968 literature, unearthed an extremely large number of surveys, reviews, comparisons, and bibliographies on the subject of file-management software, attesting to the strength of the search for decision-helping information. The literature of 1971 contains far fewer of these publications and Seiden's 1970 report (186) surveying some 150 interactive on-line retrieval systems (with detailed comparisons of 26 general-purpose and 11 bibliographic systems) is probably still the best such study around. Simms (191) provides a comparison of the advantages and disadvantages of specific- and general-purpose software. deBoer (39) evaluates the possible use of generalized systems for the proposed Center for Information Services (CIS) at UCLA and provides a concise and intelligent set of reasons for opting for specialized bibliographic-oriented software to avoid "unnecessary inefficiency" and "inadequate capability." Kreger & Nathanson (100), in an article detailing one of the first attempts to use all the features of IBM's Generalized Information System (GIS) package, include a succinct discussion of the most critical features of data-management systems. Crow & Elchesen (37) describe the use of a file-management system called Master Control for the monitoring and retrieving of completed literature search packages. Tillmanns et al. (208) describe the use of Informatics' MARK IV File Management System to operate the Atlas Biomedical Literature System (ABLS). In general, however, there was less interest in attempting to perform the evermore-complicated and specialized document retrieval operations with generalized software and more interest in (1) improving and standardizing generalized data-base management systems, and (2) installing given specialized packages (i.e., bibliographically oriented packages) at specific locations. It seems as if we have entered a period of consolidation and of great interest in the transferability of specialized software (as witness CCM Information Corporation's *Computer Programs Directory*, International Computer Program's *ICP Quarterly*, NASA's *Computer Program Abstracts*, Science Associates' directory of *Computer Programs in Science and Technology*, the activity at the University of Georgia's Computer Software Management and Information Center (COSMIC), and the growth in informal local user groups for given bodies of software).

Of particular interest, with respect to generalized packages, is the work of two professional user groups. As reported by Patterson (149), a special GUIDE/SHARE committee attempted to state explicitly a set of requirements, a standard philosophy, and an idealized set of objectives that should be strived for by anyone building a generalized DBMS. The Conference on Data Systems Languages (CODASYL) Systems Committee (27), with a similar long-range objective to develop "the specification of the common language and functions for a unified data-base system," approached the task somewhat more concretely by preparing a review of the current state of the art. This review analyzes in depth several DBMS packages, most of which are commercially available, and compares them with respect to their most significant features. Systems analyzed were: IBM's GIS, IMS, and NIPS/FFS; General Electric's IDS; Informatics' MARK IV; Auerbach's and Western Electric's SC-1; System Development Corporation's TDMS; Radio Corporation of America's UL/1. The CODASYL review presents a highly informative discussion and comparison of how each of the generalized systems handles the "Interrogation Function." Examples of features that are tabulated and compared are relational operators, arithmetic operators, logical operators, string matching, precedence rules for unparenthesized expressions, and levels of nesting.

It is obvious that this topic is getting steadily more complex. The systems in the DBMS class are acquiring more capablities. At the same time, tailored, customized systems are being adapted to data bases other than the one they began on. There is a gray area in between. When does an adapted special series of programs become a "generalized" system?

There are numerous specialized document-retrieval packages on the commercial market today. We will mention some of them here briefly and without technical details, simply to group them by system, for reader convenience.

Lockheed's well-known DIALOG proprietary system continues to extend its impressive list of users with the addition of the AEC and of the Office of Education's ERIC network. The available literature on the system this year was primarily in the form of user manuals for these two systems (Lockheed, 109, 110). DIALOG operates on an IBM 360/40, or larger, computer. At this writing, Lockheed is currently implementing plans to: (1) offer the public on-line retrieval services against the ERIC data base on a commercial basis, (2) add a natural-language text-searching capability to its heretofore index-term-oriented system. Closely related to DIALOG is NASA's RECON (REmote CONsole) system, which is essentially DIALOG as modified at one time to operate against the NASA data base and so-called STIMS (Scientific and Technical Information Modular System) files (Wente, 235). At the NASA Scientific and Technical Information Facility, RECON functions on a dedicated IBM 360/50 and supports approximately 20 terminals. Coles (26) and Wolfe (243) both evaluate the performance of RECON. Since RECON is in the public domain, it represents an attractive "free" software package, albeit with considerable implementation complexities. Kissman (92) describes an ongoing effort to implement RECON for the National Library of Medicine's Toxicology Information Program (TIP) data base.

System Development Corporation also continues to extend its ORBIT system, a major proprietary system optimized for large files and sophisticated retrieval. Seiden (187) provides the latest information on the improved version of the system known as ORBIT II. ORBIT II currently functions on an IBM 360/67. McCarn (118, 119) describes the use of ORBIT II at the National Library of Medicine on a file known as Abridged Index Medicus (AIM) and using typewriter-type terminals. The system as a whole is commonly known as AIM-TWX and the retrieval program as ELHILL II (after NIH's Lister Hill National Center for Biomedical Communication), a localism for a modified version of ORBIT. Moll (136) reports favorably on AIM-TWX from the user's point of view at the University of Virginia. Though no literature yet exists on it, SDC also inaugurated, in late 1971, an on-line commercial search service (SDC/ERIC) with access to the Office of Education's ERIC data base.

Infodata System's proprietary INQUIRE system, while not as well suited as either DIALOG or ORBIT for very large data bases and multiple terminals, nevertheless continues to show itself to be versatile and customer-pleasing in the right application. Starker et al. (200) describe its installation at Warner-Lambert Research Institute. Frycki (50) and Bennett & Frycki (16) describe its installation within the Squibb Science Information System (SSIS).

Though technical details have not been reported of late, the Mead DATA CENTRAL system, one of the first proprietary systems to concentrate on natural-text approaches, seems to have solved some of its technical difficulties relating to file update and presented itself in 1971 in a very attractive red, blue, and yellow color television format, with the colors cleverly utilized for coding purposes to aid the user in scanning output. Porter et al. (154) describe the use of the system, at the National Institute of Neurological Diseases, on 8,000 abstracts from the *Epilepsy Abstracts* data base. Schultz (184) and McCabe (117) provide some nontechnical descriptions of the Ohio Bar Automated Research (OBAR) system developed with Mead by the Ohio State Bar Association. The OBAR data base is currently claimed to contain over 500 million characters. The Mead system has also been used on an experimental basis against the American Psychological Association's *Psychological Abstracts* data base, although no reports appear to have been published. Being a natural-language-based system, Mead is, of course, at the center of the great debate raging over indexing via the automatic processing of natural text versus indexing via human assignment of terms from a controlled vocabulary. Hersey et al. (66, 67), working with the data base of the Science Information Exchange (SIE) and with the Mead retrieval system, report on a comparison of retrieval efforts based on free-text versus those based on manual indexing by scientists; results favored the latter.

From IBM we have the TEXT-PAC, CFS (or CFSS - Combined File Search System), and DPS (Document Processing System) systems. TEXT-PAC appeared on the scene several years ago at the IBM Technical Information Retrieval Center (ITIRC) and ever since, IBM manuals dealing with information retrieval have not-so-subtly pushed natural language approaches. TEXT-PAC is described briefly in an IBM manual (77) devoted specifically to searching normal text. Artandi & Struminger (7) describe the use of TEXT-PAC at the Rutgers University Graduate School of Library Science as a tool for teaching information science. Ilukka (71) and Katajapuro (84) report on the use of TEXT-PAC at the Helsinki University of Technology for an SDI system based on the INIS and NSA tapes. The most prolific of authors on TEXT-PAC is Standera (196, 197, 198) who is represented by three excellent reports describing his search operation at the University of Calgary, against the Engineering Index COMPENDEX data base. CFS is represented by the long-awaited three-volume final report by Sessions & Sloan (188) on the experimental Project URBANDOC. DPS is covered by the seven-part final report on the SUPARS (Syracuse University Psychological Abstracts Retrieval Service) Project (Cook et al., 28), and by the report by Scheffler et al. (172) on the CIRCOL (Central Information Reference and Control On-Line) system at the Air Force's Foreign Technology Division, Wright Patterson AFB. From the academic and nonprofit sector, there is the University of Oklahoma's GIPSY (General Information Processing System) and Battelle's BASIS-70 (Battelle Automated Search Information System). Kowitz et al. (99) describe GIPSY as used at Oklahoma on the ERIC data base. The National Oceanographic Data Center (220) uses GIPSY for its internal Biology Information Retrieval Program. GIPSY is widely used in metropolitan Washington, D.C., and an informal user group meets periodically in the area. BASIS-70 appears to have been used to date largely internally within Battelle and for its own various information-center operations. Covington (36) describes its use for the Copper Data Center. Penniman (151) discusses its design, implementation, and operation at Battelle. Fried (49) concentrates on the user interface. A standard user manual (Battelle, 14) completes the picture.

Search Strategies

The best introduction to this subject this year is an incisive paper by Vickery (224) that relates the function to be performed (i.e., search strategy) to the particular kind of retrieval language necessary to permit the exercise of that function.

Relevance feedback. The most written-about search strategy during 1971 was what has most commonly come to be known as "relevance feedback." This "more-of-the-same" strategy is based on user interaction and can take various forms but basically involves feeding back, to the retrieval system, information concerning the utility of certain documents already known to the user. The information can be positive (concerning relevant documents), negative (concerning irrelevant documents), or of both types. The usual process is for query to be automatically updated using judgments supplied by the user following an initial search. Salton (165), working with the experimental SMART retrieval system, finds this post-search method much superior in performance (measured by recall and precision) to all pre-search interactive methods. Vernimb (223), searching operationally for the EURATOM Nuclear Documentation System (ENDS), describes a technique wherein a sample is taken of the results of a batch search; relevant documents are identified in the sample and are used as a base; the entire output of the search is then sorted in accordance with indexing "similarity" to the relevant documents; the relevance ratio for the sample (e.g., 15%) is then used as the cutoff point for the re-ordered set of documents. Using this technique, Vernimb reports final relevance ratios on the order of 94%. Williams, in two items (237, 238), provides probably the year's best general discussion of the relevance feedback technique. His experimental BROWSER text-retrieval system (238) accepts, as a non-Boolean free-form query statement, a title, abstract, text extract, or any combination thereof from a given bibliographic entity, with the objective of finding similar entities in the file. He automatically deletes from the query the substantive terms that occur in false hits but do not occur in relevant hits; he adds terms occurring in the top ranking relevant documents that had not previously been used in the query. Over several iterations, the density of relevant documents at the "top" of the search gradually increases. Tested on an NTIS data base of 8,000 documents, the system reached a maximum performance level after four cycles. Williams claims that via this interative browsing technique it is possible to consistently work up to 80% recall and 80% precision, but that pushing recall higher, for example to 96%, led to precision dropping to 48%. Like many others working with on-line systems, Williams finds the Boolean two-valued logic useful and essential, but simplistic in its rigid insistence on a true-false/yes-no decision. He craves some measure of degree. Information theory states that symbols having a low probability of occurrence carry the greatest amount of information. The weight of each term in Williams' inverted file is calculated as the ratio of the number of times used to the total documents in the base, expressed as a logarithm. This "information value" measures the amount of information conveyed by an index term in a particular data base. Low postings equals high information value. Each abstract in a BROWSER data base is scored by what he calls his "combinatorial search" algorithm according to the number of search terms it contains and the weight of each term, providing a ranked search output.

Borbash (18), using the term "pattern recognition," and Stanfel (199), using the term "sequential adaptation," report theoretical work on the development of mathematical models for the relevance feedback process.

Weighted searching. Term weighting strategies in searching are indicative of a desire to discriminate amongst output documents. Mathews (125) has for several years been in the forefront of those advocating search-term weighting and makes excellent use of weights in his operational document retrieval systems at Imperial Chemical Industries. Weighted strategies permit easier coding of the "any X of N terms" type of specification (INSPEC calls this "quorum logic"), but their sole unique advantage over Boolean systems is in permitting ranking of the output. Weighted term search can provide a "rating of probable pertinence" or "document score." Goom (57) describes an SDI system in operation at Guest, Keen, and Nettlefolds, Ltd. in which term weighting was selected primarily as a technique to minimize computer search time. The Aerospace Research Applications Center (ARAC) has based its SDI service on weighted term searching. In an interesting attempt to automate the maintenance of their current-awareness profiles (Counts, 33), ARAC developed a profile analysis program which: (1) analyzes the index terms assigned to a batch of documents identified by the user as relevant or nonrelevant, (2) calculates new weights for each profile term, basing its decisions on five decision rules or algorithms. The algorithms involved change of sign, linear weight modification, exponential weight modification, and mixes of both. Counts concluded that "it should be possible to maintain profiles automatically and successfully in almost all operational situations." Barker et al. (13), working at the United Kingdom Chemical Information Service (UKCIS), corroborate these conclusions although using different techniques. There are today a great many systems that make use of weighted term-searching techniques, usually as a useful adjunct to the search armamentarium rather than as the sole approach. Systems that permit the searcher to distinguish between major or published index terms and minor or unpublished index terms are sometimes referred to as weighted search schemes but are better thought of as members of the class of systems weighting index terms on input instead of the class of systems permitting search terms to be weighted.

Citation searching. Citations accompanying a report or article are today in experimental efforts well recognized to be extremely useful content indicators. Garfield's contention that by using references "we are in reality using an army of indexers" is becoming the consensus viewpoint. Salton (163), with the SMART system, and Schiminovich (176), at the American Institute of Physics, report on experiments involving both the automatic indexing of documents via their citations and the use of citations contained in known relevant papers to assist in framing inquiries. Both confirm the usefulness of citations. Salton finds the expected results "fully comparable to that obtained by standard subject indicators at the low recall-high precision end of the performance range"; he recommends for future designers that documents processed for a retrieval system should normally and routinely carry bibliographic citation data in addition to standard content indicators. Nevertheless, operational systems using citations for retrieval are rare, doubtless because of the high input costs. MIT's Technical Information Project (TIP) was one of the of the first to work this area and popularize in the literature the term "bibliographic coupling." The largest search system to routinely utilize citations is the Institute for Scientific Information's Automatic Subject Citation Alert (ASCA) (72). ASCA is now in its fourth generation and, as ASCA IV, provides significantly increased search capabilities over previous versions—e.g., specific words in title, phrases in title, negative terms, stems (initial, terminal, floating), cited reference (i.e., what articles cite a particular earlier work), cited book, cited author, cited journal, cited thesis, cited patent, source author, source journal, source organization. The "cited" capabilities are unique to the ISI approach and provide it with its own particular kind of search power. Garfield (51) outlines these as follows: ability to identify the relatedness of documents that are overlooked by subject indexing; effectiveness at cutting across arbitrary disciplinary boundaries; ability to overcome translation and idiom problems with respect to foreign-origin literature. A much-needed state-of-the-art report on the use and value of citations in both experimental and operational systems has been prepared for INSPEC by Hall (58). This is a comprehensive study and covers all types of usages; an excellent 85-item bibliography is appended.

Classification. The theoretical impossibility of a perfect stable classification scheme in any complex field may be widely agreed upon (Sharp, 190); nevertheless, classification as a practical retrieval device will always have its adherents, and rightly so. Speaking out strongly for it in 1971 were Schneider (180, 181) and the UNISIST report (UNESCO, (212, 213). In a well-researched review of SDI systems published in the influential journal *Science*, Schneider (181) argues strongly that detailed, enumerative hierarchical classifications, requiring only "single-hit matching," should be substituted for existing indexing systems. Such classifications would be so specific that an article indexed under any one of the categories assigned to a user would have an extremely high probability of being useful to that user. His own system, called HICLASS for Hierarchical Classification, operates at the National Cancer Institute and covers the field of cancer. Schneider comes to his position via the firm belief that SDI systems must have a high degree of precision or users will become disenchanted with them and quit using them. The UNISIST report (212, 213) recognizes the important role a commonly agreed upon classification could play in international cooperation. The Universal Decimal Classification (UDC) receives most of their attention and they recommend "A continuing program to strengthen UDC and further studies and experiments to test its applicability to retrieval systems."

Meredith (130) describes an innovative experimental on-line system known as REFSEARCH for hunting for reference works which have the best chance of containing the answer to a given question. The reference works are coded by a variety of categories or "channels" (such as "persons"), "qualifiers" (such as "living"), and "services" (such as "defines"). This coding vocabulary, fairly small at 254 separate characteristics, is a good example of the lack of a rigid dividing line between classification and other kinds of indexing.

Efforts at clustering or clumping anything into like groupings are essentially classificatory. Jackson (78) develops a general mathematical model for classification which permits the determination of retrieval performance for various classification choices. Salton's new textbook (168) on the SMART retrieval system deals in Part IV with "Cluster Generation and Search." Most of the automatic document classification algorithms described (e.g., those of Rocchio and Dattola) deal with word coincidence data. In Chapter 13 of this same text Worona takes the interesting next step of clustering the queries as well as the documents. Results were inconclusive but encouraging. Schiminovich (176) describes a technique for clustering documents on the basis of their citations, using an algorithm called the Bibliographic Pattern Discovery Algorithm (BPDA). The BPDA routine can be added to a system as a new search strategy, a storage organizing strategy, or both. Cooper (30) offers a provocative theoretical suggestion pertaining to the use of "second level associations" for the purpose of expanding search coverage and thereby increasing recall performance. Hersey et al. (67) report on a significant experiment from the Science Information Exchange (SIE). A collection of 4,600 research projects, which had been manually indexed using the SIE classification scheme, were searched using both this scheme and free text searching (Mead Data Central system) against the full project text. The SIE scheme scored 30-40% higher in recall and 15-20% higher in relevance than the full text system. This experiment, a genuine confrontation between manual indexing/classification and full-text systems, is interesting but will have to be corroborated. Insufficient detail is presented to determine whether the full-text search system got a "fair shake" in the experiment.

Classification frequently finds an effective niche along with (rather than instead of) other approaches. INSPEC, after detailed investigation into the merits of various indexing approaches via their Direct Evaluation of Indexing Languages (DEVIL) system, selected a three-pronged approach: free language indexing for machine retrieval; controlled vocabulary, thesaurus-based subject headings for printed indexes; hierarchical classification for arrangement of announcements (Aitchison, 1).

Specific search commands. A large variety of interesting search capabilities can be assembled from any review of specific systems. The terminology is very far from being standardized and it is not unusual to find essentially the same option existing in several systems under different names or a purported new option put forward that would better be regarded as a subset of a known strategy. For example, a capability to specify every term beginning "Explo" *except* those beginning "Exploi" or "Explor" might in one system be described as an "Ignore" capability and elsewhere as a "Conditional Not" capability. Schieber (174) provides a very well done report on the International Labour Office's Integrated Scientific Information System (ISIS). An interesting search feature is the ANY instruction. Various collective terms, such as "Europe" or "Education" have had tables built for them containing all their "narrower" terms. These tables are stored in the computer and may be called for automatically, e.g., ANY Education. It can be used to handle any frequently used cluster or family of terms where the user wishes to avoid excessive coding effort. Bennertz (15) describes the same option within the Defense Documentation Center's on-line retrieval system, where it is called the "Descriptor Hierarchy" option and gathers together Related Terms as well as Narrower Terms. Thiel & Heaps (206) describe a variation of this called the DEF instruction which permits a term to be defined early in a search and in subsequent usages to be treated as its definition, e.g., "Foreign DEF (Russian OR American)."

Text searching is particularly prolific of search strategies and instructions. Carmon (24), IBM (77), Kowitz et al. (99), Negus (140), Penniman (151), Schieber (174), Thiel & Heaps (206), and Townley (209) describe some of the operators that can be found at work in string searching to specify: (1) precedence, adjacency, same sentence, distance ("WITH" logic - words must appear within so many words of each other), frequency (word must appear so many times in given record), or other properties variously referred to as contextual, syntactical, or relational; (2) Roots/stems/truncations, prefixes, infixes, suffixes, generalized masking, "universal," "open," or "I don't care" characters, etc., or the whole range of capabilities that attempt to allow for the bewildering multiplicity of spellings, grammatical inflections, hyphenations, word forms, etc. that face the user of un-normalized natural text. The variations on these instructions are endless. Schieber (174), forexample, describes a "dot" feature which, when used, allows hits on the specified search terms *only* if they appeared in the "first" part of the abstract. The theory is that an abstract is always written so that the most important terms appear in its first few sentences. Many of the ASIDIC centers, where searching activity is primarily of the current-awareness variety, against update tapes instead of entire retrospective files, are operating with character-string-searching systems and are reporting good results (Williams, 240; Carmon, 24). The work of the IIT Research Institute is particularly notable for the variety and ingenuity of the tools they provide the profile encoder faced with the text search problem. For example, a "Truncation Guide" provides an easy-to-read reference as to which and how many of the terms appearing in the data base would be subsumed by each right-truncated form (e.g., analyt-). A Key-Letter-in-Context Index (KLIC) provides a lexicographic ordering of all terms in a data base by each character in the term or character string. This is a permuted arrangement sorted by character with the balance of the term wrapped around. By consulting the KLIC, the retrieval capability of a particular letter combination or term fragment can be determined. These tools are prepared separately for each data base. The IIT Research Institute is also notable in providing statistics about the nature of their profiles. This is a neglected field and it clearly should be standard practice for major searching centers to perform such analyses, in order to determine what capabilities are put to practical use. The following kinds of statistics are of interest, for example: truncation modes used (none, left, right, both) versus data-element fields used against; use of AND, OR, NOT and number of times each used in each profile; number of sets of parentheses and depth of "nesting" of parentheses in each profile.

Man-machine interface. Many useful search system "strategies" do not pertain directly to searching itself, but can have a great impact on the success of the search. McAllister & Bell (116) report on the highly user-oriented IBM Experimental Library Management System (ELMS). ELMS is an experimental system for total library management, operating on-line with an IBM 360/40, or higher, through IBM 2260 and 2741 terminals. The system is designed to handle large amounts of highly variable information and gives on-line computer services for all library operations, including, as a by-product, some retrieval capability. Many ELMS features were specifically designed to facilitate user interaction: techniques for tutoring the inexperienced user, adaptability for the experienced user (command chains and a standard set of four-letter mnemonic codes for higher level control), minimization of keying (line numbers, one-character mnemonic codes used with procedures, and use of default options), performance of clerical tasks by exception notification, and collection of operational statistics to help improve the system. Cuadra (38) provides a major synthesis of ideas about on-line systems, in the course of which he devotes considerable space to essential interface provisions. Nevertheless, he does not believe in sacrificing the system to the user. In his view the system designer must understand and make appropriate allowances for present user habits while at the same time helping to move the user's skill level gently, but firmly, forward. Prominent in Cuadra's synthesis is Katter's earlier taxonomy of on-line interface characteristics, e.g., pacing, error control, tutorials, options in selecting the level of instruction, "peephole effect" (file contents viewed little pieces at a time), "fishbowl effect" (lack of privacy; terminal in abrasive public area), "bullying" (system continually putting user "on the spot"), speed, etc. Cuadra provides a carefully considered list of good design features worth repeating here: (1) Ability to enter any command at any time, i.e., there should not be any ordering or sequential requirements on inputs; (2) Ability to select which records and which elements of the record to print; (3) Ability to qualify or limit retrievals on the basis of cataloging data such as publication date and publication language; (4) Ability to print either on-line or off-line; (5) Unrestricted use of Boolean operators and number of search terms; (6)

Ability to issue compound specifications linking search statements and/or commands; (7) Use a "universal," "open," or "I don't care" character to handle uncertain spellings, root searching, etc.; (8) Unambiguous cues from system as to when user participation required; (9) "Nesting" of search statements to at least five levels; (10) Inputs permitted in various forms, with mixing permitted, e.g., symbolic or coded, short or mnemonic, or full word; (11) On-line thesaurus; (12) Ability to formulate search statements which will search any element of any files, e.g., "Taylor," whether it is an author, publisher, or corporate source; (12) Protection against unintentional destruction of files or programs; (13) User query language as close as practical to natural language in order to minimize the effort required to learn and use the system.

However, the best treatment during the year of the man-machine interface was provided by Walker (228) in the proceedings of a workshop which was restricted to the major information scientists actually working in this area. This book is a notable "first" in its attempt to assess our current knowledge about the user/computer interface from the user's perspective.

Specialized searching devices. General Electric (53) actively marketed their GESCAN Rapid Search Machine (RSM) though there did not appear to be any reports published on installations. GESCAN is a high-speed tape searching device with an attached operator's console which can be a CRT. Searching is done linearly, on the natural text stored on the tape, at a rate of 120,000 characters a second (or a million words a minute). Eastman Kodak (Glassman, 55) offered a system called EICON (Electronic Index Console) consisting of a minicomputer, electric typewriter, and magnetic disk with 13-million-bit capacity. Searching is done linearly and is said to take 35 seconds to scan the entire disk. Varian ADCO (221) offered a new large device for the storage of microfilm and the rapid retrieval of specific segments of the file. The basic system, called the 626, handles 360,000 pages and is expandable in modular increments of the same size. Access time is guaranteed to be less than 10 seconds, no matter how many pages are stored. Storage costs are said to be 3¢ a page. The microfilm retrieved is set before a TV monitor and the image can be transmitted to remote CRT's. The system operates on a stand-alone basis with access by document number, but can be interfaced with a computer "to provide even more sophistication such as extensive attribute search and complicated table look-up." The New York Times' long-awaited newspaper "morgue" system, termed their Information Bank, has installed a prototype of the Remote Console Information Corporation's Foto-Mem Record

Information Storage and Retrieval (RISAR) system. RISAR handles standard COSATI microfiche in 250 "cells" each containing 1,000 fiche, for a standard complement of 25,000 fiche or 2,500,000 frames maximum. Each fiche can be retrieved in 2-4 seconds, with specific frames displayed on closed circuit television. Indexes are stored on an associated IBM 2311 disk and searched via a Centaur mini-computer. Further development and additional planned installations of this device have, however, been cancelled by the manufacturer, as of this writing. Smith & Herr (193) report on searches being made at the Lawrence Radiation Laboratory on one of the largest mass memory units available to date, the IBM 1360 Photodigital Storage System (CHIPSTORE). On-line capacity of the IBM 1360 is one trillion bits. The physical unit of the system is a 35x70mm "chip" of high resolution film, each of which can hold 5 million bits of information on a direct access basis.

Several other special purpose microform-related devices are described in the General Services Administration's *Microform Retrieval Equipment Guide* (217).

Evaluation, Testing, Measurement

Though the literature dealing with evaluation is voluminous, there have actually been very few systematic evaluations of operational retrieval systems. Lancaster's assignment at the National Library of Medicine still comes to mind as the beau ideal. King & Bryant (90) see this situation changing and predict that we are moving from the let's-try-it-and-see-if-it-works innovative period of the 60's into a "period of evaluation" in the 70's. They have provided the profession with the first comprehensive textbook dealing solely with the evaluation of information services. Evaluation is seen as an "analytical and diagnostic procedure applied to measure performance level, disclose major system weaknesses, and suggest ways in which the performance may be improved." This is an excellent book, heavily oriented toward quantification and statistical analysis, and should be read by all contemplating the evaluation of any type of bibliographic system for current-awareness or retrospective search.

Evaluation models. Evaluation is a subject that frequently calls for model-building. King & Bryant (90) and Lancaster (105) both construct detailed system models depicting the relations among system features, costs, performance, and benefits. Hjerppe & Lindquist (70) develop a strictly theoretical evaluation model in which they take the maverick position of downgrading precision and recall as "quite inadequate," hopelessly oriented toward the system designer and operator, and as having acquired "undeserved importance as evaluation parameters."

Saracevic (170) reports on the results of a major four-year project at Case Western Reserve University entitled the Comparative Systems Laboratory (CSL). The aim of the project was to conduct a comprehensive inquiry into the testing of information-retrieval systems; the effort necessarily involved the construction of a system model and is closely related to other large-scale testing projects such as those conducted by Cleverdon, Salton, and Lancaster. Conclusions of the CSL project were: (1) Question analysis and search strategies affect performance to a great extent; (2) The evidence on indexing languages is inconclusive—it may be possible that indexing languages do not affect performance; (3) The depth of indexing (i.e., the variation in number of index terms per document) seems to affect system performance more than does the indexing language; (4) Contact with users slightly decreased performance (one wonders about this conclusion!); (5) Testing of total retrieval systems, taking into account and controlling *all* inside and environmental factors, seems neither feasible nor possible at present.

Some evaluation models restricted themselves to relatively narrow areas. Plotkin & Epstein (153) and Konigova (98) both develop mathematical models concerned with utilizing noise performance to evaluate retrieval systems. Welch (234), in an abstruse mathematical modeling exercise, concludes that retrieval efficiency is determined primarily by catalog size (amount of information stored) and not by file organization.

SMART. The retrieval evaluation system most reported on over the past several years, Salton's SMART at Cornell, is finally going online. The design for an on-line, real-time SMART is provided by D. and R. Williamson in the latest project report (Salton et al., 166). Another welcome direction being taken is to design and perform experiments involving larger document populations than heretofore. The regular SMART data bases have always seemed on the small side to these reviewers, considering the widespread importance attached to the results reported. Since a listing of SMART data bases and their sizes is rarely seen in one place, we assemble it below:

SMART DATA BASE	*SUBJECT*	*SIZE*
ADI	Documentation	82 full text of papers
CRAN-1	Aerodynamics	1400 + 200 keywords and abstracts
IRE-3	Computer Literature	780 abstracts

ISPRA	Documentation	1200 abstracts
MEDLARS	Medical	270 keywords and abstracts

Though SMART was always intended to be an experimental system for laboratory use, it has lately had to get more "operational" in the sense that it has had to admit the user to the environment for the system to obtain user feedback data for use in experimental interactive searches (Salton, 168). Some of the principal conclusions reported by SMART in 1971 were as follows: (1) Abstracts are better than titles alone; (2) Large text portions can be superior to abstracts, but not on a consistent cost-effective basis; (3) Weighted content identifiers are better than nonweighted ones; (4) Word normalization procedures work best for redundant and nontechnical vocabularies; (5) Dictionaries providing synonym recognition produce better retrieval results than word-stem matching procedures; (6) Feedback procedures based on user relevance judgments during first iterations are effective in producing large-scale retrieval improvements; (7) Cluster techniques offer drastic reductions in search time at only minor costs to recall and precision; (8) Automatic procedures are inferior, but not substantially inferior, to manual indexing methods (for large and heterogeneous collections, automatic procedures may be superior because of indexer variability); (9) Citation searching is always useful and in some special situations even more effective than keywords; (10) Phrases are downgraded as content indicators. The value of refined content analysis indicators resides in their effectiveness in separating lexically similar but semantically different documents. Existing document collections are too sparse and do not contain many "close" documents; (11) "Negative feedback," where the user can only point to nonrelevant items identified thus far, is a feasible variation of relevance feedback.

User surveys. Specific systems can be evaluated via use and user studies, the comparative method, or programs of testing. Wood (246) reviews one hundred user studies performed from 1966 to 1970 and provides some interesting conclusions for those who have ever wondered about the use being made of computerized document retrieval systems. He states, "Mechanized information retrieval systems, at least in their present form, do not seem likely to supplant the more traditional methods of gathering information." This statement is based largely on some National Lending Library (NLL) studies which indicate that mechanized systems such as MEDLARS, RINGDOC,

CBAC, etc., provided only 2% of the biological references and 4.6% of the medical references utilized by borrowers of biomedical and social science literature from NLL. Wood speculates that "Possibly mechanized services are too remote from users to be used as much as their value might warrant." User surveys at specific locations were reported in 1971 by Coles (26), Cook et al. (28), Kuney & Daugherty (103), Meyer et al. (133), Scheffler & March (173), Wolters & Brown (245). George (54) provides a major report, based on both user reaction and cost analyses, on the Defense Documentation Center's Automated Services and Products (ASP) program, later designated Selective Documentation Services (SDS).

Comparisons and tests. Wolfe (243) performs probably the year's major nonexperimental comparative evaluation in his in-depth examination of three on-line retrieval systems: MIT's TIP, NASA's RECON, and the unnamed new system of DDC. By assembling the best features of all systems and hypothesizing capabilities to make up for existing weaknesses, Wolfe generates a set of specifications for an ideal on-line system. Some of these are: tutorial display sequences; natural English query language; hierarchical expansion; masking; Boolean operations; weighting; limited text search (supported by on-line thesaurus); automatic query formulation based on relevant items (similarity match on *all* data fields). It is necessary, however, to have Wolfe's full report in order to determine the support for his recommendations. The journal article based on his work (244) is largely a catalog of "shoulds" without supporting argument or example.

Aitchison (1) describes the use of INSPEC's Direct Evaluation of Index Languages (DEVIL) automated system for conducting test searches and calculating performance measures, as a prelude to design of the INSPEC international system. INSPEC defined five index languages: title, abstract/title, subject headings and notations of content, free indexing, and controlled vocabulary. Controlled vocabulary achieved superior performance on all measures. Free indexing was best of the uncontrolled approaches. Title had good precision and low recall. Abstracts/title had low precision and good recall. The paper contains insightful remarks on the use of natural text for indexing purposes and recommends the use of an automatically generated "thesaurus" to keep track of word forms and alternative terms coming into the system in the free indexing situation. Hersey et al. (66, 67) test compare manual indexing by scientists using the Science Information Exchange (SIE) classification scheme against free text searching using the Mead DATA CENTRAL system, with the experimental results favoring manual indexing by a wide margin.

Evaluation of retrieval efforts may, of course, center on data bases, indexing practices, or search techniques and not just on specific retrieval systems. Hansen (60) compares five major data bases to obtain information concerning their coverage and currency when used for retrieval. Miller (134) investigates the adequacy of titles in the MEDLARS file as sources of indexing information. Eighty-six percent of the published index terms were found in the titles. Barker at al. (11, 12) investigated the relative merits of searching titles, keywords, or abstracts, and the currency and relative performance of four major chemical data bases. Parker (148) tested the comparative efficiencies of natural language searching (on titles) and keywords on the *Nuclear Science Abstracts* data base. There appeared to be little difference between the two approaches in terms of relevance, however the keyword approach retrieved 20% more relevant references than the natural-language approach. Svenonius (203) attempts to evaluate the effect of indexing specificity on retrieval performance. Her conclusions were: (1) In a search with multiple coordinations, the retrieval power of broad and narrow terms tends to become equalized; (2) When precision is desired, narrow indexing is preferable to broad indexing; (3) Deleting narrow terms never improves precision and can make both recall and precision worse; (4) Deletion of broad terms is sometimes a better means of improving precision than increasing coordinations; (5) The amount of material retrieved is not a function of depth of indexing; (6) Results for weighted (at input) index terms were disappointing. Hall (58) provides a comprehensive state-of-the-art review of the use of citations for indexing and retrieval, citing the results of all major studies to date.

Evaluation of evaluation. Evaluation procedures and measurements can, of course, themselves be evaluated. Harter (63) and Swanson (204) evaluate the design of the Cranfield II experiments. This is of prime significance because the Cranfield results have been so widely promulgated. Also, other investigators (such as Salton) have used the Cranfield collection as one of the "standard" data bases. Research based on a supposedly "solved" or thoroughly understood collection would be affected if the "facts" assumed for the collection contained aberrations. The major flaw detected is that there were, in actuality, many documents in the collection that were relevant to the queries used but that were not detected by the Cranfield judges (students). It is demonstrated that numerical measures of retrieval effectiveness for various indexing approaches and retrieval methods can be greatly altered by consideration of the "missing" relevant documents.

Performance measures. Miller (135) provides an interesting report that reviews seven methods for estimating Recall when large files are involved (the methods of Aitchison, Cleverdon, Rolling, Fels, Goffman, and Rogers). Disadvantages or weaknesses of each statistical approach are described. He criticizes Recall as ignoring the relation between the file and its users; Recall can be high only if the file's coverage of the user's interest area is high. He develops a new performance measure to detect the extension of the user's knowledge as a result of using the system. The Extension Ratio is the ratio of the number of relevant references the user knows of after the search to the number he knew about before he searched. Unfortunately for the future of this measure, very high values may reflect the user's ignorance as well as the capability of the system. The measure is related to Project INTREX's Discovery Ratio (the ratio of relevant documents found by the search, and which are not in standard bibliographies, to the total relevant documents found by the search, whether in bibliographies or not) (MIT, 124). Salton (165) reviews perceptively the particular kinds of evaluation problems caused by the interactive environment. He examines previous performance measures such as recall, precision, novelty ratio, and relative recall and argues that new measures are needed to measure interactive performance.

SPECIFIC SYSTEMS

In the tables immediately following this chapter, some 76 computerized document-retrieval systems are listed, together with basic information concerning the software used, the computers they operate on (in a batch or interactive mode), whether they offer retrospective or current awareness services, their operational or experimental status, and the search mode generally used. It must be emphasized that this list makes no attempt to be complete. The systems listed are solely those that produced written reports during 1971 that came to our attention. Note that a given transferable proprietary package may be listed both under the company offering it and under one or more of its installations.

Under "Search System," the word "internal" means that the software being used was custom developed for the application and is being used solely at the one installation. The computer column refers to the machine being used, not the the minimum machine. Surprisingly, this information is not reported in the literature with any great consistency. Sometimes technical indications appear in reports that an IBM 360 is being used; we have included these even when a model number is not available. As can be seen, on-line interactive systems usually require a model 360/40 or higher (or equivalent computing power), though Storie (201) reports on an interactive system on a machine as small as an IBM 1130. The main proprietary packages usually have the flexibility to operate in either a batch or interactive mode, as the user prefers. Certain systems, originally designed as batch systems, have been modified by users in the field to function in an on-line mode, e.g., IBM's DPS. When systems are being used for current-awareness searching, they frequently are also used for retrospective searching. Only a few systems are exclusively devoted to current awareness. The tags "operational" or "experimental" are sometimes difficult to assign accurately. For example, the SMART system was designed to run experiments with. It is frankly "experimental" and was not intended to be anything else, though it is fully "operational" in performing this function. Certain library school efforts involving TEXT-PAC and DPS are also in this hybrid class. The most difficult characterization to make is "Search Mode." Many systems combine aspects of text searching (e.g., words in title, character strings in abstract) or classification, with basic Boolean logical operators. In other words, the ability to combine things logically (AND, OR) is usually a fundamental capability whether character strings or classification codes are being retrieved. For these reasons, the true search mode used by a given system is usually a more complicated picture than can be fully expressed in an abbreviated tabular structure.

The tables are subdivided by what has become a traditional set of categories, i.e., systems developed in government (domestic, foreign, international), industry, and nonprofit organizations.

CONCLUSION

Prospects for the 1970's are exciting, for during the next decade computerized document retrieval systems will probably become a routine feature of our everyday professional lives. Batch systems will continue for mass input and mass output tasks and interactive systems will supplement (not supplant) them. Text-processing techniques will continue to advance, putting pressure on document surrogates from the point of view of quality, title/abstract adequacy, standardization of format, and availability in machine-readable form. Search strategies will show great variety, as the many ways that bibliographic entities can be looked for become better understood. At the same time, the culture-wide trend toward relieving the human user of the need to explicitly code and direct each step of the process will be prominent. Interactive systems, having gotten through the initial design and engineering test phase, are also concentrating more on human factors matters. Their major purely technical problem during the 1970's will be to increase the number of terminals that systems will handle simultaneously without excessive degradation of response.

Looking back over the year and the literature gathered during that year, we are struck with the widespread nature of the activity. Computerized document retrieval systems are no longer reserved for large government agencies or corporations. Through the use of existing software packages and commercially available data bases, it is possible for many modest operations to engage in searching files via computers. Also, there are more search activities that must support themselves, either within their own organization or by selling their services outside. The theoretical in searching is giving way to the practical, as time, the users, and relentless economics winnow out the techniques that really work and the approaches that information consumers really want to take—and pay for. In the course of this "popularization," we are arriving at an information community much more sophisticated than ever before in the ways of computer searching.

SPECIFIC SYSTEMS

1. SYSTEMS DEVELOPED IN GOVERNMENT

INSTITUTION	NAME	SEARCH SYSTEM	COMPUTER	Batch (B) or On-line Interactive (I)	Current Awareness (C) or Retrospective (R)	Operational (O) or Experimental (E)	*Search Mode: Boolean (B); Text (T); Weighted (W); Citation (C); Classif. (CL); Relevance Feedback (RF)	REFERENCES
DOMESTIC								
Air Force – Aerospace Materials Information Center (AMIC)	–	Internal	–	B	C, R	O	B	Scheffler & March (173)
Foreign Tech. Div., Wright-Patterson AFB	Central Information Reference and Control On-Line (CIRCOL)	IBM's DPS	360/65	I	R	O	T	Fong (47) Scheffler et al. (172)
Judge Advocate General	Legal Information Thru Electronics (LITE)	Internal	360/65	B	R	O	T	Air Force (215) McCarthy (120)
Atomic Energy Commission	AEC/DIALOG	DIALOG	360/40	I	R	O	B	Lockheed (110)
Nuclear Safety Information Center (NSIC)	–	Internal	–	I	C, R	O	–	Cottrell & Buchanan (32)
Defense Documentation Center (DDC)	–	Internal	UNIVAC-1108	I	R	E	B	Bennertz (15) Fong (47) Wolfe (243) Woods (247)
National Aeronautics and Space Administration	NASA/RECON	NASA/RECON (Version of Lockheed's DIALOG)	360/50	I	R	O	B	Coles (26) Fong (47) Wente (235)
National Cancer Institute (NCI)	HICLASS (Hierarchical Classification)	Internal	360/20	B	C	O	CL	Schneider (181)
National Inst. of Neurological Diseases	Epilepsy Abstracts Retrieval System (EARS)	Mead DATA CENTRAL	360/50	I	R	E	T	Porter et al. (154)
National Library of Medicine –	Medical Literature Analysis and Retrieval System (MEDLARS)	MEDLARS	I : H-800 II : 360/50	B	R	O	B	Fong (47) NLM (219)
	Abridged Index Medicus [By] Teletypewriter Exchange (AIM-TWX)	ELHILL II (Version of SDC's ORBIT II)	360/67	I	R	E	B	McCarn (118, 119) Moll (136)
	Toxicology Information Program (TIP)	NASA/RECON		I	R	E	B	Kissman (92)
National Oceanographic Data Center (NODC)	Biology Information Retrieval System	GIPSY	340/40	B	R	O	B	NODC (220)
Navy	Navy Medical Information Storage and Retrieval System (Navy MEDISTARS)	Internal	–	B	R	O	–	Ramsey-Klee (157)
Office of Education – Educational Resources Information Center (ERIC)	ERIC/DIALOG	DIALOG	360/40	I	R	O	B	Lockheed (109)
	SDC/ERIC	ORBIT II	360/67	I	R	O	B	–
Patent Office	Project Potomac (Patent Office Techniques of Mechanized Access and Classification)	Internal	–	I	R	E	–	Nugent (142)
Science Information Exchange (SIE)	–	Internal	360/30	B	R	O	CL	Hersey et al. (66, 67)

Note: Text (T) Searching Implies Boolean Logic (B) as well.

1. SYSTEMS DEVELOPMENT IN GOVERNMENT (continued)

INSTITUTION	NAME	SEARCH SYSTEM	COMPUTER	Batch (B) or On-line Interactive (I)	Current Awareness (C) or Retrospective (R)	Operational (O) or Experimental (E)	*Search Mode: Boolean (B); Text (T); Weighted (W); Citation (C); Classif. (CL); Relevance Feedback (RF)	REFERENCES
FOREIGN								
Centre National de la Recherche Scientifique Centre de Documentation	Programme Appliqué à la Sélection et à la Compilation Automatique de la Littérature (PASCAL)	Internal	–	B	R	O	B	Dusoulier & Buffet (41)
Fisheries Research Board of Canada	–	Internal	360/65	B	R	O	B	Lee et al. (108)
Institut für Dokumentation, Information und Statistik. Deutsches Krebsforschungszentrum	Système Automatique de Bibliographie, d'Information et de Recherche (SABIR)	Internal	360/30	B	R	O	B	Kohler & Wagner (97) Sandor (169)
National Science Library, Canada	CAN/SDI	Internal	360/50	B	C	O	B, T, W	Brown (20) Mauerhoff (126) Wolters & Brown (245)
National Science Library/University of Saskatchewan	Selective Dissemination of MARC (SELDOM)	Internal	360/50	B	C	O	B, W	Mauerhoff & Smith (127)
U.K. Atomic Energy Authority (UKAEA)								
Culham & Harwell Labs	–	Internal	KDF9	B	C	O	B	Hall & Terry (59)
Culham Lab	–	Internal	KDF9	I	R	E	B	Negus (140)
	Heat Transfer and Fluid Flow Service (HTFS)	Internal	360/75	B	C, R	O	B	Cousins (35)
INTERNATIONAL								
EURATOM	European Nuclear Documentation System (ENDS)	Internal	360/40	B	R	O	B, RF	Vernimb (223)
International Atomic Energy Agency (IAEA)	International Nuclear Information System (INIS)	Internal	360/30	B	R	O	B	El-Hadidy (43) IAEA (75) Pelzer et al. (150) Woolston et al. (248)
	Computer Index of Neutron Data (CINDA)	Internal	–	B	R	O	B	IAEA (74)
International Labour Office (ILO)	Integrated Scientific Information System (ISIS)	Internal	360/30	B, I	R	O	B	Schieber (174)

Note: Text (T) Searching Implies Boolean Logic (B) as well.

2. SYSTEMS DEVELOPED IN INDUSTRY

INSTITUTION	NAME	SEARCH SYSTEM	COMPUTER	Batch (B) or On-line Interactive (I)	Current Awareness (C) or Retrospective (R)	Operational (O) or Experimental (E)	*Search Mode: Boolean (B); Text (T); Weighted (W); Citation (C); Classif. (CL); Relevance Feedback (RF)	REFERENCES
Atlas Chemical Industries	Atlas Biomedical Literature System (ABLS)	Mark IV (Informatics)	360/50	B	C,R	O	B	Tillmanns (208)
British Steel Corp.	–	Internal	–	B	C	O	CL	McCash & Carmichael (121)
Celanese Research Co.	–	Internal	–	B	C	O	B	Meyer et al. (132, 133)
Dow Chemical Co.	–	Internal	B-5500	B	C	O	T, W	Bowman & Brown (19)
Guest, Keen, and Nettlefolds, Ltd.	–	Internal	–	B	C	O	W	Goom (57)
Hercules Inc.	"Multiterm" System	Internal	–	B	C, R	O	B	Skolnik & Clouser (192)
Infodata Systems, Inc.	–	INQUIRE	360/40	B, I	C, R	O	T	Bennett & Frycki (16) Starker et al. (200)
Institute for Scientific Information (ISI)	Automatic Subject Citation Alert	ASCA IV	360/30	B	C	O	B,C,T,W	Garfield (51) ISI (72)
International Business Machines (IBM)	Experimental Library Management System	ELMS	360/40	I	C, R	E	B	McAllister & Bell (116)
	BROWSER	BROWSER	360/	I	R	E	RF, T	Williams (237, 238)
	TEXT-PAC	TEXT-PAC	360/	B	R	O	T	Artandi & Struminger (7) Fong (47) IBM (77) Standera (196, 197, 198)
	Combined File Search System	CFSS	IBM-1401	B	R	O	B	Sessions & Sloan (188)
	Document Processing System	DPS	360/	B, I	C, R	O	T	Cook et al. (28) Scheffler et al. (172)
Lockheed Palo Alto Research Laboratory	DIALOG	DIALOG	360/40	I	R	O	B	Lockheed (109, 110)
Mead DATA CENTRAL	–	Mead DATA CENTRAL	360/40	I	R	O	T	Fong (47) McCabe (117) Porter et al. (154) Schultz (184)
New York Times	New York Times Information Bank	Internal	360/50	I	R	O	B	Fong (47)
Société-Nationale Industrielle Aerospatiale (France)	–	Internal	360/65 CII-10070	B	R	O	B	Roeper (161)
E.R. Squibb and Sons, Inc.	Squibb Science Information System (SSIS)	INQUIRE	360/40	B	C, R	O	T	Bennett & Frycki (16) Frycki (50)
System Development Corp. (SDC)	On-line Retrieval of Bibliographic Text	ORBIT II	360/40	B, I	R	O	B	Fong (47) Seiden (187)
Warner-Lambert Research Institute	–	INQUIRE	–	B	C, R	O	T	Starker et al. (200)
Xerox Education Group	Selective Dissemination of Information – Xerox	SDI-X	–	B	C	O	–	Xerox (249)

Note: Text (T) Searching Implies Boolean Logic (B) as well.

3. SYSTEMS DEVELOPED IN ACADEMIC, PROFESSIONAL, AND NON-PROFIT INSTITUTIONS

INSTITUTION	NAME	SEARCH SYSTEM	COMPUTER	Batch (B) or On-line Interactive (I)	Current Awareness (C) or Retrospective (R)	Operational (O) or Experimental (E)	*Search Mode: Boolean (B); Text (T); Weighted (W); Citation (C); Classif. (CL); Relevance Feedback (RF)	REFERENCES
Battelle Memorial Institute	Battelle Automated Search Information System	BASIS-70	CDC-6400	B, I	R	O	B[1]	Battelle (14) Covington (36) Fried (49) Penniman (151)
University of California. Lawrence Radiation Laboratory	–	Internal (CT)	IBM-7094	B	C	O	T	Hilliker (68)
	–	Internal (NSA)	CDC-6600	B	C, R	E	B	Smith & Herr (193) (Smith et al. (194)
University of California, Los Angeles, Institute of Library Research	Center for Information Services (CIS)	Internal	360/50	B	R	E	B, T, W	de Boer (39) Forrest (48) Watson (230)
University of Calgary, Information Systems and Services Division	–	TEXT-PAC	360/	B	C, R	O	T	Standera (196, 197, 198)
City University of New York	Project URBANDOC	CFSS	IBM-1401	B	R	E	B	Sessions & Sloan (188)
Cornell University	Salton's Magical Automatic Retrieval Technique/ System for the Mechanical Analysis and Retrieval of Text	SMART	360/65	B	R	E	B,C,T, RF, W	Salton (166, 168)
Czechoslovak Academy of Sciences. Centre for Inventions and Scientific Information		INDORES-4	EPOS-2	B	R	O	B,CL,T	Merta (131)
University of Georgia, Information Center	–	Internal	360/65	B	C, R	O	T	Carmon (24) Park et al. (147)
Helsinki University of Technology	–	TEXT-PAC	360/40	B	C, R	O	T	Ilukka (71) Katajapuro (84)
Illinois Institute of Technology Research (IITRI). Computer Search Center	–	Internal	360/40	B	C, R	O	T	Schipma et al. (178) Williams (240, 241)
University of Illinois. Coordinated Science Lab.	–	PLATO	–	I	R	E	–	Lyman (115)
Indiana University. Aerospace Research Applications Center (ARAC)	–	Internal	CDC-6600	B	C, R	O	W	Counts (33)

[1]Weighted and Text Searching Planned

Note: Text (T) Searching Implies Boolean Logic (B) as well.

3. SYSTEMS DEVELOPED IN ACADEMIC, PROFESSIONAL, AND NON-PROFIT INSTITUTIONS (continued)

INSTITUTION	NAME	SEARCH SYSTEM	COMPUTER	Batch (B) or On-line Interactive (I)	Current Awareness (C) cr Retrospective (R)	Operational (O) or Experimental (E)	*Search Mode: Boolean (B); Text (T); Weighted (W); Citation (C); Classif. (CL); Relevance Feedback (RF)	REFERENCE
Institution of Electrical Engineers	Information Service in Physics, Electro-Technology and Control (INSPEC)	Internal	–	B	C, R	O	T	Aitchison (1) Institution of Electrical Engineers (73)
Massachusetts Institute of Technology	Project INTREX (Information Transfer Experiments)	Internal	IBM-7094	I	R	E	T	MIT (124) Overhage (146)
	Technical Information Project (TIP)	Internal	IBM-7090	I	R	O	T	Wolfe (243)
University of Newcastle	U.K. MEDLARS Service	MEDLARS	–	B	R	O	B	Harley (61)
Oklahoma University	General Information Processing System	GIPSY	360/	B, I	R	O	T	Kowitz et al. (99)
Roswell Park Memorial Institute	Automatic Coder Report Narrative	ACORN	–	B	R	E	T	Shapiro & Stermole (189)
Royal Institute of Technology (Sweden)	AB Atomic Energy Computerized User Oriented Services	ABACUS	360/30	B	C	O	T	Gluchowitz (56) Tell et al. (205)
Rutgers University. Graduate School of Library Science	–	TEXT-PAC	360	B	R	E	T	Artandi & Struminger (7)
Stanford University	Bibliographic Automation of Large Library Operations Using a Time-Sharing System	BALLOTS	360/67	I	R	E	B	Epstein et al. (45)
Syracuse University	Syracuse University Psychological Abstracts Retrieval Service (SUPARS)	IBM's DPS	360/50	I	R	E	T	Cook et al. (28)
United Kingdom Chemical Information Service (UKCIS)	–	Internal	–	B	C, R	O	T	Barker et al. (11, 12) UKCIS (214)
University of Virginia	Abridged Index Medicus [By] Teletypewriter Exchange (AIM-TWX)	ELHILL II (ORBIT II)	360/67	I	R	E	B	Moll (136)
University of Washington	–	–	IBM-1130	I	R	O	T	Storie (201)

Note: Text (T) Searching Implies Boolean Logic (B) as well.

REFERENCES

(1) AITCHISON, T. M. Finding the correct indexing language. Presentation made to the Association of Scientific Information Dissemination Centers, Rochester, New York, 23 September 1970. The Institution of Electrical Engineers, The International Information Service in Physics, Electrotechnology, Computers and Control, London, England, 1970, 5 p.

(2) AMERICAN CHEMICAL SOCIETY. CHEMICAL ABSTRACTS SERVICE. Standard distribution format technical specifications. Revised. American Chemical Society, Columbus, Ohio, 1971, 57 p. (ISBN-8412-0106-4).

(3) AMERICAN INSTITUTE OF PHYSICS. INFORMATION DIVISION. SPIN: Searchable Physics Information Notices—technical specifications. American Institute of Physics, New York, New York, January 1971, 20 p. (AIP-ID-715).

(4) AMERICAN NATIONAL STANDARDS INSTITUTE. American national standard for bibliographic information interchange on magnetic tape. American National Standards Institute, New York, New York, 1971, 34 p. (ANSI-Z39.2-1971).

(5) AMERICAN NATIONAL STANDARDS INSTITUTE. American national standard guidelines for thesaurus structure, construction, and use. University of North Carolina Library, Chapel Hill, North Carolina, 1 September 1971, 34 p. (Draft).

(6) AMERICAN PSYCHOLOGICAL ASSOCIATION. Manual for users of psychological abstracts magnetic tape records. American Psychological Association, Washington, D.C., 1971, 37 p.

(7) ARTANDI, SUSAN; STRUMINGER, L. TEXT-PAC for teaching information science: a library manual. Rutgers University, Graduate School of Library Science, New Brunswick, New Jersey, 1971, 42 p. (PB 198 493).

(8) ASLIB COMPUTER APPLICATIONS GROUP. WORKING PARTY ON INFORMATION RETRIEVAL. USER-REACTION SUBGROUP. Criteria for computer output in information systems program. Program, 5:3 (July 1971) 165-169.

(9) ASSOCIATION FOR COMPUTING MACHINERY; NATIONAL AERONAUTICS AND SPACE ADMINISTRATION. Symposium on Information Storage and Retrieval. College Park, Maryland, 1-2 April 1971. Proceedings. Edited by Jack Minker and Sam Rosenfeld. University of Maryland, Conference and Institute Division, College Park, Maryland, 1971, 291 p. (ED 049 796).

(10) ASSOCIATION FRANÇAISE DES DOCUMENTALISTES ET DES BIBLIOTHÉCAIRES SPÉCIALISES (ADBS). L'Automatisation documentaire en France, et dans les pays d'expression française. Documentaliste, revue d'-information et de techniques documentaries, numéro special, hors-serie - 1971, 96 p.

(11) BARKER, F. H.; BATTEN, W. E.; VEAL, D. C.; WYATT, B. K. Some studies on computerised information retrieval techniques based on CA condensates. Presented at International Conference on Information Science, Tel-Aviv, Israel, 29 August - 3 September 1971, 6 p.

(12) BARKER, F. H.; VEAL, D. C.; WYATT, B. K. Comparative efficiency of searching titles, abstracts, and index terms in a free-text data base. Presented at the Third Cranfield International Conference on Mechanised Information Storage and Retrieval Systems, Cranfield Institute of Technology, Cranfield, England, July 1971, 16 p.

(13) BARKER, F. H.; VEAL, D. C.; WYATT, B. K. Towards automatic profile construction. Presented at the Third Cranfield International Conference on Mechanised Information Storage and Retrieval Systems, Cranfield Institute of Technology, Cranfield, England, July 1971, 13 p.

(14) BATTELLE MEMORIAL INSTITUTE. BASIS-70—A user guide. 3d ed. Battelle Memorial Institute, Columbus, Ohio, November 1971, 16 p.
(15) BENNERTZ, RICHARD K. Development of the Defense Documentation Center remote on-line retrieval system—past, present, and future. Defense Documentation Center, Alexandria, Virginia, March 1971, 51 p. (AD 720 900. DDC-TR-71-2. ED 050 799. N71-27868).
(16) BENNETT, RALPH E.; FRYCKI, STEPHEN J. Internal processing of external reference services. Journal of Chemical Documentation, 11:2 (May 1971) 76-83.
(17) BERUL, LAWRENCE H. Document retrieval. In: Cuadra, Carlos A.; ed. Annual review of information science and technology, vol. 4. Encyclopaedia Britannica, Chicago, Illinois, 1969, 203-227.
(18) BORBASH, STEVEN R., JR. Design of a document retrieval system using pattern recognition and mathematical programming techniques. University of Pittsburgh, Pittsburgh, Pennsylvania, 1970, 286 p. (Ph.D. thesis N71-24072).
(19) BOWMAN, CARLOS M.; BROWN, MARILYN T. The development, cost, and impact of a current awareness service in an industrial organization. Journal of Chemical Documentation, 11:2 (May 1971) 72-75.
(20) BROWN, JACK E. The CAN/SDI project training of users. Presented at the FID International Congress of Documentation, Buenos Aires, 21-24 September 1970. National Council for Scientific and Technical Research, Buenos Aires, Argentina, 1970, 11 p.
(21) BROWN, PATRICIA L.; JONES, SHIRLI O. Document retrieval and dissemination in libraries and information centers. In: Cuadra, Carlos A.; ed. Annual review of information science and technology, vol. 3. Encyclopaedia Britannica, Chicago, Illinois, 1968, 263-288.
(22) BURCHINAL, LEE G. ERIC: The National Education Documentation Retrieval System of the United States. Bulletin of the International Bureau of Education, Number 178 (First Quarter 1971) 9-15.
(23) CALESS, T. W.; FOSKETT, A. C.; LANGRIDGE, D.; MILLS, J.; PERREAULT, J. M. Strategies for manipulating Universal Decimal Classification relationships for computer retrieval. George Washington University, Biological Sciences Communication Project, Washington, D.C., December 1970, 40 p. (AFOSR-70-2926 TR. AD 717 212).
(24) CARMON, JAMES L. To expand the University of Georgia information center. Annual report to NSF covering the period 1 October 1969—30 September 1970. University of Georgia, Athens, Georgia, 1970, 76 p. (PB 195 274).
(25) CHOUEKA, Y.; COHEN, M.; DUECK, J.; FRAENKEL, A. S. Full text document retrieval: Hebrew legal texts (Report on the first phase of the Responsa Retrieval Project). In: Association for Computing Machinery. Symposium on Information Storage and Retrieval. College Park, Maryland, 1-2 April 1971. Proceedings. University of Maryland, Conference and Institute Division, College Park, Maryland, 1971, 61-79.
(26) COLES, VICTOR L. Remote evaluation of a remote console information retrieval system (NASA/RECON). Paper presented at the Forum on Interactive Bibliographic Systems, National Bureau of Standards, Washington, D.C., October 5, 1971. National Aeronautics and Space Administration, Washington, D.C., September 1971, 29 p.
(27) CONFERENCE ON DATA SYSTEMS LANGUAGES. SYSTEMS COMMITTEE. Feature analysis of generalized data base management systems. Association for Computing Machinery, New York, May 1971, 520 p. (ED 050 760).
(28) COOK, KENNETH H.; TRUMP, LYNN H.; ATHERTON, PAULINE; KATZER, JEFFREY. SUPARS: Syracuse University Psychological Abstracts Retrieval Service. Large scale information processing systems. Final report to the Rome Air Development Center. Syracuse University, School of Library Science, New York, July 1971. (Six sections in 7 vols.).

(29) COOPER, W. S. A definition of relevance for information retrieval. Information Storage and Retrieval, 7:1 (June 1971) 19-37.
(30) COOPER, W. S. On higher level association measures. Journal of the American Society for Information Science, 22:5 (September/October 1971) 354-355.
(31) CORBETT, L. Controlled versus natural language: a report on the great debate. The Information Scientist, 5:3 (September 1971) 115-120.
(32) COTTRELL, WILLIAM B.; BUCHANAN, J. R. NSIC computerized information techniques. Oak Ridge National Laboratory, Oak Ridge, Tennessee, August 1971, 27 p. (ORNL-NSIC-92).
(33) COUNTS, RICHARD W. The automated maintenance of current awareness profiles. Final report. Indiana University Foundation, Aerospace Research Application Center, Bloomington, Indiana, [n.d.], 90 p. (NASA-CR-94749. N68-86139).
(34) COUNTS, RICHARD W. The changing role of the information dissemination centers. Paper presented at the 1970 Annual Conference of the National Federation of Science Abstracting and Indexing Services, Boston, Massachusetts. Indiana University, Aerospace Research Applications Center, Bloomington, Indiana, 1970, 8 p.
(35) COUSINS, L. B. The Harwell Heat Transfer and Fluid Flow Information Centre. In: Advisory Group for Aerospace Research and Development. Conference Proceedings Number 78 on Information Analysis Centers. Neuilly-sur-Seine, France, February 1971, 4-1 - 4-6. (AGARD-CP-78-71. AD 719 716).
(36) COVINGTON, MARY W. Information center profile: Copper Data Center. Information, 3:4-5 (July-August/September-October 1971) 269-272.
(37) CROW, NEIL B.; ELCHESEN, DENNIS R. Monitoring and retrieving literature searches using a generalized file management system. In: American Society for Information Science. Annual meeting. 34th, Denver, Colorado, 7-11 November 1971. Proceedings, vol. 8: Communication for decision-makers. Greenwood Publishing Corp., Westport, Connecticut, 1971, 169-175.
(38) CUADRA, CARLOS A. On-line systems: promise and pitfalls. Journal of the American Society for Information Science, 22:2 (March/April 1971) 107-114.
(39) de BOER, AEINT. Center for information services. Phase II: detailed system design and programming. Part I: a modular computer program for reference retrieval. University of California, Institute of Library Research, Los Angeles, California, 1 March 1971, 46 p. (PB 201 754).
(40) DOLLAR, CHARLES M. Documentation of machine-readable records and research: a historian's view. Prologue, 3:1 (Spring 1971) 27-31.
(41) DUSOULIER, N.; BUFFET, P. Le Systeme P.A.S.C.A.L. Centre National de la Recherche Scientifique, Centre de Documentation, Paris, France, 1 July 1971, 18 p.
(42) EBERSOLE, JOSEPH L. Some probable technological trends and their impact on an information network system. Center for Applied Linguistics, Washington, D.C., May 1970, 13 p. (LINCS-3-70).
(43) EL-HADIDY, A. R. World-wide cooperation in scientific information—INIS. In: International Atomic Energy Agency. Handling of Nuclear Information, Vienna, Austria, 16-20 February 1970. Proceedings. International Atomic Energy Agency, Vienna, Austria, 1970, 623-630. (IAEA-SM-128/26. Available from UNIPUB Inc., P.O. Box 433, New York, New York).
(44) ELIAS, ARTHUR W.; ed. Key papers in information science. American Society for Information Science, Washington, D.C., 1971, 230 p. (ED 050 800).
(45) EPSTEIN, A. H.; FERGUSON, DOUGLAS; MONTAGUE, ELEANOR. An on-line network—cooperative planning with several libraries. In: American Society for Information Science Annual Meeting. 34th, Denver, Colorado, 7-11 November 1971. Proceedings, vol. 8: Communication for decision-makers. Greenwood Publishing Corp., Westport, Connecticut, 1971, 227-231.

(46) EPSTEIN, A. H.; FERGUSON, DOUGLAS; MONTAGUE, ELEANOR; SCHROEDER, JOHN; VEANER, ALLEN B. Bibliographic automation of large library operations using a time-sharing system: phase I. Final report. Stanford University Library, Stanford, California, April 1971, 334 p. (ED 049 786).
(47) FONG, ELIZABETH. A survey of selected document processing systems. National Bureau of Standards, Washington, D.C., October 1971, 67 p. (NBS-TN-599. GPO: C 13:46:599. ED 058 892).
(48) FORREST, KATHRYN S. Center for information services. Phase II: Detailed system design and programming. Part II: A study of customized literature searching using CA Condensates and CT magnetic tape data bases. University of California, Institute of Library Research, Los Angeles, California, 1 March 1971, 90 p. (PB 201 755).
(49) FRIED, J. B. BASIS-70 user interface. Presented at the AFIPS Information Systems Committee Workshop on the User Interface for Interactive Search of Bibliographic Data Bases, Palo Alto, California, 14-15 January 1971. Battelle Memorial Institute, Columbus, Ohio, 1971, 19 p.
(50) FRYCKI, STEPHEN J. Information transfer from source to user utilizing a pharmaceutical data base. In: National Information Retrieval Colloquium. Annual meeting. 8th, Philadelphia, Pennsylvania, 6-7 May 1971. Proceedings, 306-333.
(51) GARFIELD, EUGENE E. The role of man and machine in an international selective dissemination of information system. Ways to compile more effective user profiles, based on ISI's five years of SDI system experience. Paper presented at the International Congress of Documentation, Buenos Aires, Argentina, 21-24 September 1970, 26 p.
(52) GEISE, JOHN. The role of the regional dissemination centers in NASA's technology utilization program. National Aeronautics and Space Administration, Washington, D.C., May 1971, 110 p. (NASA CR-1763).
(53) GENERAL ELECTRIC COMPANY. SPACE DIVISION. GESCAN rapid search machine—a new dimension in information retrieval. 1971, 8 p. (Advertising brochure).
(54) GEORGE, RAY L. Automatic selective documentation services. Defense Documentation Center, Alexandria, Virginia, March 1971, 105 p. (AD 722 425. N71-74270).
(55) GLASSMAN, DAVID M. A high-speed computer system for searching file indexes. In: American Society for Information Science. Annual meeting. 34th, Denver, Colorado, 7-11 November 1971. Proceedings, vol. 8: Communication for decision-makers. Greenwood Publishing Corp., Westport, Connecticut, 1971, 247-255.
(56) GLUCHOWITZ, ZOPHIA. Selective dissemination from the user co-ordinators viewpoint. In: International Atomic Energy Agency. Handling of Nuclear Information, Vienna, Austria, 16-20 February 1970. Proceedings. International Atomic Energy Agency, Vienna, Austria, 1970, 227-237. (IAEA-SM-128/46. Available from UNIPUB Inc., P.O. Box 433, New York, New York).
(57) GOOM, H. H. SDI systems—A United Kingdom approach. Special Libraries, 62:12 (December 1971) 535-538.
(58) HALL, ANGELA M. The use and value of citations: a state of the art report. INSPEC, London, England, November 1970, 32 p. (Report no. R70/4).
(59) HALL, J. L.; TERRY, J. E. Development of mechanized current awareness services at Culham and Harwell. In: International Atomic Energy Agency. Handling of Nuclear Information, Vienna, Austria, 16-20 February 1970. Proceedings. International Atomic Energy Agency, Vienna, Austria, 1970, 201-209. (IAEA-SM-128/23. Available from UNIPUB Inc., P.O. Box 433, New York, New York).
(60) HANSEN, BERG. A comparative study of some information retrieval systems in chemistry and biomedicine. Industrie Chemique Belge, (December 1971) 1859-1865.

(61) HARLEY, A. J. On-line MEDLARS in the United Kingdom. Library Network/MEDLARS Technical Bulletin, May 1971, 5-8.
(62) HARMON, GLYNN. On the evolution of information science. Journal of the American Society for Information Science, 22:4 (July/August 1971) 235-241.
(63) HARTER, STEPHEN P. The Cranfield II relevance assessments: a critical evaluation. Library Quarterly, 41:3 (July 1971) 229-243.
(64) HEILIK, J. Information retrieval and MARC at the National Science Library. Canadian Library Journal (March/April 1971) 120-123.
(65) HENDERSON, KATHRYN LUTHER; ed. Proceedings of the 1970 Clinic on Library Applications of Data Processing: MARC use and users. University of Illinois, Graduate School of Library Science, Urbana, Illinois, 1971, 113 p.
(66) HERSEY, DAVID F.; FOSTER, WILLIS R.; STALDER, ERNEST W.; CARLSON, WILLIAM T. Comparison of on-line retrieval using free text words and scientist indexing. In: American Society for Information Science. Annual meeting. 33d, Philadelphia, Pennsylvania, 11-15 October 1970. Proceedings, vol. 7: The information conscious society. Greenwood Publishing Corp., Westport, Connecticut, 1970, 265-268.
(67) HERSEY, DAVID F.; FOSTER, WILLIS R.; STALDER, ERNEST W.; CARLSON, WILLIAM T. Free text word retrieval and scientist indexing: performance profiles and costs. Smithsonian Institution, Science Information Exchange, Washington, D.C., 1971, 24 p.
(68) HILLIKER, BRIGITTA. Selective dissemination of information using the Chemical Titles tape service. Journal of the American Society for Information Science, 22:5 (September/October 1971) 356-357. (Letters to the editor).
(69) HISINGER, B. A multi-disciplinary and computerized SDI service for industry and research—practical experience and costs. Information Storage and Retrieval, 7:4 (November 1971) 175-187.
(70) HJERPPE, E. ROLAND; LINDQUIST, MATS G. A model for the evaluation of information retrieval systems considering the decision situation of the user. In: American Society for Information Science. Annual meeting. 34th, Denver, Colorado, 7-11 November 1971. Proceedings, vol. 8: Communication for decision-makers. Greenwood Publishing Corp., Westport, Connecticut, 1971, 77-81.
(71) ILUKKA, ERKKI. Search programs used for INIS in Otaniemi. In: Library Occasional Paper #4, Helsinki University of Technology, Otaniemi, Finland, 1971, 7 p.
(72) INSTITUTE FOR SCIENTIFIC INFORMATION. ASCA IV—ISI automatic subject citation alert. Institute for Scientific Information, Philadelphia, Pennsylvania, [1971], 12 p. (Advertising brochure).
(73) INSTITUTION OF ELECTRICAL ENGINEERS. INFORMATION SERVICE IN PHYSICS, ELECTROTECHNOLOGY AND CONTROL (INSPEC). SDI user manual. Institution of Electrical Engineers, London, England, 1971, 24 p.
(74) INTERNATIONAL ATOMIC ENERGY AGENCY. CINDA 71: An index to the literature on microscopic neutron data. International Atomic Energy Agency, Vienna, Austria, February 1971, 1270 p. (TID-25736).
(75) INTERNATIONAL ATOMIC ENERGY AGENCY. INIS reference series. International Atomic Energy Agency, Vienna, Austria, 1969-1971, 14 vols. (IAEA-INIS-1 through 13A).
(76) INTERNATIONAL BUSINESS MACHINES CORPORATION. An introduction to information retrieval. International Business Machines Corporation, Data Processing Division, White Plains, New York, February 1971, 36 p. (GE-20-0348-0, ED 050 794).
(77) INTERNATIONAL BUSINESS MACHINES CORPORATION. Searching normal text for information retrieval. International Business Machines Corp., White Plains, New York, May 1970, 18 p. (IBM Data Processing Application GE20-0335-1).

(78) JACKSON, DAVID M. Optimal classification and its consequences. In: Association for Computing Machinery. Symposium on Information Storage and Retrieval. College Park, Maryland, 1-2 April 1971. Proceedings. University of Maryland, Conference and Institute Division, College Park, Maryland, 1971, 217-224.

(79) JACOB, M. E. Selective dissemination of information systems: problems and decisions. LASIE, Information Bulletin of the Library Automated System Information Exchange (Australia), 1:5 (January/February 1971) 12-24.

(80) JAHODA, GERALD. Information storage and retrieval systems for individual researchers. Wiley-Interscience, New York, 1970, 135 p.

(81) JAHODA, GERALD; FOOS, FEROL A. The development of an on-line searched coordinate index for use in teaching and research. Florida State University, Computer-Assisted Instruction Center, Tallahassee, Florida, 30 September 1970, 32 p. (Technical memo 22).

(82) JOHNSON, CLAIRE; BRIGGS, ELEANOR. Holography as applied to information storage and retrieval systems. Journal of the American Society for Information Science, 22:3 (May/June 1971) 187-192.

(83) JONES, KEVIN P. Compound words: a problem in post-coordinate retrieval systems. Journal of the American Society for Information Science, 22:4 (July/August 1971) 242-250.

(84) KATAJAPURO, LEENA. Finnish experience from SDI-service based on Nuclear Science Abstracts (NSA). In: Library Occasional Paper #4, Helsinki University of Technology, Otaniemi, Finland, 1971, 8-12.

(85) KATCHER, A. M. Efficient utilization of limited access archival storage in a time shared environment. In: Association for Computing Machinery. Symposium on Information Storage and Retrieval. College Park, Maryland, 1 - 2 April 1971. Proceedings. University of Maryland, Conference and Institute Division, College Park, Maryland, 1971, 197-205.

(86) KATTER, ROBERT V.; HOLMES, EMORY H.; WEIS, RICHARD L. Interpretive overlap among document surrogates: effects of judgemental point of view and consensus factors. System Development Corporation, Santa Monica, California, 15 January 1971, 87 p. (SP-3573. PB 196 798).

(87) KEENAN, STELLA. Organization profile: National Federation of Science Abstracting and Indexing Services. Information, 3:1 (January/February 1971) 53-56.

(88) KENT, ALLEN. Information analysis and retrieval. Wiley-Becker-Hayes, New York, 1971, 367 p. (Based on Textbook on Mechanized Information Retrieval, 1962 and 1966).

(89) KENT, ALLEN; LANCOUR, HAROLD; eds. Encyclopedia of library and information science. Marcel Dekker, Inc., New York, 1968- (Projected 18 volume set; 4 volumes published through 1971).

(90) KING, DONALD W.; BRYANT, EDWARD C. The evaluation of information services and products. Information Resources Press, Washington, D.C., 1971, 306 p. (ISBN-O-87815-003-X).

(91) KING, DONALD W.; CALDWELL, NANCY W. Cost-effectiveness of retrospective search systems. American Psychological Association, Washington, D.C., March 1971, 28 p. (OC-3/71-TR#14).

(92) KISSMAN, HENRY M. Toxicology information program of the National Library of Medicine. Paper presented before the American Chemical Society National Meeting, 162d, Washington, D.C., 13 September 1971, 31 p.

(93) KLINGBIEL, PAUL H. The future of indexing and retrieval vocabularies. Defense Documentation Center, Alexandria, Virginia, November 1970, 31 p. (DDC-TR-70-4. AD 716 200).

(94) KLINGBIEL, PAUL H. Machine aided indexing. National Technical Information Service, Alexandria, Virginia, March 1971, 152 p. (DDC-TR-71-3. AD 721 875).

(95) KNOTT, GARY D. A balanced tree storage and retrieval algorithm. In: Association for Computing Machinery. Symposium on Information Storage and Retrieval. College Park, Maryland, 1-2 April 1971. Proceedings. University of Maryland, Conference and Institute Division, College Park, Maryland, 1971, 175-196.

(96) KOCH, H. WILLIAM. Current physics information. Science, 174:4012 (26 November 1971) 918-922.

(97) KOHLER, C.; WAGNER, G. Erste erfahrungen mit dem SABIR-System in Heidelberg. II. Programmtechnische aspekte. (Present experience with the SABIR-System in Heidelberg. II. Program aspects.) In: Lettre, H.; Wagner, G.; eds. Actual problems from the area of cancer research III. Springer-Verlag, Berlin, Germany, 1971, 208-213.

(98) KONIGOVA, MARIE. Mathematical and statistical methods of noise evaluation in a retrieval system. Information Storage and Retrieval, 6:6 (May 1971) 437-444.

(99) KOWITZ, GERALD T.; REEVES, RONALD R.; PRATHER, JERRY R. General Information Processing System: The GIPSY/ERIC abstract retrieval system. University of Oklahoma, Norman, Oklahoma, 1971, 89 p. (Information science series monograph 5. ED 047 763).

(100) KREGER, ALAN; NATHANSON, JANET. The tribulations and triumphs of GIS. Datamation, 7:20 (15 October 1971) 20-25.

(101) KRUZAS, ANTHONY T.; SCHNITZER, ANNA ERCOLI; eds. Encyclopedia of information systems and services. 1st ed. Edwards Brothers, Ann Arbor, Michigan, 1971, 1109 p.

(102) KUGEL, PETER. Dirty Boole? Journal of the American Society for Information Science, 22:4 (July/August 1971) 293-294.

(103) KUNEY, JOSEPH H.; DOUGHERTY, VINCENT E. An experiment in selective dissemination—the ACS single article service. Journal of Chemical Documentation, 11:1 (February 1971) 9-11.

(104) KURTZ, PETER; LOWE, THOMAS C.; BAKERT, THOMAS A. On-line retrieval. Informatics, Inc., Bethesda, Maryland, August 1971, 407 p. (RADC-TR-71-157. AD 730 305).

(105) LANCASTER, F. WILFRID. The cost-effectiveness analysis of information retrieval and dissemination systems. Journal of the American Society for Information Science, 22:1 (January/February 1971) 12-27.

(106) LANDAU, HERBERT B. Can the librarian become a computer data base manager? Special Libraries, 62:3 (March 1971) 117-124.

(107) LANDAU, HERBERT B. Document dissemination. In: Cuadra, Carlos A.; ed. Annual review of information science and technology, vol. 4. Encyclopaedia Britannica, Chicago, Illinois, 1969, 229-270.

(108) LEE, P. J.; HANSEN, JUDITH A.; MARSHALL, K. E. Storage and retrieval of indexed and annotated bibliographic references. Fisheries Research Board of Canada, Winnipeg, Manitoba, Canada, 1971, 47 p. (Technical report no. 209).

(109) LOCKHEED PALO ALTO RESEARCH LABORATORY. DIALOG terminal users reference manual [For ERIC/DIALOG]. Lockheed Palo Alto Research Laboratory, Palo Alto, California, 1971, 21 p.

(110) LOCKHEED PALO ALTO RESEARCH LABORATORY. Users manual AEC/DIALOG online retrieval system. Lockheed Palo Alto Research Laboratory, Palo Alto, California, August 1970, 32 p. (TID-25730).

(111) LONG, PHILIP L.; KILGOUR, FREDERICK G. Name-title entry retrieval from a MARC file. Journal of Library Automation, 4:4 (December 1971) 211-212.

(112) LONG, PHILIP L.; RASTOGI, K. B. L.; RUSH, J. E.; WYCKOFF, J. A. Large on-line files of bibliographic data: an efficient design and a mathematical predictor of retrieval behavior. In: International Federation for Information Processing. IFIP Congress 1971. Ljubljana, Yugoslavia, 23-28 August 1971. Proceedings. North Holland Publishing Co., Amsterdam, The Netherlands, 1971, Booklet TA-3: Computer software, 145-149.

(113) LOWE, THOMAS C. Effectiveness of retrieval key abbreviation schemes. Journal of the American Society for Information Science, 22:6 (November/December 1971) 374-381.

(114) LUTZ, RAYMOND P. Costing information services. Bulletin of the Medical Library Association, 59:2 (April 1971) 254-261.

(115) LYMAN, ELISABETH R. An on-line document retrieval strategy using the Plato system. University of Illinois, Coordinated Science Laboratory, Urbana, Illinois, June 1971, 14 p. (UILU-ENG 71-2217. AD 726 921).

(116) McALLISTER, CARYL; BELL, JOHN M. Human factors in the design of an interactive library system. Journal of the American Society for Information Science, 22:2 (March/April 1971) 96-104.

(117) McCABE, DIANA FITCH. Automated legal research—a discussion of current effectiveness and future development. Judicature, 54:7 (February 1971) 283-289.

(118) McCARN, DAVIS B. AIM-TWX: an experimental on-line bibliographic retrieval system. Presented at the AFIPS Information Systems Committee Workshop on the User Interface for Interactive Search of Bibliographic Data Bases, San Jose, California, 14-15 January 1971. National Library of Medicine, Lister Hill National Center for Biomedical Communications, Bethesda, Maryland, January 1971, 24 p.

(119) McCARN, DAVIS B. Networks with emphasis on planning an on-line bibliographic access system. Paper presented at the Third Cranfield International Conference on Mechanized Information Storage and Retrieval Systems, Cranfield Institute of Technology, Cranfield, England, 20-23 July 1971. National Library of Medicine, Lister Hill National Center for Biomedical Communications, Bethesda, Maryland, 1971, 13 p.

(120) McCARTHY, WILLIAM E. LITE (Legal Information Thru Electronics)—A progress report. Law Library Journal, 64:2 (May 1971) 193-197.

(121) McCASH, W. H.; CARMICHAEL, J. J. UDC user profiles as developed for a computer-based SDI service in the iron and steel industry. Journal of Documentation, 26:4 (December 1970) 295-312.

(122) MAGNINO, JOSEPH J., JR. Document retrieval and dissemination. In: Cuadra, Carlos A.; ed. Annual review of information science and technology, vol. 6. Encyclopaedia Britannica, Chicago, Illinois, 1971, 219-245.

(123) MARRON, HARVEY; SULLIVAN, PATRICIA. Information dissemination in education: a status report. College and Research Libraries, 32:4 (July 1971) 286-294.

(124) MASSACHUSETTS INSTITUTE OF TECHNOLOGY. Project INTREX, semiannual activity report, 15 March 1971—15 September 1971. Massachusetts Institute of Technology, Cambridge, Massachusetts, 15 September 1971, 125 p. (ED 053 772).

(125) MATHEWS, FRED W. Weighted term search: a strategy for searching a large file by computer for document retrieval. In: American Society for Information Science. Annual meeting. 33d, Philadelphia, Pennsylvania, 1970. Proceedings, vol. 7: The information conscious society. Greenwood Publishing Corp., Westport, Connecticut, 1970, 315-317.

(126) MAUERHOFF, GEORG R. NSL profiling and search editing. In: American Society for Information Science, Western Canada Chapter. Annual meeting. 2d, Vancouver Public Library, 14-15 September 1970. Proceedings. Edited by F. T. Dolan. 32-53. (ED 050 791).

(127) MAUERHOFF, GEORG R.; SMITH, RICHARD A. A MARC II-based program for retrieval and dissemination. Journal of Library Automation, 4:3 (September 1971) 141-158.

(128) MEETHAM, ROGER. Information retrieval—the essential technology. Doubleday, Garden City, New York, 1970, 192 p. (SD-18).

(129) MENKUS, BELDEN. Retention of data for the long term. Datamation, 17:18 (15 September 1971) 30-32.

(130) MEREDITH, J. C. Machine-assisted approach to general reference materials. Journal of the American Society for Information Science, 22:3 (May/June 1971) 176-186.

(131) MERTA, AUGUSTIN. INDORES 4—A mechanized system of information retrieval in the field of information science. In: Foskett, D. J.; de Reuck, A.; Coblans, H.; eds. Proceedings of the Second Anglo-Czech Conference of Information Specialists, Archon Books, Hamden, Connecticut, 1970, 103-106.

(132) MEYER, ROGER L.; MESKIN, AMY J.; MRACEK, JOHN J.; SCHWARTZ, JAMES H.; WHEELIHAN, EMMA C. A systematic approach to current awareness and SDI. Journal of Chemical Documentation, 11:1 (February 1971) 19-24.

(133) MEYER, ROGER L.; MESKIN, AMY J.; MRACEK, JOHN J.; SCHWARTZ, JAMES H.; WHEELIHAN, EMMA C. User study of current awareness and SDI at Celanese Research Company. Journal of Chemical Documentation, 11:1 (February 1971) 24-29.

(134) MILLER, WILLIAM L. The efficiency of MEDLARS titles for retrieval. Journal of the American Society for Information Science, 22:5 (September/October 1971) 318-321.

(135) MILLER, WILLIAM L. The extension of user's literature awareness as a measure of retrieval performance, and its application to MEDLARS. Journal of Documentation, 27:2 (June 1971) 125-135.

(136) MOLL, WILHELM. AIM-TWX Service at the University of Virginia. A review and evaluation. Bulletin of the Medical Library Association, 59:3 (July 1971) 458-462.

(137) MULFORD, JAMES E.; RIDALL, RICHARD K. Data compression techniques for economic processing of large commercial files. In: Association for Computing Machinery. Symposium on Information Storage and Retrieval. College Park, Maryland, 1-2 April 1971. Proceedings. University of Maryland, Conference and Institute Division, College Park, Maryland, 1971, 207-215.

(138) NANCE, RICHARD E. Organization profile: Special Interest Group on Information Retrieval of the Association for Computing Machinery. Information, 3:4-5 (July-August/September-October 1971) 277-278.

(139) NATIONAL FEDERATION OF SCIENCE ABSTRACTING AND INDEXING SERVICES. Data element definitions for secondary services. Philadelphia, Pennsylvania, June 1971, 12 p. (NFSAIS-R-3).

(140) NEGUS, A. E. A real time interactive reference retrieval system. Information Scientist, 5:1 (March 1971) 29-44.

(141) NEWMAN, WILLIAM L.; BUCHINSKI, EDWIN J. Entry/title compression code access to machine readable bibliographic files. Journal of Library Automation, 4:2 (June 1971) 72-85.

(142) NUGENT, WILLIAM R. The U. S. Patent Office data base: a full text communications format for computer-aided classification, retrieval, and examination of patents. In: American Society for Information Science. Annual meeting. 34th, Denver, Colorado, 7-11 November 1971. Proceedings, vol. 8: Communication for decision-makers. Greenwood Publishing Corp., Westport, Connecticut, 1971, 179-184.

(143) OLSEN, HAROLD ANKER. The economics of information: bibliography and commentary on the literature. ERIC Clearinghouse on Library and Information Sciences, Washington, D.C., January 1971, 30 p. (ED 044 545).

(144) ONDERISIN, ELAINE M. The least common bigram: a dictionary arrangement technique for computerized natural-language text searching. IIT Research Institute, Chicago, Illinois, [n.d.], 18 p.

(145) ORGANISATION FOR ECONOMIC CO-OPERATION AND DEVELOPMENT. Inventory of major information systems and services in science and technology. Organisation for Economic Co-operation and Development, Paris, France, 1971, 340 p. (ED 051 839. PB 201 134).

(146) OVERHAGE, CARL F. J. Project INTREX: a brief description. Massachusetts Institute of Technology, Cambridge, Massachusetts, 1971, 26 p.

(147) PARK, M. K.; CAUGHMAN, M. C.; HAMILTON, H. J. Education in the use of modern information retrieval techniques. Journal of Chemical Documentation, 11:2 (May 1971) 100-102.

(148) PARKER, JANET E. Preliminary assessment of the comparative efficiencies of an SDI system using controlled or natural language for retrieval. Program, 5:1 (January 1971) 26-34.

(149) PATTERSON, ALBERT C., IV. Requirements for a generalized data base management system. In: American Society for Information Science. Annual meeting. 34th, Denver, Colorado, 7-11 November 1971. Proceedings, vol. 8: Communication for decision-makers. Greenwood Publishing Corp., Westport, Connecticut, 1971, 185-187.

(150) PELZER, CHARLES W.; TURKOV, ZHAN; WOOLSTON, JOHN E. The International Nuclear Information System. An exercise in international co-operation and a service to nuclear scientists and engineers. Paper presented at the Fourth United Nations International Conference on the Peaceful Uses of Atomic Energy, Geneva, Switzerland, 6-16 September 1971, 13 p. (A/CONF.49/P/206 IAEA July 1971).

(151) PENNIMAN, WILLIAM D. BASIS-70—Design, implementation, and operation. Presented at the Seventh Annual Symposium on On-Line Systems sponsored by the New York Chapter of American Society for Information Science, 9 October 1971. Battelle Memorial Institute, Columbus, Ohio, 1971, 19 p.

(152) PICKFORD, A. G. A. Some problems of using an unstructured information retrieval language in a co-ordinate indexing system. Aslib Proceedings, 23:3 (March 1971) 133-138.

(153) PLOTKIN, M.; EPSTEIN, S. D. Noise—its effect on depth of file search. Information Storage and Retrieval, 7:2 (August 1971) 79-87.

(154) PORTER, ROGER J.; PENRY, J. KIFFIN; CAPONIO, JOSEPH F. Epilepsy Abstracts Retrieval System (EARS): a new concept for medical literature storage and retrieval. Bulletin of the Medical Library Association, 59:3 (July 1971) 430-432.

(155) PRICE, DOUGLAS S. Collecting and reporting real costs of information systems. Prepared for the Tutorial Session sponsored by the ASIS Special Interest Group on Costs, Budgeting and Economics at the 1971 Annual Meeting of the American Society for Information Science. American Society for Information Science, Washington, D.C., November 1971, 170 p.

(156) RAITT, D. I. Space Documentation Service: operations handbook. European Space Research Organization, Neuilly-sur-Seine, France, May 1971, 47 p. (ESRO-SP-63).

(157) RAMSEY-KLEE, DIANE M. Navy Medical Information Storage and Retrieval System (Navy MEDISTARS): Design and development of the Navy MEDISTARS system and indexing of the initial research data base. R-K Research and System Design, Malibu, California, April 1971, 65 p. (Technical Report No. 1-71: Part one. AD 724 306).

(158) RATHER, JOHN C. The realities of interchanging machine-readable bibliographic records. U.S. Library of Congress, Washington, D.C., May 1971, 14 p.

(159) REES, ALAN M. Interface of technical libraries with other information systems. A synthesis. U.S. Department of the Army, Office of the Chief of Engineers, Washington, D.C., March 1971, 132 p. (TISA-35).

(160) RESNIKOFF, H. L.; DOLBY, J. L. ACCESS: a study of information storage and retrieval with emphasis on library information systems. R & D Consultants Company, Los Altos, California, 21 May 1971, 218 p. (ED 050 773).
(161) ROEPER, Y. J. Un centre de documentation specialise: son organisation-ses methodes-son efficacite. In: Advisory Group for Aerospace Research and Development. Conference Proceedings Number 78 on Information Analysis Centers. Neuilly-sur-Seine, France, February 1971, 3-1—3-9. (AGARD-CP-78-71. AD 719 716).
(162) ROLLING, L. N. Progress in information retrieval. In: International Atomic Energy Agency. Handling of Nuclear Information, Vienna, Austria, 16-20 February 1970. Proceedings. International Atomic Energy Agency, Vienna, Austria, 1970, 251-265. (IAEA-SM-128/52. Available from UNIPUB Inc., P.O. Box 433, New York, New York).
(163) SALTON, GERARD. Automatic indexing using bibliographic citations. Journal of Documentation, 27:2 (June 1971) 98-110.
(164) SALTON, GERARD. Computers and libraries—a reply. Library Journal, 96:18 (15 October 1971) 3277-3288.
(165) SALTON, GERARD. Evaluation problems in interactive information retrieval. Information Storage and Retrieval, 6:1 (May 1970) 29-44.
(166) SALTON, GERARD; et al. Information storage and retrieval—reports on analysis, dictionary construction, user feedback, clustering, and on-line retrieval. Cornell University, Department of Computer Science, Ithaca, New York, October 1970, 523 p. (ISR-18. ED 048 910. PB 198 069. N71-26306).
(167) SALTON, GERARD. New approaches to automatic document processing. Cornell University, Ithaca, New York, December 1971, 46 p. (CU-CSD-71-117. PB 205 605).
(168) SALTON, GERARD; ed. The SMART retrieval system—experiments in automatic document processing. Prentice-Hall, Inc., Englewood Cliffs, New Jersey, 1971, 556 p.
(169) SANDOR, L. Erste erfahrungen mit dem SABIR-System in Heidelberg. I. Datenerfassung und datenverarbeitung. (Present experience with the SABIR-System in Heidelberg. I. Data collection and data processing.) In: Lettre, H.; Wagner, G.; eds. Actual problems from the area of cancer research III. Springer-Verlag, Berlin, Germany, 1971, 208-213.
(170) SARACEVIC, TEFKO. Selected results from an inquiry into testing of information retrieval systems. Journal of the American Society for Information Science, 22:2 (March/April 1971) 126-139.
(171) SARACEVIC, TEFKO; comp. & ed. Introduction to information science. R. R. Bowker Company, New York and London, 1970, 751 p.
(172) SCHEFFLER, F. L.; DODSON, A. T.; BOZDECH, J. O. Development and application of lexicographic decision making criteria to the building of files for a document processing system. University of Dayton Research Institute, Dayton, Ohio, June 1971, 142 p. (UDRI-TR-71-15).
(173) SCHEFFLER, F. L.; MARCH, J. F. Evaluation of the Selective Dissemination of Information (SDI) program for the Aerospace Materials Information Center. U.S. Air Force Materials Laboratory, Wright-Patterson Air Force Base, Ohio, March 1971, 78 p. (AFML-TR-71-11. AD 725 036. ED 050 775).
(174) SCHIEBER, WILLIAM D. ISIS (Integrated Scientific Information System): a general description of an approach to computerised bibliographical control. International Labour Office, Geneva, Switzerland, 1971, 115 p. (ED 054 801. Available from International Labour Office, Washington Branch, 666 Eleventh Street, Washington, D.C.).
(175) SCHIEBER, WILLIAM D.; THOMAS, GEORGE W. An algorithm for compaction of alphanumeric data. Journal of Library Automation, 4:4 (December 1971) 198-206.

(176) SCHIMINOVICH, SAMUEL. Automatic classification and retrieval of documents by means of a bibliographic pattern discovery algorithm. Information Storage and Retrieval, 6:6 (May 1971) 417-435.

(177) SCHIPMA, PETER B. Term fragment analysis for inversion of large files. IIT Research Institute, Chicago, Illinois, 4 June 1971, 16 p.

(178) SCHIPMA, PETER B.; LOUTHAN, BARBARA LYNN; BOONE, BARBARA A. Use of PL/1 in a bibliographic information retrieval system. IIT Research Institute, Chicago, Illinois, 15 January 1971, 17 p. (ED 048 907).

(179) SCHIPMA, PETER B.; WILLIAMS, MARTHA E.; SHAFTON, ALLAN L. Comparison of document data bases. Journal of the American Society for Information Science, 22:5 (September/October 1971) 326-332.

(180) SCHNEIDER, JOHN H. A preliminary annotated bibliography of papers related to the use of classifications in automated information systems. National Cancer Institute, Bethesda, Maryland, August 1971, 29 p. (PB 202 462).

(181) SCHNEIDER, JOHN H. Selective dissemination and indexing of information. Science, 173:3994 (23 July 1971) 300-308.

(182) SCHULER, S. C. Selective dissemination of information: a system review. In: Advisory Group for Aerospace Research and Development. Scientific and technical information—Why? Which? Where? and How? London, England, February 1971, 20 p. (AGARD-LS-44-71. N71-23501. AD 721 730).

(183) SCHULTZ, LOUISE. Measuring the requirements for exchange of toxicology information. Paper presented at the Division of Chemical Literature, American Chemical Society Meeting, Los Angeles, California, 30 March 1971. Bioscience Information Service, Philadelphia, Pennsylvania, 1971, 18 p.

(184) SCHULTZ, LYNN. Information retrieval in law. Computers and Automation, 20:1 (November 1971) 12-14.

(185) SCOTT, E. J.; TOWNLEY, H. M.; STERNE, B. T. A technique for the evaluation of a commercial information service and some preliminary results from the DRUGDOC service of the Excerpta Medica Foundation. Information Storage and Retrieval, 7:4 (November 1971) 149-165.

(186) SEIDEN, HERBERT R. A comparative analysis of interactive storage and retrieval systems with implications for BCN design. System Development Corporation, Santa Monica, California, 12 January 1970, 62 p. (TM-4421).

(187) SEIDEN, HERBERT R. ORBIT II system information. System Development Corporation, Santa Monica, California, March 1971, 27 p.

(188) SESSIONS, VIVIAN S.; SLOAN, LYNDA W. URBANDOC / A bibliographic information system. The City University of New York, New York, 1971, 3 vols. Vol. 1: Demonstration report. 166 p. (URBANDOC-71-1. ED 051 821). Vol. 2: Technical supplement 1/general manual. 208 p. (URBANDOC-71-2. ED 051 822). Vol. 3: Technical supplement 2/operations manual. 243 p. (URBANDOC-71-3. ED 051 823).

(189) SHAPIRO, PAUL A.; STERMOLE, DAVID F. ACORN (Automatic Coder Report Narrative): An automated natural-language question-answering system for surgical reports. Computers and Automation, 20:2 (February 1971) 13-18.

(190) SHARP, JOHN R. Where do we go from here? Aslib Proceedings, 23:1 (January 1971) 33-46.

(191) SIMMS, DANIEL. A brief comparison of specific and general purpose software. The LARC Reports, 4:1 (1971) 7-23.

(192) SKOLNIK, HERMAN; CLOUSER, BENN E. Designing an information awareness and retrieval system for chemical propulsion literature. Journal of Chemical Documentation, 11:1 (February 1971) 39-43.

(193) SMITH, GLORIA L.; HERR, JOANNE, J. Searching the Nuclear Science Abstracts data base by use of the Berkeley Mass Storage System. University of California, Lawrence Radiation Laboratory, Berkeley, California, February 1971, 13 p. (UCRL-20286).

(194) SMITH, GLORIA L.; HERR, JOANNE J.; WAKERLING, R. K. An SDI system based on NSA magnetic tapes. In: International Atomic Energy Agency. Handling of Nuclear Information, Vienna, Austria, 16-20 February 1970. Proceedings. International Atomic Energy Agency, Vienna, Austria, 1970, 251-265. (IAEA-SM-128/33. Available from UNIPUB Inc., P.O. Box 433, New York, New York).

(195) SPARCK JONES, KAREN; BARBER, E. O. What makes an automatic keyword classification effective? Journal of the American Society for Information Science, 22:3 (May/June 1971) 166-175.

(196) STANDERA, OLDRICH R. COMPENDEX profile adjustment manual. Information Retrieval Research Council of Alberta, Edmonton, Canada, November 1970, 21 p.

(197) STANDERA, OLDRICH R. COPENDEX/TEXT-PAC retrospective search. University of Calgary, Information Systems and Services Division, Calgary, Alberta, Canada, May 1971, 62 p. (Report no. 9. ED 051 862).

(198) STANDERA, OLDRICH R. TEXT-PAC input, bulletin and indexes. University of Calgary, Information Systems and Services Division, Calgary, Alberta, Canada, January 1971, 22 p.

(199) STANFEL, L. E. Sequential adaptation of retrieval systems based on user inputs. Information Storage and Retrieval, 7:2 (August 1971) 69-78.

(200) STARKER, LEE N.; OWEN, K. C.; MARTIN, J. W., JR. Multi-level retrieval systems: IV. Large systems. Presented before the 161st Meeting of the American Chemical Society, Los Angeles, California, March 30, 1971. Warner-Lambert Research Institute, Morris Plains, New Jersey, 1971, 21 p.

(201) STORIE, J. MICHAEL. An interactive key word information retrieval system for the IBM 1130 computer. University of Washington, Urban Data Center, Seattle, Washington, 1971, 184 p. (PB 201 591).

(202) STUEART, ROBERT D. An analysis of the Universal Decimal Classification as a term system for nuclear science and technology. Library Resources and Technical Services, 15:3 (Summer 1971) 399-411.

(203) SVENONIUS, ELAINE. The effect of indexing specificity on retrieval performance. University of Chicago, Chicago, Illinois, March 1971, 426 p. (Ph.D dissertation. ED 051 863).

(204) SWANSON, DON R. Some unexplained aspects of the Cranfield tests of indexing performance factors. The Library Quarterly, 41:3 (July 1971) 223-228.

(205) TELL, B. V.; LARSSON, R.; LINDH, R. Information retrieval with the ABACUS program—an experiment in compatibility. In: International Atomic Energy Agency. Handling of Nuclear Information, Vienna, Austria, 16-20 February 1970. Proceedings. International Atomic Energy Agency, Vienna, Austria, 1970, 183-200. (IAEA-SM-128/21. Available from UNIPUB Inc., P.O. Box 433, New York, New York).

(206) THIEL, L. H.; HEAPS, H. S. Program design for retrospective searches on large data bases. Presented at the Third Cranfield International Congress on Mechanized Information Storage and Retrieval Systems, Cranfield Institute of Technology, Cranfield, England, July 1971. University of Alberta, Department of Computer Science, Edmonton, Alberta, Canada, 1971, 38 p.

(207) THOMPSON, DAVID A. Interface design for an interactive information retrieval system: A literature survey and a research system description. Journal of the American Society for Information Science, 22:6 (November/December 1971) 361-373.

(208) TILLMANNS, EMMA-JUNE H.; BOYLEN, JOYCE B.; KENDIS, MERWIN S. Atlas Biomedical Literature System—a computerized current awareness and information storage and retrieval system. Journal of Chemical Documentation, 11:4 (November 1971) 242-248.

(209) TOWNLEY, HELEN M. A look at natural language retrieval systems. Information Scientist, 5:1 (March 1971) 3-15.
(210) TURSKI, W. M. On a model of information retrieval system based on thesaurus. Information Storage and Retrieval, 7:2 (August 1971) 89-94.
(211) UNESCO. Guidelines for the establishment and development of monolingual scientific and technical thesauri for information retrieval. UNESCO, Paris, France, 6 July 1970, 14 p. (SC/MD/20).
(212) UNESCO. UNISIST: Study report on the feasibility of a world science information system. UNESCO, Paris, France, 1971, 161 p. (ED 054 808).
(213) UNESCO. UNISIST: Synopsis of the feasibility study on a world science information system. UNESCO, Paris, France, 1971, 92 p. (ED 050 752).
(214) UNITED KINGDOM CHEMICAL INFORMATION SERVICE. Computer-based services—general descriptions. United Kingdom Chemical Information Service, Nottingham, England, March 1971, 17 p.
(215) U.S. DEPARTMENT OF THE AIR FORCE. OFFICE OF THE JUDGE ADVOCATE GENERAL. LITE BRANCH. The LITE (Legal Information Thru Electronics) System. 1 March 1971, 22 p.
(216) U.S. NATIONAL ARCHIVES AND RECORDS SERVICE. OFFICE OF RECORDS MANAGEMENT. Managing information retrieval. Information retrieval systems. U.S. Government Printing Office, Washington, D.C., 1970, 150 p. (Records Management Handbook FPMR 101-11.3).
(217) U.S. NATIONAL ARCHIVES AND RECORDS SERVICE. OFFICE OF RECORDS MANAGEMENT. Managing information retrieval. Microform retrieval equipment guide. U.S. Government Printing Office, Washington, D.C., 1970, 64 p. (Records Management Handbook FPMR-101-11.3. ED 051 865).
(218) U.S. NATIONAL BUREAU OF STANDARDS. Federal information processing standards index. U.S. Government Printing Office, Washington, D.C., 1 January 1971, 143 p. (FIPS-PUB-12. ED 048 904).
(219) U.S. NATIONAL LIBRARY OF MEDICINE. Guide to MEDLARS services. A brief description of the system with emphasis on the automated bibliographic search service. U.S. National Library of Medicine, Bethesda, Maryland, Revised August 1971, 22 p. (DHEW-NIH-72-255).
(220) U.S. NATIONAL OCEANOGRAPHIC DATA CENTER. Biology information retrieval system. U.S. National Oceanographic Data Center, Rockville, Maryland, 2 December 1970, 11 p.
(221) VARIAN ADCO. 626 information storage and retrieval system. Varian ADCO develops rapid document storage and retrieval system. Varian ADCO, Palo Alto, California, 1971, 4, 4 p. (Advertising brochures).
(222) VEAZIE, WALTER H., JR. Information center profile: Electronic Properties Information Center. Information, 3:2 (March/April 1971) 102-104.
(223) VERNIMB, C. Retrieval optimization by feedback. In: International Atomic Energy Agency. Handling of Nuclear Information, Vienna, Austria, 16-20 February 1970. Proceedings. International Atomic Energy Agency, Vienna, Austria, 1970, 221-226. (IAEA-SM-128/53. Available from UNIPUB Inc., P.O. Box 433, New York, New York).
(224) VICKERY, B. C. Structure and function in retrieval languages. Journal of Documentation, 27:2 (June 1971) 69-82.
(225) VICKERY, B. C. Techniques of information retrieval. Archon Books, Hamden, Connecticut, 1970, 262 p.
(226) VILLERS, JAMES J.; RUTH, STEPHEN R. Bibliography of data compression and data compaction literature with abstracts. U.S. Navy Fleet Material Support Office, Mechanicsburg, Pennsylvania, February 1971, 85 p. (AD 723 525).
(227) WAGONER, DONALD GLENN. The implementation of an algorithm for the retrieval of patent applications. University of Illinois, Coordinated Science Laboratory, Urbana, Illinois, March 1971, 30 p. (R-503. UILU-ENG-71-2206. AD 720 643).

(228) WALKER, DONALD E.; ed. Interactive bibliographic search: the user/computer interface. Proceedings of a Workshop on "The User Interface for Interactive Search of Bibliographic Data Bases" held in Palo Alto, California, on 14-15 January 1971. AFIPS Press, Montvale, New Jersey, 1971, 400 p.

(229) WASSERMAN, PAUL; ed. LIST 1971: library and information science today, an international registry of research and innovation. Science Associates/International, Inc., New York, 1971, 397 p.

(230) WATSON, PETER G. Center for information services. Phase II: Detailed system design and programming. Part VI: CIS seminars. University of California, Institute of Library Research, Los Angeles, California, 1 April 1971, 126 p. (PB 201 759).

(231) WEEKS, DAVID C.; BENTON, MILDRED; THOMAS, MARY LOUISE. Universal Decimal Classification: a selected bibliography of UDC literature. George Washington University, Biological Sciences Communication Project, Washington, D.C., January 1971, 40 p. (AD 727 076).

(232) WEIL, B. H. Document access. Journal of Chemical Documentation, 11:3 (August 1971) 178-185.

(233) WEINSTOCK, MELVIN. Availability, sources, terms and conditions of lease, and copyright aspects of major machine readable bibliographic data files. Paper presented at the Colloquium on Machine-Readable Bibliographic Data Bases: Their Creation and Use, State University of New York, School of Library Science, Albany, New York, 20-21 April 1971, 19 p.

(234) WELCH, TERRY A. Bounds on information retrieval efficiency in static file structures. Project MAC, Massachusetts Institute of Technology, Cambridge, Massachusetts, June 1971, 166 p. (Ph.d thesis. MAC-TR-88. AD 725 429).

(235) WENTE, VAN A. NASA/RECON and user interface considerations. Presented at the AFIPS Information Systems Committee Workshop on the User Interface for Interactive Search of Bibliographic Data Bases, San Jose, California, 14-15 January 1971. 15 p.

(236) WENTE, VAN A.; YOUNG, GIFFORD A. Current awareness and dissemination. In: Cuadra, Carlos A.; ed. Annual review of information science and technology, vol. 5 Encyclopaedia Britannica, Chicago, Illinois, 1970, 259-295.

(237) WILLIAMS, JOHN H., JR. Functions of a man-machine interactive information retrieval system. Journal of the American Society for Information Science, 22:5 (September/October 1971) 311-317.

(238) WILLIAMS, JOHN H., JR. An iterative browsing technique. International Business Machines, Federal Systems Division, Gaithersburg, Maryland, April 1971, 28 p. (AD 722 672. N71-30815).

(239) WILLIAMS, MARTHA E. Cooperative data management for information centers. Presented at Joint Meeting of Association of Scientific Information Dissemination Centers and National Federation of Science Abstracting and Indexing Services, Washington, D.C., 24 February 1971. 12 p.

(240) WILLIAMS, MARTHA E. Experiences of IIT Research Institute in operating a computerized retrieval system for searching a variety of data bases. Presented at the Third Cranfield International Conference on Mechanised Information Storage and Retrieval Systems. Cranfield Institute of Technology, Cranfield, England, 21 July 1971, 38 p.

(241) WILLIAMS, MARTHA E. Handling of varied data bases in an information center environment. Presented at the Conference on Computers in Chemical Education and Research, Northern Illinois University, DeKalb, Illinois, 23 July 1971, 22 p.

(242) WILLIAMS, MARTHA E. Use of machine readable data bases by scientists and engineers. Paper presented at the Annual Meeting of the American Society for Engineering Education, Annapolis, Maryland, 21-24 June 1971, 18 p.

(243) WOLFE, THEODORE. An evaluation of on-line information retrieval system techniques. U.S. Naval Ship Research and Development Center, Washington, D.C., December 1970, 60 p. (AD 723 214. ED 050 754).

(244) WOLFE, THEODORE. Suggestions for exploiting the potential of on-line remote access retrieval and display systems. Journal of the American Society for Information Science, 22:3 (May/June 1971) 149-152.

(245) WOLTERS, PETER H.; BROWN, JACK E. CAN/SDI system: user reaction to a computerized information retrieval system for Canadian scientists and technologists. Canadian Library Journal (January/February 1971) 20-23.

(246) WOOD, D. N. User studies: a review of the literature from 1966 to 1970. Aslib Proceedings, 23:1 (January 1971) 11-23.

(247) WOODS, W. A. The Defense Documentation Center Natural English Preprocessor. Bolt, Beranek, and Newman, Inc., Cambridge, Massachusetts, 31 July 1971, 272 p. (BBN-2182. AD 727 992).

(248) WOOLSTON, J. E.; ISSAEV, L. L.; IVANOV, M. V.; DEL BIGIO, G. The design and implementation of an international nuclear information system. In: International Atomic Energy Agency. Handling of Nuclear Information, Vienna, Austria, 16-20 February 1970. Proceedings. International Atomic Energy Agency, Vienna, Austria, 1970, 607-619. (IAEA-SM-128/48. Available from UNIPUB Inc., P.O. Box 433, New York, New York).

(249) XEROX EDUCATION GROUP. Selective dissemination of information—Xerox (SDI X). Xerox Education Group, Stamford, Connecticut, 8 p. (Advertising brochure).

11 Information Systems Applications in the Humanities

JOSEPH RABEN
Queens College,
City University of New York

and

R. L. WIDMANN
University of Pennsylvania

INTRODUCTION

The application of computers to research in the humanities, now being fully reported for the first time in the *Annual Review*, has a respectable history at least a decade long. Although the subject matter is generally "soft," scholars have recognized a wide spectrum of problems, some of which in themselves form the basis for relatively objective studies, and others of which require a "hard" base for more subjective interpretation. So far, surprisingly few of the approaches have been strikingly innovative; rather, the computer has been turned to for assistance in reducing many age-old complexities and ambiguities, often where the magnitude of data has prevented manual operations. Perhaps there has not yet been adequate encouragement for humanists attempting to work with computers; sometimes they must be grateful even for tolerance, especially among their more mechanophobic colleagues. Despite the uphill fight that they must sometimes wage for acceptance, however, both in the computer world and in their home disciplines, humanists are not only demonstrating that the application of computer techniques can improve the study of the liberal arts in ways which their associates can accept but are also developing techniques and principles that should prove beneficial to all other workers in the general field. A brief overview of their activities, followed by a more detailed report on the major areas, will reveal many points of mutual concern for all practitioners of computer information science.

Language and Literature

In the early sixties, scholars in substantial numbers began to employ the computer's capacity for rapid and accurate alphabetizing to compile concordances and verbal indexes (Raben, 116); that activity has continued and expanded until now there are no major projects to produce concordances and dictionaries without mechanical aid (Leyerle, 81). Various other directions have been followed by students of language and literature seeking evidence that can be found only through restructuring vast bodies of data (as by alphabetizing or classifying according to content) or locating items according to clearly defined parameters. In attempting content analysis by dictionary look-up, some have followed the social scientists in attempting content analysis. Others have concerned themselves with the formal aspects of literature, such as overall structure, sentence- and word-lengths, alliterative patterns, or frequency-rates of repetition in the lexicon. Occasionally, they have employed statistics in this work, but, in general, the students of literature have sought to keep their attention on the traditional focal points—aesthetics, philosophy, technique, classification—with a natural emphasis on the most objective aspect of their field of interest, the word itself.

Music

In several significant ways, the work of musicologists has paralleled that of the literary scholars: like the word, the note has served as a natural focus, enjoying the same relative definiteness as a concept and the same relative standardness of codification. But because both these areas are fuzzy around the edges, a certain amount of confusion has been generated when scholars have confronted the computer's refusal to accept even the slightest degree of ambiguity. As the students of written expression have developed increasingly sophisticated organizations of phrases, so the students of musical expression have analyzed the combinations of notes that may identify a work or suggest a link to one or more other works. As yet, the problems of producing readable music (detailed below) have deterred the production of indexes to match those in literature, but the determination and vision of this segment of humanists promises that comparable research tools and results will eventually become available. On the level of theory, in fact, the musicologists seem to be ahead of the literary scholars by virtue of their already having designed at least one system to accept music played on a piano-type keyboard and encoded it for computer analysis (Knowlton, 75).

History

Among the historians, two circumstances have combined to thrust almost all activity into a peculiarly objective mode. The advent of the computer as a tool of historical research coincided with a major intellectual development among the historians, bringing their discipline closer to the new social sciences. The early decades of the century had witnessed a revision of historical theory, a shift of emphasis away from heroic individuals and catastrophic events to an awareness of mass attitudes and actions and of the small, slowly accumulating changes that are now thought to account for much (if not all) historical movement. Evidence for this type of historical interpretation has always been available; in fact, it was too plentiful for pre-computer analysis. In voting records (of both citizens and their representatives), in economic statistics, in birth and death records, and in data on mobility (social, economic, local), education, union membership, or church affiliation—in almost any social relationship that could be numerically represented—the historians had always been overwhelmed by the prospect of attempting to analyze the flood of information that each recorded act by a group of individuals has produced. It is clearly no historical coincidence that the Hollerith card, the key to all future data processing activities, was a technological response to the spiraling demands of the U.S. Census, which found that a decade's worth of information collected on the country's expanding population was too much for manual analysis of the information.

"A New History." As the desire increased to analyze these files of quantified information, the computers of the late fifties and early sixties immediately provided a means. And these machines, developed by mathematicians and engineers, readily accepted numerical input, performed a variety of statistical operations on it, and produced numerical output. The inevitable consequence is that the "new history" has become regarded by many as sociology in a temporal dimension. Such a change may in itself be desirable as an extension of older historical techniques; the cries of its opponents seem to smack more of prejudice, fear, ignorance, or all three than of rational reservations. But it

must be recognized at the same time that the ease with which quantifying approaches have dominated computerized historical research has discouraged extensions of the traditional methods. Biography, for example, has not been computerized, although the possibility of storing and linking records now suggests a totally new magnitude of such studies. The intricacies of family involvements in the British Parliament of the eighteenth century, for example, can probably be disentangled only with machine assistance. So far, the number of projects that have begun from historical premises and borrowed or developed suitable computer techniques is disproportionately small compared to those in which statistical packages were taken off the shelf and applied to a handy file of data. The art of historical research will be advanced further when historians are forced to think out both their areas of interest and their means of analysis. Simultaneously, the adherents of the older approaches must recognize that difficult or redundant effort does not, in itself, produce superior results.

Art History

Unlike the musicologist, the art historian is at a great disadvantage when he contemplates the potentialities of the computer. Over the centuries, music has evolved a relatively standard, relatively useful system of notation, so that computer-aided analysis of a score has required the comparatively straightforward task of translating that system into an input code. But in visual arts there seems as yet no way of using computers to analyze a work of art itself. While a piece of music can be reconstructed from its coded record, there is no method available to us for reconstructing a painting from a coded record, and we consequently devote much of our intellectual energy to analyzing the circumstances surrounding the work.

Someday advances in technology may assist in comprehending the contents of art: scanners may develop sufficient sophistication to encode every subtlety of a two-dimensional art work; holography may permit us to encode statues and other three-dimensional constructs. But if art historians wish to consider also the content of the works of art they study, how far can they go and how can they proceed? Do moods, color "temperatures," material textures, religious associations, political attitudes of the artist (can *Guernica* ever be studied with no reference to the Spanish Civil War?), and all the possible nonobjective aspects of art lend themselves to computerization? If not, do art historians not distort their studies if they concentrate only on the more readily quantified elements? With no agreement, nor even an attempt at agreeing, on just what they are concerned with or how to reduce it to forms a computer can absorb, will they fail to benefit from the computer revolution? With so many millions of paintings and sculptures requiring their attention, with not even a beginning for a universal catalog of their discipline, with the need for cross-cultural studies increasingly evident, the theoretical benefits of machine assistance are obvious; the means of achieving them may evolve from the tentative steps now being taken.

Related Disciplines

Of less apparent importance at the moment, both because fewer people are involved and because the obstacles to success seem to be almost insurmountable, are the activities of researchers in humanities-related social sciences such as anthropology, archaeology, and folklore. These scientists experience the same difficulties already noted under other disciplines: vagueness of the limits of the area under study, absence of a standard notation, and lack of perceptions transcending the statistical approach. To date, there have been few reported efforts to utilize computer techniques, in these disciplines, even for such obvious and already well-developed applications as bibliographic control and information retrieval. Perhaps the scholars in these fields are wise to wait until their needs are met by the more heavily funded disciplines, or until the inevitable centers for humanities research include them in their more general scope. Certainly a new generation of students, observing the accomplishments of their colleagues in related fields, will recognize the unrealized potentialities for their own investigations. The day may come, before too long, when some important development, intended primarily to advance research in one of these areas, will show the way to scholars who are presently among the leaders in reshaping computer technology to suit the needs and principles of humane studies.

Limitations

A subject as vast as the humanities, even if restricted to its tangency with computers, far exceeds the limits imposed by space and by the competence of the authors. Some topics that might have been discussed at length here can only be touched on. Among these are the twin problems of educating the humanist to use the computer and using the computer to educate the humanist. Both areas suffer somewhat from an inherent mechanophobia, but when that is overcome, the special needs of humanities programming will broaden many concepts in other areas of computer use, just as finding computer-assisted ways to encourage learning in humanities areas must increase our knowledge of both the learning process and the role computers can play in it. Another limitation of this chapter is that it does not systematically list the computer-aided generation of poetry, music, or visual art; these areas are not customarily considered among the humanities, perhaps on the analogy that playwriting and dramatic performance are distinct from the study of drama as a literary form. Finally, the emphasis here is essentially on activities in the United States, largely because information has been easier to obtain; the reader can expect these general patterns to hold in other parts of the world (chiefly Western Europe) where computers are available.

General Status

For information scientists in general, no matter how scientific or technological their immediate areas of specialization, all activities in the humanities should be of major concern. Not only should they fear that computers will remain identified with a scientistic orientation toward the world, with all the amoral and technocratic consequences we have already begun to witness, but on the positive side they must recognize that advances in the non-material sphere may well open to their imaginations totally new concepts and techniques. Language, for example, is the primary focus of hundreds of scholars in all the departments of literature around the world where computers are being directed toward increasingly subtle organizations and analyses of the written word. Humanities scholars are constantly increasing the size of their data banks, which often are of the magnitude of Shakespeare's complete works (Howard-Hill, 67; Spevack, 136); the experience gained here should have carry-over into other fields of activity.

For the analysis of this material, new ways of utilizing programming languages (and according to Barnett, 7), even whole new languages are required; these likewise should present new possibilities elsewhere. Humanists are acquiring special experience in the physical storing of large bodies of text. The tapes in these collections do not contain the customary data of computer centers, but rather duplicate the words contained in conventional books. Hence there is a strange mixture of the problems of acquisitioning, storing, and circulating a new type of material among a new type of clientele; recognizing and solving these problems should show the way for other complex applications in information science. Likewise, the efforts to encode music and data in fine arts, archaeology, anthropology, history, and all other disciplines where no obvious means of entry exist cannot fail to suggest approaches for handling parallel problems in mathematics, chemistry, physics, and all the other studies where abstract representations must —if computerization is to succeed—be translated into the binary notation required.

LANGUAGE AND LITERATURE

Basic Areas of Activity

The bulk of computer-oriented research in humanities is probably concentrated in literary and linguistic data processing. Why there should be this affinity between those segments of the scholarly community that generally seclude themselves from machinery is a question often asked at cocktail parties; perhaps some future intellectual historian will discern a pattern here of cause and effect. This historian may want to consider why such a large proportion of these scholars come from the less populated academic sectors, such as classics, biblical studies, and lexicography, where visible progress is most evident: The first centralized literary data bank was sponsored by the American Philological Association; the first computer-driven photocomposition of a concordance was David W. Packard's work on Livy (110); the first summer institute devoted to a single humanistic discipline was, again, sponsored by the APA. It has been suggested that the specialists in these fields, which are not particularly glamorous today, are seeking machine assistance that elsewhere would be supplied by graduate students. Another possible explanation is that these disciplines have always demanded the manipulation of large bodies of text, more than even the most numerous and devoted human assistants could perform, and that the recent availability of computers has only satisfied a centuries-old demand (Raben, 116).

In any case, the results, after a decade or so of computer orientation, can be roughly categorized into two major divisions: large alphabetized lists, usually verbal indexes or concordances, and searches for particular types of linguistic or stylistic phenomena. Neither of these is exclusive, since the lists are often prepared in the expectation that they will support other research, either by the original scholar or by others who will benefit from that work, while projects that go beyond listing often begin by alphabetizing the textual data. Each has benefited from the practical advances of the other and from the theoretical discussions in which they exchange philosophies. To the extent that the technical demands of computerization have compelled scholars from many fields to meet and talk together, all scholarship may be said to have gained by this dramatic new direction in which traditional research is moving.

Verbal Indexes, Concordances, Dictionaries, and Data Banks

Verbal indexes. Any study of a body of text can obviously benefit from a simple alphabetic list of the words it contains. To note, for example, how often Melville uses words associated with madness in *Moby-Dick* can suggest to the literary critic a line of investigation that may open whole new levels of meaning in that multilayered novel. If the student is further aided by having that list restructured in other dimensions—by frequency of occurrence, for example—he can recognize many other verbal clues to the meanings of his text. Another technique readily available to the computer-oriented scholar is reversed alphabetization, bringing together many related words that are scattered when they are conventionally alphabetized. Case- and tense-endings, for instance, can indicate the approximate proportion of plurals, preterites, or present participles. The final elements in compound forms can also be conveniently grouped for inspection. Whether such information is then published for wider use, merely printed out for the use of the individual researcher, or even displayed only temporarily on a CRT terminal, it can serve to stimulate the imagination and curiosity of the scholar who in the past could only dream of questions that, as long as their answers required man-years of manual copying and sorting, could never be answered (41, 92, 154).

Concordances. Simply adding a small amount of context to each listed word turns a verbal index into a concordance. The amount depends on the format chosen: a page of printout will permit at least 100 characters, enough to reveal almost any aspect of the word the user may desire to know; printed books are generally restricted by costs to a more restricted selection. If half the words in a text are significant enough to merit concording, and the entire line is repeated for each significant listing, then the resultant concordance is approximately five times as voluminous as the text it is based on, and the economics of publishing for a severely limited market may prevent its publication.

How far the editor of a concordance goes beyond supplying the headword, a suitable context, and the citation depends on the nature of the text, the editor's own interests, and the anticipated uses of this work. A recent concordance to John Milton's *Paradise Lost* (Misek,

101), for example, finds space for numbers and abbreviations that indicate the position of the word in the line, the scene where the speaker utters the word, who is speaking (a character or the narrator), who is listening, and the number of previous occurrences of that word in the poem as a whole and in its various parts. From these discriminations, it is possible to arrive at many conclusions about Milton's technique as an epic poet and about his attitudes toward the various characters (Satan, for one, comes off better than would be expected of the "villain").

Dictionaries. Although the making of dictionaries is too complex an activity to have submitted totally to data processing techniques, some aspects have employed the computer. Frequency counts and concordances have provided bases for lexicographical analysis from which human specialists have been able to advance more rapidly to the subtle work of grammatical classification and semantic discrimination. While most projects in this category are European, work along these lines is now beginning in North America (Leyerle, 81).

Data banks. Anticipating the general need for carefully structured data banks to serve a multiplicity of functions, including that of a standard against which to measure statistical analyses, several groups have begun to compile carefully designed samplings of text. One of these, headed by Professors Henry Kučera and W. Nelson Francis of Brown University, has made available to all interested users a taped million-word corpus of American English selected to correspond to the proportions of each type in common use, e.g., prose fiction, scientific writing, sports journalism (Kučera & Francis, 77). An analogous project, directed by Professor William S-Y. Wang at the University of California at Berkeley, is a dictionary of Chinese (Streeter, 138). At Dartmouth, Professor Steven V. F. Waite has collected tapes of machine-readable classical texts for safe storage and general dissemination. Reports of similar work in other parts of the world indicate that a real need for these data banks is being recognized and met.

Stylistic and Verbal Analyses

Collation. A major problem in dealing with older texts—manuscripts and early printed books—and sometimes even with more recent ones, is establishing exactly how they should read. Between copying errors by scribes, composing errors by typesetters, and emendations silently made by both editors and the authors themselves in successive editions, vast and significant changes can seriously alter the sense of many works. These changes can be as substantial as the omission of seditious passages (like the abdication scene in Shakespeare's *Richard the Second*, suppressed in all published editions during Elizabeth's lifetime), or the rearrangement of chapters in order to alter the flow of a novel's narrative, or substantial substitutions of punctuation. Identifying these changes and deciding which reading probably reflects the author's final intent has strained the attention and eyesight of numerous devoted editors. Technology came to their aid only after World War II, when an adaptation of a photo-reader originally designed to measure bomb damage permitted the simultaneous examination of two apparently identical pages and the rapid pinpointing of any discrepancies. This device, the Hinman Collator, obviously worked only for revisions or press corrections within the same edition (a common problem in Elizabethan texts); when a work had been reset, the only method of comparison was ocular inspection.

The potentiality of the computer here has been recognized by several scholars: Dearing working on John Dryden (36), Silva & Love on Thomas Southerne (134), Petty & Gibson on Henry James (111), Sarna & Schiffman on Old Testament (128), Widmann on Shakespeare (152), Cabaniss on a translation from Old French (22), and Mullen on Old and Middle English manuscripts (105). The significance of this type of work, outside its immediate scope, is that it concentrates on the most objective aspect of a literary text, the very letters, spaces, and punctuation marks that carry the coded information. Here, there are no "trivial details," for the slightest deviation from a precise encoding vitiates the entire project.

Analysis of substituted values. The researcher, when concerned with some value other than the word itself, must engage in greater or lesser amounts of preparation before the computer phases of an investigation can be performed. If, for example, his concern is with grammar, as in the influential work of Milic (98), a manual replacement of words with numerically represented classes may suffice. Such a procedure, however, may reduce some of the objectivity that computerization is intended to introduce, and the volume of effort entailed usually reduces the scope of the study to a sample rather than the entire body of text. Procedures to parse sentences automatically are reported to be almost perfect, but the remainder of untreated material continues to bother the developers of this technique. An approach borrowed from the social scientists, automated content analysis, has sought to retain both objectivity and the large-scale operation that have attracted some literary scholars to the computer. The general mode of operation is to store a thesaurus in the computer and to match the text against it; the equivalents substituted by the program may then be considered as constituting the meanings of the text. Chief among the practitioners of this method of literary analysis is Sally Y. Sedelow, whose projects to determine the "meaning" of several translated Soviet Air Force manuals and later some of Shakespeare have been reported in several places (130, 131). If a study is to center on images, the problem of subjectivity increases immediately, for the measure of how much an image rests in the external world and how much in the mind of the viewer can never be finally determined. (Wordsworth is famous for his lament that, in a materialistic age, even he could no longer "have sight of Proteus rising from the sea," as he assumed was natural for the ancient Greeks.) Still, allowance having been made for the fluidity of the initial interpretation, there can be value in bringing together all instances of particular categories of images, even in charting them to demonstrate the increase and decrease of certain emotional devices to parallel the action of a novel (Smith, 135).

From here it is a simple step to the ultimate quantification, the attempt to analyze every aspect of a literary work that can be expressed as a numerical value. The most intricate work of this type is that done by Wachal (150), who has demonstrated both amazing ingenuity in recognizing categories to count and a competence with statistics that permits him to penetrate to many new levels of interpretation. Among the practical ends to which such statistical analyses have been put is the attempt to resolve questions of disputed authorship. The best known of these, by Mosteller & Wallace, employs a variety of statistical techniques to attribute several of the *Federalist* papers to Madison or Hamilton (104).

Linguistic atlases. Among the early attempts to put linguistics on an objective basis was the procedure of plotting records of selected words on maps to represent the location of each speaker. Both the term used (*frying-pan? fry pan? skillet? spider?*) and the exact pronunciation could presumably serve to differentiate identifiable groups of speakers, whose ancestry, affiliations, and external contacts could thus be measured. These specialized atlases, because they require the exhausting volunteer field work of a few dedicated linguists, and then a fantastic input of energy to prepare the maps, have not appeared in large numbers. But when the line plotter is programmed to record the phonetic transliterations at the precise points of their collection, at least the output phase can be diminished substantially. This redistribution of energy permits more concentration on the field collection, where the enlarged horizons of the linguist can expect to find realization. In particular, the speech of the densely packed cities, rather than only that of the sparsely populated countryside, can now be included, as modern social and linguistic concerns would dictate. The volume and intricacy of linguistic studies in our huge metropolitan complexes forced the early compilers of linguistic atlases into the villages; computers and plotters may invite them back to where most of the people (and probably the provocative problems in language study) are to be found.

Intellectual Affiliations

One of the most challenging areas of literary studies is the history of ideas. Here the scholar attempts to trace the paths by which great and creative minds have adopted each other's concepts, enhanced them, or rebutted them. Among the means of establishing their sources, authors frequently quote verbatim or make clear allusions to the actual words of their predecessors. Although recent taste has placed a premium on "originality" and condescended toward obvious "borrowing," the bulk of literary history is concerned with adaptation as the norm of creativity. Shakespeare's audience, for example, did not expect original stories, and judged *Macbeth* or *Antony and Cleopatra* not only for the playwright's skill in reworking familiar material but also for his deftness at integrating direct quotations from his sources. The study of these "influences" had a certain vogue in scholarship a generation or two back, but the number of them that could be identified by ocular inspection was so small and the interpretations that could therefore be built on them were so relatively insignificant that the entire effort fell into disesteem.

Computers now make it possible to perform this type of analysis on a level where meaningful results can develop (Raben, 115). As data banks increasingly make available new quantities of machine-readable text, advancing studies should reveal more and more of these intellectual affiliations between authors, permitting us to recognize how much of any literary work is indebted to particular antecedents. Networks of ideas exist; tracing them should widen our grasp of the entire creative process, which is obviously never reducible to formulas but equally obviously can be better understood than it is now.

MUSIC

Fundamental Problems

Unlike the students of literature, who have begun to accumulate large quantities of text in machine-readable form, the musicologists are off to a slow start because they have not even agreed on what system to employ for encoding the scores they wish to study. If we consider only a few of the aspects of music that enter into a meaningful analysis, we can recognize the magnitude of the task they have assumed. Perhaps the best analogy would be a play, but not merely its printed form, the script. To be complete, our record would have to show exactly how each word was spoken: at what pitch, for what duration, even at what volume. Furthermore, in music usually, but only rarely in drama, many voices are sounding simultaneously, for their combination is one of the prime effects the composer strives for in harmony, disharmony, contrast of voices, interplay of rhythms, etc. When all the discrete qualities of a single moment of music are encoded, the record may require dozens of symbols. To input a full mass or symphony, therefore, is to embark on a project fraught with tedium, error, and expense. Here lies the basic difficulty in applying the computer to musicological research.

The input problem is balanced by the problem of output. Musical notation has, over the centuries, become such an intricate and arbitrary system that the direction of the note stem is as important as all the dots, braces, dynamic abbreviations, and slurs that guide the performer or student. Two approaches that promise at least partial solution are the plotter (Byrd, 21) and special slugs for the line printer (Lincoln, 84). A more ambitious plan, and one that is, therefore, likely to require a longer time to realize, uses photocomposition to produce graphic-arts-quality camera copy (Bauer-Mengelberg, 8) To a certain degree, the adherents of these output processes are also committed to a particular input process, with the consequential disagreement over the merits of each, including the simple fact that a particular system may already exist, even partially, or that the compilers and computers available on a particular campus restict the researcher to their use.

Input languages. Apparently only two input languages have been adopted outside the institutions of their origin. One of these, the "plaine and easie code system" (Brooks, 16), has been described as especially suitable for musical indexes (discussed below). The other, called "DARMS" (alternately known as the Ford-Columbia code) (Erickson, 45), has been promoted as most useful in string manipulation. Various other systems have been developed by individual who often, unfortunately, were unaware that others were seeking solutions to the same problem; few of their solutions seem to have found any broad acceptance (Lincoln, 85).

Current Activities

Musical indexes. Just as the researcher in literature benefits from various rationalized lists of words—the vocabulary of a particular poet, group of poems, or group of poets—so the musicologist has sought to bring together in some orderly arrangement the great masses of manuscript and printed music that are the basis of most of his research. (The chronological catalog for the works of Mozart originated by L. von Köchel is probably the best known of these [Hill, 61]). The computer's promise of more rapid, thorough, and error-free organization of such catalogs has inspired several scholars to store the *incipits* (opening notes) of various bodies of musical literature, for example, the sixteenth-century chanson (Bernstein & Olive, 11). That computer storage is superior to index cards is an assumption that is yet to be proved but one that seems manifest by the very nature of the problem.

Style analysis. Getting beyond lists into some meaningful investigation of musical properties has immediately raised, as it has in other disciplines, the fundamental question: what is style? As elsewhere, the response has often been expressed in numerical and/or statistical terms. How often, for example, does a particular type of chord occur? At what intervals? What are the intervals between the notes in the chords (Mendel, 94)? Questions of this kind seem not only to begin to supply answers but also to impress upon the musicologists the need for more objective descriptions and extensions of their technique beyond the numerical. If the energy devoted to encoding, programming, and printing can ultimately produce a general theory of musical style, then it may replace much of the confusion and ambiguity that plagues this discipline.

Publications

In the use of computers to store and retrieve information *about* music, the progress made has been most impressive. *RILM* (Repertoire International de la Littérature Musicale), a joint pilot project of the American Council of Learned Societies and the City University of New York, has successfully organized a network of international collaborators to funnel author abstracts of all articles and books on every aspect of music—composition, performance, study—to a central office where they are edited on a specially designed computer terminal and published in a journal. The present design calls for photo composition and retrieval according to descriptors, in order to compile special collections for publication or ad hoc requirements.

Also apparently unique to musicology is the number of books devoted solely to computer applications. The energies of several editors—Brook (15), Lefkoff (80), Heckmann (59), and Lincoln (83)—have resulted in impressive compendia of technical and general articles. From these, both the interested layman and the fledgling musicologist can rapidly bring himself up to date on the state of the art.

HISTORY

Background

If any general trend can be discerned in the decade or so in which computers have served the historian, it is, as in language and literary studies, a natural extension of philosophies and practices that originated at least as far back as the nineteenth century. At that time, a combination of interest in the "masses" (partly a liberal identification, partly a concern to avoid the revolutions of the recent past) with the new scientific objectivity produced a reaction among historians against the old political history. In addition to "heroes," history needed to understand the little people, to see the world "from the bottom up." Throughout the past century, new disciplines have contributed to this movement by stimulating historians to broaden their interests, to widen the foundations of their conclusions. Archaeology put its emphasis necessarily on the non-destructible remnants of cultures, often the dwellings of common men. Anthropology stressed the fundamental humanness of all races and all levels of civilization. Sociology sought for "rules" of human conduct to parallel those of physics or chemistry, while psychology strove for a parallel system within the individual. New generations of historians, trained in the elementary levels of one or more of these new disciplines, also acquired a smattering of the physical sciences that had inspired them. Functioning in an environment where they could observe both the essential value of these approaches to truth and the often-exaggerated value given them by the dispensers of social and material rewards, they could in many cases see their "new history" as a modern response to the inadequacies of the older styles of thought. In "the century of the common man" the actions of the inconspicuous individual, at least in their aggregate, required the attention of the historian.

Early Studies

The foundations of current computer-oriented historical research can thus be seen in the work of such men as James Harvey Robinson and Charles A. Beard, eminent popularizers of cultural and social history, and Frederick Jackson Turner, who postulated the influence of the frontiersman on the unique evolution of American institutions. From Turner to Merle Curti, the earliest historian (or one of the first) to employ data processing equipment (34), is a direct line: Curti was the first occupant of the Turner Professorship of History at the University of Wisconsin. At nearby Iowa, William Aydelotte was seeking to identify the collective impact of nameless British farmers and townsmen by analyzing the votes of their representatives in the recently reformed Parliament of the 1840's. He turned to the computer for relief from the overwhelming task of attempting to discern patterns in all the confusion of party loyalties, regional identifications, and individual commitments (Aydelotte, 4). Along similar lines, Rabb sought to measure the involvement of middle class investors in the colonization of America (114), Thernstrom analyzed the demographic changes that suburbanized Boston (143, 144), and Alexander studied the votes of Southern Representatives in the pre-Civil War Congress to measure their movements toward national or sectional interests (3).

Whatever its present successes or failures, into whatever dangers it may in the future lead the whole discipline of history, it must be said of this computer-oriented research that at its noblest it is conceived as pandisciplinary and democratic. It will not close its mind to any lesson it can learn from another field of study. It will not ignore the individuals who leave no large mark on the records of their time, and must be studied only through the cumulative impact of their numbers. It will not trust to impressions, either its own or those of past writers who were even more limited in their range of observation. It will not, finally, descend into a quarrel over a false distinction between "humanistic" and "scientific" history. These terms may describe techniques, but they are in themselves meaningless; the goals of their users must be the ultimate determiners.

Availability of data. A relatively rapid and easy evolution has changed the type of history written until the middle of this century, which was original in its emphasis on social, economic, and cultural elements but traditional in its techniques. Now it may be a totally new kind of history, at least insofar as it has begun to use the charts, tables, and statistics of those disciplines that call themselves "sciences." This metamorphosis has resulted in large measure from the vast quantity of objective numerical data ready for investigation: Curti (34) used census records; Rabb (114), shipping registers; Aydelotte (4) and Bailyn (5), voting records; and Thernstrom (143, 144), building permits. Almost every type of record compiled by some government agency has been turned into a data bank to support a study of human behavior. And a central repository exists, the Interuniversity Consortium for Political Research at Ann Arbor, to house and distribute these files for further study (132). The existence and growth of this institution has already had several significant results, for its prestige has enhanced the techniques it supports, it offers advanced instruction on the post-doctoral level, and it permits, as has never been true in the humanities, the repetition of identical procedures on identical data, so that results may be checked, as they routinely are in the sciences. By such a distinct departure from their traditional modes of operation, the computer-oriented historians may have effected an irreversible "chromosomatic mutation" in their discipline.

Other forces. Computerized historical research has capitalized on several developments that were not intended primarily for its benefit. The first of these is the computerization of the U.S. Census. Magnetic tapes of all the various data compilations have been offered to all investigators, who now can access them at institutions around the country (and probably in various other parts of the world). Similar use is being made of other valuable computerized data, such as public opinion polls. While this kind of information is presently still on the wrong side of the temporal line to be called history, and must be technically assigned to political science or some other social science, it will remain available to future historians, augmented by the additions of further censuses and of other collections that have served their primary purpose and can now support retrospective analyses.

The other major advantage enjoyed by computer-oriented historians is the development of packaged programs for standard statistical analyses. These have been supported by social scientists, but are not restricted to contemporary applications; if the data to which they are applied are from the past, they will easily render historical statistics. The programs, the manuals, and even formal instruction are increasingly available to the historian who wishes to explore their applicability to his own field of interest. Here, if anywhere, lies the danger for history: with canned data and canned programs, the lazy or crafty individual may produce "instant" scholarship, devoid of value. But the only acceptable safeguard against such intellectual fraud is what it has always been, scrutiny by peers and the exposure of rubbish. The injunction against confusing babies and bathwater has always been valid.

Current Status of Computerization in History

Special publications. As yet, the historians have no regular journal concentrating on computer studies; perhaps the general acceptability of scholarly articles and books will permit them to employ traditional channels of publication. Their special need to communicate with one another is served by the *Historical Methods Newsletter* (62) published at the University of Pittsburgh. To guide newcomers into the field, several textbooks have appeared: Holsti's *Content Analysis for the Social Sciences and Humanities* (64), and Dollar & Jensen's *A Historian's Guide to Statistics: Quantitative Analysis and Historical Research*

(39). Swierenga has compiled an excellent anthology of essays under the title *Quantification in American History: Theory and Research* (141).

Data banks. In addition to the Interuniversity Consortium for Political Research, mentioned above, data banks of several types are in various stages of development. At the University of California, Berkeley, a biographical file is being compiled for political leaders (Nasatir, 108). The Center for the Study of Liberty in America at Harvard University has encoded vital statistics on 2500 graduates of Harvard and Yale between 1642 and 1745, when these were essentially the only colleges in America; this data bank can reveal some surprising generalizations about the social and economic functions of higher education in the colonial period. This bank is supplemented by entries for the 15,000 men and women listed in the *Dictionary of American Biography.* Others can be located through published inventories (Merritt, 96; Merritt & Rokkan, 97).

Undeveloped areas. At least two approaches seem not to have attracted the historians' attention to any substantial degree. Content analysis, by which the underlying sense of a document (perhaps unapparent even to its author) can be brought to the surface, has failed to impress historians with its potentiality. Perhaps the need to begin such projects with the careful encoding of large samples of text has deterred potential employers of this technique. Much of what is called "literature," however, can also serve the needs of historical research; when the literary data banks become more generally available, students of history may find them satisfactory. They will, of course, need to clarify their thinking about the validity of the whole method, which has sometimes been called into question. The other technique that has been exploited in other fields but not in history is concordancing. It has been asserted from time to time that much of a public figure's thought could be revealed by an alphabetic list of his vocabulary with enough context to suggest the environments in which particular words are typically found. Experiments with General de Gaulle's television speeches, for example, have revealed high counts for *moi, nous, France,* and *grandeur.* Talk of a concordance to the complete writings of Karl Marx has apparently died away. (Perhaps this will be the first major work to come out of the USSR, just as the Italians have spent many years on an index to St. Thomas Aquinas.) Here again, however, the initial problem is input; until some adequately funded institution begins to encode the writings of historically significant authors, or until those works become available as the by-product of an investigation in some other field (which by-product, of course, is most likely to be a concordance!), it seems probable that historians using computers will capitalize on the availability of quantitative data crying for analysis and on statistical techniques designed to perform it.

ART

Primary Area of Activity

Art museums, custodians of objects that society has caused to be valued at billions of dollars, are, ironically, among the least well supported of our public institutions. Paintings that are insured for over a million dollars often cannot be exhibited because a few thousand dollars cannot be budgeted for a guard to protect them. Without massive infusions of money from millionaire patrons, museums cannot even maintain their current methods of operation. A move into the computer age, therefore, even though it fascinates many individual museum administrators, seems almost beyond possibility. And yet, the few advances that have been made suggest a vast potential not only to improve their current operations but also to open important new modes of service to their several classes of clientele.

Information retrieval. The concentration of museum computerization efforts on the single area of information retrieval is the natural consequence of the poverty just mentioned and the vagueness of the whole area, discussed earlier. It also responds to an urgent need for accurate and timely catalogs where none exist, for the penury that limits the visible staff in the exhibition halls also prevents museums from hiring the catalogers in the back rooms to maintain records on their acquisitions. Such records are desperately needed because of the total irrationality of almost all collections: chance, idiosyncrasy, the fortunes of war, the refusal to part with any item once it is acquired—these essentially irrelevant factors most often determine the nature of a collection rather than any principles of systematic acquisition. If even the administrators of museums cannot be certain of what they have, what they are supposed to have but do not, or what they once had but do not any longer, the prospect is particularly dim for outsiders—art historians, for example—who wish to locate and study a particular set of objects. Only by physically examining the part of the museum's holdings that is accessible can any scholar know what has survived that is of relevance to a particular study, or where it is at any given moment. Even printed catalogs would be of tremendous assistance to the curators and the students of art around the world.

The accomplishment of a single museum, The Museum of Modern Art in New York, in producing such a printed catalog, is of great import; the step from zero to one is always the hardest (Vance & Heller,

147). Having demonstrated the feasibility of computerization, experienced the difficulties of designing the system and of implementing it, and also succeeded in persuading their financial controllers to fund this innovation, they have shown the way to the more tradition-oriented museums, which should follow their lead and benefit from their experience.

Other possibilities. In their projections of future computer applications, museum personnel have come up with two that seem particularly suited to their special needs. One is a network of on-line terminals to permit searching of all files from any node. Because of the vast number of items to be stored and their uniqueness, it would be almost impossible to update printed catalogs for all museums, or to distribute and store them, even if they could be produced. Continuous update of computer files at a central site and remote access to all users is the only feasible (if still utopian) solution.

A further application to solve a special problem of museums results from the recent recognition that they have an educational function that exceeds their role as collectors and preservers. The best place to educate a museum visitor is in the presence of particular works of art, but the varying degrees of sophistication of the museum's visitors precludes the use of conventional teaching aids. An on-line terminal, however, preferably a CRT coupled to a slide projector, could respond to queries from users on their level of knowledge and interest. As in all CAI applications, the computer would be the ideal interlocutor, infinitely knowledgeable, infinitely patient.

RELATED DISCIPLINES

The two social sciences that seem, from their subject matter and technique, to overlap the area of the humanities most are archaeology and cultural anthopology. (History, also discussed, is also often classified among the social sciences.) In both, the use of computers is potentially large, for most of the conditions for successful application are present: there is a great deal of information to be sorted, there is (at least in some areas) a pre-existing code that can serve as a basis for computer input and output, and there are relatively objective criteria for classification. Some of the activity reported reveals an excitement over the possibility of substantially advancing these disciplines.

Archaeology. From one point of view, archaeology is the art history of the prehistoric period. As such, it shares the problems already discussed under the "museums" heading. Although the archaeological museums and the fine arts museums have yet to agree on a common system of classification or other joint procedures, it is to be hoped that a recognition of their greater area of mutual interest will generate greater cooperation. Apart from museum-related concerns, the work in archaeology, unlike that in fine arts, tends to emphasize the generic rather than the unique. The archaeological record is still so incomplete that the scholars in this discipline naturally strive to block out only the general outlines of civilization over a million years. Here, however, is one of the most challenging opportunities for computer-oriented archaeologists, the comparative analysis of apparently discrete cultures to discover what characteristics they share, attempting to discover whether such phenomena as pyramid-building efforts in Egypt and Central America reflect a cultural community, parallel but separate evolutions, or simply coincidence. At the moment, such large-scale projects have not yet been tackled; rather, the emphasis, as reported in a special newsletter *(Newsletter of Computer Archaeology*, 109), has been on structuring limited collections of artifacts—pottery, for example, or arrowheads—but from this basic work larger advances can be expected.

The latest report on computer advances in this field (Whallon, 151) stresses the intellectual ferment caused by the rapid introduction of computers with the consequent availability of statistical techniques borrowed from the social sciences and retrieval techniques from information science. With this wealth of new assistance, the archaeologists are being forced to consider the fundamental question, just what is it they are studying? The number of aspects to be discerned in a single artifact is so fantastic that a file that can hold up to one million descriptors has been seriously proposed by one of the most active advocates of a universal archaeological data bank. The pressure to benefit from technology in a field that is almost overwhelmed with information has produced many efforts at international collaboration to establish common standards (Gardin, 50) and to articulate working methods. There is a special need for freedom from domination by mathematically oriented researchers without loss of the data processing power of the machine. The success of the future-looking scholars in this field may serve as a model for other humanists.

Cultural anthropology. As archaeology may be considered the art history of prehistory, so cultural anthropology may be looked upon as the study of all survivals of primitive cultures in the contemporary time dimension. With living informants, the anthropologist can examine aspects of folklore, social relations, medical practice, and many other aspects of a culture that may leave inadequate physical traces for later study. That procedure results in such a deluge of data that much work in this field has concentrated on a distinct group, preferably small and isolated. Another approach, however, is cross-cultural, as in the study of folktales. Here, the researcher may find an existing code, like Thompson's voluminous *Motif-Index of Folk-Literature* (146), a basic analysis of thousands of elements in oral literature from around the world, on the basis of which supplemental indexes have been made to cover particular regional subsets. The need for computerization of such material grows from the need to locate a particular motif in many categories at once. A single element might fit simultaneously into several of Thompson's categories: a tale of how mosquitoes were created from the bones of a slain demon could logically come under "mythology," "animals," "magic (transformations)," "marvelous creatures," and "rewards and punishments."

No books (or set of books) within manageable dimensions could adapt the amount of cross-referencing required by such analysis. But an on-line computer store would permit locating of all the elements related to a particular study with a rapidity and certainty that would release human energies from the tedious organization of the data to the more challenging comprehension of it.

The cultural anthropologists, once out of the verbal domain, are swamped by a greater deluge than the archaeologists, for they concern themselves with not only the artifacts of culture—domestic, religious, agricultural, industrial—but also the entire social fabric of kinship, marriage, child-raising, warfare, government, economics, and every function that in more sophisticated societies is the realm of the sociologist. Devising systems to structure their data and reveal underlying patterns, while simultaneously storing their data so that they (and, more importantly, future scholars) can access it, is a task that is only now being recognized, and its solution is not yet even in sight.

CONCLUSION

The introduction of computers into humanistic research has not, despite the expressed fears and animosities of some, effected any substantial change. The bulk of the activity has simply been more of the kinds of research that had been accepted for decades, even centuries, before. In history, the one discipline where a possibly new scholarship might be seen emerging, a closer examination suggests that, given the same involvement with mass social phenomena and the same availability of statistical data, most of the currently computerized projects could have been conducted with calculating machines. In fact, it is becoming customary in reporting such projects to ignore the particular means, or even to disclaim any assistance from a computer.

A "tooling up" phase. Having followed their scientific predecessors with halting feet, and still constituting a very small minority in their profession, humanists can look back on the past decade as one of necessary preparation. They are beginning to appreciate the need for standard codes and to agree on them. They have begun to establish data banks and to fix links between them. They have begun to write packaged programs for the more routine operations, as the social scientists have their statistical packages. Formal instruction for undergraduate, graduate, and postdoctoral students is being offered on an increasing number of campuses. Only one need, ironically, is still largely unmet: no textbook has yet been written to teach programming concepts and techniques for any of the popular languages; in fact, only one textbook has been written with humanists in mind, and that is based on a language, Stylized Natural-Language Processor (SNAP), that has not met wide acceptance (Barnett, 7).

Outlook. The acceptance of computer research as a legitimate activity for humanities scholars is now enough avanced that individuals who engage in it are less in danger of being blocked from promotion and tenure than they were even recently. The support of their colleagues in other disciplines has been of major importance, particularly when job opportunities are shrinking and departments have their pick of less threatening applicants. Now the older established organizations have begun to allocate time at their meetings and space in their journals to computer-oriented activities. The National Endowment for the Humanities has included such work in the list of supportable projects. The American Council of Learned Societies has conducted a special competition for fellowships to be used exclusively for computer-oriented humanities research. None of this financial support has been of great magnitude; few people, for example, have been able to take off a full year to study, and no one has been able to hire the staff or buy the equipment necessary for these new technological advances. But such poverty has always been the lot of the humanities researcher, and his compensation for inadequately funded projects is often that he gets free student aides and computer time that he would otherwise have had to pay for. With sufficient drive, he will find some means of getting his work done and its conclusion published.

We can expect, therefore, that in the future there will be more humanists in the computer centers. There will be more formal instruction offered—in established departments, in honors programs, in new structures to be implemented—to make the machine increasingly accessible to all users, not just the scientists, mathematicians, and social scientists who presently account for almost all usage. We may hope for larger programs of fellowships, more group projects, and greater cooperation through regional centers. We almost certainly will see an increased articulation of interests between workers in information science and in the humanities, two areas that can be thought of in many instances as the applied and theoretical phases of the same field of concentration. From these activities, we may see emerging a new kind of scholarship; only the future can reveal whether one is possible. But, for both the humanist and those who share the computer with him, the intellectual interaction can have only beneficial results, a sharing of points of view, an interplay of value systems, a complement of techniques. If there is any validity in the belief that all scholarship advances when conducted on a university campus devoted to the full spectrum of intellectual concerns, then the newest facility on that campus, the computer center, must also be the home for every type of study.

REFERENCES

(1) ABBOUD, VICTORINE C. The computer as an instructional device for the Arabic writing system. Computers and the Humanities, 6:4 (March 1972) 195-207.

(2) AITKEN, A. J. The literary uses of computers. Times Literary Supplement, (21 April 1972) 456.

(3) ALEXANDER, THOMAS B. Sectional stress and party strength: a computer analysis of roll-call voting patterns in the United States House of Representatives, 1836-1860. Vanderbilt University Press, Nashville, Tennessee, 1967.

(4) AYDELOTTE, WILLIAM O. Quantification in history. American Historical Review, 71 (April 1966), 803-825.

(5) BAILYN, BERNARD. The ideological origins of the American Revolution. Belknap Press, Cambridge, Massachusetts, 1967, vi-ix.

(6) BAILYN, BERNARD; BAILYN, LOTTE. Massachusetts shipping, 1697-1714: a statistical study. Harvard University Press, Cambridge, Massachusetts, 1959, 135-141.

(7) BARNETT, MICHAEL P. Computer programming in English. Harcourt, Brace & World, Inc., New York, 1969.

(8) BAUER-MENGELBERG, STEFAN. The Ford-Columbia input language. In: Brook, Barry S.; ed. Musicology and the computer. City University of New York Press, New York, 1970, 48-52.

(9) BERKHOFER, ROBERT F., JR. A behavioral approach to historical analysis. New York, 1969.

(10) BERLIND, GARY; LOGEMANN, GEORGE W. An algorithm for musical transposition. Computer Studies in the Humanities and Verbal Behavior, II:2 (August 1969) 102-108.

(11) BERNSTEIN, LAWRENCE; OLIVE, JOSEPH P. Computers and the 16th-century chanson: a pilot project at the University of Chicago. Computers and the Humanities, 3 (1969) 153-160.

(12) BERRINGER, RICHARD E. A profile of members of the Confederate Congress. Journal of Southern History, 23 (1967) 518-541.

(13) BOGUE, ALLAN G. United States: the "new" political history. Journal of Contemporary History, 3 (January 1968) 17.

(14) BOWLES, EDMUND A. Computers and European museums: a report. Computers and the Humanities, 5:3 (January 1971) 176-177.

(15) BROOK, BARRY S.; ed. Musicology and the computer. City University of New York Press, New York, 1970.
(16) BROOK, BARRY S. The simplified "plaine and easie code system" for notating music: a proposal for international adoption. Fontes Artis Musicae, XII:2-3 (1965) 156-160.
(17) BURTON, DOLORES M. Aspects of word order in two plays of Shakespeare. Computer Studies in the Humanities and Verbal Behavior, 3:1 (January 1970) 34-39.
(18) BURTON, MICHAEL L. Computer applications in cultural anthropology. Computers and the Humanities, 5:1 (September 1970) 37-45.
(19) BURTON, VIRGINIA. Computers confront the curator. The Metropolitan Museum of Art Bulletin, 26:1 (Summer 1967) 20-23.
(20) BURTON, VIRGINIA; BONIN, ALICE; LOURIE, JANICE; SPISELMAN, TOBY. The computer and archaeology. American Journal of Archaeology, 74, 221-223.
(21) BYRD, DONALD. Transcription by plotter. Random Bits, V:9 (May 1970) 1ff. (Indiana University, Research Computer Center, Bloomington, Indiana).
(22) CABANISS, MARGARET SCANLON. Using the computer for text collation. Computer Studies in the Humanities and Verbal Behavior, 3:1 (January 1970) 1-33.
(23) CAMERON, ANGUS; FRANK, ROBERTA; LEYERLE, JOHN; eds. Computers and Old English concordances. University of Toronto Press, Toronto, Ontario, Canada, 1970.
(24) CARROLL, JOHN M.; ROELOFFS, ROBERT. Computer selection of keywords using word-frequency analysis. American Documentation, 20:3 (July 1969) 227-233.
(25) CECIL, LAMAR. The creation of nobles in Prussia, 1871-1918. American Historical Review, 75 (February 1970) 757-795.
(26) CHENHALL, ROBERT G. The archaeological data bank: a progress report. Computers and the Humanities, 5:3 (January 1971) 159-169.
(27) CHENHALL, ROBERT G. Computers in anthropology and archaeology. (IBM Data Processing Application GE 20-0384-0).
(28) CHENHALL, ROBERT G. The impact of computers on archaeological theory: an appraisal and projection. Computers and the Humanities, 3:1 (September 1968) 15-24.
(29) CLOUGH, J. TEMPO: a composer's programming language. Perspectives of New Music, IX:1 (Fall/Winter 1970) 113-125.
(30) CLUBB, JEROME M.; ALLEN, HOWARD W. American Historical Association Newsletter, 6:2 (December 1967) 9.
(31) CLUBB, JEROME M.; ALLEN, HOWARD W. Computers and historical study. Journal of American History, 54 (1967) 599-601.
(32) Computers and their potential applications in museums. Arno Press, New York, 1968.
(33) CRANE, FREDERICK; FIEHLER, JUDITH. Numerical methods of comparing musical styles. In: Lincoln, Harry B.; ed. The computer and music. Cornell University Press, Ithaca, New York, 1970, 209-222.
(34) CURTI, MERLE. The making of an American community: a case study of democracy in a frontier county. Stanford University Press, Palo Alto, California, 1959.
(35) DAMERAU, FREDERICK J. Automatic parsing for content analysis. Communications of the ACM, 13:6 (June 1970) 356-360.
(36) DEARING, VINTON A. Computer aids to editing the text of Dryden. In: Gottesman, R.; Bennett, S.; eds. Art and error: modern textual editing. Indiana University Press, Bloomington, Indiana, 1970, 254-278.
(37) de TOLLENAERE, F. Encoding techniques in Dutch historical lexicography. Computers and the Humanities, 6:3 (January 1972) 147-152.

(38) DOLLAR, CHARLES M. Innovation in historical research: a computer approach. Computers and the Humanities, 3:3 (January 1969) 145-149.
(39) DOLLAR, CHARLES M.; JENSEN, RICHARD J. A historian's guide to statistics: quantitative analysis and historical research. Holt, Rinehart & Winston, New York, 1971, 332 p.
(40) DONOW, HERBERT S. Linear word count as a function of rhythm: an analysis of Shakespeare's sonnets. Hephaistos, 1 (1970) 1-27.
(41) DUDRAP, CLAUDE; EMERY, G. Sorting the French vocabulary according to word endings. In: Wisbey, Roy A.; ed. The computer in literary and linguistic research. Cambridge University Press, Cambridge, Massachusetts, 1971.
(42) DÜRRENMATT, HANS-RUDOLF; GOULD, MURRAY; LARUE, JAN. Die notierung thematischer incipits auf "mark-sense cards." Fontes Artis Musicae, XVII:1-2 (January/August 1970) 15-23.
(43) ELLIN, EVERETT. Museums and the computer: an appraisal of new potentials. Computers and the Humanities, 4:1 (September 1969) 25-30.
(44) ERDMAN, DAVID. A concordance to the writings of William Blake. Cornell University Press, Ithaca, New York, 1967. (Two volumes).
(45) ERICKSON, RAYMOND F. The Ford-Columbia music representation (DARMS). 1971. (Unpublished typescript).
(46) ERICKSON, RAYMOND F. A general-purpose system for computer-aided musical studies. Journal of Music Theory, 13:2 (1969) 276-294.
(47) FARRINGDON, MICHAEL G. Symposium on the uses of the computer in literary research: a conference report. Computers and the Humanities, 4:5 (May 1970) 315-317.
(48) FRAUTSCHI, RICHARD L. The authorship of certain unsigned articles in the Encyclopédie: a first report. Computer Studies in the Humanities and Verbal Behavior, 3:2 (August 1970) 66-76.
(49) GARDIN, JEAN-CLAUDE; ed. Archéologie et calculateurs. Editions du Centre National de la Recherche Scientifique, Paris, France, 1970.
(50) GARDIN, JEAN-CLAUDE. Archaeology and computers: new perspectives. International Social Science Journal, 23, 189-203.
(51) GIBSON, WILLIAM M.; PETTY, GEORGE R., JR. The ordered computer collation of unprepared literary text. In: Gottesman, R.; Bennett, S.; eds. Art and error, modern textual editing. Indiana University Press, Bloomington, Indiana, 1970, 279-300.
(52) GOULD, MURRAY; LOGEMANN, GEORGE W. ALMA: alphameric language for music analysis. In: Brook, Barry S.; ed. Musicology and the computer. City University of New York Press, New York, 1970, 57-90.
(53) GROSS, LOUIS N.; WALKER, DONALD E. On-line computer aids for research in linguistics. Information Processing, 68 (1969) 1531-1536.
(54) GUMB, R. D. The inapplicability of the dictionary-encyclopedia distinction to the semantics of natural languages. Information Storage and Retrieval, 6 (May 1971) 445-452.
(55) HACKNEY, SHELDON. Populism to progressivism in Alabama. Princeton University Press, Princeton, New Jersey, 1969.
(56) HARRIS, JESSICA L.; HINES, THEODORE C.; SCOTT, RALPH L. A computer-based census and local handlist system for incunabula. Computers and the Humanities, 6:2 (November 1971) 95-102.
(57) HAYS, SAMUEL P. Computers and historical research. In: Bowles, Edmund A.; ed. Computers in humanistic research. Prentice-Hall, Englewood Cliffs, New Jersey, 1967.
(58) HAYS, SAMUEL P. Quantification in history: the implications and challenges for graduate training. American Historical Society Newsletter, 4 (1966) 8-11.
(59) HECKMANN, HAROLD.; ed. Elektronische datenverarbeitung in der musikwissenschaft. Gustav Bosse Verlag, Regensburg, Germany, 1967.

(60) HIGONNET, PATRICK L. R.; HIGONNET, TREVOR B. Class, consumption, and politics in the French Chamber of Deputies. French Historical Studies, 5 (1967) 204-224.

(61) HILL, GEORGE. The thematic index to the Köchel catalog. Institute for Computer Research in the Humanities Newsletter, IV:7 (March 1969) 8-9.

(62) Historical Methods Newsletter: quantitative analysis of social, economic, and political development. University of Pittsburgh, Department of History, Pittsburgh, Pennsylvania.

(63) HODSON, F. R.; KENDALL, D. G.; TAUTU, P.; eds. Mathematics in the archaeological and historical sciences. Edinburgh University Press, Edinburgh, Scotland, 1971.

(64) HOLSTI, OLE R. Content analysis for the social sciences and humanities. Addison-Wesley, Reading, Massachusetts, 1969.

(65) HOLT, MICHAEL F. Forging a majority: the formation of the Republican Party in Pittsburgh, 1848-1860. Yale University Press, New Haven, Connecticut, 1969.

(66) HOWARD-HILL, TREVOR H. The Oxford old-spelling concordances. Studies in Bibliography, 22 (1969) 143-164.

(67) HOWARD-HILL, TREVOR H. Oxford Shakespeare concordances. The Clarendon Press, Oxford, England, 1969-1972.

(68) HYMES, DELL. The uses of computers in anthropology. Mouton and Co., The Hague, The Netherlands, 1965.

(69) JACKSON, R.; BERNZOTT, P. A musical input language and a sample program for musical analysis. In: Brook, Barry S.; ed. Musicology and the computer. City University of New York Press, New York, 1970, 130-150.

(70) JENSEN, RICHARD J.; DOLLAR, CHARLES M. Historian's Guide to statistics. Holt, Rinehart & Winston, New York, 1971.

(71) JONES, ALEXANDER M.; HOWE, HUBERT S., JR. IML: an intermediary musical language. Princeton University, Department of Music, Princeton, New Jersey, n.d.

(72) KARP, T. A test for melodic borrowings among Notre Dame Organa Dupla. In: Lincoln, Harry B.; ed. The computer and music. Cornell University Press, Ithaca, New York, 1970, 293-297.

(73) KASSLER, MICHAEL. MIR—a simple programming language for musical information retrieval. In: Lincoln, Harry B.; ed. The computer and music. Cornell University Press, Ithaca, New York, 1970, 300-327.

(74) KLEPPNER, PAUL. The cross of culture: a social analysis of midwestern politics, 1850-1900. The Free Press, New York, 1970.

(75) KNOWLTON, PRENTISS H. Capture and display of keyboard music. Datamation, 18:5 (May 1972) 56-60.

(76) KROEBER, KARL. Styles in fictional structure: the art of Jane Austen, Charlotte Brontë, George Eliot. Princeton University Press, Princeton, New Jersey, 1971.

(77) KUČERA, HENRY; FRANCIS, W. NELSON. Computational analysis of present-day American English. Brown University Press, Providence, Rhode Island, 1967.

(78) LAND, RICHARD I. The blind lead the blind. Computers and the Humanities, 4:1 (September 1969) 65-73.

(79) LATHEM, EDWARD CONNERY; ed. A concordance to the poetry of Robert Frost. Holt Information Systems, New York, 1971.

(80) LEFKOFF, GEROLD. Automated discovery of similar segments in the forty-eight permutations of a twelve-tone row. In: Lincoln, Harry B.; ed. The computer and music. Cornell University Press, Ithaca, New York, 1970, 147-153.

(81) LEYERLE, JOHN. The dictionary of Old English: a progress report. Computers and the Humanities, 5:5 (May 1971) 279-283.

(82) LIEBERMAN, F. Computer-aided analysis of Japanese music. In: Lincoln, Harry B.; ed. The computer and music. Cornell University Press, Ithaca, New York, 1970, 181-192.

(83) LINCOLN, HARRY B.; ed. The computer and music. Cornell University Press, Ithaca, New York, 1970.

(84) LINCOLN, HARRY B. A computer application in musicology: the thematic index. In: Proceedings of the International Federation for Information Processing Congress, 1968, 957-961.

(85) LINCOLN, HARRY B. The thematic index: a computer application to musicology. Computers and the Humanities, II:5 (1968) 215-220.

(86) LININGTON, R. E. Techniques used in archaeological field surveys. Philosophical Transactions of the Royal Society of London (A), 269, 89-108.

(87) LOCKWOOD, LEWIS. A stylistic investigation of the masses of Josquin Desprez with the aid of the computer: a progress report. In: Brook, Barry S.; ed. Musicology and the computer. City University of New York Press, New York, 1970, 19-27.

(88) LONGYEAR, CHRISTOPHER R. Linguistically determined categories of meaning: a comparative analysis of meaning in "The Snows of Kilimanjaro." Humanities Press, New York, 1971.

(89) LYMAN, ELIZABETH R. An on-line document retrieval strategy using the PLATO system. University of Illinois, Coordinated Science Laboratory, Urbana, Illinois, June 1971, 20 p. (AD 726 921).

(90) McCALLA, GORDON I.; SAMPSON, JEFFREY R. MUSE: a model to understand simple English. Communications of the ACM, 15:1 (January 1972) 29-40.

(91) MACRAE, DUNCAN, JR. Issues and parties in legislative voting: methods of statistical analysis. Harper & Row, New York, 1970.

(92) MANIET, ALBERT; PAQUET, ANNETTE. Plaute, Amphytrion: index verborum, lexiques inverses, relevés lexicaux. Olms, Hildesheim, Germany, 1970.

(93) MASON, ROBERT M. An encoding algorithm and tables for the digital analysis of harmony. Journal of Research in Music Education, XVII:3 (Fall 1969) 286-300; XVII:4 (Winter 1969) 369-387.

(94) MENDEL, ARTHUR. Some preliminary attempts at computer-assisted style analysis in music. Computers and the Humanities, 4:1 (September 1969) 41-52.

(95) MERRITT, RICHARD L. National building in America: the colonial years. In: Deutsch, Karl W.; Foltz, William J.; eds. Nation building. Aldine Publishers, Chicago, 1966.

(96) MERRITT, RICHARD L. Symbols of American community, 1735-1775. Yale University Press, New Haven, Connecticut, 1966.

(97) MERRITT, RICHARD L.; ROKKAN, STEIN. Comparing nations: the use of quantitative data in cross-national research. Yale University Press, New Haven, Connecticut, 1966.

(98) MILIC, LOUIS T. A quantitative approach to the style of Jonathan Swift. Mouton and Co., The Hague, The Netherlands, 1966.

(99) MILLER, WARREN E. Promises and problems in the use of computers: the case of research in political history. In: Bowles, Edmund A.; ed. Computers in humanistic research. Prentice-Hall, Englewood Cliffs, New Jersey, 1967.

(100) MISEK, L. D. Automated contextual analysis of thematic structure in natural language. Case Western Reserve University, Cleveland, Ohio, 1970.

(101) MISEK, L. D. Context concordance to John Milton's "Paradise Lost." Case Western Reserve University, Andrew R. Jennings Computing Center, Cleveland, Ohio, 1971.

(102) MORTENSON, GLENN R. Development and use of computerized procedures for scoring sight reading of rhythms to compare the effectiveness of metric and representational notation with conventional notation. Northwestern University, Evanston, Illinois, 1970. Dissertation Abstracts, XXXI:8 (February 1971) 4205-A. (Ph.D. dissertation).

(103) MORTON, ANDREW Q.; WINSPEAR, ALBAN D. It's Greek to the computer. Harvest House, Montreal, Quebec, Canada, 1971.
(104) MOSTELLER, FREDERICK; WALLACE, DAVID L. Inference and disputed authorship: "The Federalist." Addison-Wesley, Reading, Massachusetts, 1964.
(105) MULLEN, KAREN A. Using the computer to identify differences among text variants. Computers and the Humanities, 5:4 (March 1971) 193-202.
(106) MURPHY, GEORGE G. S. Historical investigation and automatic data processing equipment. Computers and the Humanities, 3:1 (September 1968) 1-13.
(107) MURPHY, GEORGE G. S.; MUELLER, M. G. On making historical techniques more specific: "real types" constructed with a computer. History and Theory, 6 (1967) 14-32.
(108) NASATIR, DAVID. BEAR (Berkeley Elites Automated Retrieval). Computers and the Humanities, 4:5 (May 1970) 348.
(109) Newsletter of Computer Archaeology. Edited by Sylvia Gaines. University of Arizona, Department of Anthropology, Tempe, Arizona.
(110) PACKARD, DAVID W. A concordance to Livy. Harvard University Press, Cambridge, Massachusetts, 1968. (Four volumes).
(111) PETTY, GEORGE R., JR.; GIBSON, WILLIAM M. Project OCCULT: the ordered computer collation of unprepared literary text. New York University Press, New York, 1970.
(112) PREREAU, DAVID S. Computer pattern recognition of standard engraved music notation. Massachusetts Institute of Technology, Cambridge, Massachusetts, 1970. (Ph.D. dissertation).
(113) PRICE, JACOB M. Recent quantitative work in history: a survey of the main trends. History and Theory; Studies in the Philosophy of History, Beiheft [supplement] 9 (1969) 1-13.
(114) RABB, THEODORE K. Investments in English overseas enterprise, 1575-1630. Economic History Review, 19 (1966) 70-81.
(115) RABEN, JOSEPH. A computer-aided study of literary influence: Milton & Shelley. Literary Data Processing Conference Proceedings, 9-11 September 1964. IBM, Yorktown Heights, New York, 1964.
(116) RABEN, JOSEPH. The death of the handmade concordance. Scholarly Publishing, 1:1 (1969), 61-69.
(117) RADDAY, YEHUDA T. An analytical linguistic concordance to the "Book of Isaiah." In: Baird, J. Arthur; Freedman, David Noel; eds. Biblical Research Associates, The College of Wooster, Wooster, Ohio, 1971.
(118) RADDAY, YEHUDA T. Isaiah and the computer: a preliminary report. Computers and the Humanities, 5:2 (1970) 65-73.
(119) RADDAY, YEHUDA T. The unity of Isaiah in the light of statistical linguistics. Verlag Gerstenberg, Hildesheim, Germany.
(120) REGENER, ERIC. A multiple-pass transcription and a system for musical analysis by computer. In: Heckmann, H.; ed. Elektronische datenverarbeitung in der musikwissenschaft. Gustav Bosse Verlag, Regensburg, Germany, 1967, 89-102.
(121) ROBISON, TOBIAS D. IML-MIR: a data-processing system for the analysis of music. In: Heckmann, H.; ed. Elektronische datenverarbeitung in der musikwissenschaft. Gustav Bosse Verlag, Regensburg, Germany, 1967, 103-135.
(122) ROSS, DONALD, JR.; RASCHE, ROBERT H. EYEBALL: a computer program for description of style. Computers and the Humanities, 6:4 (March 1972) 213-221.
(123) ROTHGEB, JOHN. Musical research by computer: some current limitations. Computers and the Humanities, 5:3 (January 1971) 178-182.
(124) ROWNEY, DON K.; GRAHAM, JAMES Q.; eds. Quantitative history: selected readings in the quantitative analysis of historical data. Homewood, Illinois, 1969.
(125) RUBENSTEIN, NANCY O. A FORTRAN computer program for transcribing Franconian rhythms. Washington University, Seattle, Washington, 1969. Dissertation Abstracts, XXX:12 (June 1970) 5474-A. (Ph.D. dissertation).

(126) RUMMEL, R. J. Understanding factor analysis. Journal of Conflict Resolution, 11 (1967) 440-478.

(127) SALTON, GERARD. Automatic processing of foreign language documents. Journal of the American Society for Information Science, 21:3 (May/June 1970) 187-194.

(128) SARNA, DAVID E. Y.; SCHIFFMAN, LAWRENCE H. Computer-aided critical editions of Rabbinic texts. Hebrew Computational Linguistics, Bulletin no. 2, 47-63. (Bar-Ilan University, Ramat-Gan, Israel).

(129) SCANLAN, RICHARD T. Computer-assisted instruction in Latin. The Classical Journal, 66:3 (February/March 1971) 223-227.

(130) SEDELOW, SALLY Y.; et al. Automated analysis of language style and structure—1969-1970. North Carolina University, Chapel Hill, North Carolina, 1 September 1970, 163 p. (AD 711 643).

(131) SEDELOW, SALLY Y. The computer in the humanities and fine arts. Computing Surveys, 2:2 (June 1970) 89-110.

(132) SHORTER, EDWARD. The historian and the computer: a practical guide. Prentice-Hall, Englewood Cliffs, New Jersey, 1971.

(133) SILBEY, JOEL H. The shrine of party: congressional voting behavior 1841-1852. University of Pittsburgh Press, Pittsburgh, Pennsylvania, 1967.

(134) SILVA, GEORGETTE; LOVE, HAROLD. The identification of text variants by computer. Information Storage and Retrieval, 5 (1969-1970) 89-108.

(135) SMITH, JOHN B. RATS: a middle-level text utility system. Computers and the Humanities, 6:5 (May 1972) 277-283.

(136) SPEVACK, MARVIN A. A complete and systematic concordance to the works of Shakespeare. Georg Olms, Hildesheim, Germany, 1969-1970. (Six volumes).

(137) STERNE, LAURENCE; STERNE, NOEL. A concordance to Milton's English prose. Southern Illinois University Press, Carbondale, Illinois. (In press).

(138) STREETER, MARY L. DOC, 1971: a Chinese dialect dictionary on computer. Computers and the Humanities, 6:5 (May 1972) 259-270.

(139) SUCHOFF, BENJAMIN. The computer and Bartók research in America. Journal of Research in Music Education, XIX:1 (Spring 1971) 3-16.

(140) SWIERENGA, ROBERT P. Clio and computers: a survey of computerized research in history. Computers and the Humanities, 5:1 (September 1970) 1-21.

(141) SWIERENGA, ROBERT P.; ed. Quantification in American history: theory and research. Atheneum Press, New York, 1970.

(142) TEXTOR, R. B. A cross-cultural summary. Human Relations Area Files Press, New Haven, Connecticut, 1967.

(143) THERNSTROM, STEPHAN. The historian and the computer. In: Bowles, Edmund A.; ed. Computers in humanistic research. Prentice-Hall, Englewood Cliffs, New Jersey, 1967, 73-81.

(144) THERNSTROM, STEPHAN. Poverty in historical perspective. In: Moynihan, Daniel P.; ed. On understanding poverty: perspectives from the social sciences. Basic Books, New York, 1969.

(145) THERNSTROM, STEPHAN; SENNETT, RICHARD; eds. Nineteenth century cities: essays in the new urban history. Yale University Press, New Haven, Connecticut, 1969.

(146) THOMPSON, STITH. Motif-index of folk-literature. Indiana University Press, Bloomington, Indiana, 1955-1958. (Six volumes).

(147) VANCE, DAVID; HELLER, JACK. Structure and content of a museum data bank. Computers and the Humanities, 6:2 (November 1971) 67-84.

(148) VELDMAN, DONALD J. FORTRAN programming for the behavioral sciences. Holt, Rinehart & Winston, New York, 1967.

(149) VENEZKY, RICHARD L. BIBCON: a 3600 program for producing concordances to prose, poetry and bibliographic references. University of Wisconsin, Computer Sciences Department, Madison, Wisconsin, 1969. (Technical report no. 34).

(150) WACHAL, ROBERT S. The machine in the garden: computers and literary scholarship. Computers and the Humanities, 5:1 (September 1970) 23-28.
(151) WHALLON, ROBERT, JR. The computer in archaeology: a critical survey. Computers and the Humanities, 7:1 (September 1972).
(152) WIDMANN, R. L. The computer in historical collation: use of the IBM 360/75 in collating multiple editions of "A Midsummer's Night's Dream." In: Wisbey, Roy A.; ed. The computer in literary and linguistic research. Cambridge University Press, Cambridge, Massachusetts, 1971, 57-63.
(153) WIDMANN, R. L. Computers and literary scholarship. Computers and the Humanities, 6:1 (September 1971) 3-14.
(154) WISBEY, ROY A. A complete concordance to the Vorau and Strassburg "Alexander," with a reverse index to the graphic forms, an index of rhymes, and ranking list of frequencies. W. S. Maney, Leeds, 1968.
(155) WISBEY, ROY A.; ed. The computer in literary and linguistic research. Cambridge University Press, Cambridge, Massachusetts, 1971.
(156) WISBEY, ROY A. Recent scholarship in literary and linguistic research. Computers and the Humanities, 7:1 (September 1972).
(157) WISHART, DAVID; LEACH, STEPHEN V. A multi-variate analysis of Platonic prose rhythm. Computer Studies in the Humanities and Verbal Behavior, 3:2 (August 1970) 90-99.
(158) ZEMSKY, ROBERT M. Numbers and history: the dilemma of measurement. Computers and the Humanities, 4:1 (September 1969) 31-40.
(159) ZETTERSTEN, ARNE. Current Scandinavian computer-assisted language and literature research. Computers and the Humanities, 5:4 (March 1971) 203-208.

12 Information Systems Applications in the Criminal Justice System

ALFRED BLUMSTEIN
Carnegie-Mellon University

Probably the single greatest technical limitation on the criminal justice system's ability to make its decisions wisely and fairly is that the people in the system often are required to decide issues without enough information... Existing procedures must be devised, so that information can flow more fully and swiftly among the system's many parts. (24, p.13)

INTRODUCTION

When President Johnson's Crime Commission set a staff of "19 commissioners, 63 staff members, 175 consultants, and hundreds of advisors" to examine the operation of the criminal justice system (CJS) in 1965-67, it found a system operating in the technological dark ages in trying to deal with a problem of increasing social concern. Reported victim crimes had been increasing at an annual rate of about 10-20 percent and that rate of increase slowed only slightly to 11 percent in 1970 (23).

The rising crime rate has focused public attention on the nation's criminal justice system. That system appears to have been trying to reverse the trends, but because of the system's fragmented structure and antiquated practices, the futility of that effort has become increasingly evident.

Friel (6) has documented the size and scope of the CJS. He estimates that the system in 1970 comprised the activity of 420,000 law enforcement officers in over 40,000 separate agencies at a total operating budget of 2.5 billion dollars a year; the decision-making of some 3700 superior court judges and 15,000 lower court judges responsible for the sentencing of two million felons and 30 million misdemeanants a year; the handling of more than one million juveniles, 600,000 of whom can be categorized as delinquent; the operation of more than 3400 county and county-city jails and 50 state penal systems; and the employment of 121,000 correctional workers who have custody over 1.3 million people at a total operating budget of 1.5 billion dollars a year.

At the time of the Crime Commission's work in 1966, the actual implementation of computer systems was determined by a Crime Commission survey of criminal justice agencies (11, pp.161-165). Implementation at that time was limited largely to a few IBM 1401-size computers used for general management purposes by police departments, two real-time police inquiry systems for checking on stolen automobiles, two small computer systems in use by criminal courts, and no reported use of any computers in corrections agencies.

Stimulated subsequently by the passage of the Omnibus Crime Control and Safe Streets Act of 1968 (Public Law 90-351, enacted June 19, 1968), and the infusion of over two billion Federal dollars into the criminal justice system through the Law Enforcement Assistance Administration, the use of computer-based information systems has expanded to remedy many of the technological aspects of the information deficiencies emphasized so strongly by the Crime Commission.

Some of these developments are discussed here on two principal dimensions—"case-following" (CF) systems and "resource-management" (RM) systems. Case-following systems record and follow a particular event or individual as the case and its downstream consequences unfold in the operation of the CJS. Resource-management systems focus more on the institutions of the CJS, the measurement of their operations, and the allocation and scheduling of their resources.

The case-following systems include reports of individual crimes and approaches to solution of the crime by such means as the crime-pattern records ("modus operandi" or "MO") of habitual criminals. A second kind of case-following system is a police operational real-time *inquiry* system, which provides police officers in the field with rapid file-search capability to resolve an instantaneous encounter, e.g., to determine whether the automobile they have just stopped is a stolen car, whether the man driving it is wanted elsewhere, or whether the color TV set on the back seat has been reported stolen. Once an individual is arrested, another CF system maintains a "*subject-in-process*" record to keep track of his status through preliminary arraignment, pretrial detention or bail, preliminary hearing, indictment, trial, appeal, and correctional treatment; this system could be augmented by background information about the individual to improve the quality of the decisions made about him in the course of his processing. Finally, a *criminal history* is maintained on each individual to aid in police investigation of a new offense and to provide a basis for prescribing future treatments.

The resource-management system is much more concerned with aggregate agency statistics reflecting the operation of the individual criminal justice agencies, the flows they process, their resource requirements, and efficient use of those resources, including the allocation of police officers to shifts and precincts and to beats within a precinct and the scheduling of cases before a court.

PROJECT "SEARCH"

The most significant developments in criminal justice information systems in recent years have been those organized under Project SEARCH (System for Electronic Analysis and Retrieval of Criminal Histories), an effort sponsored by the Law Enforcement Assistance Administration to develop a national network among the states for the maintenance and exchange of criminal histories. Reports on the various aspects of this project were given at a *National Symposium on Criminal Justice Information and Statistics Systems* held on November 10-12, 1970 (18).

Project SEARCH was created to develop a common prototype computerized criminal history information system for a group of 15 states coordinated by the California Council on Criminal Justice. As defined by Wormeli (27, p. 17), the coordinator of the project, the effort is intended to "establish and demonstrate a multi-state prototype system and capability which will:

(a) establish and demonstrate the feasibility of an on-line system allowing for the interstate exchange of offender files in the states based on a compatible 'criminal justice offender record,' integrating police, prosecution, court and correctional offender data;

(b) design and demonstrate a computerized criminal justice statistics system (e.g., offense and arrest statistics, court statistics, probation and parole statistics, etc.) which would permit access by LEAA and by police, court, correctional, and planning agencies."

In order to create its prototype operational interstate system for transferring criminal history data, the project established three subsidiary objectives:

(a) agree upon a standardized minimum set of data elements with standardized definitions for each data element in the areas of offender identification, offenses, and dispositions;

(b) create a prototype centralized index that can be accessed by a state requesting information on a properly identified offender, and the index would then provide the names of states holding data on that offender;

(c) demonstrate and evaluate the capacity for interstate transfer of criminal histories and response to requests for criminal histories (27, p. 17).

This concept of a central index follows the recommendation of the President's Crime Commission, which had struggled with the tradeoff between the efficiency of a large comprehensive central national "data bank" containing all the relevant information and the protection afforded by a highly decentralized state-based system. The Crime Commission's recommendation (24, p.268) for "a national law enforcement directory that records an individual's arrests for serious crimes, the disposition of each case, and all subsequent formal contacts with criminal justice agencies related to those arrests" was thus reflected in the SEARCH development.

Criminal Histories

In the Project SEARCH system (27), detailed files on offenders are maintained in the states, and the national central index keeps only summary data on each state-held file. A user can query the system by providing, for an individual of interest, either the FBI number, the operator's license number, the Social Security number, miscellaneous identification numbers, or the group [name/sex/date of birth]. The central index reponds to an inquiry by providing basic personal information (name, sex, race, date of birth, height, etc.) and various identifying numbers (state identification number, FBI number, Social Security number, operator's license number, and fingerprint classification) whenever these are recorded. In addition, the user is told which state is the "agency of record," i.e., the state assigned to maintain the full criminal history record on that individual.

The state agency of record maintains the basic information indicated above and records each criminal justice transaction involving the individual, including information on the arrest by charge, outcome of the pretrial hearing, trial disposition and sentence, and correctional assignment.

Project SEARCH began in 1969 with 10 states (Arizona, California, Connecticut, Florida, Maryland, Michigan, Minnesota, New York,

Texas, and Washington) agreeing on common data formats and the design of a system for communication of criminal history information. This prototype system was operated with each of seven states providing a converted data base of 10,000 offenders' records, and the operation of the network was demonstrated in the summer of 1970. In the demonstration, Michigan's B-5500 computer served as the central index and was connected to each state by a single low-speed (110 baud) line. By the fall of 1970, the program had advanced sufficiently to warrant transfer to an operational agency, and the FBI assumed responsibility for the program under its Computerized Criminal History program. This service was closely coupled to the FBI's National Crime Information Center, which since 1967 had been maintaining a police real-time inquiry system on stolen cars, wanted offenders, and stolen property.

Shumate (20, p.249), an early pioneer in the development of criminal justice information systems, reacted somewhat skeptically to the demonstration: "It is fair to say that it has been no real surprise that the initial results of the project have demonstrated that technologically it is feasible to store, retrieve, and transmit data between a group of computers....Systems of this general class have been in use on a significant scale both within the criminal justice establishment and in a wide range of military, industrial and general governmental agencies." He emphasized the need to relate costs of these systems to their potential benefits and the fundamental difficulties that develop in dealing with large files (in the order of 10^7 as opposed to 10^5) when erroneous hit rates become high, data error rates become troublesome, and retrieval becomes much more complex.

Another problem, emphasized by Marx (15, p. 229), coordinator of the Technical Evaluation Team of Project SEARCH, is the shifting responsibility associated with designating as the agency of record for an individual the last state in which he was arrested. That agency is then responsible for maintaining, converting, and updating his SEARCH record. This introduces questions of interstate consistency of records and crime designations, consistency of format, rights to purge, etc. These problems derive from different rules by state on criminal codes (e.g., a purse-snatching is a robbery in one jurisdiction and a larceny in another; a larceny exceeding x dollars is a felony, but x may be $50 in one state and $200 in another). An alternative, of course, is for each state to maintain permanent control over the subset of an individual's record based on activities within that state, or—as a somewhat less efficient practice—for each state to maintain the entire record of each individual ever arrested within that state. This, of course, introduces the difficulty of multiple versions of the same record, and these may well be inconsistent.

Some arbitrary procedures (e.g., for the last state of record to maintain the "official" record) will always be required, but the fundamental technical differences between jurisdictions will continue to plague efforts to establish consistent national systems in criminal justice. And these local differences, even though they are usually of a minor and arbitrary sort, will not be readily changed simply for reasons of achieving national standardization.

Subject-in-Process Record

In contrast to the coarse-grain criminal history record, a subject-in-process record provides a fine-grain track of an individual as he is processed through the successive processing stages of the CJS. Each processing stage (e.g., a magistrate, prosecutor, judge, probation officer) updates the record as it completes its actions and decisions.

Maintaining such a record requires agreement on format and definitions at each of the processing stages within a criminal justice system. Most of the current differences in terminology, identification method, coding formats, and charge and crime type designation, even within a single jurisdiction, will have to be negotiated away.

A model subject-in-process format has been reported by Stevens (21) and applied by Stevens et al. (22) to 3000 records in the Fort Worth, Texas area. The basic format of that record is reproduced here as Table 1 from Stevens et al. (22, pp. 101-102). When such a subject-in-process record is correctly generated by each of the criminal justice agencies, a new level of cooperation, compatability, and completeness will have been reached in the CJS. Any agency will be able to learn of the status of any individual anywhere in the system. Monitoring reports will flag individuals who may have gotten lost in the process (e.g., those who are sitting in detention awaiting a bail decision). Future workloads downstream in the system will be reasonably predictable because today's court trial represents an extra case for the probation officer tomorrow. Finally, a full set of basic operating statistics can be generated for each of the operating agencies within a system.

The arrival of that state of affairs, however, is still somewhat less than imminent. Many of the smaller police departments (Allegheny County, Pennsylvania, with its 115 police departments is a good example) would require considerable adjustment before they would participate in this kind of reporting. Few justices of the peace and other similar dispensers of the work-a-day justice (that is far more common than the Perry Mason jury trial) are in the habit of filling out reporting forms, and many might regard a requirement to do so as an infringement on their judicial independence. Increasing control is being exercised, however, by the state and Federal governments, which are increasingly requiring regular reporting in order to share in Federal criminal justice funding. Also, aggregation of the smaller jurisdictions is taking place, stimulated largely by the development of larger information systems and by the growing recognition of the inefficiency as well as ineffectiveness of small departments. Thus, the next decade might well see considerable progress in the development and wider use of subject-in-process record formats.

Statistical Reporting

Under the expectation that reporting by the component CJS agencies is complete, it would be possible to develop an adequate statistical system from a set of subject-in-process records, augmented perhaps by a few data elements such as prior record not normally contained in a subject-in-process record.

Project SEARCH, under Steve Kolodney as Statistical Coordinator, developed a prototype statistical system based on reports from the four principal processing stages (police action, felony pre-trial, felony trial, and corrections). The data elements in this system are based on the CJS transactions, and are shown in Table II, from Kolodney (14). These data were developed for 250 adult defendants of the pilot states in the SEARCH project, and they provided a basis for assessing the difficulty of collecting even these fundamental data in the various states.

Here again, the development of such a statistical system would be hampered in many ways. Incompatabilities across jurisdictions (even within the state and more so between states) will lead to ambiguous definitions, and therefore erroneous counting. Individual local agencies will have to revise their practices considerably to replace their fragmented and occasional counting with consistently reliable and complete records. A number of states have tried to create a statewide criminal justice statistical system; but, with the striking exception of California's Bureau of Criminal Statistics pioneered in 1946 by Beattie (1), success has been only limited. Even more difficult, therefore, is aggregation at the national level as long as criminal justice operations and the associated freedom not to report remain essentially local. When all transactions are recorded into a national criminal justice information system, then this system might provide the elements from which the gross national statistics, as well as subsidiary statistics, could be developed.

	Description	*Length*		*Description*	*Length*
1.	Name	30	51.	Date Subject Transferred to County Jail	5
2.	Sex	1	52.	Amount Bond Set	4
3.	Race	1	53.	Date Bond Posted	5
4.	Date of birth	6	54.	Type of Bond	1
5.	Place of Birth	3	55.	Place Held When Bond Posted	7
6.	Height	3	56.	Name of Bondsman	30
7.	Weight	3	57.	Date of Grand Jury Indictment	5
8.	Eyes, color	1	58.	Indictment Number	6
9.	Hair, color	2	59.	Indictment Charge A	4
10.	Visible marks	49	60.	Indictment Charge B	4
11.	Address, residence	30	61.	Indictment Charge C	4
12.	Census Tract and Block	9	62.	Date of Formal Arraignment	5
13.	Occupation	6	63.	Court Arraigned (Judge)	2
14.	Driver's License Number	8	64.	Plea Entered	1
15.	Driver's License State	3	65.	Amount Bond Set	4
16.	Social Security Number	9	66.	Date Bond Posted	5
17.	Miscellaneous Numbers	15	67.	Type of Bond	1
18.	First Offense, Code	4	68.	Place Held	7
19.	Offense Location, Address	30	69.	Name of Bondsman	30
20.	Census Tract and Block	9	70.	Date Applied for Counsel	5
21.	Offense Date	5	71.	Date Counsel Assigned	5
22.	Offense Time	4	72.	Name of Counsel	29
23.	Offense Day of Week	1	73.	Name of Prosecuting Attorney	29
24.	Type of Place of Offense	2	74.	Date of Pretrial Conference	5
25.	Second Offense, Code	4	75.	First Pretrial Motion	2
26.	Third Offense, Code	4	76.	Date	5
27.	Arrest Date	5	77.	Outcome	1
28.	Arresting Agency Code	7	78.	Second Pretrial Motion	2
29.	Arrest Number	6	79.	Date	5
30.	Offense Number	7	80.	Outcome	1
31.	Arrest Agency File Number	8	81.	Third Pretrial Motion	2
32.	Fingerprint Classification	20	82.	Date	5
33.	Previous Offense Code, No. 1	4	83.	Outcome	1
34.	Date	5	84.	Fourth Pretrial Motion	2
35.	Conviction	1	85.	Date	5
36.	Previous Offense Code, No. 2	4	86.	Outcome	1
37.	Date	5	87.	Fifth Pretrial Motion	2
38.	Conviction	1	88.	Date	5
39.	Previous Offense Code, No. 3	4	89.	Outcome	1
40.	Date	5	90.	Sixth Pretrial Motion	2
41.	Conviction	1	91.	Date	5
42.	Alias	30	92.	Outcome	1
43.	Skin Tone	1	93.	Seventh Pretrial Motion	2
44.	Trademark	30	94.	Date	5
45.	Driver's License, Year Expires	2	95.	Outcome	1
46.	FBI Number	8	96.	Eighth Pretrial Motion	2
47.	DPS Number	10	97.	Date	5
48.	Preliminary Hearing Date	5	98.	Outcome	1
49.	Preliminary Hearing Magistrate	2	99.	Trial Judge	2
50.	Date Charges Filed in J.P. Court	5	100.	Date Trial Called	5

Table I — Data Elements in Subject-in-Process Record

	Description	*Length*
101.	Trial Disposition Date	5
102.	Disposition	4
103.	Type of Sentence	4
104.	Type of Length of Sentence	4
105.	Duration of Sentence (in months)	5
106.	Amount of Fine (in 00's)	4
107.	Date of Appeal to Texas Court of Criminal Appeal	5
108.	Disposition	1
109.	Date Appeal to Federal Court of Criminal Appeal	5
110.	Disposition	1
111.	Date Appeal to U.S. Supreme Court	5
112.	Disposition	1
113.	Date Entered Probation	5
114.	Probation Officer Assigned	1
115.	Date of Motion for Probation Revocation	5
116.	Reason	4
117.	Date Revoked	5
118.	Disposition From Revocation or Attempt to Revoke	4
119.	Date Entered Correctional Institution	5
120.	TDC Number	6

	Description	*Length*
121.	Institution Held	2
122.	Institution Rehabilitation Program Participation	2
123.	Date Re-entered	5
124.	Unit Re-entered	2
125.	Date Parole Granted	5
126.	DPO Assigned	3
127.	Date Parole Revoked	5
128.	Reason	4
129.	Date Exited From System	5
130.	Reason	4
131.	Charges Reduced to Misdemeanor	4
132.	Extradicted to ___ (State)	3
133.	Education	2
134.	IQ	3
135.	Narcotics Use (Yes or No)	1
	Previous Arrests Not Listed Before	
136.	Offense Code	4
137.	Date	5
138.	Offense Code	4
139.	Date	5
140.	Offense Code	4
141.	Date	5

Table I (continued)

OFFENDER CHARACTERISTICS

State
State ID Number
Age at Time of Arrest
Sex
Race
Number of Arrests
Number of Convictions
Number of Jail 90 Days
Number of Jail 90 Days
Number of Jail 90 Days
Number of Prison (State Institution)
Status at Time of Arrest
State of Supervision

STAGE 1—POLICE ACTION

Date of Arrest (Mo/Day/Yr)
Arresting Agency
Type of Arrest
Apparent Intended Offense
Primary Charged Offense (Most Serious)
Police Disposition

STAGE 2—PRE-TRIAL (FELONY)

Pre-Trial Cycle Number
Proceeding Type
Offense Charged
Date of Initiation
Date of Completion
Disposition
Release Actions
Offense Charge at Disposition
Plea
Length of Jail Term (Days)
Length of Probation (Months)
Amount of Fine ($)

STAGE 3—FELONY TRIAL

Date Filed
Offense Charged
Initial Plea
Final Plea
Type of Trial
Release Action
Disposition
Date of Disposition
Reason for Dismissal
Convicted Offense
Pre-Sentence Report Available
Length of Prison
Length of Probation (Months)
Length of Jail (Days)
Amount of Fine ($)
Length of Work Furlough
Type of Defense Counsel
Non-Supervisory Sentence

STAGE 4—CORRECTIONS

Corrections Cycle Number
Receiving Agency
Date of Receipt
Date of Termination
Reason for Termination

Table II — Data Eelements for
SEARCH Prototype Statistical System

INTEGRATED CRIMINAL JUSTICE INFORMATION SYSTEMS

Reflecting the basic concept of the Safe Streets Act to foster closer coordination among the agencies of the CJS, and the efforts of Project SEARCH to accomplish this with respect to information systems at a national level, some areas such as Philadelphia and Montgomery Valley, Ohio (around Dayton), are already developing integrated information systems to serve the information needs throughout the local CJS. This requires compatible formats and the kinds of inter-agency agreements discussed earlier. The results of these initial attempts will provide better indications of the feasibility of achieving the kind of compromises necessary for this compatibility and will also provide a basis for assessing the value of the mutual information-sharing. Clearly, some data elements such as personal identifiers are collected redundantly in various parts of the system and some information like that relating to ties to the community is retained in one part of the system and could be of value elsewhere. In general, however, if the police, courts, and corrections agencies have organized their information needs into three separate and effective comprehensive systems, and if common identification numbers are available across the system, it is doubtful that very much additional value would be gained by organizing these three into a single total system. Police need highly formatted current operational data on a real-time basis; correctional decisions require detailed historical and analytical data about individuals, and time pressures are rare; and the courts need information much more for internal management of the court process than for keeping a record of individual defendant characteristics. If each of the subsystems had an information system of its own that adequately met its needs, and if opportunities were provided for communication between these subsystems (by their sharing each other's identification numbers of subjects in process, for instance), then there is some question about the value of attempting a full integration of all the component information systems into a single, centrally controlled system.

POLICE INFORMATION SYSTEMS

The principal needs that the police have in information systems are for real-time inquiry systems. There has been extensive development and implementation of inquiry systems by which a field officer can radio a dispatcher and ask for a file search for an automobile license number, or for information on an individual or an identifiable piece of property. The first such operational system was the California Highway Patrol's

Auto-Statis System, introduced in 1965 to provide checks on stolen automobiles within California. At about the same time, a similar system was introduced by the St. Louis and Chicago Police Departments. Inquiry systems have since been extended for use by a large number of police departments, and are used nationally by the FBI in their National Crime Information Center (NCIC). In addition to the national NCIC, such systems operate at the state level (e.g., LEIN in Michigan and CLEAN in Pennsylvania), and the local level (e.g., ALERT in Kansas City, CLEAR in Cincinnati and surrounding Hamilton County), and new ones are continually being introduced. As the scope of the jurisdiction narrows, the threshold of seriousness or importance of the information contained in the file is reduced, so that local systems might contain files of habitual parking violators, while the NCIC record would include only individuals wanted for an extradictable offense.

Information systems also have important potential police value in the analysis of information about crimes and criminals, to identify patterns of a criminal's operations ("modus operandi"), and to spot the likely perpetrator when an offense is somewhat out of the ordinary. Attempts to develop this capability have been proceeding for a number of years at the Los Angeles Police Department (LAPD), with System Development Corporation's Project PATRIC (12, 13), an acronym for Pattern Recognition and Information Correlation. This invokes manual judgment and various statistical correlation approaches to estimate likely patterns. In the PATRIC system, records are maintained of the frequency of occurrence of various attributes of criminal or investigative events (e.g., personal characteristics of offender, vehicle license number), and use attributes of high information content (i.e., those that are relatively rare and unique) and correlation among them to derive patterns of crimes or of an identifiable criminal. The system is currently being tested in the operational environment of LAPD. In the tests, the feasibility of the system will be explored to determine the nature and frequency of its successes (e.g., correct identification of an offender) and its more general impact on crime (e.g., reflected as a reduction in rates of certain "repressible" crimes).

COURT INFORMATION SYSTEMS

Criminal court operation is one of the more complex parts of the criminal justice system and in many respects represents the keystone of the process. Also, courts are probably the least advanced in their use of modern information systems. Perhaps the most advanced operational criminal court information system is that of the City of Philadelphia (17).

In view of the complexity of processing through the court, and the multitude of independent participants in that process (including prosecutors, defense counsels, bondsmen, judges, defendants, police jail wardens, and witnesses), there is a major need simply for orderly scheduling and management of the operation. As a minimum, there must be an assignment of a time and place for each scheduled event, with notice going to each participant enough in advance so he can resolve a conflict if one occurs. The information and scheduling process must assure that all participants are available and will appear for the appropriate hearing. This is particularly important because repeated continuances not only cause delay but also harass lay witnesses and disillusion them with the CJS; repeated appearance costs them at least annoyance and even several days' earnings. Continuances derive from the unavailability of one of the hearing participants at the appointed time and place; because the time and place are usually known well in advance, schedules can be prepared to avoid the problem. If each court and each participant organizes and schedules independently, then conflicts in schedule are inevitable. An information system could organize conflict-free schedules and report the schedules to the participants sufficiently in advance so that if there were conflicts they could report it in time for a revised schedule to be made available to all participants.

Two additional case-following systems are needed. First, a system is needed to provide for collection of information on the defendant, his likelihood of appearance for trial (a critical component of the bail decision) and his prior record and risk to the community if he is convicted (a critical component of the sentencing decision). Needed here, of course, is a better set of information based on analysis of past decisions. Most information is presently treated in a model that tries to estimate a "base expectancy" or probability of recidivism (p_r); the critical issue is not so much an average probability of recidivism, but rather a conditional probability (p_{r_i}), which measures the probability of recidivism associated with treatment i. Since different treatments are differentially effective with different classes of offenders, this critically requires matching of the treatment to the offenders, and effective classification dimensions are needed. Then, research experiments are needed to develop recidivism probabilities $p_{r_{ij}}$ reflecting the probability of recidivism when treatment i is applied to defendants of class j. Some of the work of Warren et al. (25) and the California Community Treatment Project represents a prime example of the application of those concepts and procedures. In that project, delinquent youths were classified to identify the best treatment for them, and they were randomly assigned to the new or the conventional treatment programs. Comparison between the treatment and control groups can then be causally meaningful.

The second major case-following need is that each criminal justice official and associated participant (e.g., defense counsel) be able to learn the current status of all cases for which he is responsible and that involve people of concern to him. Any information system meeting those needs can also monitor the status of case flow and backlog, and make a projection of future requirements.

In the Philadelphia court information system, all cases and defendants are recorded at the conclusion of the preliminary arraignment, which is held within 24 hours of arrest. At that point, information on the defendant, the arrest, and the charges is used to generate a basic record for the individual case. At the conclusion of each step in the process, the outcome is recorded, dates for subsequent stages are identified, and reports are thereby generated for each of the appropriate participants to inform them of their future responsibilities in the process. There are two principal branch points: one at the lower or Municipal Court, and an expanded file for the higher Court of Common Pleas subsequent to grand jury indictment. Cases are scheduled subject to appropriate time and resource availability constraints for both arraignment and trial. Reports of the result of arraignment, pre-trial motions, and other critical events are given to the system and appropriate notices to the appropriate participants are computer-generated. These include subpoenas for witnesses, defendants, and arresting officers; trial calendars; prisoner bring-up lists; attorney letters; and appropriate program calendars.

The information system provides an inquiry capability at nine display terminals located at seven points throughout the courthouse, at the detention center, and at the police central booking facility. Thus, each participant in the process has the opportunity to retrieve appropriate information on any case or individual of interest to him.

Also derivable from these basic data are a variety of statistical reports for both the system participants and managers and/or the general public on the performance of the court system. This includes data on backlog, flow of cases, use of resources, and other measures of the efficiency of the court processing system. It is, of course, much more difficult to relate such data to the more fundamental considerations of quality of justice or of "correctness" of judicial decisions. It is possible, however, to obtain measures of excessive detention, excessive trial delays, and recidivism associated with the various kinds of sentences, and feed this information back to the judges and court administrators for general improvement of the operation of the court system.

CORRECTIONAL INFORMATION SYSTEMS

In corrections, the basic problems of information systems are markedly different from those of police operations. In police operations there is much more need for instantaneous retrieval, inquiry systems, and highly formatted information. This is because of the frequency with which information is required by policemen on the street, especially with regard to suspicious individuals, where the policeman must make a decision on whether to arrest within seconds or minutes. Furthermore, the structure of the information regarding individuals or criminal events are readily classified into a reasonably well-defined number of fundamental characteristics, as reflected, for example, in the format structure of NCIC, CLEAN, and other related information systems. The general use of these information systems is characterized by a well-defined structure, a set format, and a need for aggregating the information gathered from quite dispersed and highly fragmented police agencies. In corrections, the problems are very different. On one hand, the kinds of information relating to an individual are much more complex and combine information about many aspects—prior history, results of psychological examination and interviews, background investigation, etc. Also, especially for prisoners in custody in institutions, time lags of days or even weeks are acceptable, and instantaneous responses are rarely necessary.

A major project to identify information needs and design a correctional information system was the Correctional Decision Information Project (CDIP) conducted by the American Justice Institute (10).

In correctional programs as well as in the other parts of the system, a distinction between case-following and resource-management information systems is also useful. Case-following records include the individual, his designated status in terms of correctional control options, background information, constraints on the nature of his sentence and treatment, diagnostic information regarding the appropriate correctional treatment, and a record of the treatments assigned to him. In resource-management, a variety of information is, in principle, obtainable from the case-following records. This includes information on the number of sentenced offenders waiting for assignment to an institution, availability of space in either physical facilities, probation offices, or other correctional treatment agencies, projected availabilities based on known information on times of release from supervision, future budgets, and resource requirements. Certainly at the state level, such data can be compiled as aggregations of the individual case records, once these are appropriately committed to computer format and the appropriate software developed.

One of the most fundamental needs in the organization or management of correctional information systems is a guideline for correctional decisions in terms of the effectiveness of different treatments on individual offenders. Initial attempts have been undertaken to relate treatment effectiveness to treatment design. An example of this is the *Uniform Crime Reports* Careers in Crime Program (23, pp. 37-42), which attempts to review recidivism as a function of the treatments individuals have undergone. The fundamental problem here of such an analysis is the lack of experimental control in the analysis. To the extent that the decision-makers may have prescribed a treatment related to their somewhat accurate prior expectation of the individual's subsequent performance, the results would be subject to all the problems of self-fulfilling prophesy. When offenders given more lenient treatment show less or less serious recidivism, it can never be clear whether they were properly judged less likely to recidivate or whether the more lenient treatment induced rehabilitation. Thus, in order to provide effective evaluation and research on such issues, it is essential that controlled experiments be undertaken. Here, the judge or the associated correctional official makes an appropriate choice of a correctional treatment where such is clearly indicated. Where there is ambiguity about the correct choice, however, then some randomized procedure should be used to make the assignment of treatment to the individual. Then, the results of this controlled experiment can be used to specify much more rigorously what worked with what types of individuals. Only with this kind of control will the decisions go beyond the level of hunch to a level of empirical validity.

Even in the design and operation of such experiments, many sources of bias readily enter. Individuals who know they are in a selected treatment program, especially if that is a new or novel program, may well perform better—the well-known Hawthorne effect. New or innovative programs are more likely to be operated by more effective individuals, largely because of the self-selection of those individuals to the creation of such new programs. Thus, even after evaluation of the new program, uncertainty continues about how that program would operate in the hands of a more average operating team. These efforts will fundamentally require much greater use of randomization and controlled experiments in an environment where the tradition militates against that notion of "rolling dice with people's lives." Until the concept of experimental randomization becomes part of the routine operations within the criminal justice system, however, that system will continue to operate in the realm of darkness and myth, subject to changing contemporary ideologies as they evolve.

CRIMINAL JUSTICE PLANNING

A fundamental intent of the Safe Streets Act was to foster comprehensive planning for the total CJS. This planning has been carried out only to a limited extent so far. In large part, this results from the need for an adequate methodology. An appropriate methodology using a simulation-like model characterizing the flow through the CJS was reported by Blumstein & Larson (3), but that was not readily adopted, largely because of the complexity and apparent remoteness of the model when used on normal batch-processing mode. The program was revised by Belkin et al. (2) and emerged as Justice System Interactive Model (JUSSIM), an interactive version of that model. In JUSSIM, the criminal justice system is characterized by an initial set of flows (say crimes or arrests) by crime type; by a flow diagram comprising a sequence of processing stages; by branching ratios that reflect the portion of flow from each stage into each possible subsequent stage; by a set of resources (e.g., detectives, courtrooms, probation officers) with associated unit costs, annual availabilities, and capacity constraints; and by a set of unit workloads representing the consumption of each resource at each processing stage per unit of flow. The user starts with a data file of the "base case," all the above parameters characterizing the current operation of his Criminal Justice System. At the terminal, he then creates a "test case" by changing any combination of those parameters. He then calls for output, which provides comparative test-case and base-case estimates on costs, flows, resource workloads, and resources required for any stage or group of stages in the system. Largely as a result of its interactive operation, the JUSSIM model has already been implemented in Pittsburgh. In Pittsburgh, the base-case data file was developed over three months by three graduate students (5) and analyses were conducted shortly thereafter by a Carnegie-Mellon University project (4). In Philadelphia, the JUSSIM model was revised undertaken by Renshaw and Goldman of Government Studies & Systems, Inc. and William Braybrook of the Philadelphia Regional Planning Council (19) emerging as an alternative model called Philadelphia Justice Improvement Model (PHILJIM). Vermont; Washington, D.C.; Delaware; Alaska; and other jurisdictions are now actively developing their own data bases to implement JUSSIM.

EVALUATION

A fundamental problem inherent in CJS planning, and particularly in the design and evaluation of criminal justice information systems, is difficulty in evaluating their contribution to the performance of the criminal justice system itself in its delivery of crime control with justice. This evaluation must be conducted in terms of operational measures of the CJS (e.g., reduction in crimes, evaluation of correctness of decisions, speed of decisions, etc.) as well as those pertaining to the information systems themselves (e.g., response time, inquiry rate, etc.). This need for evaluation is certainly inherent in most tests. Auto theft retrieval systems have been available and operating for more than five years. Auto thefts have risen from 557,000 in 1966 to 921,400 in 1970 (284 to 453 reported auto thefts per 100,000 population), but there is no indication of whether the rate would have been greater, less, or the same if there were no retrieval systems. One could explore whether the cities or states with auto theft inquiry systems have a lower auto-theft rate than those without them. Such tests, of course, are easily performed, but have not yet been undertaken. It is significant that the Technical Evaluation Team (15) of Project SEARCH addressed most of its evaluative efforts to issues of system design. For example, they estimated the distribution of offense categories per individual record (and found that 98% had fewer than 8 offenses). They identified the most frequent crime categories (and found that burglary, larceny, assault, traffic, dangerous drugs, stolen vehicle, and robbery account for 55% of all occurrences). And they discussed the technical and administrative problems in creating a single "agency of record." These are certainly important system design issues, and it is certainly premature to evaluate the operational performance of the SEARCH prototype, but it is essential that a data base and evaluation procedures be developed with which to compare the usefulness of manual and automated systems.

CRIMINAL JUSTICE STATISTICS

An important part of the development of evaluation capability is the need for improved criminal justice statistics. The creation of the National Criminal Justice Statistics Center (9) within LEAA was an important step toward the creation of a compatible national system. One of the major undertakings of this center is the development of a victimization survey on a regular basis. These data are necessary for maintaining more accurate estimates of the amount of crime in the United States and represent an important follow-up to the initial victimization surveys conducted by the President's Crime Commission. When available, these data will provide corrections on the unreported crimes to the reported crime statistics maintained by the FBI in the *Uniform*

Crime Reports. These two data points will also provide, for the first time, an estimate of the *trend* in the non-reporting rates.

Zeisel (28) reviews the status of crime and criminal justice statistics for the President's Commission on Federal Statistics. In this review, he emphasizes the need to measure offender-based recidivism statistics only if recorded by an official conviction. This concept reflects the basic legal view that an individual is innocent until proven guilty, and certainly, in any formal use of the criminal sanction against an individual, this view must prevail. This does not preclude the use of other less stringent statistical measures when those are not applied to a particular individual.

Ideally, when used for statistical purposes, recidivism estimates should measure the incidence of the recommission of crime. Since such events are not normally reported, we must settle for recognizing as recidivist events those in which an individual is arrested or, more conservatively, convicted. Both cases reflect two kinds of errors, the error of commission in counting crimes by those who did not in fact commit them, and the error of omission by ignoring events that actually occurred but without their being sufficient proof for a legal conviction "beyond a reasonable doubt." In the case of individuals, of course, our legal system has decided to minimize the error of commission and accept a reasonable (although decidedly finite) error of omission. With regard to statistical estimates, however, this heavy weighting is far less appropriate. In view of the high rate of dismissal of charges by the criminal justice system based on evidence standards and procedural grounds, it is probable that the net error is less when arrest rather than conviction is used as the basis for estimating recidivist behavior.

PROTECTION OF INDIVIDUAL PRIVACY

The problems of "computer data banks," which have been discussed with increasing concern since Westin's seminal study (26), and more recently by Miller (16), are perhaps most delicate with regard to individuals' criminal histories. One of the salutary efforts of the SEARCH Project was the formation of a Security and Privacy Committee under the direction of Robert Gallati, director of New York State's Identification and Intelligence System (NYSIIS). The committee was asked to develop a set of guidelines and procedures to assure that security and privacy considerations were properly adhered to in Project SEARCH as well as in other criminal justice information systems (8).

A central issue involved in all considerations of criminal justice information systems is the question of privacy of the information contained therein. The concerns were represented by a proposal passed by the American Civil Liberties Union in June 1970:

> Whenever a government amasses files about its citizens an inherent threat to liberties exists. The ACLU...should work toward statutes setting forth rigorous tests of compelling need. When personal information is transferred between agencies...special protection must be established. The National Data Bank proposals exemplify such use; the seeming insensitivity of its proponents for safeguards underscores the need for legislative protections. The ACLU should oppose the establishment of centralized dossier-type data collections. The ACLU believes that the process of converting manual records to computer processing poses a great risk to privacy and due process. . . .The ACLU should act as a public spokesman in the defense of personal privacy and civil liberty in this area. (7)

These concerns derive from a growing recognition that the complexity and inefficiency of creating, updating, and searching manual files provide an inherent constraint on their accessibility and, thereby, a built-in privacy protection. Even so, Gallati found that relations between private detective agencies, credit bureaus, or personnel managers and police officials who have access to such records allow for a relatively free access to the data contained in those records, thus providing information that is of obvious value to the private investigative bodies. Herein, of course, lie the complexities and difficulties. No matter how carefully one protects the security of a system from external access, individuals who have access to such a system can always serve as proxies for those who cannot gain access.

The SEARCH Security and Privacy Committee included civil liberties lawyers, computer technicians, police officials, statisticians, and lawyers. The Committee explored the issues in the tradeoff between efficient record systems and protection of privacy, and wrote a document that set forth 23 major policy recommendations. Among the important ones were the following:

(1) Only data that are matters of public record should be included in the system;

(2) All participants should maintain a careful program of data verification and systematic audits;

(3) Purging procedures should be developed;

(4) A model state statute for protecting and controlling data should be drafted and adopted by all participating states;
(5) Direct access to the system should be restricted to members of criminal justice agencies;
(6) Each participating state should build its data system around a central computer through which each inquiry must pass for screening and verification;
(7) The various state "freedom of information" laws permitting public access to governmental records should be examined in order to provide appropriate exemptions and limitation on access to criminal justice information about arrested persons;
(8) All use of system data for research should involve stringent restrictions to preserve privacy;
(9) The citizen's right to have access to and to challenge the contents of his own record should form an integral part of the system, consistent with state law (this would require the individual to make positive identification of himself to gain that access);
(10) Civil remedies should be provided for those injured by misuse of the system where not otherwise provided for by state law;
(11) System participants should elect a board of directors to establish policies and procedures governing the central index operation;
(12) The system should remain fully independent of data systems not associated with criminal justice functions and be exclusively dedicated to the service of the criminal justice community;
(13) A systems audit should be made periodically by an outside agency;
(14) A permanent committee or staff should be established to consider problems of security and privacy and to conduct studies in that area.

In addition to these considerations, are a number of policy statements derived from the work of the Security and Privacy Committee to assure the integrity of the system and its information. These require that the input, modification, cancellation, and retrieval of information from the system should be limited to authorized terminals, with dissemination only to authorized final users. The information in the system must be protected against unauthorized access, alteration, loss, or misuse.

Monitoring misuse by those who have legitimate access to the data in the system will always be a problem. This seems to be an inherent risk and can best be dealt with by auditing and review procedures that compare each user's use of the system with his anticipated use. There must be a permanent log of all inquiries by each user, and he should be required to maintain a record of all dissemination he makes of individual records obtained from the system. Where this fails to inhibit misuse, it could serve as a means of apprehension in a periodic audit procedure.

The concept of purging was emphasized by the SEARCH Security and Privacy Committee as a counter to the increasing availability of individuals' records that becomes possible when the manual system is replaced by a computer-based one. Presumably, for each class of offense within a certain period of time, records of that arrest and even conviction are first transferred to a secure file from which they are accessible only in limited extreme circumstances, and after another specified time, they are purged completely from the system. An exploration of the needs for access, the times between entries, and other observations of the actual use of such a system would provide very reasonable estimates for the appropriate time values for purging. In most cases, individuals who have not come to the attention of the system for five to ten years are very unlikely to reappear and their records could very properly be kept in an inactive (and relatively inaccessible) file, and then finally purged. Such a study would provide legislatures with an appropriate basis for establishing fair record-retention rules that do not seriously inhibit police operations.

FUTURE DEVELOPMENTS OF CRIMINAL JUSTICE INFORMATION SYSTEMS

It is clear that there will be an increasing use of computer-based information systems throughout the criminal justice system, spurred on by the availability of the technology, imitation of the leaders, and infusion of Federal funds for those purposes. It is also clear that the development of those systems will be less than efficient as long as they are undertaken in a fragmented way. The Project SEARCH concept of organizing a consortium of states that are the leaders in a particular field represents an appropriate way to organize the operation of many aspects of criminal justice information systems. If each state, city, and county develops its own system with its own indicators and its own software packages, where these differ only in small detail, it is like requiring each automobile owner to design and custom-build his own vehicle. The costs are particularly high, and the value of the differences is minor. There is a clear need for efforts at a national level to provide basic software utility packages, which can then be selected and modified by each individual jurisdiction to reflect its own coding procedures and jurisdictional alternatives. Once these basic accomplishments have been attained, then we will see efficient development of such systems.

Many of these same problems relate to the need for development of statistical systems. It is obviously desirable, but probably wishful thinking, to expect that the inherent drive for autonomy throughout the criminal justice system will be relinquished sufficiently to permit the collection of a national set of statistical data on the criminal justice system as a result of the development of an identified statistical structure. We can reasonably expect that the pressure for standardization and the introduction of state or national standards as a condition for receiving funds will foster some conformity. Thus, as a goal, we have the SEARCH statistical system and related programs. In the meantime, statistical systems must be developed to provide both operational and analytical support for management of the constituent agencies within the system.

REFERENCES

(1) BEATTIE, RONALD H. Offender-based criminal statistics. California Crime Technological Research Foundation, Sacramento, California, March 1971. (Project SEARCH special report no. 3).

(2) BELKIN, JACOB; BLUMSTEIN, ALFRED; GLASS, WILLIAM. JUSSIM, an interactive computer program for analysis of criminal justice systems. Carnegie-Mellon University, School of Urban and Public Affairs, Urban Systems Institute, Pittsburgh, Pennsylvania, July 1971.

(3) BLUMSTEIN, ALFRED; LARSON, RICHARD. Models of a total criminal justice system. Operations Research, 17:2 (March/April 1969).

(4) COHEN, JACQUELINE; LETTRE, MICHEL; STAFFORD, RICHARD. Analysis of the Allegheny County Criminal Justice System: present operations and alternative programs. Carnegie-Mellon University, School of Urban and Public Affairs, Urban Systems Institute, Pittsburgh, Pennsylvania, February 1972.

(5) FIELDS, KENNETH; LETTRE, MICHEL; STAFFORD, RICHARD. A preliminary description of the Allegheny County Criminal Justice System. Carnegie-Mellon University, School of Urban and Public Affairs, Urban Systems Institute, Pittsburgh, Pennsylvania, August 1971.

(6) FRIEL, CHARLES M. Criminal statistics—state of the art statistical development. In: Project SEARCH; Law Enforcement Assistance Administration. National Symposium on Criminal Justice Information and Statistics Systems. Dallas, Texas, 10-12 November 1970. Proceedings. Edited by George A. Buck. California Crime Technological Research Foundation, Sacramento, California, 1971, 265-270.

(7) GALLATI, ROBERT R. J. SEARCH—security and privacy considerations. In: Project SEARCH; Law Enforcement Assistance Administration. National Symposium on Criminal Justice Information and Statistics Systems. Dallas, Texas,

10-12 November 1970. Proceedings, Edited by George A. Buck. California Crime Technological Research Foundation, Sacramento, California, 1971, 27-32.

(8) GALLATI, ROBERT R. J. Security and privacy considerations in criminal history information systems. California Crime Technological Research Foundation, Sacramento, California, July 1970. (Project SEARCH technical report no. 3).

(9) HALL, GEORGE E. The National Criminal Justice Statistics Center. A long-range program. In: Project SEARCH; Law Enforcement Assistance Administration. National Symposium on Criminal Justice Information and Statistics Systems. Dallas, Texas, 10-12 November 1970. Proceedings. Edited by George A. Buck. California Crime Technological Research Foundation, Sacramento, California, 1971, 261-263.

(10) HILL, HARLAND L. An integrated approach to correctional information system design. In: Project SEARCH; Law Enforcement Assistance Administration. National Symposium on Criminal Justice Information and Statistics Systems. Dallas, Texas, 10-12 November 1970. Proceedings. Edited by George A. Buck. California Crime Technological Research Foundation, Sacramento, California, 1971, 183-193.

(11) INSTITUTE FOR DEFENSE ANALYSIS. Task force report: science and technology, a report to the President's Commission on Law Enforcement and Administration of Justice. Institute for Defense Analysis, Arlington, Virginia, 1967, 228 p. (Available from U.S. Government Printing Office, Washington, D.C.).

(12) KELLY, DON R. PATRIC user's manual. System Development Corporation, Santa Monica, California, 14 May 1971, 358 p. (TM-L-2520).

(13) KELLY, DON R.; BOYER, JAMES K. PATRIC—Pattern Recognition and Information Correlation—PATRIC data collection/analysis plan. System Development Corporation, Santa Monica, California, 11 June 1971, 122 p. (TM-L-2521).

(14) KOLODNEY, STEVE E. Project SEARCH statistical system: results and evaluation of the prototype. In: Project SEARCH; Law Enforcement Assistance Administration. National Symposium on Criminal Justice Information and Statistics Systems. Dallas, Texas, 10-12 November 1970. Proceedings. Edited by George A. Buck. California Crime Technological Research Foundation, Sacramento, California, 1971, 271-278.

(15) MARX, ROBERT L. Evaluation—Criminal History Exchange System. In: Project SEARCH; Law Enforcement Assistance Administration. National Symposium on Criminal Justice Information and Statistics Systems. Dallas, Texas, 10-12 November 1970. Proceedings. Edited by George A. Buck. California Crime Technological Research Foundation, Sacramento, California, 1971, 227-232.

(16) MILLER, ARTHUR R. The assault on privacy: computers, data banks, and dossiers. University of Michigan Press, Ann Arbor, Michigan, 1971, 333 p.

(17) POLANSKY, LARRY P.; WHITE, JEAN M. A comparison of an ideal criminal court information system to the Philadelphia Criminal Court Information System. In: Project SEARCH; Law Enforcement Assistance Administration. National Symposium on Criminal Justice Information and Statistics Systems. Dallas, Texas, 10-12 November 1970. Proceedings. Edited by George A. Buck. California Crime Technological Research Foundation, Sacramento, California, 1971, 133-170.

(18) PROJECT SEARCH; LAW ENFORCEMENT ASSISTANCE ADMINISTRATION. National Symposium on Criminal Justice Information and Statistics Systems. Dallas, Texas, 10-12 November 1970. Proceedings. Edited by George A. Buck. California Crime Technological Research Foundation, Sacramento, California, 1971, 320 p.

(19) RENSHAW, BENJAMIN H.; GOLDMAN, CHARLES I.; BRAYBROOK, WILLIAM M. Application of an indicator-based planning system and simulation modeling to a criminal justice planning process: a Philadelphia "first-try." Paper presented at the 41st National Operations Research Society of America (ORSA) Meeting held in New Orleans, Louisiana, 26-28 April 1972: (Paper is available

from the authors. Renshaw & Goldman—Government Studies & Systems, Inc., Philadelphia, Pennsylvania. Braybrook—Philadelphia Criminal Justice Planning Council, Philadelphia, Pennsylvania.).

(20) SHUMATE, ROBERT P. Some problems associated with the development of a National Criminal History Information System. In: Project SEARCH; Law Enforcement Assistance Administration. National Symposium on Criminal Justice Information and Statistics Systems. Dallas, Texas, 10-12 November 1970. Proceedings. Edited by George A. Buck. California Crime Technological Research Foundation, Sacramento, California, 1971, 249-254.

(21) STEVENS, JAMES W. Subject-in-process: a dynamic inventory of a criminal justice process. In: Project SEARCH; Law Enforcement Assistance Administration. National symposium on Criminal Justice Information and Statistics Systems. Dallas, Texas, 10-12 November 1970. Proceedings. Edited by George A. Buck. California Crime Technological Research Foundation, Sacramento, California, 1971, 91-102.

(22) STEVENS, JAMES W.; BUTCHER, ALLAN K.; KEITHLEY, FREDERIC. A computerized subject-in-process system: development of a regional prototype for Texas. California Crime Technological Research Foundation, Sacramento, California, June 1971. (Project SEARCH special report no. 4).

(23) U. S. FEDERAL BUREAU OF INVESTIGATION. Uniform crime reports for the United States—1970. U.S. Federal Bureau of Investigation, Washington, D.C., 31 August 1971, 208 p. (Available from the U.S. Government Printing Office, Washington, D.C., Stock number 2701-0008).

(24) U.S. PRESIDENT'S COMMISSION ON LAW ENFORCEMENT AND ADMINISTRATION OF JUSTICE. The challenge of crime in a free society. U.S. President's Commission on Law Enforcement and Administration of Justice, Washington, D.C., 1967. (Available from the U.S. Government Printing Office, Washington, D.C.).

(25) WARREN, R.; et al. An evaluation of community treatment for delinquents; California Youth Authority Community Treatment Project. California Youth Authority, Sacramento, California, 1966. (Research report no. 7, and subsequent reports).

(26) WESTIN, ALAN F. Privacy and freedom. Atheneum Publishers, New York, New York, 1967, 487 p.

(27) WORMELI, PAUL K. Project SEARCH—System for Electronic Analysis and Retrieval of Criminal Histories. In: Project SEARCH; Law Enforcement Assistance Administration. National Symposium on Criminal Justice Information and Statistics Systems. Dallas, Texas, 10-12 November 1970. Proceedings. Edited by George A. Buck. California Crime Technological Research Foundation, Sacramento, California, 1971, 17-25.

(28) ZEISEL, HANS. The future of law enforcement statistics: a summary view. In: Federal statistics, report of the President's Commission on Federal Statistics, 1971, Volume II, Chapter 12. (Available from the U.S. Government Printing Office, Washington, D.C.).

IV
The Profession

Libraries and other information facilities are becoming more complex as they increase their range of holdings and services and move toward advanced information processing techniques. These changes, together with increasing demands for accountability, are creating a need for new and more effective management techniques. Leimkuhler and Billingsley describe the progress made in developing these techniques, as well as in applying them to the managerial functions of planning, programming, budgeting, operations and evaluation.

The development of management information systems for libraries and information centers is still receiving very little attention in the literature. Much greater attention is being given to PPBS (planning, programming, and budgeting systems), a management-oriented tool that unites three of the major managerial functions. Leimkuhler and Billingsley feel that use of the PPBS approach by decision-makers would provide them, in a systematic manner, with the essential information needed to implement and operate their programs effectively. They emphasize the special importance of the planning aspect of PPBS and the potential value of operations research as a part of the planning process in libraries.

Studies of the evaluation function are being done but much more work is needed in this area of the library field, especially in analyzing cost-effectiveness and cost-benefits of operating and experimental systems. As Leimkuhler and Billingsley note, some of the techniques of product and market analysis may be useful in improving library and information center management.

13 Library and Information Center Management

FERDINAND F. LEIMKUHLER
Purdue University

and

ALICE BILLINGSLEY
U.S. Postal Service

INTRODUCTION

In a review of the literature on the management of libraries and information centers, a difficulty arises in that there is no widely accepted definition of management or a manager's job. It is useful, however, to recognize two aspects of the term "management": the action-taking aspect and the decision-making aspect. The former is more concrete, more personal, more specific, and is difficult to generalize, analyze, or automate. The decision-making aspect, on the other hand, is amenable to scientific treatment and quantitative analysis, and it is on this aspect that this review will focus.

There are some who, for good reason, would define management as "that which is not automatable," and would thus distinguish it from the science and tools of management. This is similar to the notion of separating scholarship from scholarly information. Like the scholar, however, the manager must communicate, and it is better that he do this in a formal, organized manner. For this reason, many current developments in management science find practical expression in the establishment of management information structures and systems. Managers cannot avoid using and being responsible for such developments, and, faced with increasingly complex problems in achieving his organizational objectives, today's manager is turning more and more to the discipline of management systems and their orderly development and maintenance.

Managers need to establish, evaluate, and adjust goals; to develop plans and standards and initiate action; to measure actual performance and take appropriate action when performance varies from the standard; and to assess achievements (Sanders, 138, p. 9). The historical functions of management include planning, organizing, staffing, directing, and controlling. Newer management techniques span several of these traditional functions, and management systems themselves are composed of the arrangement and integration of personnel; equipment services; and data for effective planning, direction, and control of an organization. As libraries and information centers, along with the rest of the economy, are becoming increasingly constrained to make explicit justifications for their activities and give greater attention to their productivity, their need for managerial systems is increasing.

APPROACH

The approach in this review calls attention to newer tools and techniques of management ("technique" being used in the sense of a method to accomplish a desired goal) as informational media in their own right. That is, they are efficient ways of collecting, processing and transferring managerial data, and logical deductions from that data. We include as techniques some major areas of management knowledge, broad concepts, and some specialized procedures or tools.

DonVito (36) identifies the five basic functions of management as planning, programming, budgeting, operations, and evaluation. Operations is the action-taking part of management and the object of the other managerial functions, which are the main concern in this review because they are a way of studying operations in an analytic and generalizable manner.

The five areas to be covered in this review are: Management Information Systems (MIS); Planning, Programming, and Budgeting Systems (PPBS); planning; operations research and systems analysis; and cost effectiveness.

The development of MIS for libraries and information centers is still receiving only cursory attention in the literature and one suspects that this is a measure of the effort being expended. More attention is being given to the second area, that of Planning, Programming, and Budgeting Systems (PPBS), as a unified treatment of these three managerial functions. The development of PPBS techniques for governmental agencies is beginning to filter down to their supporting information centers and services and is spinning off to see use in similar institutions.

Because of its importance in management, planning is given added attention in this review as a separate area. The fourth area of interest is the field of operations research and systems analysis. For practical purposes, the terms are synonymous. Operations Research (OR) has grown, along with information science, to be a new field of academic study and professional practice, emerging from World War II as part of a deliberate effort to organize and apply science to socially useful ends. In the management field, OR has made its greatest contributions in providing not only a more scientific approach to decision-making but also the rationale for MIS developments. For a very long time, there has been a small but significant interface between OR and the library and information science fields.

The final area of interest in this review is concerned with the evaluative function of management as revealed in current activities along the lines of cost-effectiveness and cost-benefit analysis. While much still needs to be done in the development of good cost-measurement techniques for libraries and information centers, despite the availability of a great wealth of experience with these tools in other fields, the more critical problem area is that of identification and measurement of benefits. There is room for a good deal more soul-searching and experimentation in this area at both the research and practical level of managerial interests.

MANAGEMENT INFORMATION SYSTEMS

Presumably, every organization has some form of management information system to observe or measure the results of operations and to provide a basis for managerial control. In many organizations, the information system is quite simple and depends to a great extent upon the personal communication between the manager and his staff. Some organizations have developed far more detailed systems and it is only a matter of degree of sophistication and development of various tools that separates the two.

The Management Information System (MIS) concept is a more sophisticated approach and has come about through the development and refinement of managerial tools and techniques over the years, mainly by business organizations. The concept now represents what could be called a totality, or synthesis, of these tools and techniques and their applications. But since use of these tools implies the application of scientific principles to things that frequently cannot be defined or quantified in a rigorous manner, the definitions of MIS are many, varied, and often confusing (45, 98, 146).

Weiss (161), in a review article that traces the historical development of the MIS concept, comments on the confusion and misunderstanding concerning the subject, the voluminous literature on MIS, and the need for more organization and classification of this literature. One definition of MIS, that of Kennevan (77), does provide an all-encompassing view of the factors to be included in considering the application of scientific management principles to management decision making. According to this definition, a management information system is "an organized method of providing past, present, and projection information relating to internal operations and external intelligence. It supports the planning, control and operational functions of an organization by furnishing uniform information in the proper time-frame to assist the decision-making process."

The library or information system manager needs management information if he is to make meaningful and accurate decisions on his operations within the appropriate time frame. To be reasonably sure that library operations are directed toward achievement of organizational goals and objectives, the library manager needs information on such subjects as organizational structure, staffing, stock inventories, facilities, financial and cost information, and usage data. Decisions to be made by the system manager are both large in number and complex, as he attempts to adapt to a changing environment of different and greater user demands. As the pace of technology increases, the volume of publication grows, and budgets are not increased, the manager requires more management information to accomplish his task. In addition, he rarely has absolute control over operations, since the system usually exists to serve an outside body rather than itself. Thus, we see complex institutions governed by external forces and serving outside interests. The manager must be responsive to these outside forces and interests as well as to those factors that are directly under his control. Although publications in systems management, computers, and other allied fields contain abundant literature on the subject, again, the development of MIS for libraries and information centers is still receiving only cursory attention in the literature. Material from other fields is included in this review to inform librarians and information scientists of problems in the development of a MIS.

The use of MIS as a management concept specifically directed toward libraries is discussed in only two documents in the corpus of literature reviewed. One document, a report by Booz, Allen & Hamilton, Inc. (13), contains a recommendation that MIS be developed to support program planning, evaluation and control in university libraries. The development would involve specifying (1) the types of information needed by specific functions for purposes of program planning, control, and evaluation; (2) the elements of data needed and the formats required for the collection; and (3) the methods for collecting, analyzing, storing, and retrieving the information. The second document specifically mentions management information systems within the library context. This paper, by Spencer (145), refers to MIS as a major operational concept used in the formation of a planning and programming process. Kitagawa (80), in establishing a matrix for MIS as a total system with seven aspects of information functions, regards the library only as a function for storage of information.

The reviewers noted two papers in the information field. In one, Kriebel (89) argues that information systems in the future will play a considerably expanded role in managerial problem solving processes, augmenting, and, in some cases, replacing the analytical skills that the decision maker uses today. In the other, Blackwell et al. (9) maintains that the success of any information system depends largely upon several key decisions that must be made early in the preliminary design phase.

The educational field appears to be giving consideration to the use of MIS as a management tool. Four papers (25, 26, 43, 44), distributed to California administrators participating in an Executive Information System program in San Mateo, California, provide a useful overview for those unfamiliar with MIS basic concepts, design, and development.

A seminar on the development and use of MIS for administration of higher education was held in Washington, D.C. in 1969 (110) and brought together users and developers of management information systems. The participants explored in depth the problems and possibilities of such systems for higher education institutions. The proceedings of an educational management tools training program, held at Southern Illinois University College of Education (10) provide a discussion of the philosophy of educational management systems, and MIS as an educational administrative tool.

In describing an approach to making the optimum use of limited school resources to improve the learning process, Perkins (131) states that five major categories of MIS data (pupil, program, personnel, facilities, and financial data) are required for the school administrator to make decisions on programs and budgets. Bumsted (22) maintains that educational administrators have been slow to implement computerized data processing because they fail to understand information systems or because they neglect systems planning. He goes on to say that only with a good MIS can current administrative and educational confusion be ended.

Design and Development

An interesting aspect of MIS design procedures is that there are some clearly identifiable design procedures that may be used in terminating a project, but there is little agreement on where and how a project starts. Project initiation may be considered to start with a request for a preliminary study of an existing system, a specific set of information requirements put forth by management, an operational problem to be solved, or an analysis of the organization and its environment. Guidelines must be established to define the scope of the MIS effort to determine objectives and priorities and to develop factual and realistic plans and criteria (31).

Opinions on the building of management information systems are as varied among authors as are the definitions of MIS (57, 58, 64, 127). A step-by-step description is not really appropriate, because many activities are carried out in parallel and there is much iteration or recycling to refine the design. Differences in project scope are another problem.

A definitive study of MIS by Kelly (75) discusses the nature and limits of the subject and offers a detailed analysis of the problems and considerations confronting the designers of major MIS projects. For those unfamiliar with computers, Matthews (104) provides an excellent introduction to the design of MIS.

In an overview of MIS, Chakravarti (28) gives the opinion that the shuffling of information in a business contributes to 30-40% of the cost of operating an organization and proposes that a model for an MIS can be visualized by treating the organization as one that solves an inventory of problems through the use of a data base that provides information and knowledge to solve each problem. A network of events for the accomplishments of MIS development is provided by Murdick (117), who describes a "reference" procedure as a team effort of management and systems designers. Walker (156) describes methods for structuring and documenting key elements of business information systems by multiple uses of systems codes and project code structures.

More attention is now being given to a modular approach in the development of MIS. From a conceptual viewpoint, designing one total system is possible, but there are questions as to the practicality of this approach.

The development of an MIS is a continuous process, each phase blending into the following phase, and one will achieve significant economies as well as real potential for increasing the effectiveness of the resulting system by taking a look at the building blocks already in place and building from there (124). Tolliver (153) warns that, although the more routine management functions will gradually be automated with substantial payoff during the next decade or so, the major expense and operational penalties of being a pioneer should be avoided unless the organization has a great deal to gain by such initiative.

A standard cost system as a module of an MIS is described by Cooke & Rost (32) as being significant both in actual cost savings and in more timely and complete reporting and analysis. O'Haren (125) stresses that what is needed is a framework in which manageable system development efforts can proceed. This framework should be oriented to the decisions that management makes and to the areas in which these decisions are made.

Personnel Impact

If MIS provides information that is used to make decisions, then MIS has an impact on the organization. In discussing this impact, Coleman & Riley (30) state that there has been lack of use, lack of involvement and lack of commitment in MIS in personnel applications. They go on to say that behavioral resistance has taken the form of nonproductive internal competition, nonproductive efforts, and destructive conflict.

Argyris (2) points out that management theorists and practitioners tend to agree that some day MIS will probably perform many critical managerial functions, but that the realization of this potential is still a long way off. He argues that MIS specialists are not presently equipped to deal with the emotional problems caused by their systems. "They tend to react overrationally, which is an emotional response, and have difficulty in coping with their own and the executives' feelings and behavior." Argyris foresees the emotional impact of MIS on management as taking the form of (1) restrictions on freedom; (2) psychological failure; (3) loss of executive power; and (4) decreasing feelings of essentiality. He gives considerable attention to the ways in which managers and MIS specialists can reduce this emotional impact and stresses the need for more competence in interpersonal relationships as well as competence in system technology.

Balk (6) comments that one of the critical needs in MIS development is for analytical consideration of the impact and potential of information exchanges at all levels of organizations. In discussing the use of terminal access equipment for MIS, Seese (142) calls attention to the fears of middle managers that they will be displaced or replaced as a result of the new media, and the fears of top management about security of information and the displacement of classic organizational structures. It is imperative that all levels of management be educated and involved if the MIS is to accomplish its objectives (99) and management must be sold on the program it will put into practice (7).

Management must have learned during its own education that the real success of any system project depends upon the acceptance and cooperation of the people who will be involved in the program (120). Managers must sell systems work to their organization and, because people resent change, they must be convincing. Teamwork between the manager and the systems people is also required for effective development of a MIS (7). The manager's viewpoint of MIS is discussed in an article by Fredericks (52).

Kelly (75) considers it an axiom that the top systems manager must be placed high enough in the organizational hierarchy to participate in planning and directional efforts at the strategic level to tailor efforts to the long-range plans of the organization.

Computers in MIS

Managers need to be aware of how the computer can be used to help them perform their managerial functions. While most managers are aware of the electronic data processing capabilities of computers, many of them are unaware of how the computer can be used for management problem solving. Managers should know how the computer can be used to help solve specific and non-routine problems, and an article by Watson (157) shows ways in which the computer can be used for daily management decision making.

With the development of data processing techniques, there has been much emphasis on computer technology, hardware, and programming. Dickson (35) estimates that business organizations are spending anywhere from .25% to over 2% of annual sales for the development of computer-based clerical systems and MIS. Less emphasis has been placed on data input and the choice of data that are the input to an MIS, in many cases, has been left to the discretion of the user who is unskilled in information management and in storage and retrieval methods (159).

The use of a computer to develop MIS is appealing but high conversion costs, diverse and dynamic information needs, and changes in organizational structure require discretion on the part of the system planner prior to inception of the MIS. The provision of feedback, and flexibility to changing inputs are necessary attributes of the MIS (129). Weinmeister (159) advocates that offices of information be established at appropriate levels within organizations to ensure effective utilization of the many data elements that exist within an organization.

The major technological problem in designing a comprehensive MIS is that the data—in terms of format, number of files, and structures—do not remain stationary, which often leads to prohibitive data processing costs. One approach toward anticipating system requirements over longer periods of time, proposed by Cahill (27), is the use of a dictionary/directory method for building a common MIS data base.

Several types of current generalized data base software use conventional operating systems and their access methods (54). Generalized Data Management Systems (GDMS) have been developed to cope with data problems in military applications and are expected to be useful for other organizations. Minker (108) states that GDMS, along with application programs to meet the particular needs of management, will form the major elements of an MIS and will provide management with a flexible tool.

Once the objectives of the system have been established, the user can evaluate existing packages to see if any can be used. Waites (155) poses some questions to aid in the evaluation process: (1) Is the information management system separate from the MIS function? (2) Is the system structured so that additional applications can be provided for? (3) Can existing MIS applications produce information from the investigating user's data? Waites advocates that the application programs be implemented in modules, so that each application can be considered a processing entity and the output formatting program can be considered separately from the application programs.

The development of a MIS is costly. Dickson (35) likens the expenditures to those of research and development in that heavy expenditures are required in order to produce future benefits of uncertain magnitude. Kelly (75) observes that the development of a major MIS subsystem frequently costs as much as a new product line and deserves the same kind of planning and implementation resources.

Careful attention must be given to the numbers and kinds of reports required for management decision-making; this is necessary to ensure that management is getting the required information and is not getting information that is unnecessary.

When a computer-based information system has been authorized to support management in its decision-making processes, the user soon recognizes that shortages in time, money, and manpower will prevent the implementation of all the required reports at the same time. Weiser (160) feels that values can be assigned to the importance of individual reports, in order to determine overall priorities among the reports.

PLANNING, PROGRAMMING, AND BUDGETING SYSTEMS

The Planning, Programming, and Budgeting Systems (PPBS) concept is useful for focusing attention on three aspects of managerial decision-making. These are: anticipatory decision-making, or planning; deterministic decision-making, or programming; and retrospective decision-making, or budgeting. These are discussed below at greater length. PPBS is an operational and organized process that improves the information base for policy, program, and resource-allocation decisions. It is a management-oriented tool that focuses on determination of the goals and objectives of a program, what the program hopes to accomplish at given levels of support, what resources are available, which alternative courses of action are open, and how all of these relationships can be used to achieve a coherent and comprehensive program of action.

The technique of PPBS was developed from a combination of the traditional concepts of public budgeting through the phases of central control of spending, government concern for efficient performance of work, and the planning functions of management. It was introduced to the Department of Defense (DOD) by Robert McNamara in 1961 as a means of improving the economic analysis methods that had been used by DOD until that time. In 1965, President Johnson made the use of the procedure mandatory for all of the non-defense Federal establishment.

An excellent, well-written discussion of the essential characteristics of PPBS is given in a RAND Corporation report by DonVito (36). He says that the purpose of PPBS is to provide top management with an integrated, systematic, and analytic basis for making program decisions and putting such decisions into operation. PPBS concentrates on the management functions that precede actual operations and is intended to unify these preliminary functions into a single effort. The most effective PPBSs contain five key elements: program structure, program documents, a decision-making function, a program analysis function, and an information system. The use of the program-structure element provides a way of looking at an organization with an emphasis on its outputs and its ability to achieve specific goals or objectives. Traditional organization structures focus on inputs and the conservation of resources.

In an effort to explore the feasibility of utilizing PPBS procedures in library management, Morey (112) conducted a questionnaire survey of public libraries in Michigan, Indiana, Illinois, and Wisconsin to identify commonly accepted goals, objectives, and activities. Among the conclusions of the survey were: "...the major library objectives reported in the literature are, in fact, the ones recognized by most public libraries; library objectives are extremely difficult to categorize precisely and a structure is needed for the meaningful presentation of goals, objectives, and activities."

The report also states that more study is needed before libraries can state their objectives specifically, and a means must be developed for measuring library progress toward accomplishment of their objectives. The report strongly recommends that libraries adopt those elements of PPBS that are applicable to their situations.

In the spring of 1968, an Institute on Program Planning and Budgeting Systems for Libraries was held at Wayne State University in Detroit, Michigan, funded by the Higher Education Act, Title IIB. The intent of the Institute was to introduce administrators and finance officers of large public, state, and academic libraries to the principles and procedures of PPBS. The papers presented at this Institute provide an excellent base for library managers who are not familiar with the concept and for libraries considering the application of PPBS to their operations. Some of the papers are described below.

A paper by Keller (74) investigates the theory, philosophy, and techniques of PPBS and develops a conceptual framework for its use. A history of the development of PPBS is given, and its use for measuring physical performance, approaches to physical measurement, and the application of discounted cash flow to PPBS are described.

The total beneficial impact of PPBS depends upon its evolutionary development, and, since PPBS is a dynamic and innovative process, its acceptance and application within the Federal Government have had varying degrees of success. According to Fazar (46), a wide spectrum of approaches and results have been experienced by government agencies to date. The General Accounting Office, and the Department of Health, Education, and Welfare are using PPBS and the State Department is experimenting with it. He feels benefits beyond those of traditional program decision and resource allocation practices can be obtained; and comparable efforts he feels should become the concern of libraries.

The use of PPBS by the U.S. Congress (103) and on state and local governmental levels is increasing, although not as rapidly as is systems analysis, which complements the formal methods of optimization devised for an idealized decision-making situation. Bryk (16) describes the procedures for systems analysis and the kinds of analysis required for service organization within the government for those concerned with the potential applications of systems approaches in state and local government. The use of system analysis on a state level is also discussed by Ellis (42), who describes the influence of PPBS on capital budgeting.

At the same Institute, Sturtz (149) states that the difference between conventional budgeting and PPBS is that traditional processes for budgeting are concerned with personal services, facility maintenance, equipment, etc., while PPBS is concerned with the purpose of the work. Thus, PPBS has provided greater management accountability and has altered the form and content of the information provided the manager for his decision-making.

Applications of PPBS to costing within libraries were also considered within this Institute. Cost Utility Analysis (CUA) as a management tool for library budgeting was discussed by Stitelman (147). The advantages of utilization of CUA for library managers are that some management decisions previously based on implied judgments become exposed, popular projects that may seem justified to the public can be rejected, objectives can be stated realistically, outputs rather than inputs achieve more importance, and the long-range cost implications of decisions and alternatives can be considered. He goes on to say that there are problems and limitations of CUA that reflect mainly a lack of understanding of the process and a failure to realize that all decisions, in the end, require human judgment.

Spencer (145) provides budgeting forms that can assist libraries in proceeding from conventional-type budgets to semiconventional and program budgets. Mlynarczyk (111) feels that conventional cost-accounting procedures can be applied to develop cost information for libraries and draws an analogy to the cost of operation of a small company that processes bricks. However, Hoffman (67) feels that the concept of PPBS for library budgeting cannot be implemented in an organization of reasonable size without a fairly sophisticated data processing capability, which most libraries probably do not have at the present time.

As a beginning step for PPBS, the definition of objectives is important to provide guidelines for future actions, and these definitions must be real and operable, rather than oriented toward a public relations endeavor. These objectives must be directed toward the external objectives of the organization, the internal objectives of the library, specific program objectives, and the particular activities within a program. Basic questions to be asked for the definition of overall library objectives, as well as procedures to be used in developing the definition, are given by Burness (23), who also provides an example of a possible statement of library service objectives. Nussbaum (123) lists six basic types of library problems as: inventory, allocation, sequencing, routing, replacement, and search, and suggests that operations research could be applied to these areas for problem solutions.

In discussing the measurement of library output, Palmer (128) defends the necessity for the collection of library statistics and provides recommendations for the librarian to consider in dealing with statistics for use in PPBS. Fazar (48), a well known authority on the subject of PPBS, describes PPBS as a means for libraries to enter the institutional decision-making process. He provides guiding principles for libraries to use in gaining the rewards promised by PPBS and urges libraries to take steps toward PPBS training, development, and application.

As stated earlier, the papers from this Institute should be quite helpful to libraries considering undertaking PPBS. Another helpful guide is an article by Fazar (47), which provides a quick insight into PPBS theory.

Bromberg (15) gives a basic, simplified description of PPBS and how it can be used by the practicing librarian. He argues that PPBS "seeks to get your dollar's worth for you by analyzing what you are doing in the light of what you should be doing and plan to do in the years to come and tying that back to your standard yearly budget." He identifies six important steps in PPBS: (1) critical definition of goals and objectives; (2) program structuring; (3) relation of programs to objectives; (4) identification of alternatives; (5) study of cost-effectiveness of alternatives; and (6) selection of alternatives. Tudor (154) points out that a number of standardized procedures and reports, along with analytical techniques, are needed in the planning, the allocation of resources, and the management of operations with PPBS. He provides a 258-item bibliography on the subject. Jenkins (73), Howard (68), and Meyers & Barber (106) give further insights into the application of PPBS to libraries and information centers. Applications to specific libraries are reported by Axford (4) at Florida Atlantic University, the Santa Barbara Elementary and High School District (139), Henkle (65) for the James Jerome Hill Reference Library, and by Drickamer (39) for the Department of State Library Services in Rhode Island.

PLANNING

The term "planning" as used within the context of a business environment relates to the process of deciding the objectives to be attained by the organization; the resource allocations to be utilized to attain these objectives; and the policies for acquisition, use, and disposition of these resources. "Planning" as used in the library milieu, however, seems to be mainly concerned with such factors as library standards, and the library's buildings, equipment, and related facilities; a library's planning is sometimes only reflected in a single bound document that results from an annual or periodic planning session. In library work as in other professions, however, planning must be a dynamic process, and these reviewers feel that the need for continuing and innovative efforts must be brought to the attention of the library decision makers. The documents cited below are concerned with libraries that have used planning in the manner used by the business environment.

In a document by Sewell (144) on the planning of library services, planning as a management tool is alluded to, though not specifically treated as such. He presents some arguments for establishing "reasonable" priorities for the development of library services and examines some of the problems involved in systematic planning of these services. Hindle (66) defines planning as "anticipatory decision making" and states that the process is a difficult one, that is due, in part, to the complex variables required for decision making and, in part, to the need to consider future activities in a dynamic environment. A wrong decision may be costly in terms of resources or may lead to activities to which the user community may have an adverse reaction. In some cases, a wrong decision may result in the initiation of activities that cannot be stopped or changed once they have started. Kingsbury (79) suggests that planning is an inherently difficult and complex process requiring the exercise of analytical powers over an unbounded time period.

Long-range planning involves the identification of priority programs and services and the detailing of the necessary resources (staff, equipment, facilities, and materials) required to implement these programs and services. A report on state libraries in Colorado by Harrigan (62) discusses what is involved in this process and provides a fundamental understanding of the following three basic issues: (1) What are the program goals and performance objectives? (2) What is the systems analysis approach? and (3) What is the planning process? A procedural guide for the development of a long-range plan is included with the report.

Planning on a long-range basis was also considered by Fry (53) in the development of a design study for government libraries. A series of research designs for long-range programs are described that state the objectives, the methodology to be employed, the scope of the investigation, the nature of the research, the research staff required, the time schedule, and the estimated cost.

A description of planning efforts on a statewide basis is given in an analysis of Kansas libraries by Foster (50). The analysis revealed that the implementation of an effective statewide plan for both short-term and long-term objectives was hampered because the delegation of responsibility and authority for total planning had not been clear-cut. The report concludes that the libraries in the state are under-utilized and that the situation will continue unless comprehensive plans for funding, development of inter-library cooperation of dissimilar libraries, and material and personnel resource allocation, consistent with policy objectives, are developed and the authority to implement these plans is established.

The lack of planning as an impediment to effective management was further expressed in a report on university libraries by Booz, Allen & Hamilton, Inc. (13) that indicates the need for more comprehensive planning to specify: (1) the role and requirements of the library in relation to the academic program of the university; (2) the library's objectives and plans in support of academic programs; and (3) the library resources (financial and personnel resources, physical materials, facilities, and equipment) needed to implement plans.

The most comprehensive treatment of library planning that these reviewers found is that by Kemper (76) who reviews much of the existing planning literature that speaks to the nature and significance of planning, establishes a concept for the nature of the library environment, and summarizes a method of library planning, as an attempt to stimulate more use of available planning knowledge by libraries.

Ackoff (1) has written an excellent discussion of managerial planning. While the book is directed at corporate planning, many of the basic concepts have validity for managers of libraries and information centers. Like Hindle, he defines planning as anticipatory decision-making, and he proceeds to clarify, as far as possible, many of the basic concepts associated with planning. He distinguishes three approaches to planning: "satisficing" or "making do"; optimization, or finding the best plan; and a third approach that he calls "adaptivizing." He concludes that most current planning is of the first kind, with a little of the second and just a bare start at the third, more desirable, kind of planning. "Adaptivizing" focuses on the process of planning rather than on the plan itself and seeks to develop an organization that can anticipate new situations and adapt quickly to them. Ackoff argues that the more we push from "satisficing" toward "adaptivizing," the greater the requirement for scientific methods, techniques, and tools.

A comprehensive survey of many of the considerations in the planning of information centers is given in an article by Taylor (151), who reviews the models of various types of information systems with special emphasis on the behavioral aspects of such systems. This behavioral aspect is stressed in her subsequent discussion of the requirements for planning information centers of all kinds. She strongly urges that "more consideration be given to including the leadership structure of primary user groups in the planning phases and later in evaluation phases [and] that evidence of problems and activities of the high priority user groups be sought out." She suggests that both expressed and unexpressed information needs be examined, so that actual needs might be better met, and that more effort should be made to act rather than re-act to users.

Reflections on a UNESCO seminar on Libraries and Educational Planning organized by the International Institute for Educational Planning are given by Foskett (49). A statement of policy and a plan of action by which library service and development in New York State can respond to the societal needs is given in a position paper issued by the Regents of the University of the State of New York (121). A comprehensive plan for libraries in Seattle was prepared by the Seattle Department of Community Development (141) to determine how to allocate funds in order to produce the greatest favorable impact on the library program. A statewide study of information needs, resources, and services has been issued by the Minnesota Higher Education Coordinating Commission (109). A study at the University of Durham, England, (41, 113) on evaluating library benefits provides criteria for quantitative planning in libraries. Instead of finding ways to satisfy user needs at minimum cost, the study seeks to maximize the output of library services and products within a fixed budget. The final report (41) includes chapters on simulation of the user decision-process, data collection, current awareness services for social scientists, data analysis, a historical review of the project, and suggestions for further work.

Many libraries and information centers exist as academic support facilities in institutions of higher education. The expanding demands for services in these institutions and massive increases in their facilities have called attention to the need for more effective planning and use of resources. The Higher Education Facilities Act of 1963, in addition to providing funds for the construction of educational facilities, also provides for the establishment of comprehensive planning systems at the state and national level. A major focus for much of this work has been the Western Interstate Commission for Higher Education (WICHE). Recently, in cooperation with the American Association of Collegiate Registrars and Admission Officers, WICHE has released a set of Higher Education Facilities Planning and Management Manuals. The fourth manual in this series focuses on Academic Support Facilities and was prepared by Dahnke et al. (34). The manual provides a detailed methodology for evaluating and projecting requirements for libraries, audio visual centers, and data processing computing facilities. It is an impressive document and should have considerable influence on the planning of academic and other similar types of facilities.

The Management Studies Office of the Association of Research Libraries has inaugurated a series of Occasional Papers concerning management problems facing research libraries today. The series will provide guides to important research and publications in the management field, annual summaries of trends in various management areas, and information on current developments. The first paper in the series (158) describes planning aids for the university library director to use in solving managerial problems instead of waiting for a crisis that forces the library to take drastic and sometimes poorly conceived actions on short notice.

OPERATIONS RESEARCH AND SYSTEMS ANALYSIS

Operations Research (OR) is concerned with the application of scientific methods to the formulation and solution of management-type problems, including problems of library and information system management. The seminal work in this area was done by Morse (114) at MIT. The work dates from before 1952 when Morse was elected the first president of the Operations Research Society of America. Morse's work has been imitated and amplified on many university campuses including Johns Hopkins University; the University of California, Berkeley; Purdue University; and the University of Pennsylvania. These studies began with university libraries as convenient laboratories for students of operations research, but in some instances they have developed into full-fledged courses and programs of study and research, as reported recently by Miller & Lutz (107) at the University of Oklahoma.

The most significant development in the use of OR in libraries was a conference at the University of Chicago Graduate Library School on the implications of operations research for libraries. At this conference, papers by Churchman (29), Morse (115), and Leimkuhler (93) reviewed the methodology and motivation common to many operations research studies in the library and information center environment. Newer developments in mathematical programming and graph theory with special application to information systems were presented by Glover & Klingman (55) and Korfhage et al. (86). Case studies of variable loan policies, and catalog usage were reported by Buckland (17) and Lipetz (97). An exploratory study of the design of directories for information reference networks was presented by Kochen (82). Ramist (136) reported on a study of decision-making frameworks for allocating funds among library services, which is being conducted for the Philadelphia Public Library. The concluding paper by Bookstein

(12) discussed the implications of operations research for library schools in providing management-oriented education.

It is useful to note that the Operations Research Society of America (ORSA) has devoted several sessions at recent annual meetings to the discussion of mathematical models of library and information center operations. Abstracts of these papers can be found in the announcement of the meetings held in spring 1967 (19); fall 1970 (20); and spring 1971 (21). Papers of the fall 1970 meeting include one by Senko (143) on information storage models; one by Korfhage (85) on graphical data systems; and one by Nance (118) on network models. Baker (5) defines the relation between scientific information and innovation in research organizations. At the same meeting, Kochen (83) presented his model of referential consulting networks, and Kraft (87) reported on a model of the journal selection problem. Mann (102) discussed a model for maintaining optimal library size, and Jain (72) presented a paper on document usage and storage decision rules. At the spring 1971 ORSA meeting in Dallas, Morse (116) reported on the use of search theory in browsing; King (78) presented a method for evaluating the cost-effectiveness of information transfer systems; Arsenault et al. (3) discussed models for optimizing the organization of data banks; Hamburg et al. (59) reported on the development of statistical information systems for large libraries; and Rzasa & Baker (137) reported on a study of measures of library effectiveness.

The above topics give an accurate description of the broad interest that operations researchers are showing in libraries and information systems. The common ingredient in all of these papers is the mathematical model as a scientific tool for defining managerial problems in a very precise manner. The precision is achieved through idealization of the real management problem. The researcher seeks a mathematical formulation that will yield significant analytic results and that can be applied as a guide to the design and operation of real systems. Discussions of OR studies stress the logical validity of the models, which performs a valuable information transfer function in its own right and helps to build the base for management science. At the same time, OR models provide practical guide guidance for managerial decision-making.

The subject matter of most OR studies reported in the literature is not wholly appropriate for detailed discussion here, but some studies are cited to show their collective importance as a new managerial tool for libraries and information centers. While most of these studies are intended to help guide practical managerial decision-making, their success in actually influencing management policy is, to these reviewers, very questionable thus far. Their greatest value is in showing that it is possible to establish a close working relationship between library and information center managers, on the one hand, and scientists and engineers on the other. The eventual benefit should be substantive.

Why should managers encourage research into library operations? Mackenzie (100) poses this question in describing work at the University of Lancaster, England, which aimed to provide a series of "charts and lighthouses" to enable the library manager to make decisions rationally and scientifically rather than by tradition or "less-than-divine afflatus" of his committee. Models were developed for library size, library hierarchies, loan policy and book duplication, and book processing. Current research covers planning for library size, adaptive control of loan policies, simulation of the library user's behavior, and library management games. A recent report on this research effort was edited by Buckland (18).

The importance of research in library development and planning is discussed by Haselgrove (63). In line with Penna's (130) ideas on library planning, Haselgrove believes that research is good for planning as long as the two are carefully coordinated. He refers to Whitworth's (162) criticism that many library studies do not get beyond the point of data collection and observation and fail to produce controlled experiments for the testing of hypotheses. Possibilities for more work in this area, along operations research lines are discussed.

Modeling

Woodburn (163) discussed the use of a mathematical model of academic-library operations and the library's interaction with users during a seminar on planning library services held at the University of Lancaster, England, in 1969. The model permits management decision making to be accomplished on a rational basis. The types of models he discussed were models of library space, usage and cost models, and retrieval models. A mathematical model of a hierarchical library system for universities for the storage of books, journals, and other library materials is also described. The model can be used in designing an efficient library system and is illustrated by a simplified example.

A study of decision-making procedures for acquisition of library science materials by Lane (91) could provide a basis for model formulation for library materials acquisition. This report identifies five levels of decision-making required for the acquisition operation. For each specific decision-making process, its efficiency, strength and weaknesses, and recommendations for improvement are given.

Newhouse (122) attempted to formulate a model for book selection as a tool for public libraries. He developed a simple normative theory to measure benefits from services that are provided publicly against services that are privately provided. In effect, the theory compares demand curves for books. He concludes that, although formally applicable, the theory is not too helpful in the library sphere.

Circulation and library use are two areas for which modeling has been attempted. Foust & Hughes (51) provide an equation for the prediction of circulation, but the work of Surace (150) is more definitive. She describes a model for a circulation system that is on-line and real-time. The circulation file is created from the shelf list, and the terminal inquiry system provides the capability to query or to browse to determine the availability of specific documents by title, documents in a given subject area, or documents by a certain author. She discusses four types of circulation systems—a manual system, a semi-automated system, a data collection (batch) system, and an on-line system—and compares the capabilities of each.

Humphry & Humphry (71) provide an analytical model of library use that is useful but requires further work. One determining factor in library use is the response time for the user to receive his information, and the establishment of a model for on-line document retrieval systems for an information system represents one effort to determine response time that would be applicable to libraries. In this report, linear and inverted file organizations are considered and the response times for each type are determined and compared.

The use of simulation as a teaching method in library administration courses would benefit the library education field, according to Putman (134). Beckman (8) derives a simulation model for the Guelph Library in Canada based on two measures of effectiveness: the cost of adding a volume, and per capita usage. Nance & Baker (119) used a simulation model to study library policy structure. Their modeling technique is similar to that used by Forrester at MIT in his studies of industrial, urban, and world dynamics. The model simulates the long-run effects of various control policies on the behavior of a typical university branch library. It is applied in a case study of a physics library.

More efforts will have to be made, however, if modeling techniques are to be used within the library context. Duchesne (40) suggests that members of the library profession, including its system analysts, need to become better acquainted with the OR approach and that research projects employing OR techniques in libraries would demonstrate their applicability in libraries. He further suggests that more attention be given to the study of OR in the professional education of librarians.

Burns (24) provides a generalized methodology for library systems analysis directed at the novice to guide him in conducting a systems study. He notes that, in the past six to eight years, only a few publications of merit have appeared that show how and under what conditions a systems study can be conducted in a library environment. Burns defines the systems approach as a method-part science, part art—whereby one determines the correct balance between constraints and resources to realize organizational goals. This leads to the establishment of realistic priorities based upon a thorough understanding of the total system being studied and its relationship to all other systems having a common interface.

COST-EFFECTIVENESS

Scientific management requires that a criterion be developed for evaluating the costs required to obtain the desired objectives of an organization and the benefits to be derived if the objectives are met. This concept of weighing costs (which are usually measurable) against benefits (which are frequently difficult to quantify) is known as "cost-effectiveness" and does not appear to have received a great deal of attention within the library field.

A step-by-step approach to maximizing the benefits to be gained from the library's resources is described by Morley (113). In this approach, the production possibilities of the library are found, marginal costs are determined and weighed until a linear programming solution is found, and the resulting weights are translated into "swap-rates," which are used to predict and compare the outcomes of possible changes in library policy and techniques.

A cost analysis of the California State Library by Hargrove & Stirling (61) correlates the chief activities of implementing a processing center design against the costs, according to varying rates of production, to determine cost-effectiveness. In a cost survey of the Medical Library Center of New York, Boice et al. (11) estimates income and expenditure for operation of the center to provide unit costs for each operation. However, no attempt was made to evaluate these operations or to propose alternative procedures.

An experimental and exploratory attempt at an analysis of cost-effectiveness was made by Pfister & Milliman (132). Their report highlights the economic issues that arise in making decisions about providing and financing library services. The questions that economists raise in analyzing the provision of public goods or services are presented, as well as issues and questions that must be addressed in making efficient allocation of resources.

A study by Maier et al. (101) analyzed the operating costs of a bibliographical center to allow the center to adopt the best combination of procedures with which to achieve its service objectives at the lowest possible cost to its members. This study provides data on the form of input and output in request handling and the type and degree of service required per request, so that a fee schedule can be determined. Major recommendations of the study were that the manual system be streamlined; that tasks be reassigned; that a revised fee schedule be established with a firm agreement on card contributions and input control with each member library; that administrative record-keeping be mechanized; that a budget for research and development be established; and that priorities and a schedule be developed for whatever recommendations are adopted.

The objectives of a study made by Bourne (14) were to review, analyze, and summarize published library cost data and to develop a cost model and a methodology for reporting data in a more consistent and useful way. The cost model and reporting procedure were developed and tested on the circulation system of three libraries—a large university library and two large public libraries. The model permits the computation of unit costs for component subsystems of circulation systems. Cost data are summarized and reviewed, and the cost-reporting form is included for use by other libraries. A bibliography of the 304 references that were surveyed for cost data is included.

The formulation of a general "all-purpose" cost model is difficult since libraries do not have a standard methodology for costing. Several models established for specific types of libraries do, however, provide guidelines for developing such a model. One study by Beckman (8) attempts to establish a simple model for administrative purposes in a university library system. Two measures of this system were studied: (1) the cost of adding a volume to the collection, and (2) the use of the collection on a per capita basis. However, the study requires further analysis prior to computer manipulation, and the development of a considerable amount of new data is required before full-scale models can be developed for solutions to decision-making problems.

Leimkuhler & Cooper (95) report on the use of accounting models to measure library costs and implement program budgets. A cost-flow model for a university library is developed and tested with historical data from the University of California, Berkeley, General Library. Some comparisons are given of the unit costs for different parts of the library system. Operations research models were also developed by

Leimkuhler & Cooper (94) for minimizing costs in the management of document storage and retrieval processes.

Lancaster (90) makes a distinction between cost-effectiveness and cost-benefit analysis as applied to information systems in analysis of the relationships between costs, performance, and benefits. Klinte (81) reports on a study of cost analysis as applied to a technical information unit. Goddard (56), in an economic analysis of library benefits, shows how decision rules can be used to permit libraries to make the most efficient use of their resources by focusing on those activities that yield the highest returns. Olsen (126) provides an extensive but selective bibliography with commentary on the literature of economics of information—that is, the concepts and tools of economics as they apply to information activities. He divides this literature into 14 categories. A selected bibliography of over 300 items covers most recent literature on the subject and includes monographs, technical reports, surveys, and 25 overview documents.

Dougherty (38) raises the point that a good deal of the old fashioned work-simplification and cost-reduction efforts of earlier times are still going on and even flourishing, but under fancier names such as "systems analysis."

An Aslib report by Thomas (152) with an introduction by Vickery, is offered as a third phase in a theoretical study of the record keeping tasks that are common to all libraries. The first phase considered the basic processes and data elements in such systems; the second phase considered the relationships among these activity units—inherent time sequences and similarities. As an aid to the design of more optimal systems, the report develops a procedural model using a minimum number of forms and files needed for recording all the basic activities of a library. The tool was used in two ways. First, the model was used to design a records system for a hypothetical library; and then the operating procedures for an actual library were recorded and compared to the hypothetical case, to reveal ways in which the bibliographic records might be simplified. The ultimate objective in this study is a full understanding of the optimal use of machine-readable bibliographic records.

Koenig et al. (84) provide an example of how cost analysis can be used both to justify and to guide automation programs. They apply the "net present value technique" widely used in industry to an evaluation of the performance of an automated serials record system. It is an interesting case study with some useful observations about the savings obtained through automation, because it shows that cost-effective automation may be achieved with record systems of relatively modest size (e.g., 1100 titles). They concur with Dougherty (37) about the glaring lack of cost analysis work in the field of library and information center management.

Raffel & Shishko (135) report on a large-scale cost-benefit study of the MIT libraries. Starting with a functional analysis of the libraries and various opportunities for improving efficiency, they formulated a set of alternative programs for allocating library resources, and attempted to evaluate the benefits of such programs in terms of the total library budget and user preferences. By developing and extrapolating unit cost figures, they conclude that changing current book-storage methods is not very attractive since it would save less than one percent in total costs and might cause a major loss in service to users.

Raffel and Shishko found that the library spends more on "people" space than on book space; and, in a later chapter on benefit evaluation they conclude that the MIT libraries should promote usage by the general public through current reproduction technology and paperbacks and should economize by centralizing reserve book collections. These results are drawn from a survey in which users were asked to choose from among a list of 20 alternative ways of increasing and/or reducing the library budget. The data show that three major user groups differed in the systems they would like the library to adopt. Undergraduates would sacrifice research services for book-reserve services. Graduate students would prefer lower Xerox prices and would cut study space rather than cut cataloging activities. The faculty are most willing to change storage and cataloging practices and are the primary supporters of departmental libraries. Accommodating such different and often competing service requirements in a single institution remains a difficult managerial task and more formal methods of policy making are badly needed to preserve a degree of professional autonomy and to make innovations possible.

Another management technique closely allied to cost-effectiveness is that of product and market analysis. Product analysis is a somewhat difficult process for libraries and information centers, which sell services rather than tangible items, but product analysis is important to their effectiveness. Not only do these services to users require expenditures of resources, but they also require expenditures on the part of the user in terms of time, availability and convenience. Product analysis is a means of determining which services are most desirable to the user, and why other services are used less frequently. Market analysis involves determining who the users are and grouping them according to the principal benefits they wish to obtain. With this information, one can gain further insight about the needs and wants of each group.

In a study of the library and business community, Meyer & Rostvold (105) conducted a market analysis of the needs of business firms for information required in their work, and their habits of and desires for acquiring this information. The goal of the study was to improve public library services to business and industry through cooperative library action. Among the recommendations of the analysis were: the public library should be the first point of contact; local businessmen should establish a liaison committee to advise the public library of their needs; and the public library should improve its collection, expand its staff, take on some of the attributes of the special library, conduct a vigorous program to acquaint the economic community with its services and facilities, and reexamine financial resource allocations. It was further recommended that a proposed two-year demonstration program be initiated.

Education of the users to inform them of the library services and products will be required, for maximum use of these services. User satisfaction is not only the major objective of the library, it is also the means of assuming continued use of the library and attracting new users. As stated in a recent Canadian study (140), "...the most effective public relations person will be the satisfied user."

TRENDS

A trend toward greater attention to library management problems and the application of management tools for more effective decision-making is discernable. The number of institutes dealing with management problems in libraries is also growing. A two-week library executive development program was held at the University of Washington in April 1969 (96). This program was organized to help administrators of all types of libraries to understand current issues and concepts in business and public administration, so that they would be better able to meet the needs and demands on libraries as modern information centers. Participants at the Institute discussed the function and principles of upper-level management, and application of theory in such areas as budgeting, organizing, decision-making, and problem-solving.

The Library Organization and Management Section of the American Library Association sponsored a preconference institute, prior to its 1971 annual meeting in Dallas, called "Dollar Decisions." The institute covered several types of program and performance budgeting systems. Participants had an opportunity to try these techniques in two problem-solving sessions.

A seminar on "Management Concepts for Librarians" was held in June 1971 under the sponsorship of Washington University, St. Louis.

Among the topics discussed were basic concepts of management, problem-solving and decision-making, management by objectives and performance appraisal, and the applicability of management principles to library organizations.

In November 1971, Virginia Polytechnic Institute and State University (VPISU) held a conference entitled "The Academic Community Looks at Library Management" at Blacksburg, Virginia. Topics covered included operations research, management science, and decision theory, with applications examples in collection management and automation efforts in the VPI library.

SUMMARY AND CONCLUSIONS

The new and different tools and techniques of management have profound implications for overcoming the disadvantages of present systems and responding to new demands of both users and top management. It appears from this review of the literature that libraries and information centers are attempting to attack management problems through the introduction of management concepts and decision-making techniques. However, these attacks are diversified and focus on narrow aspects of library operations, so they do not represent full use of these tools and techniques.

If library operations are to be directed toward the achievement of specific goals, the decision-making process must be involved in establishing the goals and objectives of the organization. Since, under any managerial system, there must be one person who is responsible for making the final decision, and this person is responsible to top management, the manager of a library or information center must be given adequate visibility and authority within the organizational structure to make his decisions and recommendations meaningful.

A major impact of MIS is the emphasis on the use of valid information and technical competence, rather than formal power, to manage organizations. But managerial competence is in short supply, because of three factors: (1) there is continuing pressure for higher productivity to satisfy expectations of a rising living standard; (2) the task of management is growing more difficult as we expect managers to be more sensitive to social needs, to deal with employees' complaints and demands, and to adjust more quickly to changing technology; and (3) the new management techniques take longer to learn. Research findings, management information systems, and mathematical models can help sharpen the judgment of managers, but they also require managerial time—time for the manager to learn how to use these tools effectively. Because of these pressures, the training of future managers is a primary challenge for professional education in the fields of library and information science. It will become the responsibility of the universities to produce information systems specialists and librarians who will also be capable of managing, regardless of the type of organization in which they are employed. It is gratifying to note that some efforts are being made to give attention to this problem.

REFERENCES

(1) ACKOFF, RUSSELL A. A concept of corporate planning. John Wiley & Sons, Inc., New York, 1970.

(2) ARGYRIS, CHRIS. Management information systems: the challenge to rationality and emotionality. Management Science, 17:6 (February 1971) 275-291.

(3) ARSENAULT, JAMES R.; NUMAMAKER, J. F., JR.; WHINSTON, A. B. Models for the design of data organization. Paper presented at the 39th National Operations Research Society of America (ORSA) Meeting held in Dallas, Texas, 5-7 May 1971. (Paper is available from the authors. Purdue University, Lafayette, Indiana).

(4) AXFORD, H. WILLIAM. An approach to performance budgeting at the Florida Atlantic University Library. College & Research Libraries, 32:2 (March 1971) 87-104.

(5) BAKER, NORMAN R. Scientific information and innovation in research organizations. Paper presented at the 38th National Operations Research Society of America (ORSA) Meeting held in Detroit, Michigan, 28-30 October 1970. (Paper is available from the author. Georgia Institute of Technology, School of Industrial and Systems Engineering, Atlanta, Georgia).

(6) BALK, WALTER L. The human dilemmas of MIS. Journal of Systems Management, 22:8 (August 1971) 35-38.

(7) BARNETT, ARNOLD. Preparing management for MIS. Journal of Systems Management, 23:1 (January 1972) 40-43.

(8) BECKMAN, MARGARET. Derivation of a simulation model of a university library system. Guelph University, Library Administration, Guelph, Ontario, Canada, 1968, 28p.

(9) BLACKWELL, F. W.; et al. Educational information system design; a conceptual framework. RAND Corporation, Santa Monica, California, August 1970, 18 p. (AD 711 759).

(10) BLISS, SAM W.; et al. Proceedings of the Educational Management Tools Training Program 1969-1970 at Southern Illinois University College of Education, Carbondale, Illinois, 1970, 304 p. (Final report. ED 046 111).

(11) BOICE, EUGENE T.; et al. The Medical Library Center of New York: a cost study. New York Metropolitan Reference and Research Library Agency, New York, 1970, 68 p. (ED 043 357).

(12) BOOKSTEIN, ABRAHAM. Implications for library education. Library Quarterly, 42:1 (January 1972) 140-151.

(13) BOOZ, ALLEN & HAMILTON, INC. Problems in university library management. Association of Research Libraries, Washington, D.C., 1970, 68 p.

(14) BOURNE, CHARLES P. Data collection and cost modeling for library circulation systems. Charles Bourne and Associates, Menlo Park, California, November 1970, 89 p. (ED 046 445).

(15) BROMBERG, ERIK. Simplified PPBS for the librarian. Paper prepared for the Dollar Decision Pre-Conference Institute, sponsored by the Library Administration Division of the American Library Association at Dallas, Texas, 17-19 June 1971, 13 p. (ED 047 751).

(16) BRYK, OLIVER. Application of PPB on state and local levels. Paper presented at an Institute on Program Planning and Budgeting Systems for Libraries at Wayne State University, Department of Library Science, Detroit, Michigan, Spring 1968, 11 p. (ED 045 127).
(17) BUCKLAND, MICHAEL K. An operations research study of a variable loan and duplication policy at the University of Lancaster. Library Quarterly, 42:1 (January 1972) 97-106.
(18) BUCKLAND, MICHAEL K.; et al. Systems analysis of a university library; final report on a research project. University of Lancaster Library, The Librarian, Bailrigg, Lancaster, England, 1970, 100 p.
(19) Bulletin of the Operations Research Society of America, volume 15, supplement 1, spring 1967. Operations Research Society of America, Baltimore, Maryland.
(20) Bulletin of the Operations Research Society of America, volume 18, supplement 1, fall 1970. Operations Research Society of America, Baltimore, maryland.
(21) Bulletin of the Operations Research Society of America, volume 19, supplement 1, spring 1971. Operations Research Society of America, Baltimore, Maryland.
(22) BUMSTED, ALEC R. The concept of systems management in educational data processing. System Development Corp., Santa Monica, California, 6 January 1969, 14 p. (SP professional paper 3238. ED 047 353).
(23) BURNESS, CARL G. Defining library objectives. Paper presented at an Institute on Program Planning and Budgeting Systems for Libraries at Wayne State University, Department of Library Science, Detroit, Michigan, Spring 1968, 30 p. (ED 045 116).
(24) BURNS, ROBERT W., JR. A generalized methodology for library systems analysis. College & Research Libraries, 32:4 (July 1971) 295-303.
(25) BURROWS, J. H. Information system overview. Mitre Corporation, Bedford, Massachusetts, June 1970, 58 p. (ED 046 435).
(26) BURROWS, J. H. Persistent problems in system development. Mitre Corporation, Bedford, Massachusetts, 46 p. (ED 046 436).
(27) CAHILL, JOHN J. A dictionary/directory method for building a common MIS data base. Journal of Systems Management, 21:11 (November 1970) 23-29.
(28) CHAKRAVARTI, M. B. M. Management information system: an overview. In: Documentation Systems for Industry, Eighth Annual Seminar, PART 1. Documentation Research and Training Centre, Indian Statistical Institute, Bangalore, India, 1970.
(29) CHURCHMAN, C. WEST. Operations research prospects for libraries: the realities and ideals. Library Quarterly, 42:1 (January 1972) 6-14.
(30) COLEMAN, RAYMOND J.; RILEY M. J. The organizational impact of MIS. Journal of Systems Management, 22:3 (March 1972) 13-19.
(31) CONGDON, FRANK P., JR. Advanced planning for the systems function. Journal of Systems management, 21:8 (August 1970) 13-19.
(32) COOKE, WILLIAM F., JR.; ROST, WILLIAM J. Standard cost system: a module of a management information system. Journal of Systems Management, 20:3 (March 1969) 11-16.
(33) CORDARO, J. T., JR.; CHIEN, R. T. Design consideration of on-line document retrieval systems. Illinois University, Coordinate Science Laboratory, Urbana, Illinois, February 1970, 37 p. (AD 701 972).
(34) DAHNKE, HAROLD L.; JONES, DENNIS P.; MASON, THOMAS R.; ROMNEY, LEONARD C. Academic support facilities. Higher education facilities planning and management manual four. Western Interstate Commission for Higher Education, Boulder, Colorado, May 1971, 72 p.
(35) DICKSON, GARY W. Control systems for information system development projects. AEDS Journal, 4:1 (September 1970) 29-34.
(36) DonVITO, P.A. The essentials of a planning-programming-budgeting system. RAND Corporation, Santa Monica, California, July 1969, 21 p. (AD 690 394).

(37) DOUGHERTY, RICHARD M. Cost analysis studies in libraries: is there a basis for comparison? Library Resources & Technical Services, 13:1 (Winter 1969) 136-141.

(38) DOUGHERTY, RICHARD M. Is work simplification alive & well someplace? American Libraries, 1:10 (November 1970) 969-971.

(39) DRICKAMER, JEWEL. Analytic program budgeting—Rhode Island librarians take the plunge. NELA Newsletter, 3:1 (March 1971) 22-24.

(40) DUCHESNE, R. M. Library management information from computer-aided library systems. In: Mackenzie, A. Graham; Stuart, Ian M.; eds. Planning Library Services. Proceedings of a Research Seminar held at the University of Lancaster 9-11 July 1969. University of Lancaster Library, Bailrigg, Lancaster, England, 1969, 238 p.

(41) DURHAM, UNIVERSITY OF. Project for evaluating the benefits from university libraries. Final report. University of Durham, Computer Unit, Durham, England, October 1969, 282 p.

(42) ELLIS, ARTHUR E. Influence of PPB on capital budgeting. Paper presented at an Institute on Program Planning and Budgeting Systems for Libraries at Wayne State University, Department of Library Science, Detroit, Michigan, Spring 1968, 21 p. (ED 045 123).

(43) EVANS, J. A. A framework for the evolutionary development of an executive information system. Part 1. Organizational problem-finding. Mitre Corporation, Bedford, Massachusetts, June 1970, 73 p. (ED 047 729).

(44) EVANS, J. A. A framework for the evolutionary development of an executive information system. Part 2. System design, implementation and evolution. Mitre Corporation, Bedford, Massachusetts, June 1970, 64 p. (ED 047 730).

(45) FALOR, KEN. MIS folklore—an opinion. Modern Data, 3:12 (December 1970) 48.

(46) FAZAR, WILLARD. Application of PPB to certain Federal programs. Paper presented at an Institute on Program Planning and Budgeting Systems for Libraries at Wayne State University, Department of Library Science, Detroit, Michigan, Spring 1968, 14 p. (ED 045 117).

(47) FAZAR, WILLARD. The importance of PPB to libraries. Paper presented at an Institute on Program Planning and Budgeting Systems for Libraries at Wayne State University, Department of Library Science, Detroit, Michigan, Spring 1968, 26 p. (ED 045 114).

(48) FAZAR, WILLARD. A quick insight for the uninitiated into program planning and budgeting theory. Management Notes, 33 (October 1970) 28-34.

(49) FOSKETT, D. J. Libraries and educational planning: some reflections on a Unesco seminar. Unesco Bulletin for Libraries, 25:2 (March/April 1971) 67-72.

(50) FOSTER, ROBERT D. Library resources and service centers of Kansas, with guidelines for future development and cooperative use. Kansas State University, Center for Urban Studies, Wichita, Kansas, September 1968, 58 p. (ED 048 866).

(51) FOUST, JAMES; HUGHES, WARREN R. Regional supply and demand for library services. Indiana University, Graduate Library School, Bloomington, Indiana, 1970, 52 p. (ED 044 135).

(52) FREDERICKS, W. A. Manager's perspective of management information systems. MSU Business Topics, 19 (Spring 1971) 7-12.

(53) FRY, BERNARD M.; et al. Design study for long-range research programs. Indiana University, Research Center for Library and Information Science, Bloomington, Indiana, April 1969, 117 p. (ED 044 122).

(54) FRY, JAMES P. Managing data is the key to MIS. Computer Decisions, 3:1 (January 1971) 6-10.

(55) GLOVER, FRED; KLINGMAN, DARWIN. Mathematical programming models and methods for the journal selection problem. Library Quarterly, 42:1 (January 1972) 43-58.

(56) GODDARD, HAYNES, C. An economic analysis of library benefits. Library Quarterly, 41:3 (July 1971) 244-255.

(57) GORRY, G. A.; MORTON, M. S. S. Framework for management information systems. Sloan Management Review, 13 (Fall 1971) 55-70.

(58) GRECO, R. J. MIS planning—an approach. Data Management 9:10 (October 1971) 17-22.

(59) HAMBURG, MORRIS; RAMIST, LEONARD E.; BOMMER, MICHAEL R. W. The development of a statistical information system for university and large public libraries. Paper presented at the 39th National Operations Research Society of America (ORSA) Meeting held in Dallas, Texas, 5-7 May 1971. (Paper is available from the authors. University of Pennsylvania, Wharton School of Finance and Commerce, Philadelphia, Pennsylvania).

(60) HAMBURG, MORRIS; RAMIST, LEONARD E.; BOMMER, MICHAEL R. W. Library objectives and performance measures and their use in decision-making. Library Quarterly, 42:1 (January 1972) 107-128.

(61) HARGROVE, THOMAS L.; STIRLING, KEITH H. California State Library: processing center design and specifications. Vol. V: cost analysis. Supplemental volume. University of California, Institute of Library Research, Berkeley, California, 1970, 94 p. (ED 043 356).

(62) HARRIGAN, JOAN. Suggested long-range planning format for Colorado libraries. Colorado State Library, Denver, Colorado, 1970, 14 p. (ED 046 418).

(63) HASELGROVE, J. R. How important is research to library development planning? Paper presented at the 3d Weekend Conference of the Tanzania Library Association, Dar Es Salaam, Tanzania, November 1969, 15 p.

(64) HEAD, R. V. Management information system structure. Data Management, 9:10 (September 1971) 51-53.

(65) HENKLE, HERMAN H. Final report to the board of trustees, the James Jerome Hill Reference Library. James Jerome Hill Reference Library, St. Paul Minnesota, March 1971, 50 p. (ED 049 773).

(66) HINDLE, A. Models and measures for non-profit making services. In: Mackenzie, A. Graham; Stuart, Ian M.; eds. Planning Library Services; Proceedings of a Research Seminar held at the University of Lancaster 9-11 July 1969. University of Lancaster Library, Bailrigg, Lancaster, England, 1969.

(67) HOFFMAN, WALTER. Data processing applied to library budgets. Paper presented at an institute on Program Planning and Budgeting Systems for Libraries at Wayne State University, Department of Library Science, Detroit, Michigan, Spring 1968, 5 p. (ED 045 122).

(68) HOWARD, EDWARD N. Toward PPBS in the public library. American Libraries, 2:4 (April 1971) 386-393.

(69) HOWARD, LORE. A better look at budgets. School Library Journal, (15 March 1971) 93-94.

(70) HUDZIK, JOHN K. A fiscal and organizational analysis of public libraries in Michigan. Michigan State Department of Education, Lansing, Michigan, 1970, 110 p. (ED 044 130).

(71) HUMPHRY, JOHN; HUMPHRY, JAMES, III. Library cooperation in metropolitan Baltimore: a new approach to determining library locations and services. CONSAD Research Corporation, Pittsburgh, Pennsylvania, July 1970, 42 p. (ED 044 124).

(72) JAIN, ARIDAMAN K. Document usage sampling and storage decision rules. Paper presented at the National Operations Research Society of America (ORSA) Meeting held in Detroit, Michigan. (Paper is available from the author. Bell Telephone Laboratories, Holmdel, New Jersey).

(73) JENKINS, HAROLD R. The ABC's of PPB. Library Journal, 96:17 (1 October 1971) 3089-3093.

(74) KELLER, HARRY. The development and history of the concept of PPB. Paper presented at an Institute on Program Planning and Budgeting Systems for Libraries at Wayne State University, Department of Library Science, Detroit, Michigan, Spring 1968, 22 p. (ED 045 113).

(75) KELLY, JOSEPH F. Computerized management information systems. MacMillan Co., New York, New York, 1970, 553 p.
(76) KEMPER, ROBERT E. Library planning: the challenge of change. In: Voigt, Melvin J.; ed. Advances in librarianship, vol. 1. Academic Press, New York, 1970, 207-239.
(77) KENNEVAN, WALTER J. MTS universe. Data Management, 8:9 (September 1970) 22.
(78) KING, DONALD W. Cost effectiveness of information transfer systems. Paper presented at the 39th National Operations Research Society of America (ORSA) Meeting held in Dallas, Texas, 5-7 May 1971. (Paper is available from the author. Westat Research, Inc., Rockville, Maryland).
(79) KINGSBURY, M. E. Plan by increments. Library Journal, 97:3 (February 1972) 465-467.
(80) KITAGAWA, T. Information science approaches to scientific information systems and their implications to scientific researches. In: Proceedings of the Study Committee of International Federal for Documentation Research on the Theoretical Basis of Information. Moscow, Soviet Union, 24-26 February 1970, 54-80.
(81) KLINTØE, KJELD. Cost analysis of a technical information unit. Aslib Proceedings, 23:6 (June 1971) 362-371.
(82) KOCHEN, MANFRED. Directory design for networks of information and referral centers. Library Quarterly, 42:1 (January 1972) 59-83.
(83) KOCHEN, MANFRED. Referential consulting networks. Paper presented at the National Operations Research Society of America (ORSA) Meeting held in Detroit, Michigan, 1970. (Paper is available from the author. University of Michigan, Mental Health Research Institute, Ann Arbor, Michigan. ED 027 923).
(84) KOENIG, MICHAEL D.; FINALY, ALEXANDER C.; CUSHMAN, JOANN G. SCOPE: a cost analysis of an automated record system. Journal of Library Automation, 4:3 (September 1971) 129-140.
(85) KORFHAGE, ROBERT R. Graphical data systems for library retrieval. Paper presented at the National Operations Research Society of America (ORSA) Meeting held in Detroit, Michigan, 1970. (Paper is available from the author. Southern Methodist University, Computer Sciences/Operations Research Center, Dallas, Texas).
(86) KORFHAGE, ROBERT R.; BHAT, U. NARAYAN; NANCE, RICHARD E. Graph models for library information networks. Library Quarterly, 42:1 (January 1972) 31-42.
(87) KRAFT, DONALD H. The journal selection problem in a university library. Paper presented at the National Operations Research Society of America (ORSA) Meeting held in Detroit, Michigan, 1970. (Paper is available from the author. University of Maryland, School of Library and Information Services, College Park, Maryland).
(88) KRAMER, JOSEPH. How to survive in industry. Cost justifying library services. Special Libraries, 62:11 (November 1971) 487-489.
(89) KRIEBEL, CHARLES H. Perspectives on information in management information systems. Carnegie-Mellon University, Pittsburgh, Pennsylvania, August 1969, 32 p. (AD 695 767).
(90) LANCASTER, F. WILFRID. The cost-effectiveness analysis of information retrieval and dissemination systems. Journal of the American Society for Information Science, 22:1 (January/February 1971) 12-27.
(91) LANE, DAVID O. Study of the decision-making procedures for the acquisition of science library materials and the relation of these procedures to the requirements of college and university library patrons. American Library Association, Chicago, Illinois, 1967, 123 p. (ED 047 712).
(92) LANGMEAD, S.; BECKMAN, M. New library design: guidelines to planning academic library buildings. John Wiley & Sons, New York, New York, 1971, 117 p.

(93) LEIMKUHLER, FERDINAND F. Library operations research: a process of discovery and justification. Library Quarterly, 42:1 (January 1972) 84-96.

(94) LEIMKUHLER, FERDINAND F.; COOPER, MICHAEL D. Analytical models for library planning. Journal of the American Society for Information Science, 22:6 (November/December 1971) 390-398.

(95) LEIMKUHLER, FERDINAND F.; COOPER, MICHAEL D. Cost accounting and analysis for university libraries. University of California, Office of the Vice President—Planning and Anaylsis, Berkeley, California, January 1970, 47 p. (ED 040 728. Also in College & Research Libraries, 32:6 (November 1971) 449-464.).

(96) LIEBERMAN, IRVING. Library executive development program; narrative evaluation report on the Institute for Advanced Study for Librarians under the Higher Education Act, Title II-B, 14-25 April 1969 University of Washington, School of Librarianship, Seattle, Washington, 1969, 70 p.

(97) LIPETZ, BEN-AMI. Catalog use in a large research library. Library Quarterly, 4:2 (January 1972) 129-139.

(98) LOHARA, CHARANJIT. A new approach to management information systems, part 1. Journal of Systems Management, 22:7 (July 1971) 20-25.

(99) LOHARA, CHARANJIT. A new approach to management systems, part 2. Journal of Systems Management, 22:8 (August 1971) 27-33.

(100) MACKENZIE, A. GRAHAM. Library research at the University of Lancaster. Library Association Record, 73:5 (May 1971) 90-92.

(101) MAIER, JOAN M.; et al. The Bibliographical Center for Research, Rocky Mountain Region: a cost study of the Center's present operations. Bibliographical Center for Research, Rocky Mountain Region, Inc., Denver, Colorado, 1969, 89 p. (ED 045 161).

(102) MANN, S. H. Optimal library size. Pennsylvania State University, College of Human Development, University Park, Pennsylvania.

(103) MARVIN, KEITH E. PPB as a tool in legislative planning. Paper presented at an Institute on Program Planning and Budgeting Systems for Libraries at Wayne State University, Department of Library Science, Detroit, Michigan, Spring 1968, 16 p. (ED 045 125).

(104) MATTHEWS, DON Q. The design of management information systems. Auerbach Publishers, Princeton, New Jersey, 1971, 221 p.

(105) MEYER, ROBERT S.; ROSTVOLD, GERHARD N. The library and the economic community: a market analysis of information needs of business and industry in the communities of Pasadena and Pomona, California. Pasadena Public Library, Pasadena, California, May 1969, 150 p. (ED 046 424).

(106) MEYERS, JUDITH; BARBER, RAYMOND. McNamara, media and you. School Library Journal, (15 March 1971) 91-93.

(107) MILLER, EDWARD P.; LUTZ, RAYMOND P. A unique program in library education. Special libraries, 62:9 (September 1971) 353-356.

(108) MINKER, JACK. Generalized data management systems—some perspectives. Maryland University, Computer Science Center, College Park, Maryland, December 1969, 125 p. (ED 053 755. Technical report 69-101).

(109) MINNESOTA HIGHER EDUCATION COORDINATING COMMISSION. The Minnesota library survey: a comprehensive state-wide study of information needs, resources and services. Minnesota Higher Education Coordinating Commission, St. Paul, Minnesota, 1969, 58 p. (ED 052 808).

(110) MINTER, JOHN; LAWRENCE, BEN; eds. Management information systems: their development and use in the administration of higher education. American Council on Education, Washington, D.C.; Western Interstate Commission for Higher Education, Bolder, Colorado, October 1969, 113 p. (ED 042 427).

(111) MLYNARCZYK, FRANK, JR. Measuring library costs. Paper presented at an Institute on Program Planning and Budgeting systems for Libraries at Wayne State University, Department of Library Science, Detroit, Michigan, Spring 1968, 13 p. (ED 045 120).

(112) MOREY, GEORGE E. The identification of common library goals, objectives, and activities relative to a planning, programming, budgeting system. Western Michigan University, Kalamozoo, Michigan, June 1970, 80 p. (ED 048 876).
(113) MORLEY, R. M. Maximizing the benefit from library resources. In: Mackenzie, A. Graham; Stuart, Ian M.; eds. Proceedings of a Research Seminar held at the University of Lancaster 9-11 July 1969. University of Lancaster Library, Bailrigg, Lancaster England, 1969, 238 p.
(114) MORSE, PHILIP M. Library effectiveness: a systems approach. M.I.T. Press, Cambridge, Massachusetts, 1968, 214 p.
(115) MORSE, PHILIP M. Measures of library effectiveness. Library Quarterly, 42:1 (January 1972) 15-30.
(116) MORSE, PHILIP M. On browsing: the use of search theory in the search for information. Paper presented at the 39th National Operations Research Society of America (ORSA) Meeting held in Dallas, Texas, 5-7 May 1971. 37 p. (Paper is available from the author. Massachusetts Institute of Technology, Cambridge, Massachusetts. AD 702 920).
(117) MURDICK, ROBERT G. MIS development procedures. Journal of Systems Management, 21:12 (December 1970) 23-26.
(118) NANCE, RICHARD E. Algorithmic structures for the solution of library network problems. Paper presented at the National Operations Research Society of America (ORSA) Meeting held in Detroit, Michigan, 1970. (Paper is available from the author. Southern Methodist University, Computer Science/Operations Research Center, Dallas, Texas).
(119) NANCE, RICHARD E.; BAKER, NORMAN R. Library policy structure: an industrial dynamics study. Southern Methodist University, Computer Science/Operations Research Center, Dallas, Texas, February 1970, 29 p. (Technical report CP 70002).
(120) NAVALTA, GLORINA M. Management and the systems function. Journal of Systems Management, 23:2 (February 1972) 40-41.
(121) NEW YORK STATE EDUCATION DEPARTMENT. Library service, a statement of policy and proposed action by the Regents of the University of the State of New York. New York State Library, Gift and Exchange Section, Albany, New York, October 1970, 32 p. (Position paper 8).
(122) NEWHOUSE, JOSEPH P. The simple theory of public library services. RAND Corporation, Santa Monica, California, October 1970, 14 p. (AD 714 333).
(123) NUSSBAUM, HARVEY. Operations research applied to libraries. Paper presented at an Institute on Program Planning and Budgeting Systems for Libraries at Wayne State University, Department of Library Science, Detroit, Michigan, Spring 1968, 7 p. (ED 045 121).
(124) O'BLACK, MARY JANE. Building a successful MIS. Journal of Systems Management, 22:4 (April 1971) 9-15.
(125) O'HAREN, PARTRICK J. Total systems: operating objective or planning structure. Journal of Systems Management, 21:11 (November 1970) 34-38.
(126) OLSEN, HAROLD ANKER. The economics of information: bibliography and commentary on the literature. ERIC Clearinghouse on Library and Information Sciences, Washington, D.C., January 1971, 32 p. (ED 044 545).
(127) PALMER, ALFRED L. Organizing for management information systems. Records Management Quarterly, 5:4 (October 1971) 11-13.
(128) PALMER, DAVID. Measuring library output. Paper presented at an Institute on Program Planning and Budgeting Systems for Libraries at Wayne State University, Department of Library Science, Detroit, Michigan, Spring 1968, 17 p. (ED 045 118).
(129) PANDYA, M. P. Management information system and its major attributes. In: Documentation Systems for Industry, Eighth Annual Seminar, part 1. Indian Statistical Institute, Documentation Research and Training Centre, Bangalore, India, 1970.

(130) PENNA, CARLOS VICTOR. Planning library services. Unesco Bulletin for Libraries, XXI:2 (March/April 1967) 60-92.

(131) PERKINS, JOSEPH A., JR. PPBS and MIS: their role in managing education. Paper presented at the National School Finance Conference, New Orleans, Louisiana, March 1969, 15 p. (ED 030 961).

(132) PFISTER, RICHARD L.; MILLIMAN, JEROME. Economic aspects of library services in Indiana. Indiana University, Graduate Library School, Bloomington, Indiana, 1970, 151 p. (ED 044 136).

(133) PLUMB, PHILIP W. The Cambridge University Library Management Research Unit. Library Association Record, 73:10 (October 1971) 187-188.

(134) PUTMAN, WILLIAM. Problems and issues in specifying behavorial instructional objectives for graduate courses in library administration. Catholic University of America, Department of Library Science, Washington, D.C., October 1970, 46 p. (ED 043 352).

(135) RAFFEL, JEFFREY A.; SHISHKO, ROBERT. systematic analysis of university libraries: an application of cost-benefit analysis to the MIT libraries. M.I.T. Press, Cambridge, Massachusetts, 1969, 107 p.

(136) RAMIST, LEONARD E. Decision-making framework for allocating funds among library services. Paper presented at the 35th Annual Conference of the Graduate Library School, University of Chicago, Theme: Operations Research: Implications for Libraries. 2-4 August 1971. University of Chicago, Center for Continuing Education, Chicago, Illinois, 1971.

(137) RZASA, PHILLIP V.; BAKER, NORMAN R. Measures of effectiveness for a university library. Paper presented at the 39th National Operations Research Society of America (ORSA) Meeting held in Dallas, Texas, 5-7 May 1971. (Paper is available from the authors. Georgia Institute of Technology, School of Industrial and Systems Engineering, Atlanta, Georgia).

(138) SANDERS, DONALD H. Computers and management. McGraw Hill Book Company, New York, New York, 1970.

(139) SANTA BARBARA ELEMENTARY AND HIGH SCHOOL DISTRICT. P.P.B.S. and the library: goals, objectives, program. (Report of the Librarians' Workshop. . .). Santa Barbara Elementary and High School District, Santa Barbara, California, 1971, 137 p. (ED 050 776).

(140) SCIENCE COUNCIL OF CANADA. Scientific and technical information in Canada, part II, chapter 6: libraries. Queen's Printer for Canada, Ottawa, Ontario, Canada, 1969, 49 p.

(141) SEATTLE DEPARTMENT OF COMMUNITY DEVELOPMENT. Comprehensive plan for libraries. Department of Community Development, Seattle, Washington, 1971, 117 p. (ED 052 807).

(142) SEESE, DOROTHY ANNE. The systems analyst in the terminal access environment. Journal of Systems Management, 22:3 (March 1971) 17-19.

(143) SENKO, M. E. Modeling of information systems. Paper presented at the National Operations Research Society of America (ORSA) Meeting held in Detroit, Michigan, 1970. (Paper is available from the author. IBM Research, San Jose, California).

(144) SEWELL, P. H. The planning of library and documentation services. Working draft. Paper prepared for the Seminar on the Planning of Library and Documentation Services. International Institute for Educational Planning, 7, rue Eugene-Delacroix, Paris 16e, France, 1969, 87 p.

(145) SPENCER, MILTON. Projecting program cost over an adequate time horizon. Paper presented at an Institute on Program Planning and Budgeting Systems for Libraries at Wayne State University, Department of Library Science, Detroit, Michigan, Spring 1968, 18 p. (ED 045 119).

(146) SPIRO, B. E. What's a management information system? Data Management, 9:9 (September 1971) 45-51.

(147) STITELMAN, LEONARD. Cost utility analysis applied to library budgeting. Paper presented at an Institute on Program Planning and Budgeting Systems for

Libraries at Wayne State University, Department of Library Science, Detroit, Michigan, Spring, 1968, 15 p. (ED 045 126).

(148) STOCKER, FREDERICK D. Financing public libraries in Ohio. Ohio State University, Columbus, Ohio. Center for Business and Economic Research, March 1971, 83 p. (ED 048 892).

(149) STURTZ, CHARLES. The difference between conventional budgeting and PPB. Paper presented at an Institute on Program Planning and Budgeting Systems for Libraries at Wayne University, Department of Library Science, Detroit, Michigan, Spring 1968, 12 p. (ED 045 115).

(150) SURACE, CECILY J. Library circulation systems—an overview. RAND Corporation, Santa Monica, California, March 1970, 25 p. (ED 039 001).

(151) TAYLOR, CELIANNA I. The information center: considerations in planning. Ohio State University, Department of Computer and Information Science, Columbus, Ohio, 1971, 11 p.

(152) THOMAS, P. A. Task analysis of library operations. Aslib, London, England, 1971, 68 p. (Aslib occasional publication no. 8).

(153) TOLLIVER, EDWARD M. Myths of automated management systems. Journal of Systems Management, 22:3 (March 1971) 29-32.

(154) TUDOR, DEAN. Planning-programming-budgeting systems. Council of Planning Librarians, Monticello, Illinois, March 1970, 20 p. (ED 049 778. Supplement issued April 1971, 6 p. ED 049 779).

(155) WAITES, WILLIAM G. MIS or IMS? Journal of Systems Management, 22:1 (January 1971) 32-34.

(156) WALKER, W. C. A structure for managing systems. Journal of Systems Management, 21:3 (March 1970) 22-26.

(157) WATSON, HUGH J. Computers can reduce management risks. Journal of Systems Management, 22:12 (December 1971) 13-17.

(158) WEBSTER, DUANE. Planning aids for the university library director. Association of Research Libraries, Washington, D.C., December 1971, 27 p. (Occasional papers, number one).

(159) WEINMEISTER, CARL J. The science of information management. Computers and Automation, 20:4 (April 1971) 20-24.

(160) WEISER, ALAN L. Assigning priorities to management information reports. Data Processing Magazine, 12:7 (July 1970) 29-31.

(161) WEISS, STANLEY D. Management information systems. In: Cuadra, Carlos A.; ed. Annual review of information science and technology, vol. 5. Encyclopaedia Britannica, Chicago, Illinois, 1970, 299-324.

(162) WHITWORTH, T. A. An outsider looks at research in librarianship. Research in Librarianship, 2:11 (May 1969) 121-126.

(163) WOODBURN, I. A mathematical model of a hierarchical library system. In: Mackenzie, A. Graham; Stuart, Ian M.; eds. Planning Library Services; Proceedings of a Research Seminar held at the University of Lancaster 9-11 July 1969. University of Lancaster Library, Bailrigg, Lancaster, England, 1969, 238 p.

INTRODUCTION TO INDEX

Index entries consist of names of individuals and corporate organizations as well as subject categories and cross references. Personal authors who are cited have been indexed according to the context reference rather than the bibliographic page. In cases where there are more than two authors, the first author is indexed according to the context reference and the balance of authors are indexed against the bibliographic page.

Corporate organization names appear in the index when they have been used to denote the location of individuals or ongoing work, sponsors of specific studies and manufacturers of equipment. If the corporate organization has been actively involved in developing a study or system, an appropriate subject entry has also been made.

Where possible, acronyms have been entered under the full, spelled-out form, with cross references from the abbreviated form. The few exceptions are programming languages (e.g., PL/1) and assorted projects, systems and equipment for which no full form was found.

The index is sorted in an alphabetical word-by-word sequence treating any special character as a space except for the ampersand which is treated as the spelled-out form *and* (e.g., DATA-PHONE precedes Datamation). Personal surnames precede entries for corporate names, systems, etc. (e.g., Douglas, William precedes Douglas Aircraft Corp.). *Mc* surnames are filed alphabetically by letter. In both main and sub-entries the drop words are *a*, *and*, and *the*. Numerics follow alphabetical entries (e.g., Honeywell Corp. precedes Honeywell 200 computer). Foreign designations have been indicated where possible (e.g., University of Guelph (Canada)). Italicized entries are names of journals or books.

An attempt has been made to expand and systematize index entries with a view toward enhancing accessibility. Comments and suggestions are welcomed and should be directed to:

Annual Review of Information Science
and Technology
American Society for Information Science
1140 Connecticut Avenue, N.W., Suite 804
Washington, D.C. 20036

Index